Engineering Economics

SECOND CANADIAN EDITION

James L. Riggs
Late Professor of Industrial and General Engineering
Oregon State University

David D. Bedworth
Department of Industrial and Management Systems Engineering
Arizona State University

Sabah U. Randhawa
Department of Industrial and Manufacturing Engineering
Oregon State University

Ata M. Khan
Department of Civil and Environmental Engineering
Carleton University

McGraw-Hill Ryerson Limited

Toronto Montreal New York Auckland Bogotá Caracas
Lisbon London Madrid Mexico Milan New Delhi
San Juan Singapore Sydney Tokyo

ENGINEERING ECONOMICS
Riggs, Bedworth, Randhawa, Khan
Second Canadian Edition

ISBN: 0-07-094518-7

Printed and bound in Canada

CONTENTS

PREFACE

This book is the creation of Jim Riggs but, sadly, this is the first revised edition where his creativity and writing skills could not be utilized directly. The second Canadian edition of *Engineering Economics* is based on the fourth U.S. edition. While many changes have been made between the first and second Canadian editions (and between the third and fourth U.S. editions) in order to modernize the contents and to enhance the comprehensiveness of the coverage of engineering economics, we have attempted to retain Jim's writing style and wisdom that have made his texts unique.

The curricula of most professional schools include a course in applied economics under such titles as *engineering economy, financial management, managerial economics,* and *economic decision making.* Practicing professionals usually rate their "econ" and "engr econ" course as one of the most useful subjects taken in college or university. As with the earlier editions, the second Canadian edition of *Engineering Economics* is written to try to make that "engr econ" experience as rewarding as possible as well as to provide a comprehensive reference for future applications.

This book addresses the needs of all traditional and emerging engineering disciplines (i.e., Aerospace, Chemical, Civil, Computer and Systems, Electrical, Environmental, Industrial, Manufacturing, and Mechanical) in addition to Construction, Technology, Logistics, and other related programs. Additionally, integrated science-engineering and business-engineering programs will find it useful.

The book covers in detail the knowledge base required for the practice of engineering economics in Canada, including the latest developments in depreciation and Revenue Canada tax regulations. Metric units and the Canadian information on inflation, interest rates, and examples of Canadian corporations are used. Also, given the trend of increased portability of credentials and greater mobility of engineers caused by the provisions of the North American Free Trade Agreement (NAFTA) and General Agreement on Trade in Services (GATS), an introduction to the international practice of engineering economics is provided for the benefit of the reader.

Engineering economics is a fascinating subject. Its core is decision making based on comparisons of the worth of alternative courses of action with respect to their costs. Decisions vary from those that are concerned with personal investments to those that have to do with corporate capital budgeting. They must be made at all organizational levels in both public and private sectors of the economy. Tools for decision making range from standardized worksheets for discounted cash-flow evaluations to refinements necessary for sensitivity and risk analysis. The practices followed are grounded in classical economic theory, operations research, decision theory, and other disciplines. Most of the applications are intuitively logical and computationally simple, but the underlying principles are conceptually demanding.

TEXT CONTENTS

Based on surveys completed by a large number of engineering economics instructors, we have made quite a few organizational changes in this edition. These changes should make the book adhere more closely to engineering economy topics at the expense of deleting some materials that are more logically covered in their own textual fashion. For example, the first Canadian edition covered forecasting, production economy, and resource management. These materials are now more often covered in production management or production control courses as well as in a methods analysis type of course. Other materials that have been deleted in this edition include financial analysis and topics in decision analysis such as game theory. Materials that seemed to be especially relevant from deleted chapters have been merged into other related chapters. The chapter on depreciation and income taxation has been revised to bring it up-to-date with Revenue Canada tax regulations and Canadian depreciation practices.

Chapters have been combined where it seemed to be more efficient to cover a particular topic in one chapter rather than in more than one related chapter. For example, risk analysis was involved in four chapters in the first Canadian edition and this material has now been condensed to one comprehensive chapter. Readers familiar with the first Canadian edition will recognize that other similar modifications have been made.

We have numerous excellent recommendations from experts in the area, suggesting chapter sequencing; all were more than worthy of consideration. One book cannot include all recommendations so the authors' biases have been adapted to the majority opinions of reviewers. One excellent suggestion pertains to inflation. While we retained the chapter fairly late in the book we did present a summary of the pertinent material at the beginning of Chapter 3 since the introductory material, from that point on, hinges on the assumption of "constant dollars."

Major additions to this second Canadian edition include a computer program and spreadsheet templates to assist in economic decision making. The computer program, CHEER (Computerized Help for Engineering Economy Results), is written in Visual BASIC and it provides a WINDOWS environment that is very user-friendly. Appendix B contains the user's guide for CHEER. Spreadsheet applications and use of the templates are topics thoroughly covered in Appendix C.

Specific functions of the CHEER program will be indicated when we discuss the relevant chapters in a brief organizational tour through the book. This tour should indicate how the diverse characteristics of engineering economics, as presented earlier, are coordinated into a logical flow of subjects that is both comprehensive and comprehensible.

- **Chapter 1** traces the history of engineering economic thought to show how the generic title *engineering economics* represents a blend of subjects that builds on the traditional engineering concern for operating economies to include *financial considerations, management concepts,* and *decision analysis techniques.* An extension on *supply and demand* introduces engineering as a part of the resource allocation system, describes the supply-demand relationships, and highlights features that are most pertinent to production. A second extension provides an introduction to the *international practice* of engineering economics.
- **Chapters 2 through 5** present the conventional mathematics of money and are devoted to the mechanics of time-value calculations and comparisons of alternatives based on their *equivalent annual worth, present worth,* and *rate of return. Bonds and stocks* are discussed in an extension to Chapter 3. Interest factors follow the suggested functional notations of the American Society for Engineering Education and are commonly used in Canada. The interest calculations are displayed on cash flow diagrams. A wide variety of examples and numerous worked-out review exercises are presented. Emphasis is placed on manually performing the economic analyses in order to reinforce the learning experience. Relative to Chapters 2 through 5, the computer program can be used to look up tabular interest formula values and determine present worth, annual worth, future worth, and rate of return values; but CHEER should only be utilized after the student is thoroughly familiar with the fundamentals involved, since the contents of these four chapters is basic to the remainder of the book's material.
- **Chapters 6 and 7** present ways to structure evaluations to determine a preferred *investment alternative* or *replacement policy.*

- **Chapter 8** discusses the *public sector* and those economic considerations relevant to such operations. Special emphasis will be given to *benefit-cost* analyses.
- **Chapter 9** highlights current Canadian *depreciation* and corporate *income tax considerations* needed for economic decision making. Extensions cover depreciation and income taxes in the U.S.A. and Mexico. This chapter brings the book completely up-to-date in this rapidly changing area. The computer program has a specific menu-driven section related to depreciation and income taxes.
- **Chapter 10** covers the timely topic of *inflation* and its effect on engineering economic decision making. Options are available in the computer program to include inflation in cash flow analysis.
- **Chapter 11** is the first chapter to recognize that data used in an economic study may not really be known all that well. *Sensitivity analysis* is used to determine the effect of such data and evaluate if there is a need to spend a lot of time and money in finding exact data values. A special section of the computer program allows sensitivity analysis to be applied to conventional economic analyses.
- **Chapter 12** is concerned with *break-even analyses* in examining current conditions. Multiple alternative situations are evaluated in addition to the more common two-alternative cases.
- **Chapters 13, 14, and 15** take us away from the deterministic assumptions used in the preponderance of engineering economic studies. *Risk analysis* in Chapter 13 starts with probability concepts and proceeds to the fundamental *expected-value* and *variance criteria* that guide decisions in which future conditions are uncertain and application of simulation in risk analyses are beneficial. Risk analysis is another topic that merits a menu-driven section for the text's computer program. Chapters 14 and 15 cover the topics of *multistage sequential analysis* and *decision analysis*, extend the expected-value concept to *discounted decision trees*, and address the controversial subject of "intangibles," advocating a *multi-attribute approach* that accommodates both convenient and difficult-to-quantify data for *economic decision making*.
- **Appendix Materials:** Several appendices are retained from the first Canadian edition of the book: discrete and continuous compounding interest factors tables, English and French glossaries of terms (updated), related references (updated), areas of a standard normal distribution, and answers to selected problems (revised). Two new appendices cover usage of the computer program and the use of the spreadsheets as an alternative to a computer program. Also new with this edition are glossaries of equation symbols, equations, and probability concepts.

A text on engineering economy is expected to have plenty of detailed examples and an ample assortment of practice problems. This book has them. Realistic examples are interspersed throughout each chapter, and a collection of worked-out review exercises at the end of each chapter further expands on solution techniques. Overly elaborate theoretical developments are avoided. Concepts are reinforced with examples and are related to actual practices wherever possible.

It is a little presumptuous, we feel, for authors to tell adoptees of their books how to teach the related course. The instructor should present the material as he/she feels it should be developed. The essentials of subjects presented in this book can be covered in a one-term course. On the other hand, if an in-depth coverage of all subjects is intended, a two-term course would be appropriate.

A further comment relates to the depth of mathematical derivations in the text. We have tried to hold to a middle-of-the-road course in that derivations of basic subject matter have been given in detail. The specific orientation of the course (engineering management, operations research, multi-disciplinary engineering core, etc.) will dictate if the instructor should stay with the level given or expand or decrease the level as needed.

ACKNOWLEDGMENTS (U.S. AUTHORS):

We cannot emphasize too strongly our gratitude to those experts in the field of engineering economics who reviewed the manuscript in various stages. Appreciation is tendered to Drs. Tom West and Bill Moor who ably contributed and developed the material on depreciation and taxation in the U.S.A. CHEER would not have been a reality if Mr. Zhongkai Xu had not performed so professionally in programming CHEER according to our specifications and many whimsical requests for changes. Also, the spreadsheet templates came to life under his capable hands. As always, the administration and faculty at our respective universities have been supportive in this type of endeavor. Special thanks go to Dr. Phil Wolfe and Dr. Norma Hubele (Chair and Interim Chair of the Department of Industrial and Management Systems Engineering at Arizona State University) who contributed resources to the effort. Our fellow faculty members put up with our questions, comments, and agonizing with good grace and friendly advice.

The McGraw-Hill staff has always exemplified a high degree of professionalism, friendliness, and courtesy under sometimes trying conditions. We are particularly indebted to Mr. Eric Munson, Executive Editor of Engineering and Computer Science, and his able assistant, Ms. Holly Stark. Eric took a chance on us revising Jim's manuscript and we hope we have justified his faith in us. Appreciation is also given to the McGraw-Hill production staff.

A debt of gratitude goes to Mrs. Riggs for her support of the project and for willingness to cooperate with us. Our heartfelt thanks go to Uzma and Ginny for putting up with absent husbands who were working on a seemingly never-ending project. As Cowper well wrote:

What is there in the value of life
Half so delightful as a wife;
When friendship, love and peace combine
To stamp the marriage-bond divine?

ACKNOWLEDGMENTS (CANADIAN AUTHOR):

The author acknowledges the assistance provided by the staff of Revenue Canada, Corel Corporation, Air Canada, Bank of Nova Scotia, Royal Bank, the World Bank, and McKechnie-Moore Chartered Accountants. The activity of publishing a second Canadian edition was initiated by the College Division of McGraw-Hill Ryerson. Jennifer Mix, Senior Editor, Joan Langevin, Sponsoring Editor, Dave Ward, Editor-in-Chief, Daphne Scriabin, Developmental Editor, Maria Chu, Assistant to the Senior Editor, and Gary Bennett, Marketing Manager of McGraw-Hill Ryerson helped in various stages of the development of the book. The author is grateful for their expert advice and help. The role played by McGraw-Hill Ryerson production staff in this project is appreciated, particularly Margaret Henderson, Supervising Editor, Nicla Dattolico, Production Coordinator, and especially Gail Marsden, freelance editor. Appreciation is given to Matthew Joab for producing a WINDOWS version of CHEER and also making modifications to CHEER and SHEER software in order to incorporate Canadian depreciation practice and income tax regulations. Expert advice received from reviewers of the Canadian edition of the manuscript is gratefully acknowledged, especially, from Bill Allen, Palliser Institute (SIAST); Abdel Bassyouni, Southern Alberta Institute of Technology; Michel L. Bilodeau, McGill University; Kris Dick, University of Manitoba; Dag Friis, Memorial University; C. David Sadleir, University of Toronto; Kenneth F. Sadler, Technical University of Nova Scotia; Claude Theoret, University of Ottawa. Finally, without the support and understanding of my family, the preparation of this manuscript would not have been possible.

A JIM RIGGS' GEM

To conclude, Jim Riggs liked to intersperse interesting philosophical gems into his writings. We would like to conclude this preface with this little gem from the third U.S. edition's preface.

Money is the modern equivalent of the long-sought "philosopher's stone." For centuries, alchemists vainly sought the stone that could transform one type of metal into another. Now we have that capacity, indirectly. With money as the medium of exchange, we can convert one type of resource into other types easily and rapidly, but not always wisely. The worthiness of this transformation is a subtle aspect of the mission of engineering economists. Telltale analyses of alternatives reveal the innermost workings of a project and burden the analyst with ethical responsibilities atop fiscal obligations. A prerequisite to bearing the burden is a thorough knowledge of accepted economic principles and practices. This knowledge facilitates putting a legitimate monetary value on the transformation of each resource and allows an accurate and conscientious appraisal of worthiness when combined with technical expertise about the subject. Resource commitments monetized as cash flows set a quantitative framework for ensuing qualitative value considerations. This book is dedicated to the economic analysts who contribute to resource-allocation decisions. May you do so wisely.

It can be said that those who manage people manage people who manage works, but those who manage money manage all. We hope that you accept the challenge and enjoy a satisfying and profitable experience from *Engineering Economics*.

Great is the art of beginning,
but greater the art of ending.

Henry Wadsworth Longfellow
Elegiac Verse

David D. Bedworth
Sabah U. Randhawa
Ata M. Khan

INTRODUCTION TO ENGINEERING ECONOMICS

If thou wouldst keep money, save money; If thou wouldst reap money, sow money.

Thomas Fuller
Gnomology, 1732

Engineers are planners and builders. They are also problem solvers, managers, and decision makers. Engineering economics touches each of these activities. Plans and production must be financed. Problems are eventually defined by dollar dimensions, and decisions are evaluated by their monetary consequences. Much of the management function is directed toward economic objectives and is monitored by economic measures.

Engineering economics is closely aligned with conventional microeconomics, but it has a history and a special flavor of its own. It is devoted to problem solving and decision making at the operations level. It can lead to *suboptimization*—a condition in which a solution satisfies tactical objectives at the expense of strategic effectiveness—but careful attention to the collection and analysis of data minimizes the danger.

An engineering economist draws upon the accumulated knowledge of engineering and economics to identify alternative uses of limited resources and to select the preferred course of action. Evaluations rely mainly on mathematical models and cost data, but judgment and experience are pivotal inputs. Many accepted models are available for analyses of short-range projects when the time value of money is not relevant, and of long-range proposals when discounting is required for input data assumed to be known or subject to risk. Familiarity with these models, gained from studying subsequent chapters, should guide your passage through the engineering economic decision maze (such a maze will be summarized at the end of this chapter).

ENGINEERING DECISION MAKERS

The following general questions are representative of those that an engineer might encounter:

- Which one of several competing engineering designs should be selected?
- Should the machine now in use be replaced with a new one?
- With limited capital available, which investment alternative should be funded?
- Would it be preferable to pursue a safer conservative course of action or to follow a riskier one that offers higher potential returns?
- How many units of production have to be sold before a profit can be made? This area is commonly called *break-even analysis*.
- Among several proposals for funding that yield substantially equivalent worthwhile results but have different cash flow patterns, which is preferable?
- Are the benefits expected from a public service project large enough to make its implementation costs acceptable?

Two characteristics of the questions above should be apparent. First, each deals with a choice among alternatives; second, all involve economic considerations. Less obvious are the requirements of adequate data and an awareness of technological constraints to define the problem and to identify legitimate solutions. These considerations are embodied in the decision-making role of engineering economists to

1. Identify alternative uses for limited resources and obtain appropriate data
2. Analyze the data to determine the preferred alternative

The breadth of problems, depth of analysis, and scope of application that a practicing engineer encounters vary widely. Newly graduated engineers are regularly assigned to cost reduction projects and are expected to be cost-conscious in all their operations. As they gain more experience, they may become specialists in certain application areas or may undertake more general responsibilities as managers. Beginners are usually restricted to short-range decisions for low-budget operations, whereas engineering managers are confronted with policy decisions that involve large sums and are influenced by many factors with long-range consequences. Both situations are served by the principles and practices of engineering economics.

Now let's be a little more specific with engineering economic problems than we were with the general questions just discussed. In the following typical situations, economic decisions are required.

- Should a manufacturing plant produce a part in its own production facility, knowing that major investment will be needed in new equipment and that expensive training procedures will have to be implemented, or should the plant subcontract to an outside vendor?

- Should an arid southwestern city (U.S.A.) immediately implement a manually controlled irrigation system with a planned update to an automated system in 3 years, or should a more expensive automated control system be immediately implemented? Bond issues will be required to assist in financing either alternative.
- A university is planning a new football stadium. Should the stadium be constructed now with a planned seating capacity of 80,000, or should it first be constructed with 65,000 seats with a planned end-zone enclosure to bring it to 80,000 seats in 5 years? Projected attendance revenues, expected increases in labor costs in 5 years, and potential stadium use problems during expansion are all factors that need to be considered.
- An electric utility is considering updating its computer networking capability. Should the utility upgrade its existing minicomputer file servers, or should it consider scrapping them for new IBM AS/400 minicomputer systems? If it takes the latter, should the utility buy or lease?
- An oil refinery needs to enlarge its port facilities to allow more tankers to be serviced per week. What are the potential gains associated with a dock expansion? Doing nothing is always one possible alternative.
- A manufacturing engineer is planning a high-speed production line that will use automated transfer mechanisms to move and position products from one automated workstation to the next. More complex workstations will allow more operations to be completed at a workstation at the expense of lower production rates per hour. However, such a situation could have the advantage of allowing fewer expensive transfer mechanisms. Given forecasts of product demand for the next 5 years, should the engineer plan for a one-shift operation with a certain number of transfer mechanisms or for a two-shift operation with fewer transfer mechanisms?

Lest these problems seem overly simple, which they are not (especially when we consider that the value of money changes over time), consider the following problem which was given to one of this text's authors when he worked at an oil refinery in the late 1950s. He was asked to weigh the benefits of polyvinyl chloride (PVC) piping, which was then being experimented with to transport corrosive acids, against those of the then-conventional piping systems. Unfortunately, there was no known life for PVC at the time since it had been just recently developed during World War II. Now we have a situation where we have incomplete data that might be evaluated under a variety of scenarios to give ranges of possible outcomes for the engineer's analysis. Another problem tackled at the refinery related to heat exchangers that periodically needed to be "wash-welded" to relieve lining deterioration. At what point is it more economical to replace the exchanger than to continue with the expensive wash-welding? In later chapters, after first being thoroughly schooled in the fundamentals of economic alternative evaluation, we will look at ways to evaluate situations with incomplete data, inexact data, and data that are probabilistic (uncertain).

A decision is simply the selection from two or more courses of action, whether it takes place in construction or production operations, service or manufacturing industries, private or public agencies. Some choices are trivial or largely automatic, but, as we have seen, other decisions can be challenging and exciting experiences. Most major decisions, even personal ones, have economic overtones. This consistent usage makes the subject of engineering economics especially challenging and rewarding.

1.2   ENGINEERING AND ECONOMICS

Before 1940, engineers were mainly concerned with the design, construction, and operation of machines, structures, and processes. They gave less attention to the resources, human and physical, that produced the final products. Many factors have since contributed to an expansion of engineering responsibilities and concerns.

Besides the traditional work with scientists to develop discoveries about nature into useful products, engineers are now expected not only to generate novel technological solutions but also to make skillful financial analyses of the effects of implementation. In today's close and tangled relations among industry, the public, and government, cost and value analyses are expected to be more detailed and inclusive (e.g., worker safety, environmental effects, consumer protection, resource conservation) than ever before. Without these analyses, an entire project can easily become more of a burden than a benefit.

Most definitions of engineering suggest that the mission of engineers is to transform the resources of nature for the benefit of the human race. The types of resources susceptible to engineering enrichment include everything from ores and crops to information and energy. A growing awareness of the finite limits of the earth's resources has added a pressing dimension to engineering evaluations. The focus on scarce resources welds engineering to economics.

Paul A. Samuelson, Nobel laureate in economics, and William D. Nordhaus suggest that

> Economists today agree on a general definition something like the following: Economics is the study of how people and society choose to employ scarce resources that could have alternative uses in order to produce various commodities and to distribute them for consumption, now or in the future, among various persons and groups in society.[†]

[†]Paul A. Samuelson and William D. Nordhaus, *Economics,* 12th ed., McGraw-Hill, New York, 1985.

The relation of engineering to economics can be likened to that of engineering to physics. Scientists are devoted to the discovery and explanation of nature's laws. Engineers work with scientists and translate the revelations to practical applications. The "laws" of economics are not as precise as those of physics, but their obvious application to the production and utilization of scarce resources ensures increasing attention from engineers.

1.3   ECONOMICS: A CAPSULE VIEW

Economics, like engineering, has informal roots deep in history. The construction of the pyramids is considered an engineering marvel. It was also a significant economic accomplishment in that it funneled all the necessary resources into monuments rather than consuming them in commerce. The formal roots of economics stretch back two centuries to the publication (in 1776) of Adam Smith's *The Wealth of Nations*.

Early writings deplored government intervention in commerce and promoted a laissez faire policy. In *An Essay on the Principles of Population* (1798), Thomas Malthus conjectured about the causes of economic crises, saying that population tends to increase geometrically and the means of subsistence only arithmetically; his forecasts of misery for most of the population predisposed the "dismal science" nickname for economics. Later John Stuart Mill, in his *Treatise on Political Economy* (1800), argued against Malthus' pessimism by suggesting that the laws of distribution are not as immutable as are the laws of production. Modern doomsday scenarios indicate that the issue is still in doubt.

In *Das Kapital* (1867), Karl Marx argued that capitalism would be superseded by socialism, which would then develop into communism. According to his view, workers produce more value than they receive in wages. The surplus takes the form of profit and allows capital accumulation. He argued that the capitalist system will eventually fail, owing to cyclic depressions and other inherent weaknesses. Recent dramatic changes in the political and geographical structure of eastern Europe show that the percentage of the world's population that agrees with Marx is dwindling.

"New economics" evolved from the work of John Maynard Keynes in the 1930s. In *The General Theory of Employment, Interest, and Money*, Keynes[†] clashed with classical economic theory by proclaiming, e.g., that interest rates and price-wage adjustments are not adequate mechanisms for controlling unemployment in capitalistic economies. Refinements and extensions of the original work are collectively called *keynesian economics*, which is one of many current schools of economic thought.

[†]J. M. Keynes, *The General Theory of Unemployment, Interest, and Money,* Harcourt, Brace and Co., New York, 1936.

6

Keynes' and Marx's theories deal with the entire economic system with respect to national income, flow of money, consumption, investment, wages, and general prices. This level of analysis concerned with the economy as a whole is called *macroeconomics*. It produces economywide statistical measures such as the national cost-of-living index and total employment figures.

Microeconomics is the study of economic behavior in very small segments of the economy, such as a particular firm or household. It is generally assumed that the objective of a firm is to maximize profit and the objective of a household is to maximize satisfaction. Measurement statistics for a small economic unit might be the number of workers employed by a firm and income or expenditures of a given firm or family.

Engineering economics, with its focus on economic decision making in an individual organizational unit, is closely aligned with microeconomics.

1.4 ENGINEERING ECONOMY: A SHORT HISTORY

The Economic Theory of the Location of Railways, written by Arthur M. Wellington in 1887, pioneered an engineering interest in economic evaluations. Wellington, a civil engineer, reasoned that the capitalized cost method of analysis should be utilized in selecting the preferred lengths of rail lines or curvatures of the lines. He delightfully captured the thrust of engineering economy:

> It would be well if engineering were less generally thought of, and even defined, as the art of constructing. In a certain important sense it is rather the art of not constructing; or, to define it rudely but not ineptly, it is the art of doing that well with one dollar which any bungler can do with two after a fashion.[†]

In the 1920s, C. L. Fish and O. B. Goldman looked at investments in engineered structures from the perspective of actuarial mathematics. Fish[‡] formulated an investment model related to the bond market. In *Financial Engineering,* Goldman proposed a compound-interest procedure for determining comparative values and said that

> It seems peculiar and is indeed very unfortunate that so many authors in their engineering books give no, or very little, consideration to costs, in spite of the fact that the primary duty of the engineer is to consider costs in order to obtain real economy—to get the most possible number of dollars and cents: to get the best financial efficiency.[§]

[†]A. M. Wellington, *The Economic Theory of the Location of Railways,* John Wiley & Sons, New York, 1887.
[‡]C. L. Fish, *Engineering Economics,* 2d ed., McGraw-Hill, New York, 1923.
[§]O. B. Goldman, *Financial Planning,* John Wiley & Sons, Inc., New York, 1920.

The confines of classical engineering economy were staked out in 1930 by Eugene L. Grant in *Principles of Engineering Economy.*[†] Grant discussed the importance of judgment factors and short-term investment evaluation as well as conventional comparisons of long-run investments in capital goods based on compound-interest calculations. His many contributions resulted in the recognition that "Eugene L. Grant can truthfully be called the father of engineering economy."[‡]

Modern approaches to discounted cash flow and capital rationing were influenced by the work of Joel Dean.[§] He incorporated the theories of Keynes and other economists to develop ways to analyze the effects of supply and demand for investment funds in allocating resources.

Current developments are pushing the frontiers of engineering economics to encompass new methods of risk, sensitivity, and intangible analysis. Traditional methods are being refined to reflect today's concerns for resource conservation and effective utilization of public funds.

EXAMPLE 1.1   **Economics of Energy**

The divergent missions of classical economics and engineering economics are apparent when a specific application is examined. Consider the energy problem. How serious is it? What are its dimensions? What can be done about it?

Energy supply and demand relations fit familiar economic concepts. Collection of data about who uses how much energy falls into the province of economic demographics, a growing branch of economics that deals with the consequence of changes in the characteristics of the nation's population. An optimal energy mix that best utilizes the national energy supply can be determined according to market prices and market risks, economic principles that give priority to energy sources that are cheapest and carry the least risk, other things being equal.

From an understanding of supply-demand relations, engineering effort can be unleashed to overcome technological constraints. If solar or geothermal energy appears to be the most promising source, engineers must provide the means to convert the promise to reality. Engineering economics can be applied to evaluate alternative solutions.

A proposal from the U.S. National Academy of Sciences is to ease the energy crisis by reducing waste. Amazing advances have been made since the first oil shortage in 1972, but more are needed. U.S. federal regulations that mandate progressively more efficient fuel consumption by automobiles (voluntary in Canada) have had dramatic effects on consumption per automobile as well as emissions generated. Other actions to plug energy leaks

---

[†]E. L. Grant, *Principles of Engineering Economy,* The Ronald Press, New York, 1930.
[‡]A. Lesser, Jr., "Engineering Economy in the United States in Retrospect—An Analysis," *The Engineering Economist,* vol. 14, no. 2, pp. 109–115, 1969.
[§]J. Dean, *Capital Budgeting,* Columbia, New York, 1951.

in the national economic machine include correcting heat losses in offices and homes, creating better building designs, building more energy-efficient machines and automobiles, and developing cogeneration of electricity and steam. Effects of a broad-based Btu energy tax, proposed by the Clinton administration in 1993 (not passed), as contrasted to dramatic increases in federal gasoline taxes (passed), have to be quantified with reliable data to predict the outcomes and determine the better alternative. Estimating gas flows, comparing investment proposals, and testing the sensitivity of specific energy conservation actions are tasks for engineering economists.

1.5 PROBLEM SOLVING AND DECISION MAKING

An engineering economist draws upon the accumulated knowledge of engineering and economics to fashion and employ tools to identify a preferred course of action. The tools developed so far are not perfect. There is still considerable debate about their theoretical bases and how they should be used. This concern is wholesome because it promises improved procedures, but the variety of analysis techniques can frustrate practitioners, especially inexperienced ones: There are many aspects to consider and many ways to consider them.

The fundamental approach to economic problem solving is to elaborate on the time-honored *scientific method*. The method is anchored in two worlds: the real, everyday working world and the abstract, scientifically

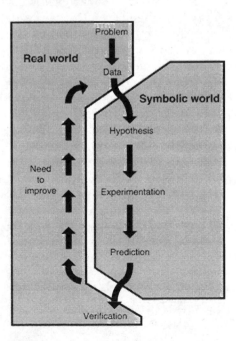

FIGURE 1.1
Problem-solving
process.

oriented world, as depicted in Fig. 1.1. Problems in engineering and managerial economy originate in the real world of economic planning, management, and control. The problem is confined and clarified by *data* from the real world. This information is combined with scientific principles supplied by the analyst to formulate a *hypothesis* in symbolic terms. The symbolic language aids the digestion of data. By manipulating and *experimenting* with the abstractions of the real world, the analyst can simulate multiple configurations of reality that otherwise would be too costly or too inconvenient to investigate. From this activity a *prediction* usually emerges.

The predicted behavior is converted back to reality for testing in the form of hardware, designs, or commands. If it is valid, the problem is solved. If not, the cycle is repeated with the added information that the previous approach was unsuccessful. Fortunately, a host of successful approaches have been discovered and validated for economic analyses; the challenge now is to use them wisely.

1.5.1 Intuition and Analysis

Because engineers generally attack practical problems with solution deadlines instead of engaging in esoteric issues for long-term enlightenment, their mission might appear relatively simple. Engineering economic evaluations could even seem mundane, since they usually rely on data from the marketplace and technology from the shelf—simply grab prices from a catalog, plug them into a handy formula, and grind out an answer. Occasionally, such a routine works. Spectacular workbench discoveries and overnight fortunes attest to the fact that plungers sometimes win. There are also innumerable instances where rule-of-thumb, skin-deep evaluations are absolutely unsatisfactory.

As represented in Fig. 1.2, a decision made now is based on data from past performances and establishes a course of action that will result in some future outcome. When the decision is shallow and the outcomes are not of much consequence, a reflex response based upon intuition is feasible. Instinctive judgments are often formalized by *standard operating procedures (SOPs)*. In economic analyses, SOPs often take the form of worksheets for the justification of investments. Such short-form justifications are typically limited to smaller investments, say, less than $10,000, that can be recaptured from savings generated by the investment within 6 months or 1 year. These SOP forms represent collective intuition derived from experience. They have a secure place in economic evaluations, but their use should be tempered by economic principles and a continuing audit to verify that previous judgments are appropriate for current decisions.

Most significant problems require both analysis and personal judgment. Initially the analyst settles on which evaluation technique to utilize and how to apply it. As the solution procedures progress, factors that are

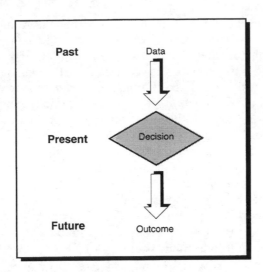

FIGURE 1.2
Decision-making process.

difficult to quantify often arise. These are called *intangibles;* they represent aspects of a problem that cannot be translated readily to monetary values. Intuitive ratings are frequently assigned to intangibles to allow them to be included in the decision process. Judgment also enters the process in determining whether a solution is well enough founded to be accepted. Thus intuition and judgment complement analysis methods by contributing to better decisions.

EXAMPLE 1.2

To Intuit or to Analyze

Most decision makers informally set boundaries for routine responses to noncritical problems of a personal and professional nature. Three possible parameters to identify routine responses are shown in Fig. 1.3. The level that separates an automatic decision from a problem that requires more investigation varies among decision makers.

Since there are limits to a decision maker's time and energy whereas the reservoir of problems often seems infinite, guidelines are necessary to confine involvement. SOPs do save time. An intuitive response is quick. Both draw upon experience to yield a reasonable solution. However, handy answers may mask better solutions than could have been exposed by analysis. What was good for yesterday's operations may not be adequate for tomorrow's.

1.5.2 Tactics and Strategy

About the only thing more frustrating than a wrong decision for an important problem is the right decision for the wrong problem. Some problems

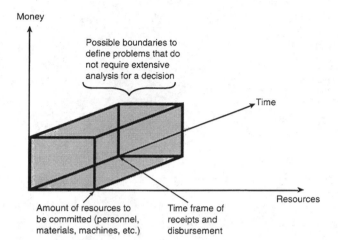

FIGURE 1.3
Criteria for routine
responses to an
economic problem.

are virtually handed to an analyst on a platter, complete with data trimmings. More commonly, a problem is ill-defined, and the analyst is forced to seek the intent of a solution before applying analytical tools. Recognizing the difference between tactical and strategic considerations may clarify the purpose.

Strategy and *tactics* historically are military terms associated with broad plans from the high command and specific schedules from lower echelons, respectively. Strategy sets ultimate objectives, and the associated tactics define the multiple maneuvers required to achieve the objectives. Strategic and tactical considerations have essentially the same meaning for economic studies.

There are usually several strategies available to an organization. A strategic decision ideally selects the overall plan that makes the best use of the organization's resources in accordance with its long-range objectives. A strategic industrial decision could be a choice from several different product designs to develop or products to promote. In government, strategic evaluations could take the form of benefit-cost analyses to select the preferred method of flood control or development of recreational sites. The measure of merit for strategic alternatives is *effectiveness*—the degree to which a plan meets economic targets.

A strategic plan can normally be implemented in a number of ways. For example, each industrial design or product has tactical alternatives, such as which kind of machine to employ or materials to use; tactics for flood control might involve choices among dams, levees, dredging, etc. The relative values of tactical choices are rated according to their *efficiency*—the degree to which an operation accomplishes a mission within economic expectations.

The relationship between strategies and tactics offers some constructive insights. The effectiveness of each strategy is initially estimated from the effect it will have on system objectives. It thus serves as a guide to the

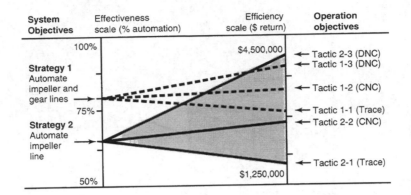

FIGURE 1.4
Relation of strategies and real-world tactics.

area in which tactics will produce the highest efficiency. The actual efficiency of each tactic is determined from a study of the activities required to conduct the tactical operation.

An aerospace engine manufacturer is considering job shop automation. Two strategies, each with three apparent means of accomplishment, are depicted in Fig. 1.4. Strategy 2 is to automate the impeller line, which will automate about 65 percent of the total shop. Strategy 1 is to automate both impeller and gear lines, which will affect about 80 percent of the facility. The company has decided that the effectiveness measure is the percentage of shop automation. The tactics shown in Fig. 1.4 represent approaches to automation. *DNC* refers to centralized, integrated direct numerical control by computer, *CNC* is local *computer numerical control* for each machine, and *trace* refers to template tracing and duplication for multiple-part setups. The efficiency, or means by which each approach is measured, in this case will be the dollar benefits from installing the new equipment. In this case, we have a situation where the best dollar return is not realized by the "most effective" strategy. Possibly, the cost of automating the gear line is relatively higher than for the impeller portion of the shop. The selection of a tactic policy must be evaluated in relation to the strategic objectives and the resources required for implementation.

1.5.3 Sensitivity and Suboptimization

The decision situation related by Fig. 1.4 has high sensitivity; i.e., it is vulnerable to small changes in the controlling conditions. With tactics 1-3 and 2-3 so close on the efficiency scale, a slight change in operating conditions or external influencing factors could switch the positions of the top tactics, or even the strategies. An insensitive situation occurs when all the tactics for a given strategy have a higher efficiency than the best tactic of any other strategy. The consequence of high sensitivity is to force a complete investigation to ensure the validity of the data being evaluated.

A *sensitivity analysis* can be conducted on any problem to explore the effects of deviations from the original problem conditions. Since most engineering economic problems extend over a period of years, future cash flows are necessarily estimated. These estimations may be quite reliable, but it is often enlightening to observe how the attractiveness of alternatives varies as the initial estimates are altered.

Whenever there are multiple objectives in a decision situation, it is probable that there is no single course of action that will optimize all the objectives simultaneously. In general, suboptimization occurs when there is a larger problem than the analyst had visualized. It is always tempting to employ a classical textbook solution to a real-world problem, whether or not it truly fits the actual conditions. The availability of "canned" computerized solutions to complex problems increases the temptation. Another cause of suboptimal solutions is the legitimate analysis technique of partitioning a large problem into a set of interdependant smaller problems during a preliminary investigation to avoid being bogged down in a deluge of details. Trouble enters when tentative solutions to the subproblems are not integrated. Advances in computer science and operations research may eventually allow analysis of an entire complex system in a single evaluation, but until then, it helps to be aware of the areas in which suboptimization is most likely to occur. Three regularly encountered perspectives that lead to suboptimization are described below.

1. *The cross-eyed view.* Both organizations and individuals can be confused by opposing objectives. An example of the danger inherent in focusing on only one parameter while blurring others is what would happen to a company that redeployed its resources to save its ailing flagship product at the expense of the rest of the product line. The rescue could boost sales for the previously eminent product while total sales declined owing to the drain on resources suffered by the rest of the company's products; thus, the battle could be won, but the war lost.

   Individuals seeking "the good life" also get caught by conflicting goals. If "good" is interpreted as "long and full," then unlimited pleasure seeking for a full life would undoubtedly jeopardize the health needed for a long life. Moderation, however, should produce a temperate plan to satisfy both goals, resulting in a life less full but longer. Of course, there are also irreconcilable objectives such as those pictured in Fig. 1.5.

2. *The shortsighted view.* Tactics based on a planning horizon of 1 or 2 years may not have the same efficiency as those based on a longer span of years. Suppose that a manufacturer anticipates using a fixed number of containers each year. The containers can be purchased, or the manufacturer can make them by acquiring new production equipment. Costs for the choices are displayed by the chart in Fig. 1.6. (This is a break-even chart, and a major discussion of such charts ensues later in this book.) A planning horizon under 2 years would indicate that purchasing is the preferable alternative; beyond 2 years it is more attractive to make the containers. Individuals face the same danger of suboptimization in lease-or-buy decisions for housing and transportation.

FIGURE 1.5
Symbolic world strategy and real-world tactics.

3. *Tunnel vision viewpoint.* Organizations are very susceptible to situations in which departments understand the common goal but individually go about working in ways that hurt the goal. A typical example is the goal to reduce material and inventory costs, as viewed by

- Purchasing: Buy in large quantities to get quantity discounts.
- Comptroller: Buy in smaller quantities to avoid paying interest on the capital required for purchases.
- Production: Larger inventories allow longer production runs that reduce manufacturing costs.
- Warehousing: Larger inventories cost more to store and increase the cost of material handling.

If each of the involved departments acts independently, inventory levels will repeatedly go up and down over time like a yo-yo. A workable plan will obviously be a compromise, probably satisfying no one com-

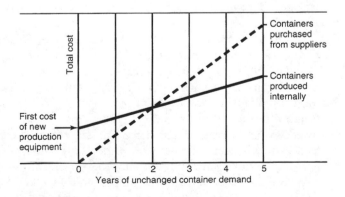

FIGURE 1.6
Pattern for potential suboptimization owing to shortsightedness.

pletely but still producing lower total material costs for the organization as a whole.

EXAMPLE 1.3   **When Optimizing Might Not Be Optimal**

Sheet-metal operations in an aircraft engine manufacturing plant pose some interesting problems, two of which might show that optimizing on a cost basis might not lead to a beneficial solution.

Problem 1. As just mentioned in the discussion of the tunnel vision viewpoint, different people in the organization can have different perspectives on reducing inventory and materials. An aircraft engine requires very complex welding operations to join intricate sheet-metal shapes. Expensive tooling is required to correctly position the parts to be welded. The time to set up parts to be welded can be lengthy, and the setup operation can cost thousands of dollars. Once the fixtures are set up, the parts can be welded in a relatively short time. The value of parts by the time they reach the welding operation can also be in the thousands of dollars. The production quantities required for each of the welded assemblies, on an annual basis, will not utilize a welding station for a very large percentage of the time. A mathematical model can be developed to optimize the total inventory charges, usually called the *lot-sizing model,* which results in the "optimum" number of parts to produce when a welding station has been set up for that part. The time to produce these parts might take, for example, 3 weeks. Then a different fixture is set up for another part. Because of the high costs of conventional tooling, it is possible that 1 or 2 months' worth of inventory for a part might be waiting to go into final assembly, thus creating congestion on the shop floor and tying up capital in the costly parts. Industry today is moving more and more to *just-in-time (JIT) production,* where just the right amount of inventory is available just when needed, relieving congestion and capital tie-up. This is very difficult to do with old, expensive fixturing. One solution is to set up a robotic welding manufacturing cell where up to four welding fixtures can be available to the robot, which can easily alternate between different parts on different fixtures. The economic evaluation for such a cell takes every ounce of skill that the engineering economist has.

Problem 2. Management makes a decision to implement a complex robotic welding manufacturing cell to handle applicable welding assemblies. The manufacturing engineer has determined that the cell can be occupied 95 percent of the time with applicable parts, and the engineering economist has determined that the system should be able to pay for itself within 12 months, much to the satisfaction of manufacturing management. Unfortunately, the people involved did not look at the rest of the system— *the total manufacturing process.* Parts coming to the robotic cell came from traditional manufacturing operations. But to keep the cell busy, management decided to always have inventory waiting to go into the cell so that it would never be idle due to lack of materials. As a result, there was congestion on the work floor around the cell. The productivity level of the cell was so good that subassembled (welded) parts were produced without consideration of when they would be needed in the final assembly line. The final assembly line then became congested with parts that might not be used for a week or so. The moral to this story is that the entire system needs to be considered when one is performing optimization studies. Yes, the robotic cell was optimized, but this turned out to be suboptimization when the entire system was considered, and the entire system was surely not optimized.

1.6 ENGINEERING ECONOMIC DECISION MAZE

Most important decisions in engineering economics entail consideration of future events. A focus on the future has always had a special and irresistible appeal, but it also encumbers the mission of engineering economists. Not only must they search the past to understand the present and survey the present for hints about the future, but also they must consolidate the accumulated results into a pattern that is susceptible to analysis and then select a decision rule to yield a verdict. The complexities involved are similar to going through a maze, as depicted in Fig. 1.7.

It would take a much larger maze to portray all the pitfalls and challenges of economic analyses, but enough are included to expose the anatomy of engineering economics and to map the contents of this book. All the channels within the maze represent subjects treated in chapters to follow. As is apparent in the decision labyrinth, there are many paths by which we could travel to get from a problem to a solution. Which path is utilized depends on the nature of the problem and the type of analysis that is most appropriate. Because problems come in such profuse variety and there are so many ways to evaluate them, engineering economics is rich in application opportunities and offers rewarding challenges to its practitioners.

1.7 OVERVIEW OF CHEER AND SHEER

CHEER and SHEER (*C*omputerized *H*elp **or** *S*preadsheet *H*elp for *E*ngineering *E*conomy *R*esults) are two computer programs that provide support for solving engineering economy problems. A text objective is to emphasize fundamentals so that the manual approach to any problem should be thoroughly understood before you use any program. CHEER can be used with no knowledge of the program structure or the programming language; CHEER provides a WINDOWS environment. User interface with CHEER is through structured screens and menus. The system provides complete file manipulation and data editing capabilities. "Logical"

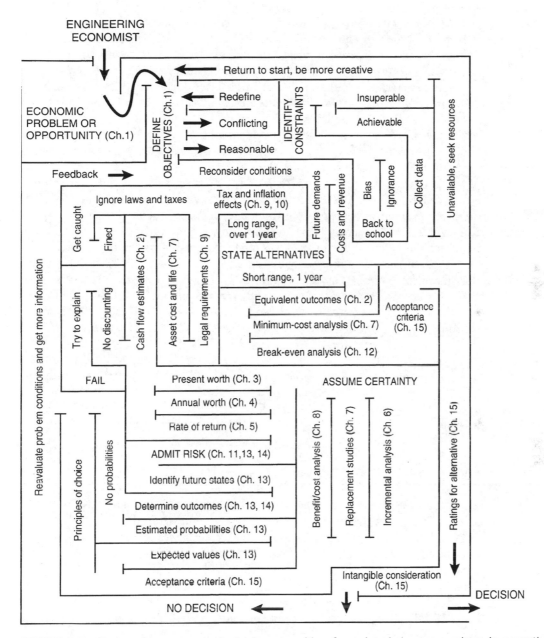

FIGURE 1.7 Engineering economic decision maze with a few related chapter numbers in parentheses (only a few of the starting and ending path arrows are shown).

error checks are built into the system; thus users are prompted for action if "out-of-bound" conditions are encountered.

CHEER provides functions for most of the concepts in engineering economics: *before-tax cash flow (BTCF) analysis,* with present worth, annual worth, future worth, and internal rate of return results; *after-tax cash flow*

(ATCF) analysis, including depreciation computations; *sensitivity analysis,* where the effect of individual factors (e.g., revenues, costs, interest rates, salvage value) on present worth of an investment is explored; and *risk analysis,* where probability distribution functions for uncertain parameters are utilized. Graphic capabilities are available for sensitivity analyses and risk analyses. *Stand-alone functions* in CHEER include (1) look-up interest formula values, (2) payback period computations, and (3) loan analysis. Although CHEER is completely integrated into one package, segments of the program can be used independently of others. For example, users can perform BTCF analysis or do a risk evaluation without using other features of the program. A complete user's guide for CHEER can be found in App. B.

SHEER gives QUATRO PRO for Windows capability for spreadsheet analysis. Tableaus with sample data and results are displayed for each of the twelve functions available to the user, and the data can be modified as needed to allow analysis of the user's specific problems. Entry to each function tableau is through a user-friendly menu. The functions handled by SHEER are: *interest formula value look-up; loan payment analysis; cash flow equivalencies* (present worth, future worth, annual worth); *internal rate of return computations*—three methods are available; *depreciation computation;* Canadian *capital cost allowance (CCA)* methods for *declining balance* and *straight-line* classes of assets; *modified accelerated cost recovery system* (MACRS)—straight line or accelerated depreciation method; and *after-tax cash flow (ATCF) analysis.* SHEER parallels much of CHEER's capability but, because of the spreadsheet attributes, functions are not integrated as well as by CHEER. SHEER's user guide is given in App. C.

1.8   PERPETUAL-MOTION MYSTIQUE

The idea of perpetual motion—something for nothing—seems to be a persistent, insidious dream of humans. It has been around a long time. Over 2000 years ago the Chinese searched for an unpowered "everlasting going." Archimedes tried to find it through hydraulics, and da Vinci experimented with gravity-powered mechanisms. In 1670, John Wilkens, the Bishop of Chester, designed a ramp leading to a pedestal where a magnet was mounted. The magnet was supposed to attract an iron ball up the ramp until it fell off onto a chute that returned it to the bottom of the ramp, again and again and . . . .

A perpetual-motion machine was exhibited in New York City in 1813. People paid to see little carriers ceaselessly moving up and down inclined planes to drive a wheel which offered free energy. Robert Fulton, of steamboat fame, exposed the hoax by showing that the contraption was connected by a hidden strand of catgut to a hand-powered crank in an adjacent room.

The mystique of perpetual-motion machines has a counterpart in economic ventures—rewards without inputs. The engineering economist has to possess a firm foundation of knowledge which has to be logically applied to a problem before economic decisions can be feasibly recommended.

| 1.9 | **REVIEW EXERCISES AND DISCUSSIONS** |

EXERCISE 1

The First Canadian Edition of *Engineering Economics* discussed the activities that would undoubtedly have far-reaching effects on engineering practices, with emphasis on

1. The passage of national, provincial, and local legislation that regulates industrial operations and developments
2. The formation of public pressure groups whose efforts are directed toward improving the quality of life
3. Concern about low productivity in industries

Does it seem that these activities are still coming into play as far as engineering practices are concerned?

SOLUTION 1

Of course, they are. Just consider the following:

Effect of legislation. Just as the Occupational Health and Safety legislation has had a profound effect on safety concerns in the factory, hospital, university, and all other occupational locations, so will the acts that deal with the welfare of the physically challenged. The effect on the design of the workplace, building design and construction, and so on, is enormous. Added costs have to be made up from the business, and so the engineering economist will see extensive needs for alternative evaluations in the years to come.

Another legislative action that is having a major effect on the way business is conducted is the North American Free Trade Agreement (NAFTA) which became effective in 1994. The potential for enlarged markets and freer competition will make economic analyses even more critical when new products are being considered as well as the effects of changing demand for products on production facilities.

Effect of pressure groups. Consumer protection groups have successfully campaigned for automobile modifications and control of waste discharges. New technologies have to be developed to protect the quality of air, water, and land; the relationship between control costs and quality levels is largely an engineering function. Management decisions are likely to be made in the light of the total environment to be affected. The nuclear power plant accidents that have been so detrimental to the environment would not have had such a profound effect if the plants' designers had taken into consideration all the factors surrounding the operation of the facility, including the possibility of human error.

Effect of productivity investments. Canada and the U.S.A are just starting to see the fruits of productivity investments. These have come about through total quality control and innovative manufacturing and assembly methods. Two prime examples include the 1993 resurgence of the automobile industry and advances in semiconductor devices. All aspects of quality and the just-in-time concept with its relative inventory reductions have been prime movers to productivity improvement. The bottom line is, of course, being able to compete on an international scale from a monetary viewpoint. The role of the engineering economist should only grow with the need for further productivity gains.

EXERCISE 2

A subassembly line has been giving the production manager nightmares for months. All kinds of minor modifications have been tried, and all failed to improve output. The current per-unit cost is $4.20, which seems reasonable, but output has failed to reach the required 10,000 units per year. A check with the purchasing department reveals that supplementary units are now being purchased for $4.75 each; but one vendor agrees to provide them at $4.50 each if the entire annual demand is ordered.

The subassembly-line supervisor suggests acquiring three new machines to mechanize successive stages of the production process. Engineers calculate that the machines' total purchase price of $100,000 would make their discounted annual cost over a 10-year machine life, coupled with yearly operating costs, amount to $27,000. The discounted annual cost takes investment rates into consideration and is a major topic that will be covered later in this text. If needed, the machines have the capacity to double the present output. At the present output level, the remaining subassembly costs using the new machines will annually total $18,000.

While investigating the problem, the engineers uncovered another alternative: All three successive operations could be combined and handled by a single machine. This one combination machine would have the same capacity, speed, life, and remaining production costs as the three-machine alternative, but ownership and operating costs would be reduced by $3000 per year.

Which alternative should be accepted, and why?

SOLUTION 2

Apparently it has been decided that something must be done to improve subassembly production, so the do-nothing alternative is eliminated. The single machine is obviously more attractive than the three-machine alternative because the combined operation costs $3000 less. The unit cost for the one-machine alternative is

$$\frac{\$27{,}000 + \$18{,}000 - \$3000}{10{,}000 \text{ subassemblies}} = \$4.20 \text{ per subassembly}$$

This unit cost is the same as the current cost, but promises greater reliability. It is also $0.30 per unit less expensive ($4.50 − $4.20) than purchasing all the subassemblies from a supplier. However, more information is needed about the long-range (10-year) expected demand for the subassemblies. Without this information, the decision is subject to the make-or-buy pattern of suboptimization shown in Fig. 1.6. The discounted cash flow computations needed for the annual costing will be covered in Chaps. 2 through 5.

1.10   PROBLEMS

1.1 There are many general definitions of engineering and specific ones for different branches of engineering. Look up one and comment on the explicit and/or implied attention paid to economic considerations.

1.2 It has been said that economists are very busy people because they have to spend all their time telling what's going to happen and then explaining why it did not. Engineering economists also work with forecasts of the future but are not usually subjected to such joking comments. Why?

1.3 *Efficiency* is defined as output divided by input (multiplied by 100 percent). Engineering efficiency is commendable when it approaches 100 percent, but financial efficiency must exceed 100 percent before it is considered adequate. Explain.

1.4 Why do economic projections for a future event tend to vary more widely than engineering estimates of performance for a new design?

1.5 Given the question in Prob. 1.4, why might there be less confidence in the economic performance than in the operating performance of a new machine?

1.6 Earlier we discussed the possibility of using lot-size computations to determine the number of parts to weld in a sheet-metal operation after the fixtures have been set up. Can you see the analogy of this process for a bookstore owner? Do you think the JIT concept would be feasible for a bookstore?

1.7 Spark Electric Company is evaluating whether to manufacture a part in its own facility or to subcontract it from the Automack Company. Spark estimates its start-up costs (equipment, fixtures, facility readying) to be $85,000. The materials-and-labor cost to produce each part is estimated to be $150. Automack submits a bid of $280 per part delivered to Spark's plant. Assuming that no other data are needed, draw a break-even chart to show the total minimum number of parts that would have to be produced to justify Spark's producing in its own facility.

1.8 For the situation in Prob. 1.7, suppose that Spark estimates that materials and labor costs will both increase at 5 percent per year for each year following the first year's production. Also Automack submits a new bid of $300 per part for the first 500 parts contracted for and $225 per part for all parts produced afterward. The estimated demand is 500 parts for the first year, 600 parts for the second year, and 450 parts for the third year. Management requires that a make-or-buy decision be based on a maximum time frame of 18 months. Would you recommend to make or to buy? Why?

1.9 Would the decision made in Prob. 1.8 change if management accepted a 36-month time horizon for the evaluation period instead of 18 months?

1.10 Why, do you think, would management in Prob. 1.8 specify a time span of 18 months rather than 36 months?

1.11 An engineer contemplates the bulging walls of a large concrete culvert under a multi-lane highway. The collapsing culvert is the result of thousands of tonnes of rock recently stockpiled on roadbed above in preparation for new construction. In a few days, the spring thaw will soak the ground and send torrents of water through the culvert. The engineer speculates on possible designs in terms of the conditions and restrictions imposed by available equipment, materials, and time. Identify the strategic or tactical nature of each decision faced by the engineer, and discuss the factors that should be considered (including sensitivity, if appropriate).

1.12 Answer the same question as just posed in Prob. 1.11, but for the following scenario: The owner of a wholesale distribution center seeks to improve her delivery service in order to meet competition. To do so, she can buy or rent more trucks, subcontract deliveries, open additional outlets, and/or improve the handling facilities. Capital is limited, and the outlook for increased volume is uncertain. First she must decide if any action is needed. If it is, she must select the most useful alternative.

EXTENSION 1A   SUPPLY AND DEMAND

1A.1   From Resources to Products

Engineering is the profession that deals with the process of converting scarce resources into desired valuable products. As shown in Figure 1A.1, design decisions and the production process play the key role in the efficient transformation of resources into products.

Decisions on how to transform valuable resources into more valuable products are made by engineers. Three main factors contribute to the efficiency of the production process: (1) the nature of the transformation process, (2) the values associated with the resources, and (3) the values of the products.

The value of resources or cost functions are usually defined by the economic market for the resources used, which also include engineering services. On the other hand, the values of products are determined either by a market or, in the absence of a market for some products such as social benefits (e.g., environmental quality), by the political process.

Engineering activities can take many forms:

- Research and development required for discovery and refinement of new products and processes
- Planning, which consists of problem definition, solution generation, solution analysis, evaluation, and choice

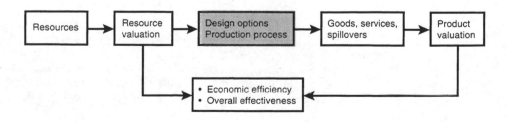

FIGURE 1A.1
Transformation of resources into products.

- Design to create an efficient production process that uses resources and produces products or services
- Coordination and supervision of activities for fabrication or construction
- Operation of a system, including testing and inspection for the evaluation of the production process
- Management of public and private projects and services

In addition to ensuring the technical and economic efficiency of the production processes, it is essential to investigate the overall effectiveness of transformation of resources into products, which depends upon economic as well as social factors. Engineering combines expertise in the physical characteristics of resources with a knowledge of the economic factors in order to optimize the transformation function.

A knowledge of the supply-demand interaction is necessary for the success of projects and systems.

1A.2 Demand Function

The relationship between price and demand shown in Figure 1A.2 indicates that as the price per unit is lowered, demand rises. On the other hand, higher prices result in a drop in sales. Therefore it is customary to show the demand curve D with a downward slope, which reflects buyers' response to changes in price. That is, a lowering of the price would attract new customers and encourage previous buyers to increase their purchases. It should be noted that for a given fixed demand curve, changes in prices are reflected in quantity demanded. For a fixed demand curve, changes in

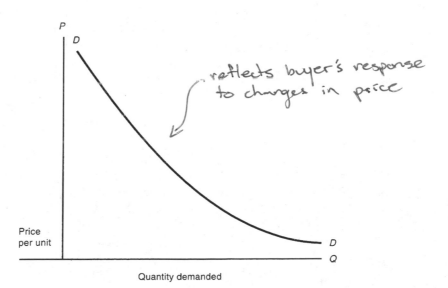

reflects buyer's response to changes in price

FIGURE 1A.2
Demand function.

quantity demanded that correspond to price changes can be found by movement along the demand curve.

1A.3 Elasticity of Demand

Marketing decisions rely heavily on the behavior of demand with changes in price. Technological advances and other cost-reduction initiatives by engineers frequently result in lower production costs. These cost savings can be used to cut prices in order to sell more units, with the expectation of an increase in total revenue. However, this may not be the case. Depending upon the response of demand to a drop in price of the product, it is possible that the lowering of the price would actually decrease the total dollar revenue for the product. In another context, a similar effect may result in the form of a drop in total revenue when a government commission permits a regulated utility to raise prices with the intent to increase revenue. The total revenue may even drop since the price rise could trigger consumer actions leading to a high drop in demand.

For improved decisions on lowering or raising prices for products, the concept of *elasticity* of demand has to be understood. It should also be noted here that for enhancing the profit, an increase in gross revenue is not a sufficient condition. In such cases, changes in total revenues as well as total costs are to be studied.

The demand function or curve can take on a variety of forms. The price elasticity of demand expresses a very important characteristic of the shape of the demand function for products. Price elasticity of demand is a measure of the rate of change of quantity demanded relative to the rate of change in price.

In general, the value of elasticity of demand at one point will differ from its value at another point. The precise definition of elasticity is based on the derivative of the demand function at a point. However, as an approximate definition, it is often defined as the percentage change in quantity demanded resulting from a 1 percent change in price.

For a demand function for which a mathematical equation is known, the elasticity at a reference point can be expressed as:

$$E_d = (dQ/dP)(P/Q)$$

(See Figure 1A.3.)

In the case of an arc shown in Figure 1A.4, the measure of elasticity of demand is the ratio of percentage change in Q to the corresponding percentage change in P. Specifically, the arc price elasticity of demand is calculated as:

$$\text{The arc price elasticity} = -\frac{\% \text{ Change in } Q}{\% \text{ Change in } P} = -\frac{(\text{Change in } Q)/\text{Avg } Q}{(\text{Change in } P)/\text{Avg } P}$$

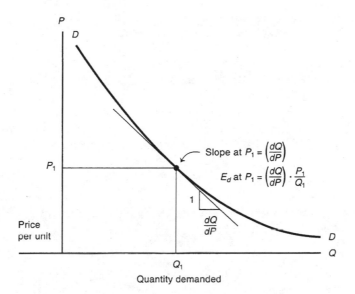

FIGURE 1A.3
Point elasticity.

$$E_d = - \frac{(Q_2 - Q_1)/[(Q_1 + Q_2)/2]}{(P_2 - P_1)/[(P_1 + P_2)/2]}$$

Where Q_1 and Q_2 represent the quantities of good demanded in response to price levels of P_1 and P_2, respectively.

Another form of the arc elasticity equation is:

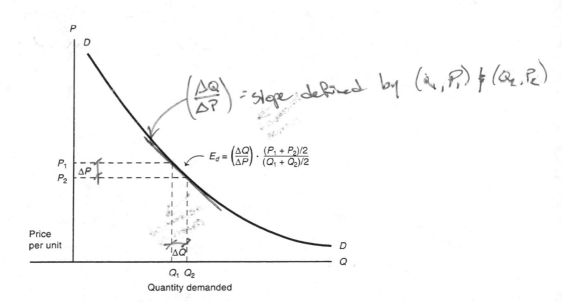

FIGURE 1A.4
Arc elasticity.

$$E_d = -\frac{(\text{Change in } Q)}{(\text{Change in } P)} \cdot \frac{(\text{Avg } P)}{(\text{Avg } Q)}$$

$$E_d = -\frac{(Q_2 - Q_1)}{(P_2 - P_1)} \cdot \frac{[(P_1 + P_2)/2]}{[(Q_1 + Q_2)/2]}$$

Demand is considered as *elastic* or *inelastic*, depending upon the relative response of quantity demanded to price changes. If the elasticity of demand in absolute terms is greater than unity, $|E_d > 1|$, demand is classified as elastic. On the other hand, $|E_d < 1|$ in absolute terms signifies inelastic behavior of demand. An absolute value of E_d of 1 reveals unit elasticity.

Taking the general case of a straight-line demand function as shown in Figure 1A.5:

$$Q = a - bP$$

The point elasticity of demand with respect to price is:

$$E_d = (dQ/dP)(P/Q) = (-bP)/Q$$

Following substitution for P, using the equation

$$E_d = 1 - (a/P)$$

P at $Q = 0$ can be found as $0 = a - bP$ or $P = a/b$

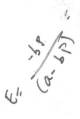

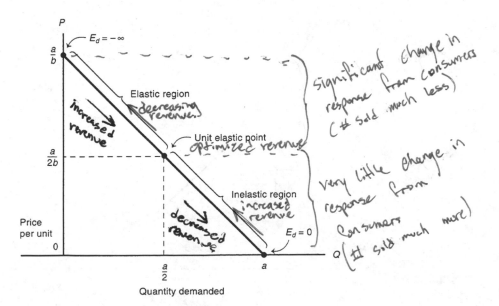

FIGURE 1A.5
A linear demand function and elasticity ranges.

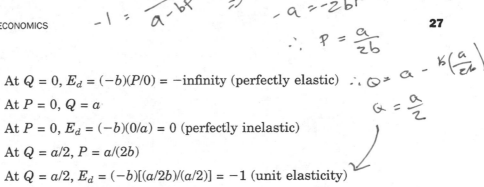

At $Q = 0$, $E_d = (-b)(P/0) = -$infinity (perfectly elastic)

At $P = 0$, $Q = a$

At $P = 0$, $E_d = (-b)(0/a) = 0$ (perfectly inelastic)

At $Q = a/2$, $P = a/(2b)$

At $Q = a/2$, $E_d = (-b)[(a/2b)/(a/2)] = -1$ (unit elasticity)

Most demand functions exhibit variable elasticity. The straight-line demand function is one such case. As for the representation of demand by this function, the hypothesis is that above a certain price the commodity would not be sold at all. At the other extreme, there is a maximum quantity that would be sold corresponding to a zero price. In the real world, such observations are, of course, rarely made at these two extreme levels of price.

Demand curves can be linear or curvilinear, depending upon the characteristics of the market for specific products. Most demand curves are variable elasticity type since these exhibit all three cases of elasticity. That is, consumers are relatively unresponsive to price changes over one range (*inelastic* demand), while for the same demand curve, over another range of price change, there is a significant response in terms of quantity purchased (*elastic* demand).

For variable elasticity curves, the E_d can be found at a selected reference point, called the *point elasticity*. For a variable elasticity curve, E_d may vary according to the reference point selected for the computation.

A linear demand function consisting of an inelastic range, a unit elasticity point, and an elastic range is illustrated in Figure 1A.5. As the price is gradually decreased in the elastic range, total revenue keeps on rising. At the unit elastic point, the total revenue reaches its highest magnitude. Beyond the unit elastic point, further reduction in price results in decreasing total revenue.

In some situations, the price elasticity of demand for a commodity can be constant. A constant elasticity situation is represented by the following mathematical function:

$$Q = aP^b$$

where a and b are constant parameters of the demand function.

The constant elasticity property of this demand curve can be seen by differentiating this function with respect to price:

$$dQ/dP = a \cdot b \cdot P^{b-1}$$

Next, substitution of the value of dQ/dP into the definition of elasticity results in:

$$E_d = a \cdot b \cdot P^{b-1} \cdot P \cdot Q^{-1}$$

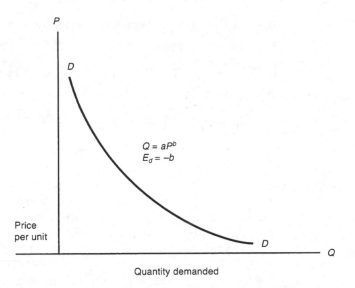

P

D

$Q = aP^b$
$E_d = -b$

Price
per unit

D

Q

FIGURE 1A.6
A constant elasticity
demand function.

Quantity demanded

Replacing Q with the original expression of demand leads to:

$$E_d = a \cdot b \cdot P^{b-1} \cdot P \cdot (1/(aP^b)) = b$$

The result is that b, the exponent or power of the price of the commodity P, is the price elasticity.

A constant elasticity demand function $Q = aP^b$ is shown in Figure 1A.6. For such a curve, E_d may be elastic or inelastic or it can be a unit elasticity curve.

As for total revenue (i.e., price × quantity), there are three possibilities that correspond to the three cases for elasticity of demand. These are summarized in Table 1.A.1.

In the first case, if the total revenue goes up with an increase in price, the demand is *inelastic*. Conversely, for inelastic demand, the total revenue drops with a decrease in price. The second case is that of *elastic* demand. In this case, the total revenue falls when the price rises, and total revenue rises when the price falls. The third case is that of *unit elasticity*, in which

TABLE 1A.1

Relationship between price (P) and total revenue ($P \times Q$) for a demand function

	Elastic demand	Unitary elasticity	Inelastic demand
P goes up	$P \times Q$ falls	Constant $P \times Q$	$P \times Q$ rises
P goes down	$P \times Q$ rises	Constant $P \times Q$	$P \times Q$ falls

a change in P and the corresponding change in Q cause no change in $P \times Q$. This case of <u>unit elasticity results in the highest revenue.</u>

EXAMPLE 1A.1

Change in Demand

The demand function for a product is given by $Q = 100,000 - 400P$, where Q is quantity demanded and P is price per unit. The current price is $50 per unit. How many extra units will be sold in response to a 10 percent drop in price?

Solution

Units sold at the price of $50/unit = $100,000 - 400 \times \$50 = 80,000$
New price/unit = $\$50 \times (1 - 0.1) = \$45$
Units expected to be sold at $45/unit = $100,000 - 400 \times \$45 = 82,000$
Percent increase in units sold = $[(82,000 - 80,000)/80,000] \times 100 = 2.5\%$

EXAMPLE 1A.2

Arc Elasticity, Revenue and Profit

The demand schedule for a product is a straight line. At sale price/unit of $0.50, 9000 units are demanded. Raising the price to $0.70/unit, 3000 units are expected to be sold. Cost of producing the product is $0.45/unit at 9000 units of production and $0.50/unit when 3000 units are produced. (a) What is the arc elasticity of demand? (b) Should the price be increased?

Solution

At $P = \$0.50$ and $Q = 9000$ units, Revenue = $P \times Q = \$4,500$, Cost = $\$4,050$

Profit = Revenue − Cost = $\$4,500 - \$4,050 = \$450$

At $P = \$0.70$ and $Q = 3000$ units, Revenue = $P \times Q = \$2,100$, Cost = $\$1,500$

Profit = Revenue − Cost = $\$2,100 - \$1,500 = \$600$

Arc E_d = (Change in Q/Change in P)(average P/average Q)
　　　 = $(6000/0.20)(0.60/6000) = 3.0$ (Elastic)

An increase in price from $0.50 to $0.70/unit results in a drop in revenue since the demand is elastic. However, due to an increase in profit, price should be increased.

EXAMPLE 1A.3

Variable Elasticity Demand Function

The demand function for a product is given by $Q = 5,000 - 10,000P$ where Q is the quantity demanded and P is price/unit. The existing sale price is $0.30/unit.

Handwritten margin notes:

a) $P \times Q = 0.5 \times 9000$
$= \$4500$

b) $P \times Q = 0.7(3000)$
$= \$2100$

Cost $= 0.45(9000)$
$= \$4050$

b) Cost $= 0.5(3000)$
$= \$1500$

$\Delta Q = -6000$
$\Delta P = 0.2$

$E = \dfrac{\Delta Q}{\Delta P} \times \dfrac{P_1 + P_2}{2} \cdot \dfrac{}{Q_1 + Q_2}$

Elastic

$E = \dfrac{-6000}{0.2} \times \dfrac{0.6}{6000} = -3$

Revenue$_a$ = 4500 - 4050
$= 450$

Revenue$_b$ = 2100 - 1500
$= 600$　∴ Increase $

(a) Find the elasticity at $P = 0$, $Q = 0$, and at $P = \$0.30$/unit.
(b) Find price and quantity for $E_d = 1$.
(c) What is total revenue at price = $\$0.24$/unit?
(d) Find total revenue at $\$0.32$/unit.

Solution

(a) At $P = 0$, $Q = 5{,}000$,

$$E_d = (dQ/dP)(P/Q) = (-10{,}000)(0/5000) = 0$$

At $Q = 0$, $P = 5{,}000/10{,}000 = \$0.50$

$$E_d = (-10{,}000)(0.5/0) = -\text{infinity}$$

To find E_d at $P = \$0.30$/unit, first we find Q that corresponds to this price level.

$$Q = 5{,}000 - 10{,}000\ (\$0.30) = 2{,}000 \text{ units}$$

Now $E_d = (-10{,}000)(0.30/2{,}000) = -1.5$ (elastic)

(b) According to theory, the unit elasticity should occur midway between $Q = 0$ and Q that corresponds to $P = 0$ (i.e., at $Q = 1/2$ of 5,000 units). The price level at $Q = 2{,}500$ is found as follows:

$$P = (5{,}000 - 2{,}500)/(10{,}000) = \$0.25.$$

(c) Revenue at the current price level of $\$0.30$/unit = (2,000 units $\times$ $\$0.30$ per unit) = $\$600$

Next, Q at $P = \$0.24$ is to be found.

$$Q = 5{,}000 - 10{,}000(\$0.24) = 2{,}600$$

Revenue at $\$0.24$/unit = (2,600 $\times$ $\$0.24$) = $\$624$

It should be noted that lowering the price from $\$0.30$/unit to $\$0.24$/unit results in the sale of 600 more units and revenue increases from $\$600$ to $\$624$. This is expected since the elasticity at $P = -\$0.30$ is -1.5 (i.e., it is in the elastic region). However, the decision to lower the price should be based on change in profit, not change in revenue alone.

(d) In order to decide whether to raise the price to $\$0.32$/unit, first we have to find Q at this price level.

$$Q = 5{,}000 - 10{,}000(0.32) = 1{,}800 \text{ units}.$$

Since demand is elastic, as a result of increasing price/unit, there is a decrease of 200 units demanded and also the revenue is expected to drop.

Change in revenue = 1,800($0.32) − 2000 ($0.30)= −$24

EXAMPLE 1A.4   **Constant Elasticity Demand Function**

The demand function for a product is given by the following equation:

$$Q = aP^b$$

Where P is price/unit, Q is the number of units demanded, and a and b are constants. The value of b was estimated to be equal to −2.50. The sales are 10,500 units/day at a price of $50/unit. The company is considering that the price should be raised to $70/unit. If the cost of producing a unit is $45 at present and it is expected to increase to $55 at the new production level following the price change, should the price be raised?

Solution

The demand schedule is $Q = a \cdot P^{-2.5}$. In order to complete the demand schedule, the value of the constant a has to be found from given information.

$$10,500 = a \cdot (50)^{-2.5} \text{ or } a = 10,500(50)^{2.5} = 185.616 \times 10^6$$

Now an increase in price from $50 to $70/unit will result in sales of:

$$Q = 185.616 \times 10^6 \times (70)^{-2.5} = 4528$$

This shows that an increase in price from $50 to $70 (a 40 percent increase) is likely to reduce the sales from 10,500 units/day to 4528 (a 56.88 percent decrease). As for change in revenue, the results are as follows: Revenue.

At $50/unit: 10,500 × $50 = $525,000

At $70/unit: 4,528 × $70 = $316,960

Loss in revenue = $208,040

As expected, for an elastic demand market, an increase in price would lead to a drop in revenue. Therefore, on the basis of revenue alone, the management should not increase the price. Next, the change in profit can be studied. On the cost side, the reduction in cost = $45/unit(10,500) − $55(4,528) = $223,460.

Now we can find change in net revenue:

Net revenue before change = $525,000 − $472,500 = $52,500

Net revenue after change = $316,960 − $249,040 = $67,920

Since net revenue increases as a result of an increase in price, therefore the price can be increased.

1A.4   Demand Shifts

For a given product, a shift in demand curve can occur due to socioeconomic and demographic changes. A movement of the demand curve reflects "demand shift." Figure 1A.7 illustrates a movement of the demand function. As a result of a shift in demand function to the right from curve D to D_1, the quantity demanded increases for a fixed price level. Demand shifts can also occur such that the curve shifts to the left, with the result that even without a rise in price the demand for a given product drops.

Demand shifts could be caused by any one or a combination of the following influences:

1. An increase in the number of buyers results in higher sales. For example, increasing business activity results in an increased market for office equipment.
2. An increase in buyers' incomes normally increases demand.
3. Consumer tastes can change, which affect market shares for competing products. Advertising could play a role in inducing changes in consumer tastes.

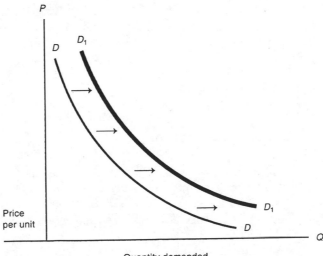

FIGURE 1A.7
Demand shift.

4. Consumers can switch their purchases by substituting more expensive higher quality products, or vice versa. The increasing market for laser printers as a substitute for dot matrix is a recent example.
5. Sharp increases in current demand can occur because of fears of inflation or shortages in the future. On the other hand, expectation of dropping prices in the future can discourage current sales.

EXAMPLE 1A.5

Demand Shift

The existing demand function for a product is represented by $Q = 200,000 - 500P$, where Q is units sold and P is price per unit. Due to an increase in population and a rise in income, the demand function after five years is expected to be $Q = 300,000 - 500P$. The present price per unit is $100. If the future price is the same as the present price/unit, what will be the increase in demand? If future price is increased by 20 percent, what will be the change in demand as compared to the present demand? Find change in revenue.

Solution

The present demand can be found by using the present demand function and current price/unit.

Present sales = $200,000 - 500P = 200,000 - 500 \times \$100/\text{unit} = 150,000$ units
Future sales at $100/unit = $300,000 - 500 \times \$100 = 250,000$ units
Percent increase = $[(250,000 - 150,000)/150,000] \times 100 = 66.7\%$
Future price/unit if price is increased by 20% = $\$100 \times (1 + 0.2) = \$120$

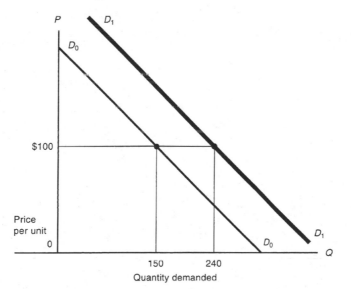

FIGURE 1A.8
Demand shift and
equilibrium points.

Percent increase in revenue = [(250,000 − 150,000) × 100]/[150,000 × 100]
= 66.7%
Future sales at $120/unit = 300,000 − 500 × $120/unit = 240,000 units
Percent increase in demand = [(240,000 − 150,000)/150,000] × 100 = 60.0%
Percent increase in revenue = {[(240,000 × 120) − (150,000 × 100)]/[150,000
× 100]} × 100 = 92.0%

1A.5 Supply Function

A supply function is a relationship between the sale price and the amount
of a particular product that producers in a given market are willing to supply. The concept of the supply function is shown in Figure 1A.9 by using
the axes of price per unit (P) and quantity supplied (Q). It shows that all
else being equal, the higher the price of a product, the greater the inducement for suppliers to increase production. The movement along one supply
function is the study of quantity supplied in response to price change while
non-price factors are held constant.

In addition to market price, there are other factors that affect supplier
decisions. These are prices of resources used to produce the product and of
technology for producing the product. For fixed prices of resources and
given technology of production, one supply function is applicable. Advances
in technology and/or a reduction in resource costs lower production costs
and thereby make more units available at lower prices, and can shift the
supply function to the right. See Figure 1A.10.

The case of a supply function shift to the right shows that at a given
price, a shift results in increased quantity supplied. On the other hand, a

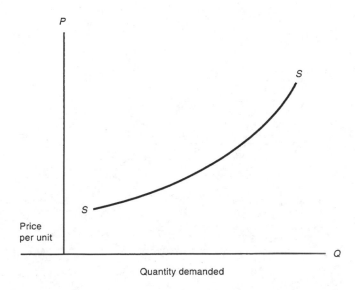

FIGURE 1A.9
Supply function.

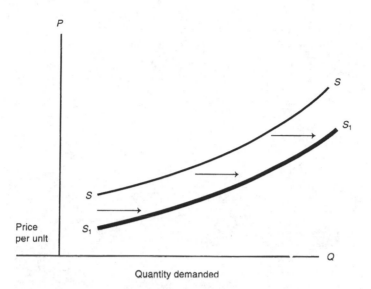

FIGURE 1A.10
Supply function
shift.

shift of the supply function to the left can result from increased prices for raw materials (Figure 1A.10). Such a shift, unless offset by technology changes, results in increased prices for finished products.

As noted above, non-price factors cause a shift in supply functions. Such a movement of the supply function results in a change in quantity of a product in the marketplace.

It is useful to make a number of observations on the behavior of suppliers. Manufacturers may expand production because of expectations of higher future prices. This of course causes the current supply to increase. Also, in case future prices do not rise, the suppliers may be obliged to sell products at low prices. Should firms leave the marketplace, this would result in a decrease of supplies. Non-market factors, such as tax policies and subsidies, can also affect supplies by causing a shift in the supply function.

1A.6 Equilibrium of Demand and Supply

Figure 1A.11 brings the demand and supply functions together for the same product in order to show the equilibrium between price and quantity at the intersection of two curves. Under the equilibrium condition, the amount of goods demanded and supplied is the same. According to the example shown in Figure 1A.11, should all other factors remain constant, the market price for product Z is estimated to be $3/unit and the suppliers are expected to produce 6000 units.

The equilibrium point E that occurs at a price of $3 and quantity of 6000 units signifies the balance between quantity demanded and supplied. That is, at this point there is no shortage or surplus. At $5/unit, the sup-

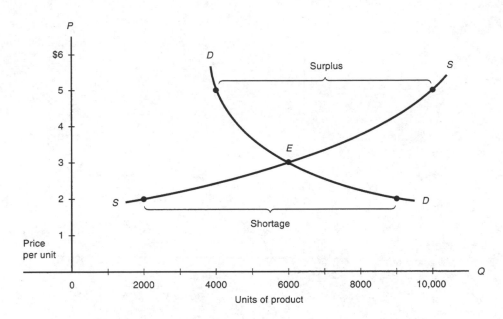

FIGURE 1A.11
Surplus, shortage, and equilibrium cases.

pliers would produce more units than will be bought, resulting in a surplus of 6000 units. In such a case, the suppliers would decrease the price with the object of selling their surplus. On the other hand, at a low price of $2 per unit, there will be a shortage of 7000 units. Consumers would be willing to pay higher prices in order to buy the product. Whether there is a surplus or shortage, the mechanisms of a competitive market would adjust prices, leading to an equilibrium of supply and demand.

EXAMPLE 1A.6

Change in Revenue Due to Shift in Supply Function

The demand function for a product is given by the equation $Q = 200,000 - 500P$, where Q is quantity demanded at price P. The supply function is represented by $P = 100 + 0.1Q$. Due to improvement in technology, a new supply function $P = 80 + 0.1Q$ is attainable. Find arc elasticity and the change in revenue due to a shift in the supply function.

Solution

Figure 1A.12 presents the equilibrium of demand and supply. The change in revenue due to a shift in supply function = $P_2Q_2 - P_1Q_1$. The equilibrium of the demand and the existing supply function is found at the intersection point of these two functions.

$P_1 = \$394.10$ and $Q_1 = 2941$. Revenue is $P_1Q_1 = \$1.159$ million.

The equilibrium of the demand and the new supply function occurs at $P_2 = \$393.70$ and $Q_2 = 3137$. Revenue is $P_2Q_2 = \$1.235$ million.

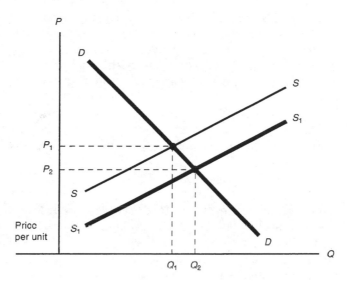

FIGURE 1A.12
Supply function shift
and equilibrium
cases.

The Arc E_d = (Change in Q/Change in P)(Average P/Average Q)
= (196/0.4)(393.90/3039) = 63.5 (Elastic).

Since the demand is elastic, a drop in price due to a shift in supply
function results in an increase in revenue.

Percentage increase in revenue = $[(P_2Q_2 - P_1Q_1)/(P_1Q_1)] \times 100 = 6.6\%$

1A.7 Supply and Demand Applications

Due to the complexity of the real world marketplace, the concepts of supply and demand alone cannot explain completely why price changes occur.
Nevertheless, a knowledge of these concepts goes a long way in enabling
forecasters to study forces that affect prices and to appreciate the evaluation methods based on supply-demand relationships. In engineering economics the demand and supply relationships are relied upon for investment and production decisions. Here, a few strategic applications are
described by way of examples.

Whether to invest in partial automation of a process, or even to go into
full automation such as the use of robotics, can be decided on the basis of
supply-demand interaction, revenues, and costs. The elasticity of demand
for the product concerned plays a part. While there could be a number of
reasons for automation (such as a reduction in production costs, avoiding
labor troubles, or enhancing safety), reducing the cost is an important
motive since such savings allow a reduction in price, leading to increased

demand. This would allow a high utilization of expensive equipment. For elastic demand, this policy may well succeed. On the other hand, an inelastic demand makes such an investment less attractive since any increase in demand arising from a price cut will be relatively small.

Although excess demand or supply are largely created by market action, other factors play a role. In order to achieve political or social objectives, governments may decide that certain prices are too high or too low and as a consequence may establish floor or ceiling prices. The supply and demand relationships explain why the price limits cause shortages or surpluses. Establishing the desirability of shortages or surpluses is not of interest here.

Wage and price controls have occasionally been imposed by governments in response to political pressures. While such controls may work well for a short period, their prolonged imposition would lead to distortions. The supply and demand curves in Figure 1A.13 illustrate that the equilibrium point without controls is at price P_e for amount Q_e. If price ceiling is imposed at 80 percent of P_e, or $0.8P_e$, and the supply and demand curves remain unchanged, at $0.8P$, the demand will be Q_d and supply will be Q_s and shortage of $Q_d - Q_s$ units would occur. This may lead to a rationing plan. Alternatively, the suppliers may be offered a subsidy. As compared to the free market condition, neither is completely satisfactory since rationing induces black markets (which are responsible for the rationed items being sold at prices above legal limits). On the other hand, subsidies are known to result in their own supply-demand distortions.

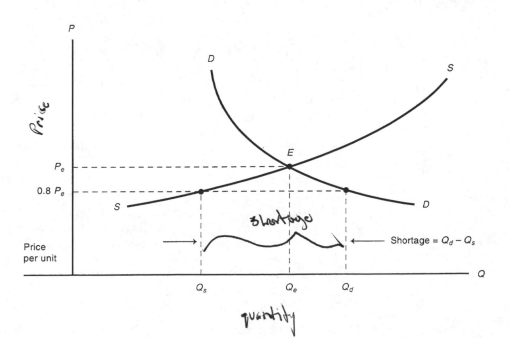

FIGURE 1A.13
Price ceiling at 80 percent of P_e and resulting shortage.

1A.8   Elasticity of Supply

The supply elasticity E_s is defined as:

$$E_s = \frac{\% \text{ Change in } Q}{\% \text{ Change in } P} = \frac{\text{Change in } Q/Q}{\text{Change in } P/P} = \frac{\text{Change in } Q}{\text{Change in } P} \cdot \frac{P}{Q}$$

Should producers be responsive to price changes, elastic supply exists. Alternatively, if producers are relatively unresponsive, then supply is regarded as inelastic.

The concept of supply elasticity is useful for production planning. Due to the nature of the production process, it tends to be greater over the longer range than in making decisions in the immediate production period.

1A.9   PROBLEMS

1A.1 The demand function for a product can be represented by a straight line connecting price/unit and units sold. Available information is provided below:

At P	Q
$0.50	3000
1.00	2000

Slope $= \dfrac{-0.5}{1000}$

$P = -0.0005\,Q + 1000$

(a) Find the equation for the demand function.
(b) What would be the sales if the price was (i) $0.75/unit, (ii) $1.50/unit.
(c) Find change in gross revenue if price is raised from $1.00 to $1.50/unit.
(d) If units can be produced at 75 percent of the sale price, should the price be raised from $1.00 to $1.25/unit?

1A.2 A computer repair company makes on site service visits in an urbanized region. The demand function for its services connects service visits and fee/visit within certain limits as follows:

$$Q = 2000 - 1000P$$

Where Q is service visits/month and P is the price (dollar/minute of site visit). The manager has the following options to increase the total revenue:

(a) attracting additional clients by expanding the service area and thus changing the demand function to $Q = 2100 - 1000P$, or
(b) encouraging more business by reducing the fee from $1.50 to $1.25 per minute. What option would you advise the manager to adopt, giving good reasons for doing so?

1A.3 The present demand function for a product is given by $Q = 5000 - 20P$, where Q is quantity demanded and P is price per unit. Due to increased market, the demand function is expected to shift to $Q = 6000 - 20P$. The present supply function is $P = 150 + 0.05Q$. The manufacturer believes that owing to improvements in the production process, the supply function will become $P = 100 + 0.05Q$. Find (*a*) the current equilibrium in terms of price and units sold, (*b*) new equilibrium price and quantity following the shifts of demand and supply functions, and (*c*) change in revenue.

1A.4 An aggregate demand function is represented by the equation $Q = 300 - 15P$ where Q is the number of trips made and P is the price per trip in dollars. Assume that the cost of serving a trip is 75 percent of the price charged.

   (*a*) Find the price elasticity of demand when $P = 20$, $P = 15$, $P = 10$, $P = 5$, $P = 0$ dollars.
   (*b*) If price is lowered from \$15/unit to \$10/unit, find change in revenue. Also find whether the price should be lowered.
   (*c*) If price is lowered from \$10 to \$5, find change in revenue. Should the price be lowered?
   (*d*) Comment on the changes in revenue and profit estimates. Also, comment on decision criteria for changing prices.

1A.5 Figure 1A.14 shows a case where both supply and demand change simultaneously. Initial supply and demand conditions are shown by curves S and D. Curves S_1 and D_1 indicate conditions when both supply and demand have increased. Although both supply and demand have increased for the same product, the price has remained constant. Please explain why such a condition may occur. Also, show and comment on cases where the price/unit following the simultaneous shift of supply and demand curves may result in higher or lower price per unit.

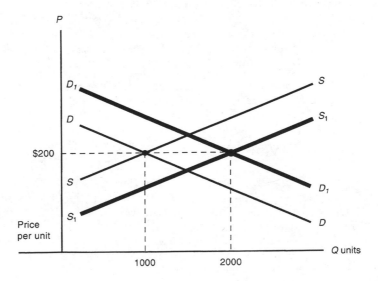

FIGURE 1A.14
Effects of supply
and demand shifts
on price and
quantity.

EXTENSION 1B   INTERNATIONAL PRACTICE

1B.1 Growing Integration of Economies

Over the past two decades, a growing integration of financial markets located in the industrial countries and major offshore centers has occurred as a result of a fundamental structural change in the world economy. This increased integration was brought about by the relaxation of capital controls and broader financial liberalization in the industrial countries. Also, the new telecommunications and computer technologies have played a role in the form of cross-border transfer of funds.

The relaxation of restrictions on external and domestic financial transactions was fostered in part by policies aiming at the improvement of financial efficiency through increased competition in domestic financial systems. Another factor that contributed to financial efficiency was to reduce financial risks by permitting domestic residents to hold internationally diversified portfolios.[†]

1B.2 Trade Blocks

Trade blocks have been on the rise in recent years. The North American Free Trade Agreement (NAFTA) became effective on January 1, 1994 between Canada, U.S.A., and Mexico.[‡] The North American Free Trade Agreement has resulted in a powerful economic block consisting of 360 million consumers in the United States, Mexico, and Canada. The combined Gross National Products of these countries was over US$6.3 trillion in 1993.[§]

NAFTA is already providing numerous opportunities to business including engineering enterprises, industry, and workers. The agreement is expected to heighten competitive market forces and will lead to greater economic integration in North America. NAFTA is expected to induce a more efficient use of North American resources—capital, land, labor, and technology.[§]

[†]Donald J. Mathieson, and Liliane Rojas-Suarez, "Liberalization of the Capital Account, Experience and Issues," International Monetary Fund, Washington, D.C., March 1993.

[‡]B. Hoekman and P. Sauve, "Liberalizing Trade in Services," World Bank Discussion Paper 243, Washington D.C., 1994.

[§]J.L. Nolan, A. Woznick, W.T. LeGro, D.C. Alexander, K.C. Shippey, E.G. Hinkelman, H.I. Vera, M.F. Pasero, "Mexico Business, The Portable Encyclopedia for Doing Business With Mexico," World Trade Press, San Rafael, CA, USA, 1994.

1B.3 Portability of Qualification

There are three elements that complement the NAFTA package on professional services such as engineering. First, an agreement was reached to remove all citizenship and permanent residency requirements associated with the licensing and certification of professional service providers (i.e., the obligation to be a "landed immigrant"). Second, detailed work programs are in place aimed at liberalizing the licensing of foreign legal consultants and engineers. Third, governing principles and rules have been developed that enable citizens of each NAFTA country to have access to the other NAFTA countries on a temporary basis in order to pursue business opportunities without meeting a labor market (or economic "needs") test.[†]

In June 1995, representatives of the engineering profession from the U.S., Canada, and Mexico signed a historic agreement on requirements for temporary as well as permanent licensing of engineers in the three countries. This is the first such agreement on professional services that was made possible by the provisions of the North American Free Trade Agreement (NAFTA).

Both NAFTA and GATS (General Agreement on Trade in Services) aim to make it easier for professionals in one country to practice in another, either on a temporary or on a long-term basis. Various requirements are specified by the agreement for temporary and permanent licensing of engineers that will be recognized in each country. This initiative is expected to lead to increased portability of credentials and greater mobility for engineers to practice in the North American market. However, for the agreement to be effective, it must be ratified by professional organizations in each country as well as state and provincial governments in the U.S. and Canada that license engineers.[‡]

NAFTA encourages each member country's professions to develop mutual recognition pacts. Also, NAFTA contains provisions for developing temporary licensing of engineers. The engineering associations that negotiated the agreement are the U.S. Council for International Engineering Practice, the Canadian Council of Professional Engineers, and the Comité Méxicano para la Practica Internacional de la Ingeniería.[‡]

1B.4 An International Perspective of Engineering Economics

Engineering economic studies are carried out for a variety of purposes and are usually undertaken by engineers or by multi-disciplinary teams.

[†]B. Hoekman and P. Sauve, "Liberalizing Trade in Services," World Bank Discussion Paper 243, Washington D.C., 1994.
[‡]ASCE News, "Engineers from Three Countries Reach Mutual Recognition Agreement," ASCE News, July 1995, V.20, No.7, American Society of Civil Engineers, New York (p.1).

Because these studies result in a report covering many aspects of this subject, it is important to have thorough analyses and a well-written report.
The purpose of such studies could encompass:

- private as well as public sector investment decisions
- design decisions
- capital allocations
- attraction of new investors
- support of loan applications from governments, the World Bank, or other development banks.

Depending upon the problem at hand, the practice of engineering economics could involve the following types of studies:

- defining "engineering economics" problems
- use of discounted cash flow or use of interest formulas
- treatment of inflation
- study of alternatives in terms of costs and revenues
- acquisition of assets—capital investments with equity funds or borrowed funds or a combination
- public projects—amortization issues, benefits, and costs
- for private sector activities—depreciation, taxes, evaluation of projects based on after-tax cash flow—reflecting government policy objectives regarding investment and other factors
- government subsidies
- evaluation of investments under risk and uncertainty
- multi-criteria evaluation
- productivity and quality studies

Governments around the world levy taxes on corporations and individuals. However, the level of taxation differs significantly. Taxes on income are paid to the federal government and in some countries to other levels of government. Private sector corporations are normally directly concerned with cash flow for depreciation and taxes.

Governments allow a certain amount of depreciation, with method and rates of depreciation specified by tax regulations. The calculation of depreciation and taxes are of special interest to private sector companies and also to private sector but regulated utilities (e.g., power companies, railways).[†]

Information on application-specific factors is required, including business environment, financial and commercial issues, risk, the security pack-

---

[†]G.A. Fleischer, *Introduction to Engineering.* PWS Publishing Company, Boston, 1994.

age, comprehensive feasibility study, and the use of well-defined evaluation criteria, depreciation practices, and tax laws.[†]

For projects funded by the International Bank for Reconstruction and Development, also called the World Bank, economic appraisal of projects is essential. Among other components of analyses, the following are required: economic costs, traffic forecasting, economic benefits, and a comparison of costs with benefits.[‡]

Given the effects of the North American Free Trade Agreement (NAFTA) and the growing integration of economies on engineering practice, it is essential that Canadian engineers become knowledgeable about the international practice of engineering economics. As a step in this direction, this Canadian edition covers the U.S. depreciation and tax regulations. Also, an introduction to depreciation and corporate income taxes in Mexico is provided.

[†]P.A. Cordukes, (Editor), "Submission and Evaluation of Proposals for Private Power Generation Projects in Developing Countries," World Bank Discussion Paper 250, 1994.
[‡]Hans A. Adler, "Economic Appraisal of Transport Projects, A Manual with Case Studies," Revised and Expanded Edition, published for the World Bank, The John Hopkins University Press, Baltimore, 1987.

TIME VALUE OF MONEY

If you would know the value of money, go and try to borrow some.
Benjamin Franklin, *Poor Richard's Almanack*, 1758

Interest is the cost of using capital. Its history extends as far back as the recorded transactions of humanity. In earliest times, before money was coined, capital was represented by wealth in the form of personal possessions, and interest was paid in kind. For example, a loan of seed to a neighbor before planting was returned after harvest with an additional increment. We can surmise that the concept of interest in its modern sense arose from such loans for productive purposes.

By the time the Greek and Roman empires were in their ascendancies, interest rates were somewhat standardized and occasionally legislated. The amount charged for loans to the most reliable borrowers was around 10 percent, ranging from 4 percent in first-century Rome to about 50 percent for grain loans in Egypt during the same period.[†]

The concept of interest has not changed much through the centuries, but the modern credit structure differs markedly from that of antiquity. Lending or investing was relatively inconvenient in ancient days because transactions were made directly between individuals. There were no banking organizations to act as intermediaries and no credit instruments in the money market. Governments were rarely able to float loans since they could not pledge the private resources of their people. Also, governments had not discovered the practice of deficit financing.

[†]S. Homer, *History of Interest Rates,* Rutgers, New Brunswick, N.J., 1963.

Today, there are many credit instruments, and most people use them. Business and government are the biggest borrowers. Businesses seek the use of capital goods to increase productivity. Governments borrow against future tax revenues to finance highways, welfare programs, and public services. Households also borrow to make purchases in excess of their current cash resources. Such borrowers, and the corresponding lenders, must acknowledge the time value of their commitments.

The following example reveals the significance of interest in economic transactions and confirms the importance of understanding how interest operates, whether it pertains to personal finances or to professional practices.

EXAMPLE 2.1

Impact of Interest Rates and Loan Periods

The purchase of a home is the largest investment most people make. By the summer of 1993, many people had refinanced their homes because interest rates dipped to the lowest levels in some 20 years. The two tables below vividly portray the impact of interest rates and loan periods. A shorter repayment period at a given interest rate or a lower interest rate for a given loan period gives a significant saving.

A $100,000 loan at 8.5% interest for four repayment periods

Repayment period, years	Monthly payment, $	Total interest, $
15	984.51	77,210
20	867.57	108,217
25	804.96	141,485
30	768.63	176,707

A $100,000 loan for 30 years at four interest rates

Interest rate, %	Monthly payment, $	Total interest, $
7.5	699.21	151,722
8.5	768.63	176,707
9.5	841.15	202,806
10.0	877.28	215,812

A further interesting historical example relates to New York City lending $1 million to the capital of the United States of America during the War of 1812. During the period of New York's financial crises in 1975, it was suggested that Washington might be billed for the original loan and the accumulated interest. At 6 percent interest compounded annually, that $1 million loan would have increased to an $11.2 billion debt.

2.1

INTEREST AND THE TIME VALUE OF MONEY

Nearly everyone is directly exposed to interest transactions occasionally and is indirectly affected regularly. Credit cards are a mainstay of commerce; they have an interest load for delayed payments. Key parts of a contract for purchasing an automobile or home are the interest stipulations.

The rate of interest paid on municipal bonds directly affects tax rates for property in the affected area. Businesses borrow to expand or simply maintain operations, and the cost of their borrowing must be repaid from more profitable operations enabled by loans. All this borrowing taken together adds up to an enormous debt, and it all has interest charges.

To fully appreciate interest charges, one must comprehend the reasons for the charges, understand how they are calculated, and realize their effect on cash flows. Interest represents the earning power of money. It is the premium paid to compensate a lender for the administrative cost of making a loan, the risk of nonrepayment, and the loss of use of the loaned money. A borrower pays interest charges for the opportunity to do something now that otherwise would have to be delayed or would never be done. *Simple interest I* is a charge directly proportional to the capital (principal *P*) loaned at rate *i* for *N* periods, so that $I = PiN$. *Compound interest* includes charges for the accumulated interest as well as the amount of unpaid principal.

A *nominal interest rate r* of 8 percent compounded quarterly, e.g., indicates an interest charge of 2 percent per quarter compounded four times per year. If *m* is the number of compounding periods per year, we will see that the equivalent *effective interest rate*, or *actual annual interest earned or paid, i* from a nominal rate is

r = nominal interest rate
m = number of compounding periods

$$i_{\text{eff}} = \left(1 + \frac{r}{m}\right)^m - 1 \tag{2.1}$$

Continuous interest i_∞ is the effective interest rate as *m* approaches infinity, and its equivalent effective interest rate is

$$i_\infty = e^r - 1 \tag{2.2}$$

as will be shown in Sec. 2.4.3.

Time-value mechanics involve the use of compound-interest factors to translate payments of various amounts occurring at various times to a single equivalent payment. Interest factors are symbolized by notations based on interest *i*, number of periods *N*, *P* = present worth, *F* = future worth, and *A* = annuity payment. An ordinary annuity is a series of equal payments, at equal intervals, with the first payment at the end of the first period. When payments in an annuity increase by a constant increment *G* each period, an equivalent ordinary annuity is determined through use of an arithmetic gradient factor.

Seven discrete interest factors are commonly used to evaluate cash flows and convert them to summary statements that define alternative uses for capital. These factors are represented by functional symbols that assist calculations; the values of the factors for different interest rates and numbers of compounding periods are tabulated in App. D. Also, they can be computed by using CHEER, the computer program supplied with this text.

The fundamental concepts of interest and the basic constructs of interest calculation introduced in this chapter are the foundations for discounted cash flow applications to be developed in the next four chapters.

REASONS FOR INTEREST

The significance of interest can be shown through a historical purchase that most of us are familiar with, the Manhattan Island purchase.

EXAMPLE 2.2   **All You Have to Do to Be Rich Is Live Long Enough**

The famous purchase of Manhattan Island from the Indians for $24 is often referred to as an exceptional bargain. This incident reputedly occurred in 1626, when Peter Minuit of the Dutch West India Company bought the rights to the island from local residents. Was it a bargain? For the sake of argument, suppose that the Indians could have invested the money at a reasonable interest rate of 6 percent compounded annually. Over the years since then, the original $24 investment would have grown as shown in the following table:

Year	Value of original $24 investment compounded at 6% per year, $
1626	24.00
1676	442.08
1726	8,143.25
1776	149,999.92
1826	2,763,021.69
1876	50,895,285.85
1926	937,499,017.25
1976	17,268,876,530.40
1996	55,383,626,485.92

Whether Minuit or the Indians got the better deal depends on the perspective taken. If they could have invested at a higher rate, say the 18 percent return earned on money market funds in 1981, the Indians' theoretical investment would have been worth, in 1981, just over

$790,000,000,000,000,000,000,000,000

or $790 septillion. On the other hand, at the 6 percent rate, a value closer to 1993 rates, its value would have increased to slightly more than $27 billion by 1984, when the assessed value of taxable real estate in Manhattan was about $24 billion.

The effect of interest should be evident from Example 2.2. The reasons for this effect become more apparent when we examine the uses of capital. In our economic environment, capital is the basic resource. It can be converted to production goods, consumer goods, or services. It has the power to earn and to satisfy wants.

From a lender's viewpoint, capital is a fluid resource. Capital can be spent on goods expected to produce a profit or on personal satisfaction. It can be hoarded or given away. It can also be loaned. If it is loaned, the lender will normally expect some type of compensation. The common compensation is interest. Interest compensates for the administrative expense of making the loan, for the risk that the loan will not be repaid, and for the loss of earnings that would have been obtained if the money had been invested for productive purposes.

From a borrower's viewpoint, a loan is both an obligation and an opportunity. A borrower must expect to repay the loan. Failure to repay leads to a damaged reputation, loss of possessions, and other consequences. The loan offers an opportunity to do something immediately that would otherwise have to be delayed. In some cases the objective would no longer exist after a delay. To take advantage of an existing course of action or to fulfill a current need, the borrower agrees to pay a certain amount in addition to the sum immediately received. This premium is the interest paid to avoid waiting for the money.

Implied in both the lender's and borrower's viewpoints is the earning power of money. For money to earn something, the owner or user must wait (waiting-earning is obviously opposed to the spending-owing use of money to gratify immediate desires). Interest payments have been likened to the reward for waiting, but it is more appropriate for engineering economists to view interest as the productive gain from the efficient use of the money resource. The prevailing interest rate is essentially a measure of the productivity to expect from the resource. An owner of money can lend it at the prevailing rate and wait to be repaid the original amount plus an extra increment. Equivalently, the borrower could reloan the money at a higher rate to acquire a gain larger than the amount to be repaid, or the money could be converted to productive goods that would be expected to earn more than the amount needed to repay the loan. In both cases the prevailing interest rate sets the minimum level of expected productivity, and both cases involve time between receipt and return of the loan to secure the earnings—the *time value of money*.

2.3   **SIMPLE INTEREST**

In the very unusual circumstance when a *simple interest rate* is quoted, the interest earned is directly proportional to the capital involved in the loan. Expressed as a formula, the interest earned I through several time periods is found by

$$I = PiN$$

where P = present amount or principal

i = interest rate per period

N = number of interest periods (usually years)

Since the principal, or amount borrowed, P is a fixed value, the annual interest charged is constant. Therefore, the total amount a borrower is obligated to pay a lender is

$$F = P + I = P + PiN = P(1 + iN)$$

where F is a future sum of money to be paid. When N is not a full year, there are two ways to calculate the simple interest earned during the period of the loan. When *ordinary simple interest* is used, the year is divided into twelve 30-day periods, or a year is considered to have 360 days. In *exact simple interest,* a year has precisely the calendar number of days, and N is the fraction of the number of days the loan is in effect that year.

An example of simple interest as the rental cost of money is a loan of $1000 for 2 months at 10 percent. With ordinary simple interest, the amount to be repaid is

$$F = P(1 + iN)$$

where N is $\frac{2}{12}$ year, giving

$$F = \$1000 \, (1 + 0.01667) = \$1016.67$$

With exact simple interest when the two months are January and February in a nonleap year, the future sum is

$$F = P\left[1 + (i)\left(\frac{31 + 28}{365}\right)\right]$$

and

$$F = \$1000 \, (1 + 0.01616) = \$1016.16$$

2.4   COMPOUND INTEREST

Again, assume a loan of $1000, this time for 2 years at an interest rate of 10 percent compounded annually; the pattern of interest compounding is shown in Table 2.1.

TABLE 2.1

Future value of $1000 loan when interest is due on both the principal and unpaid interest

Year	Amount owed at beginning of year, $	Interest on amount owed, $	Amount owed at end of year, $
1	1000	$1000 \times 0.10 = 100$	$1000 + 100 = 1100$
2	1100	$1100 \times 0.10 = 110$	$1100 + 110 = 1210$

The amount to be repaid with simple interest is

$$\$1000 \, [1 + 0.1(2)] = \$1200$$

Thus, the amount to be repaid for the given loan is now $10 greater for compound interest than for simple interest ($1210 − $1200). The $10 difference accrues from the interest charge on the $100 earned during the first year that was not accounted for in the simple-interest calculation. The formula for the calculations in Table 2.1, using previously defined symbols, is

$$
\begin{matrix}
\text{Compound} \\
\text{amount} \\
\text{due in} \\
\text{2 years}
\end{matrix}
=
\begin{matrix}
\text{amount} \\
\text{borrowed}
\end{matrix}
+
\begin{matrix}
\text{year 1} \\
\text{interest}
\end{matrix}
+
\left(
\begin{matrix}
\text{amount} \\
\text{borrowed} \\
\text{plus year 1} \\
\text{interest due}
\end{matrix}
\right)
\left(
\begin{matrix}
\text{interest} \\
\text{rate}
\end{matrix}
\right)
$$

$$
\begin{aligned}
F_2 &= P + Pi + (P + Pi)i \\
&= P(1 + i + i + i^2) \\
&= P(1 + i)^2 \\
&= \$1000(1 + 0.10)^2 \\
&= \$1000(1.21) = \$1210
\end{aligned}
$$

The key equation in the development above is $F_2 = P(1 + i)^2$. Generalized for any number of interest periods N, this expression becomes

$$F_N = P(1 + i)^N \tag{2.3}$$

and $(1 + i)^N$ is known as the *compound-amount factor*. It is one of several interest factors derived in this chapter for which numerical values are tabulated in App. D.

2.4.1 Nominal Interest Rates

Interest rates are normally quoted on an annual basis. However, agreements may specify that interest will be compounded several times per year: monthly, quarterly, semiannually, etc. For example, 1 year divided into four quarters with interest at 2 percent per quarter is typically quoted as *8 percent compounded quarterly*. Stated in this fashion, the 8 percent rate is called a *nominal annual interest rate*. The future value at the end of 1 year for $200 earning interest at 8 percent compounded quarterly is developed as

$$
\begin{aligned}
F_{3\text{ mo}} &= P + Pi = \$200 + \$200(0.02) \\
&= \$200 + \$4 = \$204 \\[4pt]
F_{6\text{ mo}} &= \$204 + \$204(0.02) \\
&= \$204 + \$4.08 = \$208.08 \\[4pt]
F_{9\text{ mo}} &= \$208.08 + \$208.08(0.02) \\
&= \$208.08 + \$4.16 = \$212.24 \\[4pt]
F_{12\text{ mo}} &= \$212.24 + \$212.24(0.02) \\
&= \$212.24 + \$4.24 = \$216.48
\end{aligned}
$$

The result of the nominal interest rate is to produce a higher value than might be expected from 8 percent compounded annually. At 8 percent compounded annually, the $200 mentioned above would earn in 1 year

$$
F_{12\text{ mo}} = \$200 + \$200(0.08) = \$216
$$

which is $0.48 less than the amount accrued from the nominal rate of 8 percent compounded quarterly. An interest rate of 1.5 percent per month is also a nominal interest rate that could appear quite reasonable to the uninitiated. Using the compound-amount factor to calculate how much would have to be repaid on a 1-year loan of $1000 at a nominal interest rate of 18 percent compounded monthly (1.5 percent per period with 12 interest periods per year) gives

$$
F_{12\text{ mo}} = \$1000(1 + 0.015)^{12} = \$1195.62
$$

This can be compared with the future value of the same loan at 18 percent compounded semiannually (9 percent per period with two interest periods per year):

$$
F_{2\text{ periods}} = \$1000(1.09)^2 = \$1188.10
$$

Thus, more frequent compounding with a nominally stated annual rate does indeed increase the future worth.

2.4.2 Effective Interest Rates

Confusion about the actual interest earned is eliminated by stating the charge as an *effective interest rate*. Efforts to protect borrowers from exotic statements of interest charges was the thrust behind the national truth-in-lending law passed in the United States in 1973. The effective annual interest rate is simply the ratio of the interest charge for 1 year to the principal (amount loaned or borrowed). For the 1-year loan of $1000 at a nominal annual interest rate of 18 percent compounded monthly,

$$\text{Effective annual interest rate} = \frac{F - P}{P} = \frac{\$1196 - \$1000}{\$1000}$$

$$= \frac{\$196}{\$1000}(100\%) = 19.6\%$$

For the same loan at 18 percent compounded semiannually,

$$\text{Effective annual interest rate} = \frac{\$1188 - \$1000}{\$1000}$$

$$= \frac{\$188}{\$1000}(100\%) = 18.8\%$$

The effective annual interest rate can be obtained without reference to the principal. Based on the same reasoning utilized previously and by using Eq. (2.1), the effective annual interest rate i_{eff} for a nominal interest rate r of 18 percent compounded semiannually is

$$i_{\text{eff}} = \left(1 + \frac{r}{m}\right)^m - 1 = \left(1 + \frac{0.18}{2}\right)^2 - 1$$

$$= (1 + 0.09)^2 - 1 = 1.188 - 1$$

$$= 0.188 \text{ or } 18.8\%$$

This means that a nominal annual interest rate of 18 percent compounded semiannually is equivalent to a compound-interest rate of 18.8 percent on an annual basis.

2.4.3 Continuous Compounding

The ultimate limit for the number of compounding periods in 1 year is called *continuous compounding*. Under this accrual pattern, m approaches infinity as interest compounds continuously, moment by moment. The effective interest rate for continuous compounding for a nominal interest rate r is developed as follows:

The interest periods are made infinitesimally small:

$$i_{\infty} = \lim_{m \to \infty} \left(1 + \frac{r}{m}\right)^m - 1$$

The right side of the equality is rearranged to include r in the exponent:

$$\left(1 + \frac{r}{m}\right)^m - 1 = \left[\left(1 + \frac{r}{m}\right)^{m/r}\right]^r - 1$$

The term inside the square brackets is recognized as the value of the mathematical symbol e [$e = 2.718$ is the value of $(1 + 1/n)^n$, as n approaches infinity]:

$$\lim_{m \to \infty} \left(1 + \frac{r}{m}\right)^{m/r} = e$$

By substitution,

$$i_\infty = \lim_{m \to \infty} \left[\left(1 + \frac{r}{m}\right)^{m/r}\right]^r - 1 = e^r - 1$$

As an example of continuous compounding, when the nominal interest rate is $r = 18.232$ percent,

$$i_\infty = e^r - 1 = e^{0.18232} - 1 = 0.20 \text{ or } 20\%$$

and, correspondingly, when the effective annual interest rate is 22.1 percent,

$$0.221 = e^r - 1$$
$$1.221 = e^r$$
$$r = \ln 1.221 = 0.20 = 20\%$$

The most obvious computational effect of using continuous interest is that it produces a larger future amount than does the same rate compounded discretely; the effective interest when $r = 20$ percent instead of $i = 20$ percent realizes a 10.5 percent increase in value:

$$\frac{0.221 - 0.20}{0.20} (100\%) = 10.5\%$$

The rationale for using continuous interest in economic analyses is that the cash flow in certain situations is best approximated by a continuous pattern; i.e., cash transactions tend to be spread out over 1 year in a more or less even distribution rather than being concentrated at particular dates. Some mathematical models are also facilitated by the assumption of continuous compounding rather than periodic compounding.

In actual practice, however, interest rates are seldom quoted on a continuous basis, and the vast majority of organizations use discrete compounding periods in their economic studies. The reason for this is probably custom or the familiarity that makes it easier to understand periodic interest charges. Accounting practices that categorize receipts and disbursements as end-of-year values and financial experiences with annual tax, insurance, or mortgage payments contribute to thinking in terms of discrete periods. Yet continuous and discrete compounding are both only approximations of true cash flow, because cash neither flows like a free stream of water nor gushes like a geyser at given intervals. Receipts and disbursements are often irregular in amount and in timing.

In the following discussion of the time value of money and in subsequent chapters on economic comparison methods, end-of-year compounding is utilized. Tables of interest factors are provided in App. D for discrete compounding and in App. E for continuous compounding. *Discrete compounding* is implied in all examples and exercises in this text unless specified otherwise.

| 2.5 | **TIME-VALUE EQUIVALENCE** |

Two things are *equivalent* when they produce the same effect. The effective interest rate computed for a nominally stated interest rate is an equivalent expression of the interest charge. Both interest charges produce the same effect on an investment. In considering time-value conversion, the equivalent numerical values of money are determined, not values with equivalent *purchasing power*. The amount of goods that can be purchased with a given sum of money varies up and down as a function of special localized circumstances and nationwide or worldwide economic conditions. Inflation is discussed completely in Chap. 10, but Sec. 3.1.1 will briefly introduce the topic. In this chapter about time-value mechanics, attention is directed toward calculations based on the *earning power* of money, which relates time and earnings to locate time-equivalent money amounts.

If $1000 were sealed and buried today, it would have a cash value of $1000 when it was dug up 2 years from now. Regardless of changes in buying power, the value remains constant because the earning power of the money was forfeited. It was observed earlier that $1000 deposited at 10 percent interest compounded annually has a value of $1000 $(1 + 0.10)^2 =$ $1210 after 2 years. Therefore, $1000 today is equivalent to $1210 in 2 years from now, if it earns at a prevailing rate of 10 percent compounded yearly. Similarly, to have $1000 in 2 years from now, one need only deposit

$$\$1000 \ \frac{1}{(1 + 0.10)^2} = \$826.45$$

today. In theory, then, if 10 percent is an acceptable rate of return, an investor will be indifferent between having $826.45 in hand or having a trusted promise to receive $1000 in 2 years.

Consider other facets of the *earning power of money*. The $1000 could have been used to pay two equal annual $500 installments. The buried $1000 could be retrieved after 1 year, an installment paid, and the remaining $500 reburied until the second payment became due. If the $1000 is instead deposited at 10 percent, $1100 would be available at the end of the first year. After the first $500 installment was paid, the remaining $600 would draw interest until the next payment. Paying the second $500 installment would leave

$$\$600 \,(1.10) - \$500 = \$660 - \$500 = \$160$$

in the account. Because of the earning power of money, the initial deposit could have been reduced to $868 to pay out $500 at the end of each of the 2 years:

First year: $868 (1.10) − $500 = $955 − $500 = $455

Second year: $455 (1.10) = $500 = second installment

Thus, $868 is equivalent to $500 received 1 year from now plus another $500 received 2 years from now:

First year: $$\frac{\$500}{1.10} = \$455$$

Second year: $$\$455 + \frac{\$500}{(1.10)^2} = \$455 + \frac{\$500}{1.21}$$

$$= \$455 + \$413 = \$868$$

The concept of equivalence is the cornerstone for time-value-of-money comparisons. To have a precise meaning, income and expenditures must be identified with time as well as with amount. A decision between alternatives having receipts and disbursements spread over a period of time is made by comparing the equivalent outcomes of the alternatives at a given date.

Figure 2.1 shows the translation of $1000 at time 0 (now) to equivalent alternative expressions of cash flow. Figure 2.1 shows that

- $1000 today is equivalent to $1791 received 10 years from now.
- $1000 today is equivalent to $237.40 received at the end of each year for the next 5 years.
- $1000 today is equivalent to $317.70 received at the end of years 6, 7, 8, 9, and 10.
- $237.40 received at the end of each year for the next 5 years is equivalent to a lump sum of $1791 received 10 years from now.
- $317.70 received at the end of years 6, 7, 8, 9, and 10 is equivalent to $1791 in 10 years from now.

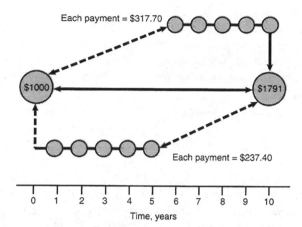

FIGURE 2.1
Equivalence outcomes with an interest rate of 6 percent compounded annually.

- $237.40 received at the end of each year for the next 5 years is equivalent to $317.70 at the end of years 6, 7, 8, 9, and 10.

Equivalence is at the heart of making engineering economic decisions. How to perform the economic evaluations, which is key to much of engineering decision making, is a major thrust of this book.

Figure 2.1 graphically shows the equivalence between cash flows, or amounts, at different times. This is similar to the popular engineering economy representation schema called *cash flow diagramming*. We will represent the cash flow relations in the development of compound-interest factors in the next section in a manner similar to Fig. 2.1. Following the compound-interest factor development, in Sec. 2.7 we formally discuss cash flow diagramming. The reason for delaying the formal discussion is that some concepts will be introduced that might cloud the compound-interest factor development.

2.6   COMPOUND-INTEREST FACTORS

Cash flow is translated to a given time by determining either its present worth or its future worth. A present-worth calculation converts a single future sum or a series of future values to an equivalent amount at an earlier date. This date is not necessarily the present. Future-worth calculations convert values occurring at any time to an equivalent amount at a later date.

Equivalent values could be determined by calculating the compound amount of each sum for each period. This tedious routine is avoided by using compound-interest tables for different present- and future-worth factors. There are two basic types of factors. The one we have already considered, in Sec. 2.4, converts a single amount to a present or future value. The other type is for a series of uniform values called an *annuity*. The tables in

App. D are based on an annuity characterized by (1) *equal payments A,* (2) *equal periods between payments N,* and (3) *the first payment occurring at the end of the first period.* Annuity factors are used to convert a series of payments to a single future or present sum and to translate single sums to a series of payments occurring in the past or future.

2.6.1 Conversion Symbols

There are seven basic interest factors for discrete compounding. Names and notations for these factors are those suggested by the engineering economy division of the American Society for Engineering Education. Each factor is described by a name (e.g., one is the *compound-amount factor,* used in Sec. 2.4 to find the future worth of a single payment) and a notational form where a functional symbol suggests the use of the interest factor, as in *(F/P, i%, N),* again for the compound-amount factor that is used to find F given P, given a specific interest rate $i\%$ and N. Time-value conversions and associated factors are summarized in Table 2.2.

The symbols for the first six time-value conversions are abbreviations for the equivalent values sought (future worth F, present worth P, or uniform series amounts A) and the data given (F, P, or A with its associated interest rate $i\%$ and number of compounding periods N). The arithmetic gradient conversion factor is used to convert a constantly increasing or decreasing series to a uniform series of amounts A that can then be an input to other interest factors. In the equation

$$F = \$1000 \; (F/P, \; 10, \; 2)$$

$1000 is the known present amount, the interest rate i is 10 percent, and F is the equivalent future worth after two periods ($N = 2$). The whole symbol stands for the numerical expression $(1 + 0.10)^2$, and the numerical value is found in App. D. To find the value for $(F/P, 10, 2)$, look for 2 in the N column of the 10 percent table, and then read across to the compound-amount factor column to find 1.2100.

TABLE 2.2

Interest factors for discrete cash flow with end-of-period compounding

Factor	To find	Given	Symbol
Compound amount	Future worth F	Present amount P	*(F/P, i%, N)*
Present worth	Present worth P	Future amount F	*(P/F, i%, N)*
Sinking fund	Annuity amounts A	Future amount F	*(A/F, i%, N)*
Series compound amount	Future worth F	Annuity amounts A	*(F/A, i%, N)*
Capital recovery	Annuity amounts A	Present amount P	*(A/P, i%, N)*
Series present worth	Present worth P	Annuity amounts A	*(P/A, i%, N)*
Arithmetic gradient conversion	Annuity amounts A	Uniform change in amount G	*(A/G, i%, N)*

The conversion descriptions and symbols indicate that certain factors are reciprocals of one another:

$$(F/P, i, N) = \frac{1}{(P/F, i, N)}$$

$$(A/F, i, N) = \frac{1}{(F/A, i, N)}$$

$$(A/P, i, N) = \frac{1}{(P/A, i, N)}$$

Other relationships are not so apparent from the abbreviations but are useful in understanding conversion calculations. The following equalities will be verified during the development of the conversion symbols:

$$(F/P, i, N) \times (P/A, i, N) = (F/A, i, N)$$

$$(F/A, i, N) \times (A/P, i, N) = (F/P, i, N)$$

$$(A/F, i, N) + i = (A/P, i, N)$$

2.6.2 Development of Interest Formulas

A better understanding of the conversion process is achieved by studying the development of the interest factor formulas. The symbols employed in the following discussion of the seven interest factors are the same as those described previously: i = interest rate per period and N is the number of compounding periods. Remember that these factors are for discrete compounding and their numerical values are tabulated in App. D; corresponding factors for continuous compounding are presented in Sec. 2.8.3.

Additional sample applications of the interest factors are provided in the review exercises at the end of this chapter.

2.6.2.1 Compound-amount factor (single payment)

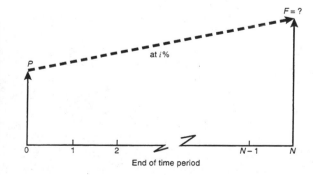

Use: To find F, given P.
Symbols: $(F/P, i\%, N)$
Formula: $F = P(1 + i)^N$
$= P(F/P, i, N)$

End of time period

The effect of compound interest on an investment was demonstrated in previous examples. The future worth of a present amount when interest is accumulated at a specific rate i for a given number of periods N, where F_1 is the future worth at the end of the first period and F_N is the future worth at the end of N periods, is found by using the development of Eq. (2.3) given earlier:

$$F_1 = P + Pi = P(1 + i)$$

$$\begin{aligned} F_2 &= F_1(1 + i) \\ &= P(1 + i)(1 + i) = P(1 + i)^2 \end{aligned}$$

$$\begin{aligned} F_3 &= F_2(1 + i) = F_1(1 + i)^2 \\ &= P(1 + i)(1 + i)^2 = P(1 + i)^3 \end{aligned}$$

$$F_N = P(1 + i)^N$$

The ratio of future worth to present amount is then expressed as

$$F/P = (F/P,\, i,\, N) = (1 + i)^N$$

2.6.2.2 Present-worth factor (single payment)

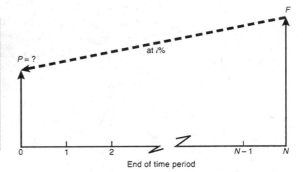

Use: To find P, given F.
Symbols: $(P/F,\, i\%,\, N)$
Formula: $P = F[1/(1 + i)^N]$
$= F(P/F,\, i,\, N)$

The present worth of a sum N periods in the future is P. Rearranging the single-amount future-value formula, Eq. (2.3), gives

$$P = F\left[\frac{1}{(1 + i)^N}\right] \qquad (2.4)$$

Then the ratio of present worth to future value is

$$P/F = (P/F,\, i,\, N) = \frac{1}{(1 + i)^N}$$

That the present-worth factor is simply the reciprocal of the compound-amount factor is confirmed by applying it to the data given in Table 2.1, where the future worth of $1000 at 10 percent compounded annually was shown to be $1210. Equivalently, $P = F(P/F, i, N)$ is the expression for present worth when the future worth is known. The numerical value of the present-worth factor $(P/F, 10, 2)$ is found in the 10 percent table of App. D at $N = 2$ to be 0.82645. Then

$$P = \$1210(0.82645) = \$1000$$

2.6.2.3 Sinking fund factor (uniform series)

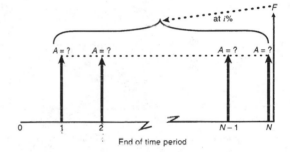

Use: To find A, given F.
Symbols: $(A/F, i\%, N)$
Formula: $A = F\{i/[(1 + i)^N - 1]\}$
$\qquad = F(A/F, i, N)$

A fund established to accumulate a given future amount through the collection of a uniform series of payments is called a *sinking fund*. Each payment has a constant value A and is made at the end of an interest period.

The growth pattern of a sinking fund is illustrated in Table 2.3. Each end-of-year payment A is equal to $1000, and payments continue for 5 years. Interest is 8 percent compounded annually. It is assumed that each payment begins to draw interest as soon as it is deposited in the sinking fund account. Thus, the first payment draws interest for 4 years, and the last payment receives no interest.

A more general expression for the future worth of an annuity develops from the use of symbols to represent the values in Table 2.3. The first payment, earning interest for $N - 1$ periods, where N is 5 years in the example, increases to a future worth of

$$F = A(1 + i)^{N-1}$$

Each of the payments is treated in the same manner and is collected to obtain the total amount F:

$$F = A(1 + i)^{N-1} + A(1 + i)^{N-2} + \cdots + A(1 + i)^{N-(N+1)} + A(1 + i)^{N-N}$$

$$F = A[(1 + i)^{N-1} + (1 + i)^{N-2} + \cdots + (1 + i)^{N-(N+1)} + (1 + i)^{N-N}] \qquad (2.5)$$

TABLE 2.3

Compound amount of a uniform series of payments

Time of payment (end of year)	Amount A of payment, $	Future worth at end of each year, $
1	1000	$1000(1.08)^4 = 1360$
2	1000	$1000(1.08)^3 = 1260$
3	1000	$1000(1.08)^2 = 1166$
4	1000	$1000(1.08)^1 = 1080$
5	1000	$1000(1.08)^0 = \underline{1000}$

Annuity value F at the end of year 5 = 5866

Multiplying Eq. (2.5) by $1 + i$ gives

$$F(1 + i) = A[(1 + i)^N + (1 + i)^{N-1} + \cdots + (1 + i)^{N-(N+2)} + (1 + i)^1] \qquad (2.6)$$

Subtracting Eq. (2.5) from Eq. (2.6) results in

$$F(1 + i - 1) = A[(1 + i)^N - 1]$$

and solving for A gives

$$A = F\left[\frac{i}{(1 + i)^N - 1}\right] \qquad (2.7)$$

The sinking fund factor can now be expressed as

$$(A/F, i, N) = \frac{i}{(1 + i)^N - 1} \qquad (2.8)$$

Now, applying the sinking fund factor to the data in Table 2.3, we have

$$A = \$5866(A/F, 8, 5)$$
$$= \$5866(0.17046) = \$1000$$

The sinking fund factor that we have just developed for a uniform series will now make it very easy for us to determine the series compound-amount factor that is used for finding F given A.

2.6.2.4   Series compound-amount factor (uniform series)

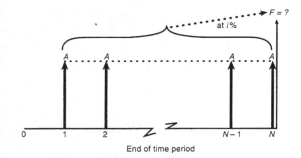

Use: To find F, given A
Symbols: $(F/A, i\%, N)$
Formula:

$$F = A \frac{(1 + i)^N - 1}{i}$$

$$= A(F/A, i, N)$$

From the development of the sinking fund formula, Eq. (2.7),

$$Fi = A[(1 + i)^N - 1]$$

which is expressed in terms of F as

$$F = A \left[\frac{(1 + i)^N - 1}{i} \right]$$

Then the series compound-amount factor to use in calculating the future worth of an annuity is

$$(F/A, i, N) = \frac{(1 + i)^N - 1}{i}$$

The future worth of the annuity composed of five annual payments of $1000, each invested at 8 percent compounded annually, as was shown in Table 2.3, is

$$F = \$1000(F/A, 8, 5)$$
$$= \$1000(5.86660) = \$5866.60$$

2.6.2.5   Capital recovery factor (uniform series)

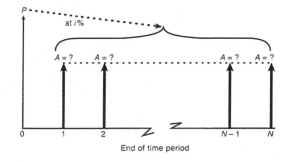

Use: To find A, given P.
Symbols: $(A/P, i\%, N)$
Formula:

$$A = P \left[\frac{i(1 + i)^N}{(1 + i)^N - 1} \right]$$

$$= P(A/P, i, N)$$

The capital recovery factor is used to determine the amount of each future annuity payment required to dissipate a given present value when the interest rate and number of payments are known. For instance, the amount of each annual payment made for 5 years in order to repay a debt of $3993 bearing 8 percent annual interest can be determined through the use of the capital recovery factor. Table 2.4 shows that it would take five $1000 payments to repay the $3993 debt.

TABLE 2.4

Present worth of a uniform series of payments

Time of payment (end of year)	Amount A of payment, $	Present worth of payments at beginning of year 1, $
1	1000	$1000(1.08)^{-1} = 926$
2	1000	$1000(1.08)^{-2} = 857$
3	1000	$1000(1.08)^{-3} = 794$
4	1000	$1000(1.08)^{-4} = 735$
5	1000	$1000(1.08)^{-5} = 681$

Present worth P of 5-year annuity = 3993

Using symbols to represent the conversions shown in Table 2.4, we find that the present worth of an annuity is

$$P = A[(1 + i)^{-1} + (1 + i)^{-2} + \cdots + (1 + i)^{-N+1} + (1 + i)^{-N}] \qquad (2.9)$$

Multiplying both sides of Eq. (2.9) by $(1 + i)^{-1}$ gives

$$P(1 + i)^{-1} = A[(1 + i)^{-2} + (1 + i)^{-3} + \cdots + (1 + i)^{-N} + (1 + i)^{-N-1}] \qquad (2.10)$$

Subtracting Eq. (2.9) from (2.10) results in

$$P[(1 + i)^{-1} - 1] = A[(1 + i)^{-N-1} - (1 + i)^{-1}] \qquad (2.11)$$

Knowing that

$$(1 + i)^{-1} - 1 = \frac{1}{1 + i} - \frac{1 + i}{1 + i} = \frac{-i}{1 + i}$$

we can multiply both sides of Eq. (2.11) by $-(1 + i)$ to get

$$P(i) = A[-(1 + i)^{-N-1}(1 + i) + (1 + i)^{-1}(1 + i)]$$
$$= A\left[\frac{(1 + i)^N - 1}{(1 + i)^N}\right]$$

and

$$A = P\,\frac{i(1+i)^N}{(1+i)^N - 1} \tag{2.12}$$

from which comes the expression for the capital recovery factor

$$(A/P, i, N) = \frac{i(1+i)^N}{(1+i)^N - 1} \tag{2.13}$$

As applied to the data in Table 2.4 where $P = \$3993$,

$$A = \$3993\ (A/P, 8, 5)$$
$$= \$3993(0.25046) = \$1000$$

The relationship between the capital recovery factor [Eq. (2.13)] and the sinking fund factor [Eq. (2.8)] is as follows:

$$(A/P, i, N) = (A/F, i, N) + i \tag{2.14}$$

This can be shown by substituting the factors from Eqs. (2.8) and (2.13) into Eq. (2.14):

$$\frac{i(1+i)^N}{(1+i)^N - 1} = \frac{i}{(1+i)^N - 1} + i = \frac{i + i(1+i)^N - i}{(1+i)^N - 1} = \frac{i(1+i)^N}{(1+i)^N - 1} \tag{2.15}$$

2.6.2.6 Series present-worth factor (uniform series)

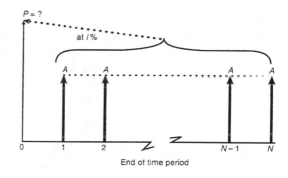

Use: To find P, given A.
Symbols: $(P/A, i\%, N)$
Formula:

$$P = A\left[\frac{(1+i)^N - 1}{i(1+i)^N}\right]$$
$$= A(P/A, i, N)$$

The present value of a series of uniform end-of-period payments can be calculated in the cumbersome fashion shown in Table 2.4. The present worth is more readily determined by use of the series present-worth factor.

Expressing the known relationship [Eq. (2.15)]

$$A = P\,\frac{i(1+i)^N}{(1+i)^N - 1}$$

in terms of P yields

$$P = A\frac{(1 + i)^N - 1}{i(1 + i)^N} = A(P/A, i, N) \qquad (2.16)$$

which is the time-value expression of the present worth of an annuity.

The reciprocal relationship between the capital recovery factor and the series present-worth factor is demonstrated by the data from Table 2.4:

$P = \$1000(P/A, 8, 5)$
  $= \$1000(3.99271) = \$3992.71$

which indicates the equivalence of having \$3992.71 in hand and a firm contract to receive five year-end payments of \$1000 each when the interest rate is 8 percent.

2.6.2.7 Arithmetic gradient conversion factor (to uniform series)

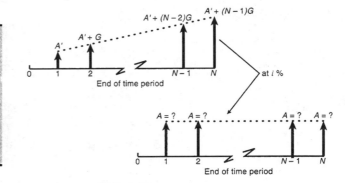

Use: To find A, given G.
Symbols: $(A/G, i\%, N)$
Formula:

$$A = G\left[\frac{1}{i} - \frac{N}{(1 + i)^N - 1}\right]$$
$$= G(A/G, i, N)$$

Enough situations occur in which series of payments increase at equal increments to warrant a special conversion factor. A series of payments that increases at a rate of \$200 per year is illustrated in Fig. 2.2. The \$200 periodic change is the gradient G, and the payment at the end of the first period is the base annuity value A'. The pattern of an arithmetic gradient is then

$$A', A' + G, A' + 2G, \cdots, A' + (N - 1)G$$

where N is the duration of the series ($N = 5$ in Fig. 2.2).

A uniformly increasing series can be evaluated by calculating F or P for each individual payment and summing the results. The calculation time is reduced by converting the series to an equivalent annuity of equal payments A. The formula for this translation is developed by separating the series shown in Fig. 2.2 into two parts: a base annuity designated A' and an arithmetic gradient series increasing by G each period. The future worth of the G values in Fig. 2.2 is calculated as

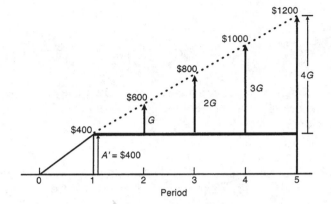

FIGURE 2.2
Uniform gradient series for five periods.

$$F = \$200\ (F/P,\ i,\ 3) + \$400\ (F/P,\ i,\ 2) + \$600\ (F/P,\ i,\ 1) + \$800$$
$$= G(1+i)^3 + 2G(1+i)^2 + 3G(1+i) + 4G \tag{2.17}$$

Multiplying Eq. (2.17) by $1 + i$ gives

$$F\ (1+i) = G(1+i)^4 + 2G(1+i)^3 + 3G(1+i)^2 + 4G(1+i) \tag{2.18}$$

Subtracting Eq. (2.18) from Eq. (2.17) yields

$$F - F - Fi = -G(1+i)^4 - G(1+i)^3 - G(1+i)^2 - G(1+i) + 4G \tag{2.19}$$

Knowing that for this case $4G = (N-1)\ G$ and multiplying both sides of Eq. (2.19) by -1, we get

$$Fi = G[(1+i)^4 + (1+i)^3 + (1+i)^2 + (1+i) + 1] - NG$$

We have, inside the square brackets, the series compound-amount factor $(F/A,\ i,\ 5)$ so that

$$Fi = G(F/A,\ i,\ N) - NG \tag{2.20}$$

To convert F to an annuity, both sides of Eq. (2.20) are multiplied by the sinking fund factor $(A/F,\ i,\ N)$, which is the reciprocal of $(F/A,\ i,\ N)$, to get

$$Fi(A/F,\ i,\ N) = G - NG(A/F,\ i,\ N)$$

Since $A = F(A/F,\ i,\ N)$, we get

$$A = \frac{G}{i} - \frac{NG}{i}(A/F,\ i,\ N)$$

or

$$A = G\left[\frac{1}{i} - \frac{N}{i}(A/F, i, N)\right] = G\left[\frac{1}{i} - \frac{N}{(1+i)^N - 1}\right] \qquad (2.21)$$

in which the bracketed expression is called the *arithmetic gradient conversion factor* with the symbol $(A/G, i, N)$, so that

$$A = G(A/G, i, N)$$

For the cash flow diagrammed in Fig. 2.2, the equivalent uniform annuity calculated at an effective interest rate per period of 10 percent is

$$A = A' + G(A/G, i, N)$$
$$= \$400 + \$200(A/G, 10, 5)$$
$$= \$400 + \$200(1.81013) = \$762$$

which means that five end-of-period payments of $762 are equivalent to five payments starting at $400 and which increase by $200 each period.

The gradient factor may also be applied to a pattern of payments that decrease by a constant increment each period. The formula would then be

$$A = A' - G(A/G, i, N)$$

As an example, assume that an endowment was originally set up to provide a $10,000 first payment with payments decreasing by $1000 each year during the 10-year endowment life. What constant annual payment for 10 years would be equivalent to the original endowment plan if $i = 8$ percent? We have

$$A = \$10,000 - \$1000(A/G, 8, 10)$$
$$= \$10,000 - \$1000(3.87131)$$
$$= \$6128.69$$

2.6.2.8 Development of geometric series formulas

A *geometric series* is a nonuniform progression that grows or declines at a *constant percentage rate* per period. The most familiar example is the effect of inflation or deflation on a cash flow stream. For instance, the rate of growth during a period of inflation could be 10 percent per period. An item priced at $1000 during the first year would then increase by 10 per-

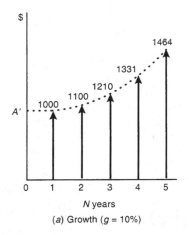
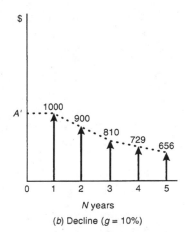

FIGURE 2.3
Geometric growth
and decline
patterns.

cent per year, as shown in Fig. 2.3*a*. A decline of 10 percent per year, starting from the same $1000 figure, would take the pattern shown in Fig. 2.3*b*.

We could determine the present worth of the geometric growth pattern in Fig. 2.3*a* in a cumbersome manner, using the appropriate *(P/F, i, N)* values:

$$P = \$1000(P/F, i, 1) + \$1100 \, (P/F, i, 2) + \$1210(P/F, i, 3)$$
$$+ \, \$1331(P/F, i, 4) + \$1464(P/F, i, 5) \tag{2.22}$$

If the interest rate *i* is 8 percent and, as we know, the geometric growth rate *g* is 10 percent, Eq. (2.22) becomes

$$P = \$1000[(P/F, 0.08, 1) + (1 + 0.10) \, (P/F, 0.08, 2)$$
$$+ \, (1 + 0.10)^2 \, (P/F, 0.08, 3) + (1 + 0.10)^3 \, (P/F, 0.08, 4)$$
$$+ \, (1 + 0.10)^4 \, (P/F, 0.08, 5)] \tag{2.23}$$

Substituting the appropriate App. D values for *(P/F, 0.08, N)* into Eq. (2.23), we get

$$P = \$1000[0.92593 + 1.1(0.85734) + 1.21(0.79383) + 1.331(0.73503)$$
$$+ \, 1.464(0.68058)] = \$4804$$

Now, let us generalize Eq. (2.22) for any *A'*, *P*, *N*, *g*, and *i*:

$$P = A'(P/F, i, 1) + A'(1 + g) \, (P/F, i, 2) + A'(1 + g)^2 \, (P/F, i, 3) + \cdots$$
$$+ \, A'(1 + g)^{N-1}(P/F, i, N)$$

which reduces to

$$P = A' \sum_{k=1}^{N} (1 + g)^{k-1}(P/F, i, k)$$

As can be seen, the equation for P is a finite series that is a function of two rates, i and g. There are two ways we can compute P; the first is direct, and the second uses existing factors in the computation.

Method 1: The previous equation can be expanded to

$$P = A' \sum_{k=1}^{N} (1 + g)^{k-1} \frac{1}{(1 + i)^k}$$

$$= \frac{A'}{1 + g} \sum_{k=1}^{N} \left(\frac{1 + g}{1 + i} \right)^k$$

We can see that if $i = g$,

$$P = \frac{NA'}{1 + g} = \frac{NA'}{1 + i}$$

When $i \neq g$, we can simplify the finite series for P by

$$P = \frac{A'}{1 + g} \sum_{k=1}^{N} \left(\frac{1 + g}{1 + i} \right)^k$$

Letting $(1 + g)/(1 + i) = x$, we get

$$P = \frac{A'}{1 + g} \sum_{k=1}^{N} x^k$$

$$= \frac{A'}{x (1 + i)} (x + x^2 + \cdots + x^N)$$

$$= \frac{A'}{1 + i} (1 + x^1 + \cdots + x^{N-1})$$

Multiplying $1 + x^1 + \cdots + x^N$ by x, subtracting the result from the previous equation, and solving for the closed form of the series give

$$P = \frac{A'}{1 + i} \left(\frac{1 - x^N}{1 - x} \right)$$

Substituting $(1 + g)/(1 + i)$ back for x results in

$$P = \frac{A'}{1+i} \left[\frac{1 - (1+g)^N/(1+i)^N}{1 - (1+g)/(1+i)} \right]$$

$$= A' \frac{1/(1+i) - (1+g)^N/(1+i)^{N+1}}{(i-g)/(1+i)}$$

$$= A' \left[\frac{1 - (1+g)^N (1+i)^{-N}}{i-g} \right]$$

For example, if we have $A' = \$1000$, $i = 0.10$, $g = 0.08$, and $N = 5$,

$$P = \$1000 \left[\frac{1 - (1.08)^5(1.10)^{-5}}{0.10 - 0.08} \right] = \$4383$$

Similarly, if the values for i and g were reversed:

$$P = \$1000 \left[\frac{1 - (1.10)^5(1.08)^{-5}}{0.08 - 0.10} \right] = \$4804$$

Method 2. We can compute the present worth of the geometric gradient by using a pseudo interest rate that depends on the relationship between i and g.

    Case 1. $g > i$
    Form $i' = (1+g)/(1+i) - 1$ and use i' in

$$P = \frac{A'}{1+i}(F/A, i', N)$$

For the earlier example with $g = 0.10$ and $i = 0.08$, we have

$$i' = \frac{1.10}{1.08} - 1 = 0.0185$$

This requires interpolation from the tables at the back of the book; or CHEER, the computer program ancillary to this text, can be used to find $(F/A, 1.85, 5)$ directly, as we will see in the review exercises at the end of this chapter:

$$P = \frac{\$1000}{1.08}(5.1585) = \$4804$$

This is exactly what we expected from our earlier direct calculation.

    Case 2. $g < i$
    Form $i' = (1+i)/(1+g) - 1$ and use i' in

$$P = \frac{A'}{1+g}(P/A,\ i',\ N)$$

If we reversed the values for i and g in the previous example, we would have i' the same as before since the larger of g or i is always in the numerator; $i' = 0.0185$.

$$P = \frac{\$1000}{1.08}\ (4.73405) = \$4383$$

2.6.2.9 Midyear accounting convention

Usually, cash flows are assumed to occur at the end of a time period, say, at the end of the year or at the end of a quarter. This might require the accumulation of multiple incomes or disbursements that occur during a time period and the use of the accumulated values at the end of the period without considering the effects of interest. The errors in using the end-of-period convention are generally insignificant. For example, the Canadian tax regulations permit half-year of depreciation allowance for a number of assets during the first year of their service. This tax deductible expense is considered as an end-of-year cash flow item. The U.S. federal government requires that an asset be placed in service at the middle of a purchase year, which forces an asset with a life of 5 years, for example, to be depreciated over 6 years. Therefore, an asset depreciated over 5 years will be assumed to have costs over 6 years. In a straight-line depreciation method, the capital cost depreciation would be split in the 6 years as follows: 10, 20, 20, 20, 20, and 10 percent at time periods 1 through 6, respectively. Further comments on depreciation rules and the midyear assumption will be given in Chap. 9, which covers the implications of income taxes on engineering economic decisions.

2.7   CASH FLOW DIAGRAMS

Figure 2.1 and diagrams with the compound-interest factor development showed how equivalence between incomes and payments made at various times can be clarified by a graphical display. Figure 2.1 is not really representative of a realistic engineering economy situation because several equivalent situations are shown on the diagram. Be that as it may, representing engineering decision data in graphical form can greatly enhance the understanding of the problem. Cash flow diagrams are tools to help the decision maker to understand and solve such problems.

During the construction of a cash flow diagram, the structure of a problem often becomes distinct. It is usually advantageous to first define the time frame over which cash flows occur. This establishes the horizontal scale, which is divided into time periods, often in years. Receipts and disbursements are then located on the time scale in adherence to problem specifications. Individual outlays or receipts are designated by vertical lines;

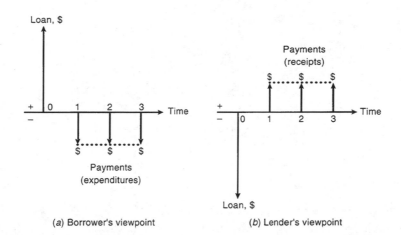

FIGURE 2.4
Perspectives for
cash flow diagrams.

(*a*) Borrower's viewpoint   (*b*) Lender's viewpoint

relative magnitudes can be suggested by the heights of lines, but exact scaling wastes time. Whether a cash flow is positive or negative (positive above the axis and negative below) depends on whose viewpoint is portrayed.

Figure 2.4*a* and *b* represents the same transaction: a loan paid off in three installments. From the borrower's viewpoint in Fig. 2.4*a,* the receipt of the loan is a positive inflow of cash, whereas subsequent installment payments represent negative outflows. Flows are reversed when viewed from the lender's perspective in Fig. 2.4*b*.

Although cash flow diagrams are simply graphical representations of income and outlay, they should exhibit as much information as possible. It is useful to show the interest rate, and it may be helpful to designate the unknown that must be solved for in a problem. Figure 2.4 is redrawn in Fig. 2.5 to represent specific problems. In Fig. 2.5*a,* the three equal payments are represented by a convenient convention that indicates a 3-year annuity in which the payment size *A* is unknown. Amount *A* may be circled to indicate the needed solution. The given interest rate ($i = 10$ percent) is entered in a conspicuous space, and the amount of the loan is placed on the arrow at time 0. The style of a cash flow diagram is important only insofar as it contributes to clarity.

In Fig. 2.5*b,* numbered years are replaced with dates, and the size of *A* is given. The problem is to find the interest rate that makes the annuity equivalent to the loan value. Sometimes it may clarify the situation to put in dashed lines for arrows that represent cash flows of unknown magnitude. This or a similar tactic is especially useful when a problem comprises several separate cash flow segments, each of which must be replaced by an equivalent value; these, in turn, are converted to a single sum representing all the segments.

The obvious requirements for cash flow diagramming are completeness, accuracy, and legibility. The measure of a successful diagram is that someone else can understand the problem fully from it. If it passes this test, you are unlikely to confuse yourself. We will utilize the concepts of

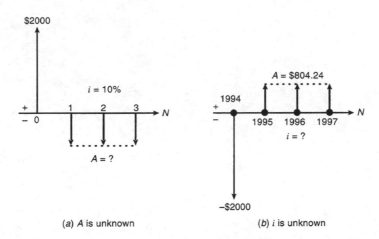

FIGURE 2.5
Different versions of
cash flow diagrams.

(a) A is unknown

(b) i is unknown

cash flow diagramming in the following sections (and in later chapters) where a series of examples will be presented.

2.8   CALCULATION OF TIME-VALUE EQUIVALENCES

Concepts concerning the time value of money will now become working tools. Compound-interest factors for both discrete and continuous interest will be applied to a variety of cash flows. The purpose of the calculations is to develop skills in converting cash flow patterns to equivalent sums that are more useful in comparing investments. The use of cash flow diagrams will be emphasized to portray receipts and disbursements associated with an economic situation.

The purpose of time-value calculations is to translate receipts and disbursements of various amounts occurring at various times to a cash flow pattern that assists an economic evaluation, which will generally be for *engineering decision making* in this text. The translation is essentially mechanical in the same way as a vector is routinely decomposed into component forces; rules of geometry direct vector operations, and time-value relations direct cash flow translations. Although errors in translation can arise from carelessness, mistakes due to incorrect problem formulations are the ones to guard against.

The notable statements in a discounted cash flow problem are the elements *P, F, A, N,* and *i*. Generally, three of the elements are known for each cash flow, and the problem entails solving for a fourth element. Several money-time translations may be required in one solution.

A variety of typical cash flow patterns are treated in the following pages. Examples are presented to put cash flow problems in a realistic setting, show different perspectives for the same type of problem, demonstrate the use of cash flow diagrams, and provide familiarity with the use of interest factors and tables. The examples given will employ discrete and continuous compounding. The diagrams and solution formulations common to discrete compounding, the compounding that most of us have some familiarity with, are equally applicable to continuous compounding.

2.8.1 Single-Payment Cash Flow

Translation of a future amount to its present worth, or the reverse from present to future, has already been demonstrated for both discrete and continuous compounding. Sometimes both present and future amounts are known, so the problem is to find the value of i or N that makes them equivalent.

EXAMPLE 2.3

Unknown Interest Rate

At what annual interest rate will \$1000 invested today be worth \$2000 in 9 years?

Solution

Given $P = \$1000$, $F = \$2000$, and $N = 9$ years, find i.

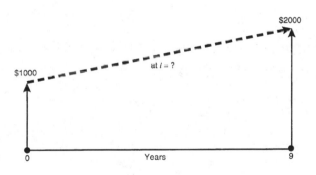

$$\frac{F}{P} = (F/P,\ i,\ 9)$$

$$\frac{\$2000}{\$1000} = 2 = (F/P,\ i,\ 9)$$

$$i = 8\%$$

The interest rate i is determined by locating the interest rate at which the single-payment compound-amount factor is equal to 2.0 and $N = 9$ (a reciprocal relation using a present-worth factor could serve as well). The numerical value of i is found by leafing through the pages of interest rates and noting the appropriate factor values for the given number of periods. Another way to find i directly is

$$(F/P, i, 9) = (1 + i)^9 = 2 \qquad i = 2^{1/9} - 1 = 0.08$$

When tables are used rather than CHEER to determine compound-interest factor values, it is often necessary to interpolate when N or i is unknown. The error introduced by linear interpolation is relatively insignificant for most practical applications. If the investment period for Example 2.3 had been 10 years instead of 9, the interest rate calculation would have been

$$(F/P, i, 10) = F/P = \frac{\$2000}{\$1000} = 2.0$$

At $i = 7$ percent, $(F/P, 7, 10) = 1.96715$; at $i = 8$ percent, $(F/P, 8, 10) = 2.15892$. Then, by interpolation,

$$
\begin{aligned}
i &= 0.07 + 0.01\left(\frac{2.0000 - 1.96715}{2.15892 - 1.96715}\right) \\
&= 0.07 + 0.01\left(\frac{0.03285}{0.19177}\right) \\
&= 0.0717 = 7.2\%
\end{aligned}
$$

Most of the inconvenience of interpolation is avoided with calculators that can be programmed, or are preprogrammed, for the interest factor formulas. CHEER, the computer program available with this text, very simply determines the values, as is possible with spreadsheet applications.

The time periods being considered in an economic analysis do not have to be yearly, although this will often be the case. The ultimate situation where subdivisions of a year are used for the time periods is where continuous compounding is used; the time periods are infinitesimally small. In engineering economic analyses, the time periods often occur quarterly, or four times per year.

EXAMPLE 2.4

Unknown Number of Interest Periods

A loan of $1000 is made today under an agreement that $1400 will be received in payment sometime in the future. When should the $1400 be received if the loan is to earn interest at a rate of 8 percent compounded quarterly?

Solution

Given $P = \$1000$, $F = \$1400$, $i = r/m - 8$ percent/4 = 2 percent, find N in quarters:

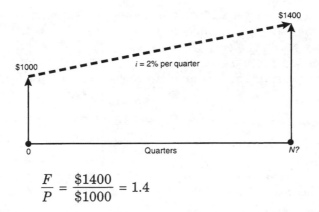

$$\frac{F}{P} = \frac{\$1400}{\$1000} = 1.4$$

By interpolation, $N = 17$ quarters, or 4 years 3 months.

Example 2.4 is slightly deceptive because it involves a nominal interest rate. The problem is clarified by noting in the cash flow diagram that the time scale is in quarters of a year and that i is given as the rate per quarter. The problem could also have been solved by converting the nominal rate to its equivalent effective annual interest rate

$$i_{\text{eff}} = \left(1 + \frac{0.08}{4}\right)^4 - 1 = 1.082 - 1 = 0.082$$

and then interpolating between the 8 percent and 9 percent interest tables and N values between 4 and 5:

$$(F/P, 8.2, N) = 1.400$$

Determine N.

$$(F/P, 8.2, 4) = 1.36049 + 0.2(1.41158 - 1.36049) = 1.37071$$
$$(F/P, 8.2, 5) = 1.46933 + 0.2(1.53862 - 1.46933) = 1.48319$$
$$N = 4 + 1\left(\frac{1.4000 - 1.37071}{1.48319 - 1.37071}\right)$$
$$= 4.26 \text{ years}$$

The result differs from 4 years 3 months only by minor roundoff errors in the interest factors.

2.8.2 Multiple-Payment Cash Flows

Practical problems customarily involve both single payments and annuities. For instance, to determine the equivalent present worth (cost) of owning a car for 3 years involves a series of payments, to purchase the car and provide gas, repair, and maintenance costs at irregular intervals, and a single payment (receipt) when the car is sold. All these receipts and disbursements would be translated to "now" and summed to find the present worth—a single sum equivalent to ownership costs for 3 years.

EXAMPLE 2.5

More Compounding Periods than Payments

"Now" is June 30, 1994. Three payments of $500 each are to be received every 2 years, starting 2 years from now, and deposited in a bank where they will earn interest at 7 percent per year. How large will the bank account be on June 30, 2002?

Solution

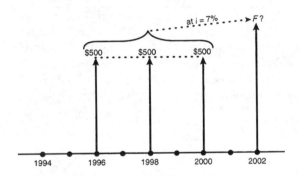

$$F = \$500\ (F/P,\ 7,\ 6) + \$500\ (F/P,\ 7,\ 4) + \$500\ (F/P,\ 7,\ 2)$$
$$= \$500\ (1.50073 + 1.31080 + 1.14490)$$
$$= \$500\ (3.95643) = \$1978$$

The equal payments in Example 2.5 do not constitute an ordinary annuity because there are fewer payments than there are compounding periods. Therefore, each payment must be translated individually to the 2002 date and added to the worth of the other payments at that date to obtain the equivalent future worth of all three payments.

Frequently in engineering economic decision making, a company will require that a minimum specified interest rate be achievable before investing in a new process or product. This means that the interest rate in the analysis will be the unknown.

EXAMPLE 2.6

Annuity with an Unknown i

A numerically controlled milling machine that can be purchased for $8065 is estimated to reduce production costs annually by $2020. The machine will operate for 5 years, at which time it will have no resale value. What rate of return will be earned on the investment? (Alternative statement of the problem: At what interest rate will a cash flow of $2020 per year for 5 years equal a present value of $8065?)

Solution

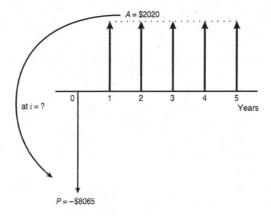

$$\frac{P}{A} = \frac{\$8065}{\$2020} = 3.993 = (P/A, \, i, \, 5) \quad \text{and} \quad i = 8\%$$

A series of payments made at the beginning instead of the end of each period is sometimes referred to as an *annuity due*. Rather than create a special factor for this annuity pattern, we divide the series into two parts. If the first payment is translated separately, the remaining payments fit the pattern for an ordinary annuity beginning at the time of the first payment. The present worth of the series is the sum of the first payment plus the product of one payment times the series present-worth factor, where N is the number of payments minus 1.

EXAMPLE 2.7

Annuity Due

What is the present worth of a series of 15 year end payments of $1000 each, when the first payment is due today and the interest rate is 5 percent?

Solution

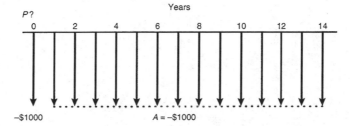

$$P = A + A(P/A, 5, 14)$$
$$= \$1000 + \$1000(9.89864)$$
$$= \$1000 + \$9899$$
$$= \$10,899$$

Another pattern for a series of payments, in which the first payment does not begin until some date later than the end of the first period, is called a *deferred annuity*. Like an annuity due, a deferred annuity is evaluated by dividing the time period into two parts. One portion is the number of payment periods. This portion forms an ordinary annuity. The second portion is the number of periods. A solution results from determining the present worth of the ordinary annuity and then discounting this value through the preannuity (deferred) periods .

EXAMPLE 2.8   **Deferred Annuity**

With interest at 6 percent, what is the worth on December 31, 1994, of a series of year-end payments of $317.70 made from the years 2000 through 2004?

Solution

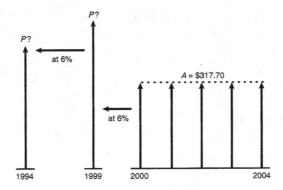

Starting from the known values of A, i, and N, we have at the end of 1999:

$$P(1999) = A(P/A, 6, 5)$$

and P (1999) now becomes the F value in calculating $P(1994)$:

$$P(1994) = P(1999) \, (P/F, 6, 5)$$

Collecting terms, we have

$$P(1994) = A(P/A, 6, 5) \, (P/F, 6, 5)$$
$$= \$317.70(4.21236)(0.74726)$$
$$= \$1000$$

The results of Example 2.8 may be recognized as one of the equivalent outcomes presented without proof in Fig. 2.1.

Many engineering economy problems require the use of an arithmetic gradient due to expected annual increases in costs or incomes.

EXAMPLE 2.9

Present Worth of an Arithmetic Gradient

Sabdave Company, which has had a rapid growth in business, finds that it is running out of storage space for raw materials. Jenna Company has offered a contract for leasing a nearby storage facility at $20,000 per year with annual increases of $1500 for 8 years. Payments are to be made at the end of each year, starting 1 year from now. The prevailing interest rate is 7 percent. What lump sum paid today would be equivalent to the 8-year lease payment plan? This present worth could then be compared with the estimated cost of expanding Sabdave's existing storage facility (including the expected present worth of added costs in running the facility).

Solution

The base annuity A' and the gradient G per period are shown on the cash flow diagram:

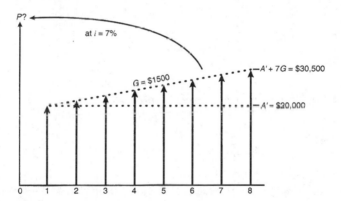

The first step in solving for the present worth of the lease payment plan is to convert the increasing annual payments to a uniform series:

$$A = A' + G(A/G, 7, 8) = \$20,000 + \$1500(3.14654)$$
$$= \$20,000 + \$4719.81$$
$$= \$24,719.81$$

The annuity is now translated to its present worth as

$$P = A(P/A, 7, 8) = \$24,719.81(5.9713)$$
$$= \$147,609.40$$

which is the amount in today's dollars equivalent to the lease contract that provides yearly payments of $20,000 with annual increases of $1500 for 8 years.

More extensive economic situations usually include income, possibly savings, and costs. Such situations are evaluated by calculating the net outcome at a certain time. A cash flow diagram incorporates receipts and disbursements by displaying income above the time line and outlays below the line. Other payment categories can be handled similarly.

EXAMPLE 2.10

Income and Outlay

The management of an expanding manufacturing firm is considering a proposal from a consulting group to introduce a new method of training inexperienced machine tool operators. The consultants claim that their program will produce savings of $7000 per year over the planned 5-year life of the project. Immediate costs to implement the program are $12,000, and annual training expenses will be $4000. The firm uses 6 percent annual interest for cost comparisons. Should the firm accept the proposal, assuming all other factors are negligible?

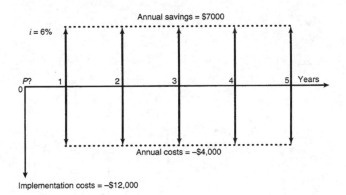

Solution

Assuming that the costs and savings occur at the end of a year, we find that

$$A = \text{annual savings} - \text{annual costs} = \$7000 - \$4000 = \$3000$$

For the proposal to be acceptable, the net return must be greater than the $12,000 initial cost. By translating the 5-year annuity to the present time, we compare the initial cost and the present worth of savings P directly:

$$P = A(P/A,\ 6,\ 5) = \$3000(4.21236) = \$12,637$$

The indicated total net savings exceed the initial cost by

$$\$12,637 - \$12,000 = \$637$$

which gives very little leeway for error in cost or savings estimates.

The same conclusion results from taking a different approach with the same data. From the capital recovery formula, the annual return on the gross savings A required for 5 years to meet a present obligation of $12,000 is

$$A = P(A/P, 6, 5) = \$12,000(0.23740) = \$2849$$

Comparing the required return with the expected annual gross savings shows annual net savings of

$$\$3000 - \$2849 = \$151$$

a marginal saving at best.

We have seen two approaches to the problem, and usually there are several ways to tackle such problems. The solutions, though, are identical. This can be seen by determining the present worth of the $151 expected to be saved annually over 5 years:

$$P = \$151(P/A, 6, 5) = \$151(4.21236) = \$636.07$$

This is the same as the present-worth saving we determined earlier (with minor roundoff errors).

So, given an engineering decision that requires an economic analysis, we have seen that there are many ways to attack the analysis. One way might be the most efficient while another might be the most logical from a management presentation perspective. Only experience will reveal the best way to go in many situations. Even if the most expedient method is not chosen, the solution should still be correct, if assumptions and data are correct.

2.8.3 Calculations with Continuous Interest

In our earlier discussion of nominal interest rates (Sec. 2.4.1), it was apparent that for a specific nominal rate, the effective interest rate gets larger as the compounding interval is shortened. The effective interest rate i for a nominal interest rate of 18 percent ($r = 0.18$) compounded semiannually ($m = 2$) was shown to be

$$i_{\text{eff}} = \left(1 + \frac{r}{m}\right)^m - 1 = \left(1 + \frac{0.18}{2}\right)^2 - 1 = 0.188 \text{ or } 18.8\%$$

and $i_{\infty} = e^r - 1$ when the interest periods are infinitesimally small. For the same 18 percent nominal interest compounded continuously,

$$i_{\infty} = e^{0.18} - 1 = 1.1972 - 1 = 0.1972 \text{ or } 19.72\%$$

Using continuous compounding in place of discrete compounding leads to an increase in the force of interest on the time value of money. A single payment earning continuous interest has a future value of

$$F = Pe^{rN}$$

where the continuous-interest compound factor e^{rN} relates to the $(1 + i)^N$ used in the F/P factor for discrete compounding.

EXAMPLE 2.11

Comparison of Continuous and Discrete Compounding

A sum of money doubles in size after 9 years, when it is invested at 8 percent interest compounded annually:

$$F = P(1 + 0.08)^9$$
$$2P = P(1.999)$$

At what rate of continuous compounding will an amount double in only one-half the time taken at the 8 percent effective rate?

Solution

It is given that $F = 2P$ at $N = 9/2 = 4.5$ years. Substituting these values into the future-worth equation and using continuous compounding, we get

$$F = 2P = P(e^{rN}) \quad \text{and} \quad 2 = e^{4.5r}$$

And r can be found in the right-hand equation by taking natural logarithms of both sides:

$$\ln 2 = 4.5r \ln e$$

and

$$0.693 = 4.5r \qquad r = \frac{0.693}{4.5} \, (100\%) = 15.4\%$$

2.8.3.1 Continuous-compounding, discrete cash flow

There are two versions of continuous interest. The *discrete cash flow* form applies continuous compounding to a payment whenever it is received, but the payment is assumed to be received in one lump sum. The other form assumes that the cash flow is continuous. The future-worth formula $F = Pe^{rN}$ and its reciprocal $P = Fe^{-rN}$ are discrete cash flows compounded continuously.

Continuous-compounding factors with *discrete payments* can be similarly developed from the end-of-period annuity formulas. First, recall from the discussion of effective interest that e^{rN} corresponds to $(1 + i)^N$ and that the effective interest rate is

$$i_\infty = e^r - 1$$

Substitution of these expressions into the sinking fund formula yields the fact that the discrete cash flow, end-of-period compounding, sinking fund formula is equal to the discrete cash flow, continuous-compounding, *sinking fund* formula when $i = e^r - 1$:

$$A = F\left[\frac{i}{(1 + i)^N - 1}\right] = F\left(\frac{e^r - 1}{e^{rN} - 1}\right)$$

and the reciprocal of the expression in parentheses is the series compound-amount factor for continuous compounding.

By similar reasoning, the capital recovery formula with continuous compounding and discrete payments is

$$A = P\left[\frac{e^{rN}(e^r - 1)}{e^{rN} - 1}\right]$$

and the reciprocal of the bracketed expression is the continuous-compounding series present-worth factor.

In every formula the A, F, and P values resulting from computations using either end-of-period or continuous compounding are identical for discrete payments when the continuous interest rate is equivalent to the effective interest rate. This relation is apparent when numbers are substituted into the sinking fund formulas displayed above. Letting $i = 22.1$ percent, which corresponds to a nominal continuous interest rate of 20 percent ($0.221 = e^{0.2} - 1$), and applying the equivalent interest rates in the two sinking fund formulas with $N = 2$ gives

End-of-period compounding   Continuous compounding

$$A = F\left(\frac{0.221}{1.221^2 - 1}\right) = F\left(\frac{e^{0.2} - 1}{e^{(0.2)(2)} - 1}\right)$$

$$= F\left(\frac{0.221}{1.491 - 1}\right) = F\left(\frac{1.221 - 1}{1.492 - 1}\right)$$

$$0.45 = 0.45$$

which shows that the factors are equal when $i = e^r - 1$ and payments are discrete.

EXAMPLE 2.12

Continuous Compounding of a Discrete-Payment Annuity

At the end of each year, a single payment of $1766 is deposited in an account that earns 6 percent compounded continuously. What is the amount in the account immediately after the fifth payment?

Solution

Given $A = \$1766$, $r = 0.06$, and $N = 5$, we calculate F as

$$F = A\left(\frac{e^{rN} - 1}{e^r - 1}\right) = \$1766\left(\frac{e^{(0.06)(5)} - 1}{e^{(0.06)} - 1}\right)$$

$$= \$1766\left(\frac{1.3499 - 1}{1.0618 - 1}\right) = \$1766(5.6618)$$

$$= \$9999$$

This future worth is not notably higher than that earned by annual compounding of the same annuity:

$$F = \$1766(F/A, 6, 5) = \$1766(5.63709) = \$9955$$

2.8.3.2 Continuous-compounding, continuous cash flow

The other version of continuous compounding occurs when the total payment for 1 year is received in continuous, small, equal payments during that year. We will let $\bar{A}$ designate the total amount of each payment per year, which continues for N years at a nominal interest rate r per year.

If we have the case of equal payments per period, the flow pattern is as follows:

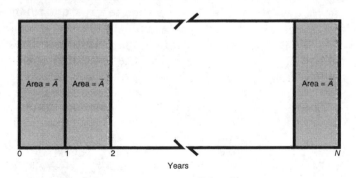

If the compounding and flow are both discrete, we have a future value after N years of

$$F = \frac{A[(1 + i)^N - 1]}{i}$$

With continuous cash flows, we are allowing $\bar{A}$ to be broken into a large number (say, m) of equal cash flows spaced at equal points within the year, so that

$$F = \frac{\bar{A}}{m} \frac{(1 + r/m)^{mN} - 1}{r/m} = \bar{A} \frac{(1 + r/m)^{mN} - 1}{r}$$

where r is the nominal annual interest rate. From our earlier continuous-interest computations, we know that

$$\left(1 + \frac{r}{m}\right)^m = e^r \qquad \text{as } m \to \infty$$

so

$$F = \bar{A} \left(\frac{e^{rN} - 1}{r}\right)$$

From a classical calculus approach, this is the same as

$$F = \bar{A} \int_{m=0}^{N} e^{rm} \, dm = \bar{A} \left(\frac{e^{rN} - 1}{r}\right)$$

The expression in parentheses is called the *continuous-compounding series compound-amount factor* for *continuous uniform payments*.

If we wanted to determine $P/\bar{A}$, we could start from the completely discrete case:

$$P = A\left[\frac{(1 + i)^N - 1}{i(1 + i)}\right]$$

and form the continuous equivalent,

$$P = \frac{\bar{A}}{m} \frac{(1 + r/m)^{mN} - 1}{r/m(1 + r/m)^{mN}}$$

As m approaches infinity, this reduces to

$$P = \bar{A} \left(\frac{e^{rN} - 1}{re^{rN}}\right)$$

TABLE 2.5

Symbols and formulas for continuous compounding of a continuous flow. Here $\bar{A}$ designates total amount accumulated in small equal payments during 1 year, N represents the total number of years for compounding, and the continuous interest rate is r per year

Application formula	Equation
$(\bar{A}/F, r\%, N)$	$\bar{A} = F\left(\dfrac{r}{e^{rN} - 1}\right)$
$(F/\bar{A}, r\%, N)$	$F = \bar{A}\left(\dfrac{e^{rN} - 1}{r}\right)$
$(\bar{A}/P, r\%, N)$	$\bar{A} = P\left(\dfrac{re^{rN}}{e^{rN} - 1}\right)$
$(P/\bar{A}, r\%, N)$	$P = \bar{A}\left(\dfrac{e^{rN} - 1}{re^{rN}}\right)$

Functional notations and formulas for four basic continuous-compounding factors for continuous-flow payments are given in Table 2.5.

The assumption of a continuous flow of disbursements and incomes throughout a year is rare as compared with the end-of-year payment pattern. However, the continuous-flow assumption is more revealing and applicable than is continuous compounding of discrete payments, because the main reason for using continuous interest in an economic evaluation is to determine the effects of continuous cash flows, not just the continuous interest on discrete payments. Consequently, tables are provided in App. E for continuous-compounding, continuous-flow interest factors. These factors follow the functional notations given in Table 2.5 and are applied to continuous cash flows according to the same logic and procedures that govern discrete compound-interest calculations.

EXAMPLE 2.13   Continuous Compounding of a Continuous-Payment Annuity

A savings plan offered by a company allows employees to set aside part of their daily wages and have the money earn 6 percent compounded continuously. What annual amount withdrawn from pay will accumulate $10,000 in 5 years? (Alternative statement of the problem: What continuous-flow annual annuity will yield a future value of $10,000 in 5 years when compounded continuously at 6 percent?)

Solution

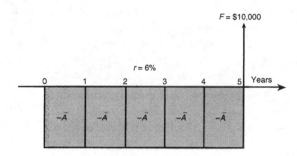

The effect of continuous compounding of continuous flow can be judged by comparing Example 2.12 with this example (where Example 2.12 accumulated $9999, a slight rounding difference from this example's $10,000).

$$\bar{A} = F(\bar{A}/F, \ 6, \ 5)$$

$$= F\left(\frac{r}{e^{rN} - 1}\right)$$

$$= F\left(\frac{0.06}{e^{0.3} - 1}\right) = \$10,000(0.1715) = \$1715$$

The amount of money to be held back per year with a continuous-payment annuity as contrasted to continuous compounding of a discrete-payment annuity is $51 less, where A from Example 2.12 is $1766:

$$A - \bar{A} = \$1766 - \$1715 = \$51$$

2.8.3.3 Role of continuous compounding in engineering economic studies

Some savings institutions advertise continuous compounding as an inducement to savers. The intent is to attract investors by paying higher effective interest than the competitors while still adhering to the nominal interest rate set by regulation. This is an example of discrete continuous compounding.

Actual flows of funds in industry, minute-by-minute incoming receipts and outgoing disbursements, are essentially continuous. Since continuous cash flow closely approximates the pattern of business transactions, it would seem reasonable to compound that flow pattern in evaluating business proposals. It seldom is reasonable. Engineering economic studies primarily rely on discrete compounding because they typically focus on aggregate payments that are assumed to take place on specified dates. If we were investigating a possible new machine, estimates of cash flow for the future use of the new machine would be even less precise than assessments of performance for existing machines; applying continuous compounding would add negligibly to the precision of the evaluation, even though cash flows are closer to being continuous than annual.

Discrete compounding is featured in this text because it is conceptually easier to grasp, provides adequate precision, and is the most widely applied method. Despite its lack of acceptance, continuous compounding is sometimes more appropriate, particularly when data show that the cash flow is indeed continuous. It is for these occasions that continuous-compounding, continuous cash flow calculations have been discussed.

2.9   **REVIEW EXERCISES AND DISCUSSIONS**

EXERCISE 1

The money earned from making a loan is evident in the contract (sometimes in fine print). A loan of $10,000 for 1 year at an interest rate of 10 percent earns the lender $10,000 × 0.10 = $1000. A borrower usually does not know in advance exactly how much will be gained from a loan to buy productive goods. It is often impossible to segregate precisely the receipts due to a certain production operation when that operation is a small part of a much larger production system. In such cases an evaluation study may be made of the amount that production costs of the system are decreased by improvements to the given operation, assuming the operation must be performed to maintain the total process. Then the earnings are in the form of "cost savings" in the system, which are compared with the investment cost of acquiring and using assets to improve the operation.

Assume a machine is purchased for $10,000 with the loan mentioned above. The machine will be completely worn out by the end of the year, and its operating costs will be $100 per month more than the costs of the present operation. How large a cost reduction must be provided by the machine for its purchase to earn a 15 percent return for the borrower?

SOLUTION 1

The costs involved include repayment of the loan plus interest charges for the loan, extra operating costs, and investment earnings resulting from the purchase of the machine:

Loan repayment (purchase price of machine)	$10,000
Interest paid on loan for 1 year = $10,000 × 0.10	1,000
Additional operating cost incurred = $100/month × 12	1,200
15% earnings on $10,000 borrowed = $10,000 × 0.15	1,500
Necessary cost reduction to support investment	$13,700

If the cost reduction turned out to be only $13,700 − $1500 = $12,200, it would cover only expenses and nothing would be gained from the machine's purchase. However, if the company could afford $10,000 of its own money for the machine rather than borrowing it, a cost reduction of $12,200 will yield a 10 percent return on the investment, which is the rate the company could earn by simply lending its money at the "going" interest rate of 10 percent. A cost reduction of $13,700 will produce a return of

$$\frac{\$13,700 - \$10,000 - \$1200}{\$10,000} = \frac{\$2500 \ (100\%)}{\$10,000} = 25\%$$

which is attractive to the company because it provides an added 15 percent beyond the cost of capital to support the project.

EXERCISE 2
A loan of $200 is made for a period of 13 months, from January 1 to January 31 the following year, at a simple interest rate of 10 percent. What future amount is due at the end of the loan period?

SOLUTION 2
Using ordinary simple interest, we find that the total amount to be repaid after 13 months is

$$\begin{aligned} F &= P + PiN \\ &= \$200 + \$200(0.10) \ (1 + \tfrac{1}{12}) \\ &= \$200 + \$200(0.1083) \\ &= \$200 + \$21.67 = \$221.67 \end{aligned}$$

If exact simple interest is used, the future value (assuming the year in question is not a leap year) is

$$\begin{aligned} F &= P + PiN \\ &= \$200 + \$200(0.10)(1 + \tfrac{31}{365}) \\ &= \$200 + \$200(0.10849) = \$221.70 \end{aligned}$$

EXERCISE 3
A credit plan charges interest at the rate of 18 percent compounded monthly. What is the effective interest rate?

SOLUTION 3
The nominal 18 percent rate constitutes monthly charges of 1.5 percent. From this statement we know that $r = 0.18$ and $m = 12$, so the effective interest rate can be calculated as

$$\begin{aligned} i_{\text{eff}} &= \left(1 + \frac{r}{m}\right)^m - 1 = \left(1 + \frac{0.18}{12}\right)^{12} - 1 \\ &= 1.015^{12} - 1 = 1.1956 - 1 = 0.1956 \text{ or } 19.56\% \end{aligned}$$

The same result can be obtained by recognizing that

$$1.015^{12} - 1 = (F/P, \ 1.5, \ 12) - 1$$

Then the tables in App. D can be used to find the value of the compound-amount factor at $i = 1.5$ percent and $N = 12$:

$$(F/P,\ 1.5,\ 12) = 1.19562$$

so

$$1.19562 - 1 = 0.1956 \text{ or } 19.56\%$$

EXERCISE 4

How much would a person have had to invest 1 year ago to have $2500 available today, when the investment earned interest at the nominal rate of 12 percent compounded monthly?

SOLUTION 4

It is first necessary to convert the nominal rate to its corresponding periodic rate: 12 percent compounded monthly means that an investment earns 1 percent per month. Next, it must be recognized that today's worth is a future worth in terms of when investment P was made, 1 year previously. It is known that $F = \$2500$, $i = 1$ percent, and $N = 12$ (12 months have passed since the original investment); therefore,

$$P = F(P/F,\ 1,\ 12) = \$2500(0.88745) = \$2219$$

EXERCISE 5

What annual year-end payment must be made each year to have $20,000 available 5 years from now? The compound annual interest rate is 6 percent.

SOLUTION 5

The 5-year annuity is a sinking fund that has a value at maturity of $F = \$20,000$. The necessary annual deposits equal

$$A = F(A/F,\ 6,\ 5) = \$20,000(0.17740) = \$3548$$

EXERCISE 6

If you deposit $10,000 today, what equal amounts can you withdraw at the end of each quarter for the next 4 years, when the nominal interest rate is 10 percent?

SOLUTION 6

The withdrawals form an annuity where $N = 16$ and $i = 10/4$ percent. Given $P = \$10,000$, the capital invested is recovered by payments of

$$A = \$10,000(A/P,\ 2.5,\ 16) = \$10,000(0.07660) = \$766$$

EXERCISE 7

An ambitious saver plans to deposit $2000 in a money market account starting 1 year from now and wants to increase annual deposits by $1000 each year for the following 6 years. Assuming that deposits earn 9 percent annually, determine what equal-payment annuity would accumulate the same amount over the 7-year period.

SOLUTION 7

The first step in using the arithmetic gradient conversion factor is to identify the base annuity A' and the gradient G. Annuity A' is the first payment of $2000, and G is the amount by which the payments increase each year, or $1000. Then

$$A = A' + G(A/G, i, N) = \$2000 + \$1000(A/G, 9, 7)$$
$$= \$2000 + \$1000(2.6574) = \$2000 + \$2657 = \$4657$$

Thus seven equal payments of $4657 are equivalent to seven payments increasing by $1000 increments from $2000 for the first one to $8000 for the last one.

EXERCISE 8

The ambitious saver in Exercise 7 has changed plans. Instead of increasing each deposit by $1000, each deposit will be raised by 20 percent over the previous one. What equal-payment annuity will accumulate the same amount over the 7-year period, when deposits earn 9 percent annually?

SOLUTION 8

The annual 20 percent change is a geometric gradient where $g = 0.20$. Given $A' = \$2000$ and $N = 7$, the present worth of the series is

$$P = A' \left[\frac{1 - (1 + g)^N (1 + i)^{-N}}{i - g} \right]$$
$$= \$2000 \left[\frac{1 - (1.2)^7 (1.09)^{-7}}{0.09 - 0.2} \right] = \$17,457$$

The equivalent uniform annuity is now

$$A = \$17,457(A/P, 9, 7) = \$17,457(0.19869) = \$3458.53$$

We could have found P by using

$$P = \frac{A'}{1 + i} \ (F/A, i', 7)$$

where

$$i' = \frac{1.20}{1.09} - 1 = 0.101$$

CHEER, this text's computer program, can be used to find any value of the discrete-compounding interest factors. To find $(F/A, 10.1, 7)$, we access the screens shown in Fig. 2.6. The first screen (Fig. 2.6a) is the initial screen obtained when

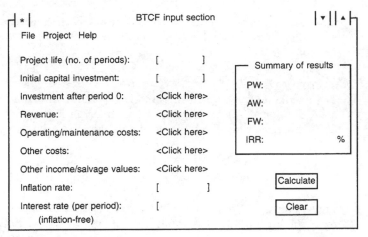

(a) Initial CHEER screen

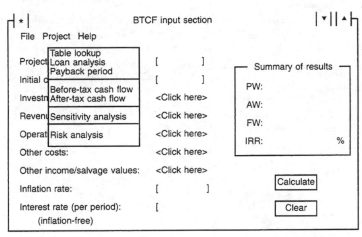

(b) "Project" menu screen

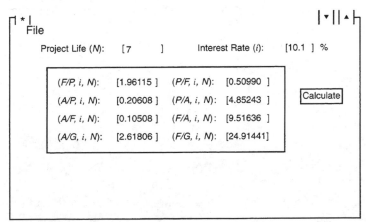

FIGURE 2.6
Using CHEER to find compound-interest factors.

(c) Compound interest factors screen

CHEER is accessed. The top menu file shows File, Project, and Help. We access Project, and we get a menu superimposed over the initial menu as shown in Fig. 2.6b. The top menu item is Table Lookup which, when accessed, brings up the third screen (Fig. 2.6c). We type in 7 for the project life and 10.1 for the interest rate, and we click Calculate. The screen shows that we get eight factor values. We can see that $(F/A, 10.1, 7)$ is 9.51636. It is a very simple matter to change the N or i values to determine any value that we need. We will not spend very much time on CHEER in the chapters prior to Chap. 5 since the reader needs to fully understand the material before relying on a computer program to assist or completely solve a problem. The reader will find that CHEER will greatly speed things in looking up compound-interest factors, especially when interpolation is called for.

Now we can complete our problem solution:

$$P = \frac{\$2000}{1.09}\,(9.51636) = \$17,461$$

This is the same value we found earlier except for minor rounding error.

EXERCISE 9

Receipts from an investment will decline by $150 each year for 5 years from a level of $1000 at the end of the first year. For an interest rate of 7 percent, calculate a constant annual series amount that is equivalent to the gradient over the following 6-year period.

SOLUTION 9

The base amount ($A' = \$1000$) is decreased by a uniform amount each year ($G = -\$150$). Given $i = 7$ percent and $N = 6$,

$$A = \$1000 - \$150(A/G, 7, 6) = \$1000 - \$150(2.30322)$$
$$= \$654.67$$

EXERCISE 10

A manufacturing firm in a foreign country has agreed to pay $25,000 in royalties at the end of each year for the next 5 years for the use of a patented product design. If the payments are left in the foreign country, interest on the retained funds will be paid at an annual rate of 15 percent.

What total amount will be available in 5 years under these conditions?

How large would the uniform annual payments have to be if the patent owners insisted that a minimum of $175,000 be accumulated in the account by the end of 5 years?

SOLUTION 10

The annual payments form an annuity. Knowing that $A = \$25,000$ per period, $i = 15$ percent per period, and there are five periods, we calculate the future worth F as

$$F = A(F/A, 15, 5) = \$25,000(6.74238) = \$168,558$$

If the patent owners insisted on an accumulated value of $175,000, the five end-of-year royalty payments would have to be

$$A = F(A/F, 15, 5) = \$175,000(0.14832) = \$25,956$$

EXERCISE 11
The inventor of an automatic coin-operated newsstand called Automag believes that the economic evaluation of the invention should be based on continuous compounding of continuous cash flow because income from the Automag will be essentially continuous and disbursements for services and purchases of materials (newspapers, paperbacks, magazines, etc.) will occur regularly and frequently. The expected life of Automag is 5 years. Annual income should average $132,000 at a good location, and the total expenses for servicing materials are expected to average $105,000 per year. What initial price could be paid for Automag (delivered and ready to operate) to allow a buyer to earn 15 percent on the investment if the income and disbursements are accurate?

SOLUTION 11
Net annual receipts from the Automag are expected to average

$$\$132,000 - \$105,000 = \$27,000$$

Since the cash flow is almost continuous, it is appropriate to apply continuous-interest discounting. After recognition that the acceptable price of an Automag is the present-worth equivalent of a continuous annuity resulting from net receipts over 5 years, we get the value of the $P/\bar{A}$ factor from App. E for $N = 5$ and $r = 13.976$ percent, which corresponds to an effective interest rate of 15 percent:

$$P = \bar{A}(P/\bar{A}, 13.976, 5) = \$27,000(3.59773) = \$97,139$$

2.10   PROBLEMS

Problems 2.1 through 2.11 are adapted from Mathematics of Finance *by L. L. Smail (McGraw-Hill, New York). This college text was published in 1925, and it shows that basic interest problems have not changed much over the years.*

2.1 What sum must be loaned at 8 percent simple interest to earn $350 in 4 years?

2.2 How long will it take $800 to yield $72 in simple interest at 4 percent?

2.3 At what rate will $65.07 yield $8.75 in simple interest in 3 years 6 months?

2.4 How long will it take any sum to triple itself at 5 percent simple-interest rate?

2.5 Find the ordinary and exact simple interest on $5000 at 5 percent for 56 days.

2.6 If the interest on a certain sum for 3 months is $63.87 at 5 percent simple interest, what would it be at 6 percent?

2.7 Find the compound amount of $100 for 4 years at 6 percent compounded annually.

2.8 What is the compound amount of $750 for 5 years at 6 percent compounded quarterly?

2.9 Accumulate a principal of $1000 for 5 years 9 months at a nominal rate of 12 percent compounded monthly. How much interest is earned?

2.10 Find the difference between the amount of $100 at simple interest and at compound interest for 5 years at 5 percent.

2.11 Find the compound amount of $5000 at 6 percent for 4, 8, and 12 years, and compare the results. Does doubling the time double the amount of interest earned?

2.12 Determine the effective interest rate for a nominal annual rate of 6 percent that is compounded
    (*a*) Semiannually
    (*b*) Quarterly
    (*c*) Monthly
    (*d*) Daily

2.13 A personal loan of $1000 is made for a period of 18 months at an interest rate of $1\frac{1}{2}$ percent per month on the unpaid balance. If the entire amount owed is repaid in a lump sum at the end of that time, determine
    (*a*) The effective annual interest rate
    (*b*) The total amount of interest paid

2.14 What nominal annual interest rate compounded monthly yields an effective annual rate of 19.56 percent?

2.15 A loan of $5000 is scheduled to be repaid in equal monthly installments over $2\frac{1}{2}$ years. The nominal interest rate is 6 percent. How large is each payment?

2.16 How much will a piece of property have to increase in value over the next 5 years if it is to earn 10 percent per year on the purchase price?

2.17 How much less would it cost to pay off a $3000 loan in 1 year with 12 equal payments when interest is 12 percent compounded monthly, as opposed to making a single payment when the effective interest rate is 12 percent?

2.18 Fred borrowed $1000 from Friendly Finance Company at a nominal annual rate of 18 percent compounded monthly. Determine how long Fred will be required to pay off his debt if he makes the following monthly payments.
    (*a*) $175.54
    (*b*) $ 49.93
    (*c*) $ 15.00

2.19 Service records for a specific piece of production equipment indicate that a replacement machine will have first-year maintenance costs of approximately $1000 and that these costs will increase by $200 per year for each additional year of service. Assuming the equipment is to be in service for 10 years and using an interest rate of 15 percent, determine the maximum amount that should be paid for a lifetime maintenance contract at the time the equipment is purchased.

2.20 Maintenance costs on a selected piece of production equipment are expected to be $1000 the first year of operation and will probably increase at a rate of 20 percent per year throughout a 10-year service life. Using an interest rate of 15 percent, compute the present worth of the expected costs.

2.21 Compare the answers obtained in Prob. 2.19 with those obtained in Prob. 2.20. What accounts for the significant difference in present-worth values?

2.22 The net income from a newly purchased piece of construction equipment is expected to be $12,000 the first year and to decrease by $1500 each year as maintenance costs increase. The equipment will be used for 4 years. What annual annuity will produce an equivalent income, when the interest rate is 8 percent?

2.23 Traffic flow over a new bridge is expected to be 1 million vehicles the first year it is in use. The average traffic rate is expected to increase by 5 percent per year.
   (a) Find the expected number of vehicles using the bridge in the 20th year of service.
   (b) Determine the total expected number of vehicles using the bridge during the 20-year period.
   (c) Comment on the relationship between conventional interest computations in financial analyses and this normal engineering problem.

2.24 Assuming that a toll of $1 per vehicle is charged for use of the bridge in Prob. 2.23, determine the present worth of all projected toll collections, using an interest rate of 8 percent.

2.25 The amount of $1200 per year is to be paid into an account over each of the next 5 years. Using a nominal interest rate of 12 percent per year, determine the total amount that the account will contain at the end of the fifth year under the following conditions:
   (a) Deposits made at the first of each year with simple interest
   (b) Deposits made at the end of each year, with interest compounded annually
   (c) Deposits made at the end of each month, with interest compounded annually
   (d) Deposits made at the end of each month, with interest compounded monthly
   (e) Deposits made at the end of each year, with interest compounded monthly
   (f) Deposits made at the end of each year, with interest compounded continuously
   (g) Deposits made continuously, with interest compounded annually
   (h) Deposits made continuously and interest compounded continuously

2.26 Today's price for materials used in a production process is expected to hold constant for this year at $100,000. Find the present worth of 5 years' supply for the same amount of material used each year, when the interest rate is 8 percent, if the price changes at a constant annual rate of
   (a) $g = -5$ percent
   (b) $g = 0$ percent
   (c) $g = 5$ percent

2.27 A building site for a new gasoline station was purchased 10 years ago for $50,000. The site has recently been sold for $120,000. Disregarding any taxes, determine the rate of interest obtained on the initial investment.

2.28 The rights to a patent have been sold under an agreement in which annual year-end payments of $10,000 are to be made for the next 10 years. What is the current worth of the annuity at an interest rate of 7 percent?

2.29 A deferred annuity is to pay $500 per year for 10 years with the first payment coming 6 years from today. Determine the present worth of the annuity, using an interest rate of 12 percent.

2.30 An inventor has been offered $12,000 per year for the next 5 years and $6000 annually for the following 7 years for the exclusive rights to an invention. At what price could the inventor afford to sell the rights to earn 10 percent, disregarding taxes?

2.31 A company 3 years ago borrowed $40,000 to pay for a new machine tool, agreeing to repay the loan in 100 monthly payments at an annual nominal interest rate of 12 percent compounded monthly. The company now wants to pay off the loan. How much would this payment be, assuming no penalty costs for early payout?

2.32 If the population of a certain suburb is 35,000 at the end of 1994 and the average annual rate of increase is estimated at 7 percent, what should its population be at the end of the year 2003 if the 7 percent growth rate remains constant?

2.33 Derive the equation for calculating the future worth of a series of discrete payments when interest is compounded continuously. Start from the expression

$$F = A + Ae^{r} + Ae^{2r} + \cdots + Ae^{(N-2)r} + Ae^{(N-1)r}$$

and follow the procedure used in developing the sinking fund factor for end-of-period compounding.

2.34 Net receipts from a continuously producing oil well add up to $185,000 over 1 year. What is the present worth of the well if it maintains steady output until it runs dry in 8 years, assuming $r = 8$ percent?

2.35 You have a chance to buy a new car with a list price of $12,000. You have to pay $2000 down, and the dealer will finance the remainder at an nominal annual rate of 6 percent, compounded monthly for 5 years.
   (a) Determine the amount of your monthly payment.
   (b) How much total interest will you pay over 5 years?

2.36 A recently developed citrus orchard will come into full bearing after 6 years. Starting in the seventh year and continuing through a productive life of 20 years, the orchard is expected to produce an average net yield of $80,000 per year. What is the equitable present cash value of the investment, if money is worth 7 percent per annum?

2.37 A company is planning to buy an inspection device (coordinate-measuring machine) for $45,000. The expected life of the device is 5 years, and the expected annual operating costs and taxes are $600 for the first year with an added increase per year of $100 for years 2 through 5. Maintenance costs will be zero in the first 2 years because of the warranty but are expected to be $1000 in year 3, $1500 in year 4, and $2000 in year 5. What is the minimum desired annual economic benefit of the device, assuming that these benefits will just offset the annual costs? The company uses an interest rate of 10 percent for economic evaluations.

2.38 Maintenance records of a certain type of machine indicate that the first-year maintenance cost of $350 increases by $70 per year over the 5-year life of the machine. Answer the following, if the maintenance cost is considered to occur at the end of the year and the firm's interest rate is 8 percent.

    (*a*) What equal annual payments could the firm justify making to a service organization to carry out the maintenance for 20 machines?

    (*b*) How much additional could be paid for a new type of machine with the same service life that required no maintenance in the first 2 years and $125 per year for each of the last 3 years?

2.39 A new piece of materials handling equipment costs $20,000 and is expected to save $7500 the first year of operation. Maintenance and operating cost increases are expected to reduce the net savings by $500 per year for each additional year of operation until the equipment is worn out at the end of 8 years. Determine the net present worth of the equipment at an interest rate of 12 percent.

2.40 Office equipment can be purchased for $6000 cash or a down payment of $1000 followed by 24 end-of-month payments of $220 each. At what effective interest rate are these terms equivalent?

2.41 Assume that you sold property today for $2421 and that you had purchased the property 4 years ago with $2000 withdrawn from your savings account. During the 4-year period your savings would have earned 6 percent compounded quarterly. For a comparison of the investments, calculate the nominal interest rate received from your property purchase.

2.42 Discuss briefly how the material we have covered so far might assist you in determining how to pay for your next automobile purchase. Could the material affect how you choose the type of automobile to buy?

CHAPTER 3

PRESENT-WORTH COMPARISONS

One today is worth two tomorrows.
Benjamin Franklin, *Poor Richard's Almanack.* 1758

We can infer quite a lot about engineering economic evaluations from the introductory quotation by Benjamin Franklin. First, any cash flows that we have at present are known and certain and from an analysis point of view can be more valuable than those uncertain values at some other time. Also, as we have learned from the previous chapter, an investment of $1000 now is currently worth more than an investment of the same amount sometime in the future. Part of the future amount will be consumed by the effect of intervening interest rates. Therefore, it is not surprising that we often make engineering economic decisions based on the expected present worth of all incomes and outlays associated with those decisions, regardless of when those activities occurred. The purpose of this chapter is to apply what we have learned in Chap. 2 in making present-worth comparisons.

Present-worth (PW) comparisons are made only between coterminated proposals, to ensure equivalent outcomes. *Cotermination* means that the lives of the involved assets end at the same time. When assets have unequal lives, the time horizon for an analysis can be set by a common multiple of asset lives or by a study period that ends with the disposal of all assets.

Net present worth, the difference between the present worths of benefits and of costs, is the most widely used present-worth model. A capitalized cost model is used when an asset is assumed to have infinite life. We discuss this concept in Sec. 3.4. Other PW models include deferred investments and valuation of property, stocks, and bonds.

Many economists prefer a present-worth analysis because it reveals the sum in today's dollars that is equivalent to a future cash flow stream, and PW models are less subject to misinterpretation. It is therefore important to become familiar with the assumptions upon which PW calculations are based and the types of comparisons that can be made.

3.1   CONDITIONS FOR PRESENT-WORTH COMPARISONS

In Chap. 2 we introduced present-worth comparisons. A present worth resulted from each calculation of P. In this chapter, the present worth of a cash flow stream is denoted by PW—the present worth of receipts and disbursements associated with a particular course of action. Each alternative is thus represented by a PW, a measure of economic merit.

The ingredients of a present-worth comparison are the amount (in dollars) and timing (N) of cash flow and the interest rate i at which the flow is discounted. Listed below are assumptions used in this and the next two chapters in introducing the basic comparison methods; also indicated are topics from subsequent chapters that make comparisons less restrictive.

1. *Cash flows are known.* The accuracy of cash flow estimates is always suspect because future developments cannot be anticipated completely. Transactions that occur now, at time 0, should be accurate, but future flows become less distinct as the time horizon is extended. Ways to evaluate riskier cash flows are discussed in Chaps. 13 and 14.

2. *Cash flows are in constant-value dollars.* The buying power of money is assumed to remain unchanged during the study period. Ways to include the effect of inflation are presented in Chap. 10. Because this is such an important assumption and the concept of *constant dollars* is paramount to the evaluation of alternatives in the next few chapters, we will summarize the salient points necessary for understanding inflation in Sec. 3.1.1.

3. *The interest rate is known.* Different interest rates have a significant effect on the magnitude of the calculated present worth, as illustrated in Fig. 3.1. The rate of return i required by an organization is a function of its cost of capital, attitude toward risk, and investment policy. Alternative courses of action for the same proposal are normally compared by using the same interest rate, but different proposals may be evaluated at different required rates of return. The sensitivity of interest rates is explored in Chap. 11.

4. *Comparisons are made with before-tax cash flows.* Inclusion of income taxes greatly expands the calculation effort for a comparison and correspondingly increases reality. Since the workings of comparison meth-

ods are featured here and in the next few chapters, inclusion of income taxes is delayed until Chap. 9.

5. *Comparisons do not include intangible considerations. Intangibles* are difficult-to-quantify factors that pertain to a certain situation. For instance, the "impression" created by a design is an intangible factor in evaluating that design and an important one for marketing, but it would not be included in a present-worth comparison unless its economic consequences could be reasonably estimated. (If a dollar value can be assigned, a factor is no longer intangible.) Ways to include intangible factors in the decision-making process are considered in Chap. 15.

6. *Comparisons do not include consideration of the availability of funds to implement alternatives.* It is explicitly assumed that funds will be found to finance a course of action if the benefits are large enough. Although financing is not a direct input for computations, the output computed can be appraised with respect to available funding. For instance, an old, inefficient machine could be kept in operation because there appears to be insufficient capital available in the organization to afford a replacement, but an engineering economic analysis might point out that the savings from replacing the outdated machine would be so great that the organization could not afford to not find funds for a replacement.

EXAMPLE 3.1	**Present Worth by the "72 Rule"**

The present worth of a future amount drops off rapidly as the time between *now* and *then* increases, particularly at higher interest rates. The pattern of this decrease in present value is shown in Fig. 3.1. Examination of the curves supports an interesting rule of thumb: The *72 rule* indicates the approximate number of years N^* at which the PW is one-half the future worth (FW) at the annually compounded interest rate i:

$$\text{72 rule: } N^* = \frac{72}{(i)(100)}$$

Another way to view the 72 rule is that $(1 + i)^N$ doubles about every N^* years. Thus, as is clear in Fig. 3.1 on page 104, the present worth is one-half of the future worth in about 14 years at $i = 5$ percent, 7 years at $i = 10$ percent, and 4 years at $i = 20$ percent.

3.1.1   Inflation and the Constant-Dollars Assumption

It was mentioned in the introductory material to this chapter that cash flows will be assumed to be in constant-value dollars where the buying

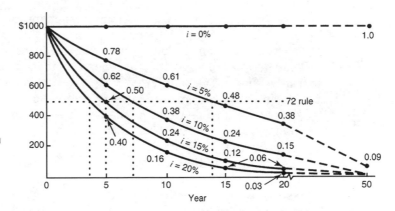

FIGURE 3.1
Present worth of
$1000 as a function
of time and interest
rates when interest
is compounded
annually.

power of money is assumed to remain unchanged during the study period. Another way to state this is to say that cash flows are in *constant dollars.* We need to clarify what this means and its effect on the analyses we will be considering in the next few chapters, primarily this chapter and Chaps. 4 through 8. Therefore it is reasonable to summarize material covered in Chap. 10 (inflation) now.

We have all felt the effects of inflation. A house bought around the mid-1960s might have cost around $20,000. The same house was selling, in the mid-1990s, for at least $96,000. Inflation causes prices to rise and decreases the purchasing power of money with the passage of time. In engineering economics studies, we have a related topic that we might need to consider: *technological stability.* Research and development cost money, and that money has to be returned in terms of increased product selling costs and/or increased volume of sales. Further, we have seen consumer products where technological improvements have been made commensurate with *reductions in prices.* Computer and many other electronic products can fall into this category. Unless stated in the associated material, we assume that we have a condition of *technological stability:* The same or similar product in a few years will have the same cost structure as it does now in constant dollars (when inflation effects are removed).

A common way to eliminate inflation effects is to convert all cash flows to money units that have constant purchasing power, called *constant,* or *real, dollars.* This approach is most suitable for before-tax analysis, when all cash flow components inflate at uniform rates. We assume that this is the way inflation has been removed in our pretax analyses through Chap. 8. Another way to handle the situation is to actually perform the analyses with the cash flows in the estimated amount of money exchanged at the time of transaction. These money units are called *future, then-current,* or *actual* dollars. The use of this approach in economic analysis is introduced in Chap. 10.

We mentioned in Chap. 2, when the geometric gradient was discussed, that inflation is an example of such a growth pattern (and deflation would follow a negative geometric gradient pattern). This means that we have a *percentage compounding* effect over a period of years. If f is the *inflation rate* over the next few years, actual dollars in year N can be converted to constant dollars by

$$\text{Constant dollars} = \frac{\text{actual dollars}}{(1 + f)^N}$$

Since $1/(1 + i)^N$ is the single-payment PW factor, we can rewrite the conversion equation as

$$\text{Constant dollars} = (\text{actual dollars})(P/F, f, N)$$

The reverse occurs if we want to convert constant dollars to actual dollars at time period N:

$$\text{Actual dollars} = (\text{constant dollars})(F/P, f, N)$$

Now we can show a cash flow series in actual dollars and the cash flow series after we have removed the inflationary effects:

End of year	Actual dollars		4% Annual inflation		Constant dollars
0	−5000	×	$1/1.04^0$	=	5,000
1	1000	×	$1/1.04^1$	=	962
2	800	×	$1/1.04^2$	=	740
3	600	×	$1/1.04^3$	=	533
4	400	×	$1/1.04^4$	=	342
5	200	×	$1/1.04^5$	=	164

If we were to perform a present-worth analysis under our constant-dollars assumption, we would use the rightmost column of cash flow data, not the second.

We will show in Chap. 10 that the *minimum attractive rate of return (MARR)* used by firms to evaluate their economic investments includes the effect of inflation. Use of this rate, referred to as the *market interest rate*, requires that all cash flows be in actual dollars. The MARR used with constant dollars is the inflation-free interest rate that represents the earning power of capital when inflation effects have been removed. Also in Chap. 10 we will show that CHEER can automatically handle the effects of an inflation rate. Until we get to Chap. 10, we assume that inflation has been removed from the cash flows and that the MARR is the inflation-free interest rate.

3.2   BASIC PRESENT-WORTH COMPARISON PATTERNS

The present worth of a cash flow over time is its value today, usually represented as time 0 in a cash flow diagram. Two general patterns are apparent in present-worth calculations: present-worth equivalence and net present worth. The former has investments in the future while the latter has an investment at time 0 followed by possible receipts and expenditures at future time periods. Both types of analysis will give the same results and interpretation; they will be presented as separate concepts due to common acceptance in the field of engineering economics.

3.2.1   Present-Worth Equivalence

One pattern determines the present-worth equivalence of a series of future transactions. The purpose is to secure one figure that represents all the transactions. This figure can then be compared with a corresponding figure that represents transactions from a competing option, or it can be compared with the option of doing nothing. A *do-nothing option* is always an alternative, even if it results only in procrastination. Often there is a go/no-go situation where each alternative is selectively weighed to decide whether it is worth exercising. For instance, a series of expenses that will occur in the future can be discounted to obtain its PW, and then a decision can be made about whether an investment of the PW amount should be made *now* to avoid the expenses. Similar reasoning guides the equivalence comparison in the following example.

EXAMPLE 3.2   **Equivalent PW of an Option**

An investor can make three end-of-year payments of $15,000, which are expected to generate receipts of $10,000 at the end of year 4 that will increase annually by $2500 for the following 4 years. If the investor can earn a rate of return of 10 percent on other 8-year investments, is this alternative attractive?

Solution

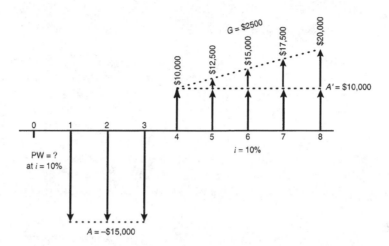

From the cash flow diagram, it is apparent that the receipts and disbursements each constitute an annuity, one positive and the other negative. Both are discounted to time 0 at 10 percent:

$$
\begin{aligned}
PW ={}& -\$15,000(P/A,\ 10,\ 3) \\
&+ [\$10,000 + \$2500(A/G,\ 10,\ 5)]\ (P/A,\ 10,\ 5)\ (P/F,\ 10,\ 3) \\
={}& -\$15,000(2.48685) \\
&+ [\$10,000 + \$2500(1.81013)]\ (3.79079)\ (0.75131) \\
={}& -\$37,303 + \$41,369 = \$4066
\end{aligned}
$$

The interpretation of the $4066 present worth is that the transactions provide a return of 10 percent on the investment *plus* a sum of $4066. This investment is therefore preferable to one that would return exactly 10 percent over 8 years.

It is common practice to drop the minus sign when the cash flow is composed of only costs. The calculated PW is then called the *present worth of costs*. This is purely a convention of convenience and is unlikely to cause confusion as long as the alternatives in a comparison are treated in the same way. We will handle each situation in the most logical manner for the case at hand.

3.2.2 Net Present Worth

The second general pattern for PW calculations has an initial outlay at time 0 followed by a series of receipts and disbursements. This is the most frequently encountered pattern, which leads to the fundamental relation

$$\text{Net present worth} = \text{PW(benefits)} - \text{PW(costs)}$$

The criterion for choosing between *mutually exclusive* alternatives is to select the one that maximizes net present worth or simply the one that yields the larger positive PW. A negative PW means that the alternative does not satisfy the rate-of-return requirement.

In addition to mutually exclusive alternatives where we can select only one alternative, we could have *independent* alternatives where more than one alternative may be selected. We will consider this later in the text, but the criterion for consideration of independent alternatives is that they should have a PW which is equal to or greater than zero.

Applications of net present worth to benefits and costs of public projects will be developed in Chap. 8. A typical industrial application might be as follows.

EXAMPLE 3.3

Net Present-Worth Comparison

Two devices are available to perform a necessary function for 3 years. The initial cost (negative) for each device at time 0 and subsequent annual savings (positive), both in dollars, are shown in the following table. The required interest rate is 8 percent.

	Year			
	0	**1**	**2**	**3**
Device *A*	9,000	4,500	4,500	4,500
Device *B*	14,500	6,000	6,000	8,000

Solution

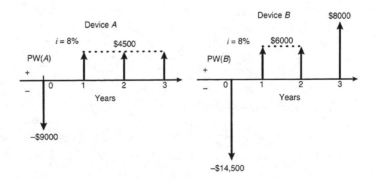

$$PW \text{ (device } A) = -\$9000 + \$4500(P/A, 8, 3)$$
$$= -\$9000 + \$4500(2.5771) = \$2597$$

$$PW(\text{device } B) = -\$14,500 + \$6000 \ (P/A, 8, 2) + \$8000(P/F, 8, 3)$$
$$= -\$14,500 + \$6000(1.78326) + \$8000(0.79383)$$
$$= \$2550$$

Both alternatives meet the minimum acceptable rate of return, because both PWs are positive, and their net present worths are close in value. In this case, other considerations must be involved in the choice, such as the availability of the extra $5500 needed to purchase device B.

In Examples 3.2 and 3.3, the alternatives were naturally coterminated. That is, in Example 3.2 the investment periods were identical, and in Example 3.3 the lives of the two devices were equal. When the lives of assets being compared are unequal, special procedures must be followed to coterminate the analysis periods.

3.3   COMPARISON OF ASSETS THAT HAVE UNEQUAL LIVES

The utilization of present-worth comparisons for *coterminated projects* implies that the lives involved have a common endpoint. The necessity for cotermination is readily apparent when a familiar decision is considered, such as the choice between paying $30 for a 3-year subscription to a magazine and paying $40 for a 5-year subscription to the same publication. A simple comparison of $30 to $40 for a subscription is inaccurate, because the extra $10 buys 2 more years of issues. *Alternatives must be compared on the basis of equivalent outcomes.*

Several variations have been proposed to accommodate present-worth comparisons of unequal-life assets.[†] Two prominent methods are described below.

1. *Common-multiple method.* Alternatives are coterminated by selecting an analysis period that spans a common multiple of the lives of the involved assets. For instance, if assets had lives of 2, 3, 4, and 6 years, the least common multiple is 12 years, which means that the asset with a life of 2 years would be replaced 6 times during the analysis period. The assets with 3-, 4-, and 6-year lives would be replaced 4, 3, and 2 times, respectively.

   Legitimate use of a least common multiple of lives depends on the validity of the assumption that assets will be repeatedly replaced by

---

[†]D. J. Kulonda, "Replacement Analysis with Unequal Lives," *The Engineering Economist,* vol. 23, no. 3, pp. 171–179, Spring 1978. Published by Institute of Industrial Engineers.

successors having identical cost characteristics. In other words, constant dollars are assumed where the purchasing power does not change with passage of time. This assumption is more often reasonable when the least common multiple of alternative lives is small. Then there is less likelihood that a technologically better asset will become available during the analysis period.

2. *Study-period method.* A more justifiable analysis is based on a specified duration that corresponds to the length of a project or the period of time the assets are expected to be in service. An appropriate study period reflects the replacement circumstances. Some of the options are to set the study period as the length of:

(a) *The shortest life of all competing alternatives*—a protection against technological obsolescence.

(b) *The known duration of required services*—a project philosophy in which each new undertaking is considered to start with new assets, continue to use similar replacements, and dispose of used assets when the project is completed. Again, as mentioned earlier, constant dollars are assumed.

(c) *The time before a better replacement becomes available*—an attempt to minimize cost by purposely upgrading assets as improvements are developed.

A study period comparison presumes that all assets will be disposed of at the end of the period. Therefore it is usually necessary to estimate the income that can be realized from the sale of an asset which can still provide useful service. This *salvage value* can be established somewhat arbitrarily by prorating the investment in the asset over its normal service life and then calculating the size of the unrecovered amount at the time of disposal. A better estimate is obtained when it is possible to accurately appraise an asset's market value at the end of the study period. The most precise study would result from also having explicit knowledge of operating costs as a function of the asset's age and future capital costs for each successor. These conditions are explored more completely in Chap. 7.

EXAMPLE 3.4 **PW Comparisons of Alternatives with Unequal Service Lives**

Assets A_1 and A_2 have the capability of satisfactorily performing a required function. Asset A_2 has an initial cost of $3200 and an expected salvage value of $400 at the end of its 4-year service life. Asset A_1 costs $900 less initially, with an economic life 1 year shorter than that of A_2; but A_1 has no salvage value, and its annual operating costs exceed those of A_2 by $250. When the required rate of return is 15 percent, state which alternative is preferred when comparison is by:

(a) The repeated-projects method

(b) A 2-year study period (assuming the assets are needed for only 2 years)

Solution

(a) The repeated-projects method is based on the assumption that assets will be replaced by identical models possessing the same costs. Equivalent service results from comparing costs over a period divisible evenly by the service lives of the alternatives; in this case the least common multiple is 12 years.

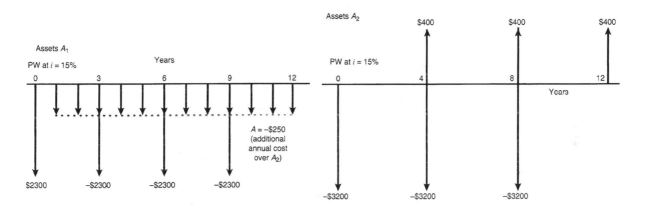

$$PW\ (A_1) = -\$2300 - \$2300(P/F,\ 15,\ 3) - \$2300(P/F,\ 15,\ 6)$$
$$- \$2300(P/F,\ 15,\ 9) - \$250(P/A,\ 15,\ 12)$$
$$= -\$2300 - \$2300(0.65752) - \$2300(0.43233)$$
$$- \$2300(0.28426) - \$250(5.42062)$$
$$= -\$6816$$

$$PW\ (A_2) = -\$3200 - \$2800(P/F,\ 15,\ 4) - \$2800(P/F,\ 15,\ 8)$$
$$+ \$400(P/F,\ 15,\ 12)$$
$$= -\$3200 - \$2800(0.57175) - \$2800(0.32691)$$
$$+ \$400(0.18691)$$
$$= -\$5642$$

The net present-worth advantage of A_2 over A_1 for 12 years of service is $-\$5642 - (-\$6816) = \$1174$.

(b) A service period comparison is utilized when a limited period of ownership of assets is set by specific operational requirements. A 2-year study period for A_1 and A_2 indicates that the service required from either asset will be needed for only 2 years and will be disposed of at that time. If possible, estimates of the worth of assets at the end of the study period should be secured. These salvage values, which we will symbolize by S, may be quite large when the service period is only a small fraction of the service life. When it is difficult to secure reliable estimates of worth after use during the ownership period, minimum resale levels can be calculated to make the alternatives equivalent.

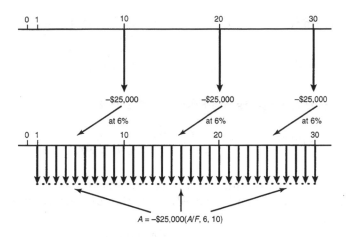

$$\text{First cost} = \$500{,}000 - \frac{\$15{,}000 + \$25{,}000(A/F,\ 6,\ 10)}{0.06}$$

$$= \$500{,}000 - \frac{\$15{,}000 + \$25{,}000(0.07587)}{0.06}$$

$$= \$500{,}000 - \$281{,}613 = \$218{,}387$$

This means that the interest earned on the amount left after allowing $218,387 for construction will cover all the anticipated upkeep indefinitely, provided that the interest rate remains at 6 percent or more or else averages about 6 percent. Also, this assumes that painting and other costs will not increase over time, which is possibly an unrealistic assumption.

3.5   COMPARISON OF DEFERRED INVESTMENTS

An occupational hazard for engineers is the habitual appeal to "get it done today, or preferably yesterday." The accustomed response to such an appeal is a workable solution that admittedly may not be the most economical long-run course of action. But keeping an operation going with a less-than-optimum solution is often less costly than the wait caused by a search for something better. For instance, suppose that flooding at a construction site was the motivation for an engineer to remedy the situation quickly. The emergency purchase and installation of a pump plus sandbags for revetments cost $4000. The pumping facility was used off and on during the 2-year construction project for a total cost discounted to the time of purchase (assuming no salvage value and $i = 12$ percent) of

First cost of pump and revetment	$4000
Pumping cost and maintenance ($460/year)	
$460(P/A,\ 12,\ 2) = \$460(1.69005)$	777
PW of emergency pumping operation	$4777

A postproject review shows that a smaller pump could have been purchased to perform the same work adequately:

First cost of smaller pump and revetment	$3100
Pumping cost and maintenance ($640/year)	
$640(P/A, 12, 2) = $640(1.69005)	1082
PW of lower-cost solution to flooding	$4182

However, if it had taken only a week longer to select and get delivery of the lower-cost pump, it is likely that the cost of 7 days of flooding would have exceeded the $4777 − $4182 = $595 potential saving.

A more typical way to analyze deferred investments is to determine the timing of capital expenditures to meet anticipated activity increases. Designs to accommodate growth usually involve the question of whether to acquire a full-sized facility now and absorb the temporary cost of unused assets or to acquire a smaller facility with a later addition and accept the extra cost of duplicated effort and dislocation inconvenience. For a given capacity, one large facility inherently has a lower per-unit cost because it is designed specifically for that level of operation, but it increases the chance of technical obsolescence and idleness, owing to changing future conditions. The economic analysis of a deferred addition is usually conducted by a present-worth comparison of the options. Piecemeal additions to existing capacity are seldom an efficient expansion program. A planning horizon too short to accommodate growth is one example of shortsighted suboptimization. Careful planning and timing are always required for such activities.

EXAMPLE 3.6

Immediate and Deferred Investments for Identical Capacity

A small novelty manufacturing company must acquire storage space in order to reduce production costs by stabilizing employment. Ninety percent of the products produced are sold during the Christmas holiday season. A resource utilization study has shown that producing at a constant rate during the year and storing output will reduce the overall manufacturing costs.

The products produced by the novelty company have been well received, and sales have increased each year. Increased capacity will be needed in the future; two alternatives have been identified. A large warehouse with sufficient space to meet all needs for 10 years can be leased for that period at $23,000 per year. Since there is some doubt about how much business will increase in the future and since the company is reluctant to go into debt deeply enough to build a warehouse as large as the one available for leasing, the other feasible alternative is to build a small warehouse now for $110,000 and make an addition to it in 3 years for $50,000. Annual costs for taxes, insurance, maintenance, and repairs are expected to be $1000 for the first 3 years and $2000 for the next 7 years. The added-to warehouse should have a resale value of $50,000 in 10 years. Based on a study period equal to the lease contract and a 12 percent cost for capital, which alternative is preferable?

Solution

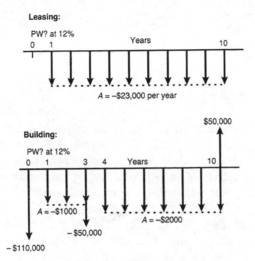

$$\text{PW(lease)} = -\$23,000(P/A,\ 12,\ 10)$$
$$= -\$23,000(5.65022) = -\$129,955$$

$$\text{PW(build and add)} = -\$110,000 - \$50,000(P/F,\ 12,\ 3)$$
$$+ \$50,000\ (P/F,\ 12,\ 10) - \$1000(P/A,\ 12,\ 3)$$
$$- \$2000(P/A,\ 12,\ 7)\ (P/F,\ 12,\ 3)$$
$$= -\$110,000 - \$50,000(0.71178) + \$50,000(0.32197)$$
$$- \$1000(2.40183) - \$2000(4.56376)(0.71178)$$
$$= -\$138,389$$

The analysis indicates that the present worth of storage costs for the next 10 years will be −$129,955 − (−$138,389) = $8434 less from leasing than building the required warehousing facility.

It should be mentioned that since we were considering only costs in this exercise, we could have treated them as positive values for positive costs and then picked the alternative with the smaller present worth. The analyst should handle the problem in the way that is most comfortable to her or him.

The major potential problem with situations involving estimates of future costs and factors relates to the accuracy of those estimates. Home mortgage rates in the early 1960s were on the order of 6 to 7 percent. Several years later there was a large increase in mortgage rates, and they were on the order of 15 percent. The early 1990s saw mortgage rates dropping close to those of the early 1960s. How then, can uncertain costs and factors be taken into consideration? The same problem that was addressed in Example 3.6 will be examined from a different perspective in Chap. 14, where it will no longer be assumed that future demands are known with certainty. If reliable probabilities for future capacity needs can be generated, they should be included in the analysis. The difficulty lies with finding a reliable way to peek into the future.

3.6   FUTURE-WORTH COMPARISONS

It is evident from the equivalence concept that a present worth can be translated to a future worth at any given time at a given interest rate. The mechanics of the translation are elementary, but the change in perspective of the analyst can be significant. For certain situations, the future worth of cash flow may be more meaningful to a decision maker than the present worth. The amount of debt or surplus accumulated at a future date could be a milestone in a financial plan or a goal that directs current activities. The potential benefits for a person about to retire certainly could be more meaningful at a future date.

Attention to future cash flows may yield more accurate estimates of receipts and disbursements because thinking tends to be in *then-current* dollars. Because the purchasing power of a unit of currency is eroded by inflation, it may be advantageous to focus on how many currency units must be available to meet needs at a later date—the quantity of then current dollars. Consequently, future-worth calculations are frequently utilized in escalation analyses, particularly for evaluating the effects of inflation.

Given the cash flow for an alternative, the future worth at any time can be calculated by

$$FW = PW(F/P, i, N) = PW(1 + i)^N$$

The decision rule based on FW has the same results as for PW since, for the same i and N, both of which are positive, the FW ranking of alternatives has to be the same as the ranking based on a PW analysis.

The future-worth perspective can be illustrated by reference to the cash flow in Example 3.2. The 8-year cash flow in Example 3.2 is composed of two annuities: annual $15,000 costs for the first 3 years followed by five equal step receipts ranging from $10,000 to $20,000.

The future value of disbursements, treated as debts for which interest at 10 percent must be paid, builds in 8 years to a total indebtedness of

$$FW(\text{disbursements}) \quad = -\$15,000(F/A, 10, 3)(F/P, 10, 5)$$
$$= -\$15,000(3.31000)(1.61051)$$
$$= -\$79,962$$

A complementary future worth at the end of year 4 will show the accumulated indebtedness before any income is generated as

$$FW(4) = -\$15,000(F/A, 10, 3)(F/P, 10, 1) = -\$54,615$$

This amount is reduced by the receipt of $10,000 at the end of year 4, but it reveals the maximum liability level.

The positive arithmetic gradient cash inflow reaches a maximum at the end of year 8, amounting to

$$\begin{aligned}FW(receipts) &= [\$10,000 + \$2500(A/G, 10, 5)](F/A, 10, 5)\\ &= [\$10,000 + \$2500(1.81013)](6.10510)\\ &= \$88,677\end{aligned}$$

The balance on hand at the end of the study period is then

$$Net\ FW = \$88,677 - \$79,962 = \$8715$$

This same result (differing only by rounding error from the interest tables) could be obtained from the previously calculated (in Example 3.2) PW = $4066 as

$$Net\ FW = \$4066(F/P, 10, 8) = \$4066(2.14359) = \$8716$$

The relative usefulness of PW and FW comparisons depends on which figure is more valuable for decision making. If knowledge of the dollars available at some impending date is critical, then a future-worth calculation is called for. Knowing when to answer such a call is the mark of a competent engineering economist.

In the majority of engineering economy cases, the present-worth analysis would be more meaningful to the decision maker for reasons given earlier in this chapter's introductory material. In many cases, annualized benefits will make more sense, for management might want to track annualized values. For example, what are the anticipated increases in annual operating expenses due to a new process being implemented? We look at annualized evaluations in the next chapter.

3.7 VALUATION

Value is a measure of the worth of something in terms of money or goods. A barter system uses a personally directed trade of goods to establish equivalent values. In an auction, the measure of worth is established by competitive monetary bids. To some extent, the selling price in an openly competitive market sets a value on goods as a result of the amount customers are willing to pay. Value is more difficult to determine before a transaction occurs. Expert appraisers are familiar with prices from previous transactions and interpolate to set values on goods that have not been exposed to the market. Works of art and land properties are subject to sometimes controversial evaluations.

Appraisals regularly encountered in financial practice are known by specific names. The *going value* is how much the assets of an organization are worth as an operating unit. It is opposite to a *liquidating value,* which is the amount that could be realized if the assets were sold separately from the organization that is using them. The going value is normally greater than the liquidating value, in recognition of the "organizational" value of a unit still in operating condition; accountants term this difference *goodwill.* The worth of an asset for accounting purposes is its *book value,* which may be quite different from its *market value*—the price at which it can be sold. The book value reflects historical cost, whereas market value is dependent upon earnings.

When the value of property depends upon its earning capacity, valuation results from discounting future probable earnings to their present worth. When risk is ignored, the "value" of such property is simply its present worth at the interest rate deemed appropriate by the appraiser. Examples of properties whose values tend to be a function of future cash flows are bonds, stocks, and rental assets.

3.7.1 Bond Valuation[†]

A bond is sold by an organization to raise money. Bonds represent a debt to the bondholders rather than a share of ownership in the organization. Most bonds bear interest semiannually and are redeemable for a specified maturity value at a given date. There are many variations designed to make bonds more attractive to purchasers, such as an option to convert them to common stock under specified conditions, or to make the bond debt more manageable for the issuing organization, as in callable bonds that may be paid off prior to maturity according to a printed repurchase schedule. Some public organizations are allowed to issue bonds for which the interest payments are not taxable income to the bondholders.

The value of a bond of a given denomination depends on the size and timing of the periodic dividends and the duration before maturity. The bond valuation is thus the present worth[‡] of the cash flow stream of divi-

---

[†]The engineer interested in applying economic analysis only to equipment replacement decisions and similar engineering evaluations may feel that a discussion of stocks and bonds is not worthwhile. Granted, this material may be bypassed for someone in that category. At least a cursory review of the material is recommended to (1) provide a better understanding of PW calculations, (2) equip oneself for possible personal financial decisions, and (3) understand some of the financial considerations at the corporate level of the enterprise.

[‡]The procedure for calculating a value is sometimes called *capitalization of income.*

dends plus the discounted value of the redemption payment. The key to the valuation is the rate of return expected by the bond purchaser. Lower rates are reasonable when there is very little risk of default. For instance, a federal Treasury bill would have less risk of nonrepayment than one issued by Fly-by-Nite Corporation; consequently, a lower discount rate would be appropriate.

Each bond has a stated redemption amount, called the *face value,* at which it can be redeemed at maturity. Bonds sell for less than their face value when buyers are not satisfied with the rate of interest promised, called the *bond rate,* and more than the face value when market interest rates drop below the bond's face rate. Interest is paid in the form of regular premiums; the flow of premiums constitutes an annuity where

$$A = \text{premium} = (\text{face value})(\text{bond rate})$$

and the number of payments per year is a function of the bond rate structure (e.g., four payments per year for a quarterly bond rate). A present-worth purchase price for a bond that satisfies a buyer seeking a return greater or less than the bond rate is calculated from the bond's maturity value F and the annuity composed of premium payment A, both discounted at the buyer's desired rate of return.

EXAMPLE 3.7

To Buy a Bond

A 10-year corporate bond has a face value of $5000 and a bond rate of 8 percent payable quarterly. A prospective buyer desires to earn a nominal rate of 12 percent on investments. What purchase price would the buyer be willing to pay?

Solution

The bond can be redeemed at $5000 in 10 years from now. During that period, four premium payments will be paid each year in the amount $A = \$5000(0.08/4) = \$5000(0.02) = \$100$. The buyer desires a return of $12/4 = 3$ percent per period. To meet the buyer's requirement, the purchase price must be the present worth of income from the bond discounted at 3 percent for 40 periods:

$$
\begin{aligned}
\text{PW} &= \$5000(P/F,\ 3,\ 40) + \$100(P/A,\ 3,\ 40) \\
&= \$5000(0.30656) + \$100(23.11477) \\
&= \$3844
\end{aligned}
$$

Bonds are traded regularly through financial markets. Depending on the prevailing interest rate, a bond may sell for a price that is less than, more than, or equal to its face value. When the owner of a bond purchased previously seeks to sell it before maturity, the original purchase price and premiums already received have no bearing on its market value; only future cash flow has consequence.

EXAMPLE 3.8

Evaluation of a Bond Purchase

A utility company sold an issue of 4 percent bonds 6 years ago. Each bond has a face value (value at maturity) of $1000, is due in 14 years, and pays interest twice a year (2 percent per period). Because interest rates on savings have climbed in recent years, the bond can now be sold on the bond market for only $760. If a buyer wants his or her investment to earn 8 percent compounded semiannually and must pay a brokerage charge of $20 to purchase each bond, is the current market price low enough to provide the desired return?

Solution

Semiannual interest payments amount to 2 percent of the face value of the bond, or $0.02 \times \$1000 = \$20$, and $1000 will be redeemed in 14 years, or 28 half-year periods. Therefore, the present value of the cash flow when the desired interest rate is 4 percent per 6-month period is

$$PW = \$20(P/A, 4, 28) + \$1000(P/F, 4, 28)$$
$$= \$20(16.66306) + \$1000(0.33348)$$
$$= \$666.74$$

Since the price of the bond is $760 + \$20 = \$780$, prospective bond purchasers should look elsewhere to obtain their desired rate of return on investments.

Assuming that an original purchaser of the utility bond in Example 3.8 paid the face value ($1000) 6 years ago and accepted $760 for it now, we find that only the original investment was recovered and no interest was earned during the 6 years it was held:

$$\$1000 = \$20(P/A, i, 12) + \$760(P/F, i, 12)$$
$$= \$20(P/A, 0, 12) + \$760(P/F, 0, 12)$$
$$= \$20(12) + \$760(1) = \$1000$$

The current market rate of interest strongly affects bond prices. Higher market rates tend to lower bond prices by decreasing the present worth of the future stream of payments promised by the bond. Figure 3.2 displays the valuation at different market rates of interest for a $1000, 20-year bond which pays $40 semiannually (4 percent) and a 3-year bond with the same face value and dividend rate.

As is apparent in Fig. 3.2, the longer the maturity of a security, the greater its price change in response to a change in the market rate of inter-

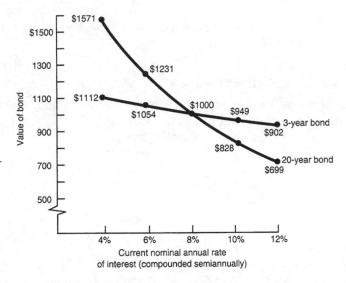

FIGURE 3.2
Value of $1000 long-term (20-year) and short-term (3-year) bonds at different market interest rates. Both bonds promise semiannual dividends of $40.

est. The fact that future interest rates are uncertain is an element of risk. Investments in short-term securities expose the investor to less chance of severe fluctuations in the market rate of interest than do comparable long-term investments.

3.7.2 Stock Valuation

Stock in a company represents a share of ownership, as opposed to a bond, which is essentially a promissory note. There are many types of stocks and bonds, varying with respect to their degree of security and associated special privileges. In general, all bonds have claims on a company's assets before stock in case of a business failure. Stock is still a popular investment because it has the potential of increasing in value and may pay higher dividends than bonds when the company is very successful. Some shareholders have voting privileges that allow major investors to have some say in company policy.

Preferred stocks usually entitle owners to regular, fixed dividend payments similar to bond interest. Characteristically, preferred stock has no voting rights and initially has a higher yield than bonds. The *par value* of a preferred stock is the amount due to the shareholder in the event of liquidation, and the *annual yield* is often expressed as a percentage of the par value. Since preferred stock has no maturity date, it may be treated as a perpetuity whose value is

$$PW = \frac{\text{annual dividend on preferred stock}}{\text{annual rate of return expected by investor}}$$

Common stocks—the most common form of equity shares in a company—are more difficult to value than preferred stocks or bonds because dividends and prices of common stocks are not constant; investors hope that they will increase over time. It is therefore necessary to forecast future earnings, dividends, and stock prices. If reliable forecasts could be made (and that is a highly questionable assumption), stock valuation would result from discounting the forecast cash flow.

To illustrate, suppose that a share of Sumplex, Inc., has a current market price of $40. It is expected to pay a $3 dividend by the end of 1 year. Since the company went public in 1985, the value of its stock has been rising at an average rate of 4 percent. Using a 1-year study period, we find that

$$\text{Present worth} = \frac{\text{dividend}}{(F/P,\, i,\, 1)} + \frac{\text{market price at end of year}}{(F/P,\, i,\, 1)}$$

$$\text{Present worth} = \frac{\text{dividend}}{1 + i} + \frac{\text{present price} \times 1.04}{1 + i}$$

Rearranging and substituting numerical data give

$$1 + i = \frac{\$3 + \$40(1.04)}{\$40} = \frac{\$44.60}{\$40} = 1.115$$

to reveal the discount rate

$$i = 1.115 - 1 = 0.115 \text{ or } 11.5\%$$

If an investor is satisfied with an 11.5 percent rate of return after considering the risk involved, shares in Sumplex, Inc., could be purchased. The same expected rate of return could be calculated as

$$i = \text{dividend rate} + \text{growth rate} = \frac{\$3}{\$40} + 0.04$$

$$= 0.075 + 0.04 = 0.115$$

3.8   PAYBACK COMPARISON METHOD

The *payback method* is an extremely simple method used to obtain a rough estimate of the time that an investment will take to pay for itself. The reader should be warned that because of its simplicity, it does not give results that are equivalent to the present-worth evaluation or the other accepted techniques that we will be looking at in Chaps. 4 and 5. The payback method (sometimes called the *payout method*) avoids the need to calculate the cost of capital and still recognizes financial concern for limited resources. It guards against unexpected price (cost) increases and utilizes a cutoff criterion by requiring proposals to return their original investment from the savings they generate in a specified period, usually of short duration. It is typically applied to relatively small investment proposals that originate from operating departments. A department manager often has the authority to accept proposals up to a given ceiling without subjecting them to outside review.

The formula for obtaining a rough measure of the time an investment takes to pay for itself is simple to use and understand:

$$\text{Payback period} = \frac{\text{required investment}}{\text{annual receipts} - \text{annual disbursements}}$$
$$= \frac{\text{first cost}}{\text{net annual savings}}$$

Data utilized in applying the formula are usually direct, *not discounted,* cash flow amounts, and no salvage values are included. The result tells us how long it will be before the amount invested is recovered in actual dollars.

Claims such as "This investment will pay for itself in 18 months" are commonly heard in industry; they usually indicate anxiety about the elapsed time before a proposed investment begins to show a profit. The payback period is an extremely popular investment criterion in Canada and throughout the world. Polls consistently reveal that the payback method is used more than any other comparison method by Canadian industry to rate investments, particularly proposals from operating units for relatively small capital expenditures to improve operations.

In actual practice, the simple payback formula is sometimes modified to recognize capital recovery through depreciation charges and to include some discounted values. The simple payback formula is still widely used without elaborations, although it yields ratings that may lead to incorrect conclusions. Its deficiencies arise from failing to give recognition to cash flows occurring *after* the payback period has passed and from ignoring the time value of money.

For instance, as an extreme illustration of payback period deception, an investment of $1000 in an asset with a life of 1 year and an associated net return of $1000 will yield

$$\text{Payback period} = \frac{\$1000}{\$1000 \text{ per year}} = 1 \text{ year}$$

Another investment of $1000 promises to return $250 per year during its economic life of 5 years and yields

$$\text{Payback period} = \frac{\$1000}{\$250 \text{ per year}} = 4 \text{ years}$$

Favoring the alternative with the shortest payback period would rate the first alternative as better, but this alternative actually earns nothing: $1000 – $1000 = 0. Meanwhile, the spurned second alternative would have provided an annual return of 8 percent:

$$P/A = \frac{\$1000}{\$250} = 4 = (P/A,\ 8,\ 5)$$

Only when independent proposals have uniform returns and equal lives do the payback and internal rate-of-return (IRR) comparison methods indicate the same preferences.

If the results of payback calculations are questionable, why are they used? There are at least two apparent reasons. First, they are simple calculations. Since both depreciation and interest effects are usually ignored, the calculations are quick and easy and the results are intuitively logical. Second, the other reason stems from a preoccupation with the flexibility of capital. If the money spent on an improvement is recovered rapidly, the funds can be allocated again to other desired projects. This concept tends to engender a false sense of security, with reasoning such as "If the project can quickly pay for itself, it must be good" or "Only the best projects can meet our short-payback-period requirement."

Even though the payback period criterion is not always appropriate, it does address the problem of working-capital management by attempting to protect a firm's liquidity position. During times of constricted income, when a firm may have trouble meeting operating expenses and may have very limited capacity for funding new investments, an extremely short payback period (as low as 6 months) ensures that only quick-profit projects will be endorsed. In such exceptional situations, cash availability considerations may be equal to or more important than total earnings. As an auxiliary criterion, requiring a short payback period guards against the chance of losses due to new technological developments. Since the payback period criterion has serious weaknesses, it should never be applied alone; it should only be applied as an aid in decision making.

EXAMPLE 3.9

Payback Period Comparisons for Alternatives with Different Lives

The supervisor of a small machine shop has received three suggestions for reducing production costs. Suggestion A is to buy new jigs and fixtures; B is to rebuild an existing machine to improve its performance; and C is to purchase a new machine to replace some manual labor. Estimates have been made for the three alternative investments:

	Alternative		
	A	**B**	**C**
First cost, $	1800	2350	4200
Economic life, years	4	4	8
Net annual saving, $	645	840	1100
Payback period, years	2.8	2.8	3.8

The supervisor selects alternative B, explaining that because of limited capital for investments, shorter payback periods are preferable. With alternatives A and B having the same payback period, B is favored because the annual savings are greater than for A. What are the fallacies in this reasoning?

Solution

The flaws in the reasoning stem from a strict reliance on the payback criterion. It surely does not take into consideration the fact that alternatives A and B would have to reinvest in new equipment after 4 years had elapsed while alternative C would not. Also, an interest rate of 0 percent is assumed. We can see the flaws by computing the present worth of each alternative over an 8-year period, assuming that alternatives A and B will have equipment costs at the end of year 4 that are identical, in constant dollars, to the costs at the end of time period 0. We will assume a desired rate of interest equal to 8 percent. For alternative A:

$$PW_A = -\$1800 - \$1800(P/F, 8, 4) + \$645(P/A, 8, 8)$$
$$= -\$1800 - \$1800(0.73503) + \$645(5.74664) = \$583.53$$

Alternative B has the same structure:

$$PW_B = -\$2350 - \$2350(0.73503) + \$840(5.74664) = \$749.86$$

Finally alternative C has

$$PW_C = -\$4200 + \$1100(P/A, 8, 8)$$
$$= -\$4200 + \$1100(5.74664) = \$2121.30$$

As expected, alternative C prevails due primarily to just one investment cost in 8 years.

This explains why the simple payback period method should not be applied to different life alternatives. It also leads to the idea of a *discounted* payback period analysis. As we will see, this also only works with situations where all lives are equal. We compute discounted cumulative cash flows instead of cumulative cash flows determined with 0 percent interest. Let's use alternative C as an example:

End of year	Cash flow, $	Discounted cumulative cash flow, $
0	−4200	−4200
1	1100	−4200(1.08) + 1100 = −3436
2	1100	−3436(1.08) + 1100 = −2611
3	1100	−2611(1.08) + 1100 = −1720
4	1100	−1720(1.08) + 1100 = −757
5	1100	−757(1.08) + 1100 = +282
6	1100	+282(1.08) + 1100 = +1405
7	1100	+1405(1.08) + 1100 = +2617
8	1100	+2617(1.08) + 1100 = +3926

We see that the discounted payback period occurs in the fifth year. Interpolating, we get

$$\text{Discounted payback period} = 4 + 1\left(\frac{-757 - 0}{-757 - 282}\right)$$

$$= 4.73 \text{ years}$$

With 0 percent interest, by the conventional payback method this period is 3.8 years. Therefore, the conventional method tends to be optimistic in addition to other problems.

If we had performed a similar calculation for alternative A or alternative B we would have arrived at the same discounted payback period for either: 3.28 years. This tells us that we would have 0.72 year of profit, but then we would be investing in new equipment at the end of the fourth year! Having a net investment after period 0 is causing trouble with the method. This backs up the earlier statement that we should consider only alternatives with equal lives. CHEER will handle discounted payback period problems, and by inputting an interest rate of 0 percent, we can handle the original simple payback period method also.

3.9   **REVIEW EXERCISES AND DISCUSSIONS**

EXERCISE 1

An entrepreneur intending to start a new business knows that the first few years are the most difficult. To lessen the chance of failure, a loan plan for start-up capital is proposed in which interest paid during the first 2 years will be at 3 percent, at 6 percent for the next 2 years, and at 12 percent for the final 2 years of the 6-year loan. How large a loan can be justified for proposed repayments at the end of years 2, 4, and 6 of, respectively, $20,000, $30,000, and $50,000?

SOLUTION 1
It is not unusual for interest rates to change during a study. Time-value equivalence is calculated by translating individual cash flows through each time period at the interest rate applicable during that period. The procedure is illustrated by considering each loan repayment independently and calculating its present worth, as

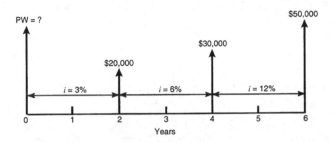

PW($20,000 payment) = $20,000($P/F$, 3, 2) = $20,000(0.94260)
                    = $18,852

PW($30,000 payment) = $30,000($P/F$, 6, 2)($P/F$, 3, 2)
                    = $30,000(0.89000)(0.94260) = $25,167

PW($50,000 payment) = $50,000($P/F$, 12, 2)($P/F$, 6, 2)($P/F$, 3, 2)
                    = $50,000(0.79719)(0.89000)(0.94260)
                    = $33,439

The loan that can be repaid by the given repayment amounts at the given interest rates is then

PW(total loan) = $18,852 + $25,167 + $33,439 = $77,458

A graph of the loan's balance over the 6-year period is shown in Fig. 3.3. From an initial value of $77,458 at time 0, the amount owed increases to $82,175 in 2 years with interest at 3 percent. Then the $20,000 payment is recorded, reducing the amount owed to $62,175. The steeper rates of increase during the later stages of the loan result from greater earnings generated by higher interest rates.

EXERCISE 2
A new rock pit will be operated for a construction project that will last 5 years. Rock can be loaded from an elevated box loader served by a conveyor from the pit or by mobile shovel loaders. The box loader and conveyor have an initial cost of $264,000 and will have no salvage value at the end of the project. Two shovel loaders, each priced at $42,000, can provide the same capacity, but their operating costs together will be $36,000 per year more than the box loader. Normal service life for a shovel loader is 3 years with zero salvage value, but a 2-year-old machine can likely be sold for $10,000. Which alternative is preferred when the interest rate is 13 percent?

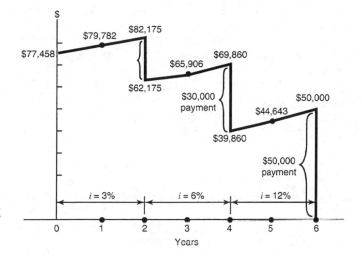

FIGURE 3.3
Loan balance during the 6-year repayment period.

SOLUTION 2

The study period is the duration of the project, 5 years. The present worth of the box-loader alternative is its initial cost: PW(box loader) = –$264,000.

Since the first two shovel loaders are replaced at the end of 3 years and the replacements will not be in service for their entire useful life, the estimated salvage value must be included as a cash inflow at the end of year 5. The additional operating costs incurred for the shovel loader alternative form a 5-year annuity of annual $36,000 payments:

$$PW(\text{shovel loaders}) = 2(-\$42,000) + 2(-\$42,000)(P/F, 13, 3) - \$36,000$$
$$\times (P/A, 13, 5) + 2(\$10,000)(P/F, 13, 5)$$
$$= -\$84,000 - \$84,000(0.69305) - \$36,000(3.51723)$$
$$+ \$20,000(0.54276)$$
$$= -\$84,000 - \$58,216 - \$126,619 + \$10,856$$
$$= -\$257,979$$

The shovel loaders appear to be more economical if the machines can be sold for the indicated salvage value after 2 years of use. Also, leverage might now be available for negotiation on the price of the box loader and conveyor.

EXERCISE 3

Kiddytoyz is a small novelty toy manufacturing company that is considering moving to a *just-in-time (JIT)* approach. JIT is a manufacturing philosophy where everything needed arrives at exactly the right time, equipment is supposed to operate without failure, and quality is perfect (zero defects). It is estimated for Kiddytoyz that the JIT first costs for equipment and tooling modifications will be $185,000. Annual maintenance and operating costs will increase due to the need for reliability improvements. These increases over the current operation are estimated to be a constant $8000 per year. Potential inventory reductions are estimated to be $32,000 for the first year with further arithmetic gradient reductions of \$4000 per year for the following 4 years (the life of the study). Also, production rates are expected to increase, leading to an increase in income of \$21,000 for the first year with \$2000 per year increases in each of the following 4 years. Should JIT be considered? An interest rate of 10 percent is used for economic justification analyses.

SOLUTION 3

Since JIT includes many intangible factors related to manufacturing, the decision of whether to implement JIT involves much more than is shown in an economic analysis. JIT is a manufacturing philosophy that requires excellence at all levels of the operation. The critical question relates to what the JIT implementation costs will be and what segments of JIT are affordable now.

The analysis of the given data indicates that a net present-worth evaluation is logical:

Net present worth = current benefits − current costs

PW (benefits) = [\$32,000 + \$4000 $(A/G, 10, 5)](P/A, 10, 5)$
  inventory savings with annual linear increase brought to present
  + [\$21,000 + \$2000 $(A/G, 10, 5)](P/A, 10, 5)$
  potential increase in income with annual linear increase brought to present
  = [\$32,000 + \$4000(1.81013)](3.79079)
  + [\$21,000 + 2000(1.81013)](3.79079)
  = \$148,747 + \$93,327 = \$242,083

PW(costs) = \$185,000 + \$8000 $(P/A, 10, 5)$
  first costs plus linear increase in maintenance and operating costs
  = \$185,000 + \$8000(3.79079)
  = \$185,000 + \$30,326 = \$215,326

So,

Net present worth = \$242,083 − \$215,326 = \$26,757

Assuming that the estimated future data are reasonable, JIT should be more than economically sound. This brings up an interesting thought: Shouldn't we be able to evaluate such alternatives even if we know that the estimates of future values are subject to variation? The answer, logically, is yes! Through sensitivity analysis we can see the effect of changing estimate values on the final solution. The computer program available with this text has that capability. We will discuss sensitivity analysis later in Chap. 11.

EXERCISE 4

The computer program CHEER can be used to solve Exercise 3. This exercise will demonstrate the process.

SOLUTION 4

Four CHEER screen displays are shown in Fig. 3.4 on pages 132 and 133. CHEER's initial screen is shown in Fig. 3.4a. The preliminary information input through this screen, from top to bottom, includes the project life of 5 years, the initial capital investment of $185,000 for JIT, and an interest rate of 10 percent. We click Revenue on the first screen's menu so that we can input expected savings through JIT. This causes the second screen to appear, shown in Fig. 3.4b. We are interpreting savings as revenues when we input data through this screen. Inventory savings are input as cash flow 1. And $32,000 is the base amount, but we have an arithmetic gradient of $4000 per year for years 2 through 5. So we input $32,000 for the amount and indicate that the cash flow covers years 1 through 5. There are three options at the right-hand side of the screen. If $32,000 were a constant flow for each of the 5 years, we would click option C (defined at the bottom of the screen). A geo-metric gradient would require clicking option G. We have an arithmetic gradi-ent, so we click option A. This causes the box under Change/period to be highlighted on the computer screen, indicating that a gradient value has to be inserted. Our gradient is $4000, and that is the value input. If we had a geometric gradient, we would need to input the percentage gradient rather than the constant-dollar gradient. The second cash flow is the expected increase in income to result from JIT.

After completing the screen 2 inputs, we click OK, and the first computer screen will appear (not shown again in the figure). Since we have additional maintenance costs to input, we click Operating/Maintenance costs and get the third screen (Fig. 3.4c). Now we have to input the expected $8000 per year additional income expected, and this is input with option C since we do not expect increases per year. We click on OK and return to the original screen.

Now we are ready to determine the present worth of savings. We click Calculate and get the last screen (Fig. 3.4d). We see four results, and the one we are interested in is PW (for present worth), which is $26,756.22. This compares with $26,757 which was found in Exercise 3 by using the compound-interest tables at the back of the book. Either way will result in the same economic decision being made.

The reader will note that the summary-of-results screen also gives the AW (annual worth), discussed in Chap. 4, FW (future worth), discussed earlier in Sec. 3.6, and IRR (internal rate of return), deferred to Chap. 5.

EXERCISE 5

Metalix Company is planning for the manufacture of an assembly that will be used in a new product for which the company has a 5-year military contract. This assembly could be produced in the company's own facility with the purchase of specialized numerically controlled equipment; or the assembly could be subcontracted to a low bidder. The cost estimates for producing the assembly in-house are as follows:

First costs	$825,000
Annual maintenance and operating costs	$125,000 for first year with 4 percent per year additional costs for subsequent years
Tooling and material costs	$525 per assembly
Equipment salvage value after 5 years	$45,000

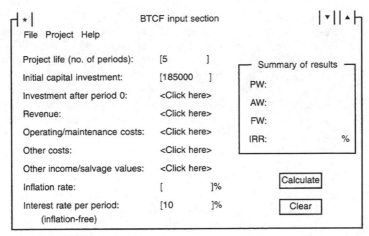

(a) Initial screen inputs

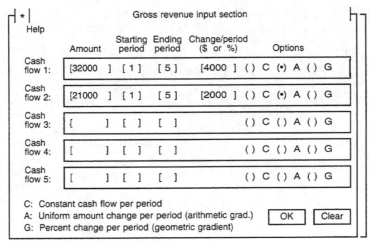

FIGURE 3.4
CHEER screens for
Exercise 4.

(b) Screen for savings input

The low-bid subcontractor bids as follows:

500– 999 assemblies in 1 year	$850 per assembly
1000–1999 assemblies in 1 year	$830 per assembly
2000–2999 assemblies in 1 year	$800 per assembly

The bidder already has the specialized equipment needed to produce the assemblies.

The Metalix contract requires the following delivery schedule:

Year	1	2	3	4	5
Number of assemblies	900	1500	2100	1800	1100

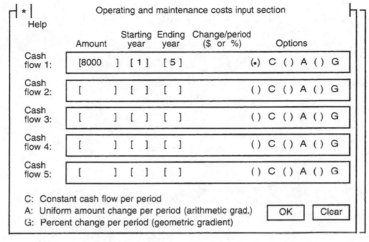

(c) Screen for cost inputs

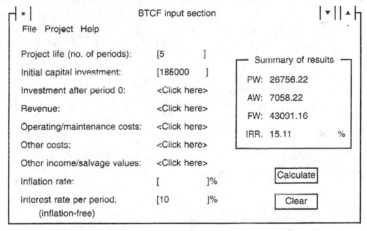

FIGURE 3.4
continued

(d) Final results screen

If an interest rate of 12 percent is used by Metalix for its economic evaluations, would you recommend that Metalix (a) subcontract or (b) manufacture in-house?

SOLUTION 5

(a) Subcontract:

$$\begin{aligned} PW &= 900(\$850)(P/F,\ 12,\ 1) + 1500(\$830)(P/F,\ 12,\ 2) \\ &\quad \text{first-year cost} \qquad\qquad \text{second-year cost} \\ &\quad \text{brought to time 0} \qquad \text{brought to time 0} \\ &\quad + 2100(\$800)(P/F,\ 12,\ 3) + 1800(\$830)(P/F,\ 12,\ 4) \\ &\quad \ \ \text{third-year cost} \qquad\qquad \text{fourth-year cost} \\ &\quad \ \ \text{brought to time 0} \qquad \text{brought to time 0} \\ &\quad + 1100(\$830)(P/F,\ 12,\ 5) \\ &\quad \ \ \text{fifth-year cost brought to time 0} \end{aligned}$$

$$= \$765,000(0.89286) + \$1,245,000(0.79719) + \$1,680,000(0.71178)$$
$$+ \$1,494,000(0.63552) + \$913,000(0.56743)$$
$$= \$4,338,860.$$

(b) Manufacture in-house:

1. First costs = $825,000.
2. *Maintenance and operations.* These are $125,000 for the first year with 4 percent increases for the following years. Using Method 1 for Chap. 2 part (a) for the geometric gradient gives

$$\text{PW} = \$125,000 \left(\frac{1 - 1.04^5 \, 1.12^{-5}}{0.12 - 0.04} \right) = \$483,810$$

3. *Tooling and maintenance.* This is a function of quantity produced in a year, similar to the subcontractor's costing, and each yearly cost would have to be brought to time 0 with the appropriate $(P/F, i, N)$ value:

Year 1:   900($525)$(P/F, 12, 1)$ = $421,876
Year 2: 1500($525)$(P/F, 12, 2)$ =   627,787
Year 3: 2100($525)$(P/F, 12, 3)$ =   784,737
Year 4: 1800($525)$(P/F, 12, 4)$ =   600,566
Year 5: 1100($525)$(P/F, 12, 5)$ =   327,691
PW(tooling and materials) = $2,762,657

4. *Salvage value:*

$45,000$(P/F, 12, 5) = \$25,534$

The in-house costs now are

$825,000 + $483,810 + $2,762,534 − $25,534 = $4,045,933

The net present worth difference for the two alternatives is

$4,338,860 − $4,045,657 = $293,927

It looks as though manufacturing in-house will be more economical than subcontracting. Possible uncertain characteristics could make management think twice about this. The state of the military complex with cost reductions might force a cancellation of the project before the 5-year period is completed. If this probability is small, management would opt to manufacture. If it is large, then management might decide to subcontract. Uncertainty characteristics are discussed later in this text.

EXERCISE 6

A bank has offered to loan the novelty company described in Example 3.6 the sum of $145,000 at 8 percent interest compounded annually to build a large warehouse immediately. The warehouse would be the same size as the small one plus the addition and would have annual expenses of $1500 per year. If its resale value at the end of 10 years were $50,000, would it be a better alternative than the other two given in Example 3.6?

SOLUTION 6

The interest rate offered by the bank should not be used in the comparison, because the required rate of return for an organization includes more than just the cost of borrowing (this is discussed further in Chap. 5). At $i = 12$ percent, the present worth of 10 years of storage from the construction of a large warehouse comparable in size to the other alternatives is

$$PW = \$145,000 - \$50,000(P/F,\ 12,\ 10) + \$1500(P/A,\ 12,\ 10)$$
$$= \$145,000 - \$50,000(0.32197) + \$1500(5.6502)$$
$$= \$137,377$$

This cost is lower than that of the build-small-and-add alternative but is more than the leasing cost. Note that the cost of construction in two phases of the same-size building exhibits the typical relation that the absolute cost (at $i = 0$ percent) of acquisition by parts is greater than the acquisition cost all at one time. However, a deferral may make the time value of acquisition by parts less expensive.

EXERCISE 7

An investor has been investigating the stock performance of two companies: Withit and Righton. Withit Corporation has consistently paid dividends that increase $0.10 per year while the selling price of the stock has averaged a 2 percent annual increase. Righton is a new glamour company that has paid no dividends because all earnings are retained for expansion, but its market price is expected to increase by $10 per year. Moreover, in about 5 years Righton is expected to start paying dividends equal to 2 percent of its price per share (a price-to-earnings ratio of 50:1). Current data about the two companies are summarized below.

	Withit corporation	Righton corporation
Dividend	$2.25 (10¢/year increase)	0 (2% of market price after 5 years)
Market price	$28 (2% annual increase)	$65 ($10/year increase)
Capitalization rate	9%	12% (risk-adjusted)

Since it is generally believed that Righton's stock is less stable than Withit's, the extra risk of investing in Righton is recognized by requiring a higher rate of return for the valuation—12 percent versus 9 percent. Note that this might be a poor way to handle risk. Later chapters will discuss probability concepts that can be used with future cash flows to reflect risk possibilities. Also, sensitivity analysis will be introduced in a later chapter to show how slightly changing values, such as rates of return, can reveal whether there is a need for extremely accurate values.

Disregarding tax effects and brokerage commissions to buy or sell, determine which stock has the greater valuation for an anticipated 10-year ownership.

SOLUTION 7

A 10-year study period is used to calculate the present worth of each stock alternative, assuming that dividends are paid at the end of the year. The valuation of Withit stock at $i = 9$ percent is

$$\text{PW(Withit)} = [\$2.25 + \$0.10(A/G, 9, 10)] (P/A, 9, 10) + \$28 (F/P, 2, 10)$$
$$\times (P/F, 9, 10)$$
$$= [\$2.25 + \$0.10(3.79777)] (6.41766) + \$28(1.21899)(0.42241)$$
$$= \$16.88 + \$14.42 = \$31.30$$

which makes the current market price of $28 appear attractive.

The valuation of Righton Company's stock based on a 12 percent desired rate of return and the assumption that dividends are paid annually after a 5-year wait is diagrammed as

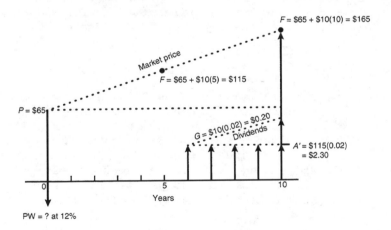

$$\text{PW(Righton)} = [\$2.30 + \$0.20(A/G, 12, 5)] (P/A, 12, 5)(P/F, 12, 5)$$
$$+ \$165(P/F, 12, 10)$$
$$= [\$2.30 + \$0.20(1.77459)] (3.60478)(0.56743) + \$165(0.32197)$$
$$= \$5.43 + \$53.13 = \$58.56$$

Since the $65 market price for Righton stock exceeds the calculated valuation, it appears that Withit stock is a better investment opportunity, assuming that risk-return ratings and forecast cash flows are reasonably accurate.

3.10   PROBLEMS

3.1   The lease on a warehouse amounts to $5000 per month for 5 years. If payments are made on the first of each month, what is the present worth of the agreement at a nominal annual interest rate of 12 percent, compounded monthly?

3.2   Determine the present worth of the lease in Prob. 3.1 if the payments are to increase at the beginning of each year equal to $250 per month for each month of occupancy.

3.3   What is the future worth at the end of 5 years of the payments to be made in Prob. 3.1? Do *not* use your PW results from Prob. 3.1!

3.4   A company borrowed $100,000 to finance a new product. The loan was for 20 years at a nominal interest rate of 8 percent compounded semiannually. It was to be repaid in 40 equal payments. After one-half the payments were made, the company decided to pay the remaining balance in one final payment at the end of the 10th year. How much was owed?

3.5   A proposed improvement in an assembly line will have an initial purchase and installation cost of $175,000. The annual maintenance cost will be $6000; periodic overhauls once every 3 years, excluding the last year of use, will cost $11,500 each. The improvement will have a useful life of 9 years, at which time it will have no salvage value. What is the present worth of the 9-year costs of the improvement at $i = 8$ percent?

3.6   The assembly line in Prob. 3.5 will have potential income increases, due to higher production volumes, of $29,000 in the first year with $3000 per year additional increases in years 2 through 5. These increases can be expected to decrease from the year 5 value at $5000 per year until the increase in year 9 is $21,000. Are the future expected increases sufficient to justify the expenditures given in Prob. 3.5?

3.7   Amjay Company is currently renting a parking lot for employee and visitor use at an annual cost of $9000, payable on the first of each year. The company has an opportunity to buy the lot for $50,000. Maintenance and taxes on the property are expected to cost $2500 annually. Given that the property will be needed for 10 more years, determine what sales price must be obtained at the end of that period in order for Amjay to break even, when the interest rate is 12 percent.

3.8   A bakery is thinking of purchasing a small delivery truck that has a first cost of $18,000 and is to be kept in service for 6 years, at which time the salvage value is expected to be $2500. Maintenance and operating costs are estimated at $2500 the first year and will increase at a rate of $200 per year. Determine the present worth of this vehicle, using an interest rate of 12 percent.

3.9   A small dam and an irrigation system are expected to cost $300,000. Annual maintenance and operating costs are expected to be $40,000 the first year and will increase at a rate of 10 percent per year. Determine the equivalent present worth of building and operating the system with interest of 10 percent over a 30-year life.

3.10   It is estimated that additional reinforcement of the dam in Prob. 3.9 in the first year at a cost of $65,000 will reduce annual maintenance costs to $25,000 in the first year with an increase of 5 percent per year over the rest of the 30-year life. Should the civil engineer in charge of the project seriously consider the proposal to do the reinforcing?

3.11 In a scenario of high petroleum prices, a newly developed electric car will cost $21,000 to purchase. Operating and maintenance costs, including home charging of the batteries, are estimated to be $350 for the first year with annual increases thereafter of $50 per year. Salvage value after 5 years is estimated to be $6500. A new gasoline runabout will cost $16,000 and will average 30 kilometers per liter. Gasoline costs $1.26 per liter and is expected to increase at a rate of $0.05 per year for each of the next 4 years. Maintenance costs are estimated to be $300 per year including warranty coverage. Salvage value is estimated to be $1500 after 5 years of service. If the vehicles are expected to be driven for 20,000 kilometers per year, determine which option will have the lower cost over 5 years. Use present-worth analysis with a 10 percent rate of interest.

3.12 Assume that the estimates for the gasoline car in Prob. 3.11 are reasonable due to past experience but that the salvage value is somewhat unclear for the electric car. What is the minimum salvage value that should be obtained after 5 years to justify consideration of the electric car over the gasoline vehicle?

3.13 Machine A has a first cost of $9000, no salvage value at the end of its 6-year useful life, and annual operating costs of $5000. Machine B costs $16,000 new and has an expected resale value of $4000 at the end of its 9-year economic life. Operating costs for machine B are $4000 per year. Compare the two alternatives on the basis of their present worths, using the repeated-projects assumption at 10 percent annual interest.

3.14 A commercial rental property is for sale at $100,000. A prospective buyer estimates that the property would be held for 12 years, at the end of which it could be sold for $90,000. During the ownership period, annual receipts from rentals would be $15,000, and average disbursements for all purposes in connection with ownership would be $6000. If a rate of return of 9 percent is expected, what is the maximum bid that the prospective purchaser should make to buy the property?

3.15 A manufacturer requires an additional 10,000 square feet (929 square meters) of warehouse space. A reinforced-concrete building added to the existing main structure will cost $850,000, whereas the same amount of space can be constructed with a galvanized building for $595,000. The life of the concrete building is estimated at 25 years with a yearly maintenance cost of $23,800. The life of the galvanized building is estimated to be 15 years, and the annualized maintenance cost is estimated to be $53,000. Average annual property taxes are 1.2 percent of first costs for the concrete building and 0.5 percent for the metal building. Assume that the salvage value of the concrete building will be zero after 25 years. Compare the present worths of the two warehouse additions, using 12 percent interest for a 25-year study period, in determining the minimum salvage value of the galvanized building after the 25-year period to make it economically comparable to the concrete building, assuming that its salvage value after 15 years is zero.

3.16 Perpetual care for a small shrine in a cemetery is estimated to be available for $500 per year. The long-term interest rate is expected to average about 5 percent. If the capitalized cost is estimated at $15,000, what amount is anticipated for the first cost of the shrine?

3.17 A proposed mill in an isolated area can be furnished with power and water by a gravity-feed system. A stream high above the mill will be tapped to provide flow for water needs and power requirements by connecting it to the mill with a ditch-and-tunnel system or with a wood-and-concrete flume that winds its way down from the plateau. Either alternative will meet current and future needs, and both will utilize the same power-generating equipment.

The ditch-and-tunnel system will cost $500,000 with an annual maintenance cost of $2000. The flume has an initial cost of $200,000 and a yearly maintenance cost of $12,000. In addition, the wood portion of the flume will have to be replaced every 10 years at a cost of $100,000.

Compare the alternatives on the basis of capitalized costs with an interest rate of 6 percent.

3.18 A company is considering the purchase of a new piece of testing equipment that is expected to produce $8000 additional income during the first year of operation; this amount will probably decrease by $500 per year for each subsequent year of ownership. The equipment costs $20,000 and will have an estimated salvage value of $3000 after 8 years of use. For an interest rate of 15 percent, determine the net present worth of this investment. Neglect taxes in your computations.

3.19 To attract industry, a city has made an offer to a corporation. The city will install all roads and services for the plant site at no immediate cost to the corporation, but the corporation will be expected to bear the cost of operation and maintenance on a cost-sharing schedule whereby $65,000 is paid the first year of the project (2 years from now), each subsequent yearly payment will be $5000 less, and the corporation's obligation will end with the last $5000 payment. What is the present worth today of this agreement, if the annual interest rate is 9 percent?

3.20 A marina has two alternative plans for constructing a small-boat landing on a lake behind the sales building; one is a wooden dock, and the other is a metal-and-concrete wharf. Data for the two plans are as shown.

	Wood	**Metal and concrete**
First cost	$35,000	$55,000
Period before replacement	10 years	15 years
Salvage value	$5000	0
Annual maintenance	$6000	$3200

Using a minimum attractive rate of return of 10 percent, compare the present worths of the two plans. Assume that both will provide adequate service and that replacement costs will be the same as the original cost.

3.21 A refining company entered into a contract for raw materials with an agreement to pay $600,000 now and $150,000 per year beginning at the end of the fifth year. The contract was made for 10 years. At the end of the third year, because of unexpected profits, the company requested that it be allowed to make a lump-sum payment in advance for the rest of the contract. Both parties agreed that 7 percent compounded annually was a fair interest rate. What was the amount of the lump sum?

3.22 A machine can be repaired today for $2000. If repairs are not made, the operating expenses will increase by $200 each year for the next 5 years. Assume that the expenses will occur at the end of each year and that the machine will have no value under either alternative at the end of the 5-year period. The minimum acceptable rate of return is 12 percent. Compare the present worths of the two alternatives.

3.23 The following alternatives are available to accomplish an objective of 12 years' duration:

	Plan A	Plan B	Plan C
Life cycle	6 years	3 years	4 years
First cost	$2000	$8000	$10,000
Annual cost	$3200	$700	$500

Compare the present worth of the alternatives, using an interest rate of 7 percent.

3.24 The lining of a chemical tank must be replaced every 3 years at a cost of $3500. A new type of lining is available that is more resistant to corrosion. The new lining costs $5100. If the minimum rate of return required is 12 percent and taxes and insurance are 4 percent of the first cost annually, how long must the improved lining last to be more economical than the present lining?

3.25 A single underground transmission circuit is needed immediately, and load studies indicate the need for a second circuit in 6 years. If provision is made for a second conduit when the conduit for the first circuit is installed, there will be no future need for reopening, trenching, backfilling, and repaving. The cost of installing a single circuit with minimum preparation for the eventual second circuit is $850,000. The installation of the second circuit will be considered to cost $800,000 at the end of year 6 in order to be in operation by the beginning of year 7. If the second circuit is installed immediately, the total cost will be $1.4 million.

Constant annual operating and maintenance costs of the circuits are 8 percent of the first cost. The average life of a circuit is 20 years. The required rate of return on such investments is 10 percent before taxes.

    (a) Compare the deferred investment with the immediate investment, using a 20-year study period.

    (b) Compare the two conduit plans on an infinite study period. Then compare this solution with that in part (a). Which is more reasonable? Why?

3.26 Autocon Company is evaluating three robots for possible use in its assembly operations. (Only one robot will be purchased.) Data associated with these robots are as follows:

	Robot A	Robot B	Robot C
First cost, $	55,000	58,000	53,000
Operating and maintenance costs, $	3000/year	4500/year	4000/year
Expected income, $	40,000/year	44,000/year	38,000/year
Estimated salvage value, $	4000	6000	4000

Assuming a technological life of 3 years and a desired interest rate of 12 percent, which robot seems to be preferable, assuming all other factors are equal? Use a net present-worth evaluation.

3.27 What would the "net future" economic evaluations be, at the end of period 3, for the robots in Prob. 3.26? Would this future evaluation make much sense when presented to the manufacturing manager?

Note: First solve this problem *without* considering your PW results from Prob. 3.26. Next, directly use your PW results from Prob. 3.26 in verifying your FW solutions.

3.28 Suppose the technological lives for robots *A* and *B* in Prob. 3.26 are both 2 years while robot *C* still has a life of 3 years. Perform the economic evaluations, assuming that the salvage values of all three robots will be $6000 after their useful lives. Also, robot first costs are expected to increase at a rate of 5 percent per year due to technological enhancements.

3.29 A wealthy industrial economist dies, and her will specifies that $5 million of her estate will go to the University of Toronto (U of T) to fund a small engineering economy building as well as 20 graduate scholarships per year over the next 20 years. The scholarships are to have a value of $12,000 per year for the first year and should increase at a rate of $1500 per year over the following 19 years. U of T requires that $15,000, starting with the third year of the bequest, be reserved for building maintenance and operating costs. These costs are to have a linear increase of $2000 per year, starting with year 4. Assuming that a 10 percent interest rate is used for such analyses, determine how much will be available for building first costs.

3.30 For the building specified in Prob. 3.29, determine the effect on potential first costs if the maintenance and operating costs increase by 12 percent per year instead of having a linear increase.

3.31 What is the maximum amount that you could afford to bid for a bond with a face value of $5000 and a coupon rate of 8 percent payable semiannually, if your minimum attractive rate of return is 10 percent? The bond matures in 6 years.

3.32 Swampwater Flood Control District is selling 20-year tax-free bonds with a face value of $2 million and a stated yield of 6 percent with semiannual interest payments. Printing and legal costs associated with issuing the bonds have totaled $50,000, and costs associated with paying the dividends are expected to be $1000 per period. What is the minimum amount the bonds must sell for such that the utility district's cost of capital does not exceed a nominal 8 percent per annum?

3.33 A bond with a face value of $5000 pays quarterly interest of $1\frac{1}{2}$ percent each period. Twenty-six interest payments remain before the bond matures. How much would you be willing to pay for this bond today, if the next interest payment is due now and you want to earn 8 percent compounded quarterly on your money?

3.34 Bonds of Overightors Corporation are perpetuities bearing 7 percent annual interest. Their par value is $1000.
   (*a*) If bonds of this type currently are expected to yield 6 percent, what is the market price?
   (*b*) If interest rates rise to the level at which comparable bonds return a yield of 8 percent, what would the market price be for Overightor bonds?

(c) How would the prices change in parts (a) and (b) if the bonds had a definite maturity date in 20 years?

EXTENSION 3A BONDS AND STOCKS

3A.1 Things to Think About When Buying Bonds

A decision to buy a bond rather than investing in a different savings option, such as stocks or a money market fund, is just the first decision. The next one is to decide which bond to buy.

A variety of government and corporate bonds can be purchased. In general, corporate bonds offer a higher stated interest rate (i.e., coupon rate) than government bonds because they suffer greater risk of nonpayment than those from "governments." Ratings are made for both corporate and government bonds by agencies that specialize in evaluating the creditworthiness of issuing organizations. Thus the yield or the effective rate of interest must be balanced against the possibility of default. The yield of a bond is based on the purchase or bid price, the coupon rate, and the maturity (i.e., face) value.

Yield typically increases for longer term bonds. On the basis of known information, either the bid price (in present worth) or the yield of a bond can be calculated. Consideration of risk, coupon rate, and maturity date leads to an acceptable purchase price. This price (present worth) should then be balanced against expected changes in prevailing interest rates. When market interest rates rise, the price an investor is willing to pay goes down for a bond with a given coupon rate. When interest expectations are higher than a bond's coupon rate, buyers are willing to pay more for shorter maturity dates.

To accurately compare the potential of bonds with other types of investments, income taxes and capital gains taxes must be figured in. Chapter 9 provides tax information.

3A.2 Stock Market Vocabulary and How It Works

A corporation is a legal entity. Like a person it can acquire resources, own assets, incur debts, and sue or be sued. Yet it is separate from the individuals who own it. The owners (shareholders) have only limited liability for the corporation's actions, risking just the amount they have paid for its stock. These stock purchases are made in anticipation of monetary gains from the organization's performance. The amount paid for a share of stock reflects the expected level of gain and the confidence of that expectation.

Organized stock exchanges facilitate the transfer of securities among buyers and sellers. Individuals can spread their risks by buying shares in a variety of corporations and can change their holdings easily and quickly. Ten of the more common terms involved in these transactions are listed below.

- *Broker*. An agent who executes orders to buy and sell shares of stock and other securities for a commission.
- *Common stock* or *equities*. Holders have a share in assets and control of the company, but few fully utilize their voting rights to exercise control.
- *Preferred stock*. Represents a part of the capital of a business, usually having fixed dividends and no voting rights.
- *Dividends*. Payments that are usually made quarterly by a company to shareholders in the form of cash or stock.
- *Listed stock*. These are traded on a stock exchange.
- *Over-the-counter*. Stocks that are not listed on exchanges are traded by direct negotiation between brokers representing buyers and sellers.
- *Margin*. Investors can purchase stocks on the margin by not putting up the full purchase price; they borrow the balance from their broker.
- *Selling short*. A technique for investors to sell stock they do not own. They borrow stock from the broker, sell it, and hope that the price will go down so they can buy shares at a lower price, return the shares to the broker, and pocket the difference.
- *Price-earnings ratio*. The relationship of the price of stock to its annual per share earnings. To calculate it, divide the latest price of the company's stock by the company's latest earnings per share. Earnings per share are calculated by taking the company's latest annual profits and dividing them by the total number of shares outstanding.
- *Yield*. The return on a security figured by dividing annual dividend rate by the price of the stock. A stock selling at $50 with an annual dividend of $5 per share has a yield of 10 percent.

3A.3 Deciphering Stock Listing

Summaries of stock movements at different exchanges are published in newspapers. The terminology used in such listings is defined below.

- *Yearly high & low*. The highest and lowest price paid for the stock in the latest 52-week period. Stock prices are quoted in fractions as low as 1/8, or 12.5 cents.
- *Div*. Dividend paid on an annual basis.
- *Yield*. Defined previously.

- *P/E*. Price-earnings ratio defined above.
- *Vol 100s*. The volume or the number of shares traded during the week.
- *Last*. The price of the stock at the final trade of the last trading day.
- *Net Chng*. The net change from the close of the previous week. For example, +1/2 shows a gain of 50 cents.

Additional notations may be used to show special conditions, such as an "x" in front of the dividend to indicate that the stock is selling *ex-dividend*—the buyer will not receive the latest declared dividend.

3A.4 Interpreting the Dow Jones Industrial Average (DJIA)

The DJIA is an indicator of stock market fluctuations that was started in 1896 with only twelve stocks. The Dow Jones "Average" is just the sum of current prices for the stocks of 30 highly respected corporations divided by the adjustment factor to account for dividends and newly issued shares. It is not a true indicator of the average stock's performance because its 30 blue chip industrials certainly do not represent the several thousand issues currently being traded, and even these 30 issues are price-weighted to give proportionately more weight to high-priced stocks than to cheaper ones. While the Dow Jones index has shortcomings, it nonetheless is a widely watched signal of stock market movement.

The DJIA is important to Canadian investors because the North American capital markets are very much integrated. Many Canadian stocks are traded in the U.S.A. and many U.S. stocks are also traded in Canada. Canadian market fluctuations are usually correlated with fluctuations in the U.S. market.

3A.5 The Toronto Stock Exchange 300 Composite Index

The major Canadian stock market indicator is the Toronto Stock Exchange 300 Composite Index, created in January 1977. It is called the TSE 300. It is composed of the 300 most important Canadian-owned stocks (from among the more than one thousand which are listed for trading) on the Toronto Stock Exchange. Each company in the Index must have been listed for at least three years. At least 25,000 shares worth at least one million dollars must have been traded in each of the three years in order for the stock to be included in the Index. The index is divided into groups and subgroups.

The TSE 300 is not a mere arithmetic average like the DJIA. It is an index number calculated by multiplying the price of each of the 300 stocks by its capitalization (the value of the outstanding shares) and relating a given day's index value to a base figure.

The base was set equal to 1000 in 1977. On July 29, 1996, the TSE Index was at 4896.30, so it has gone up by approximately 8.5 percent per year since 1977. Although fluctuations occur frequently, obviously over the 1977–1996 period the trend has been upward.

EQUIVALENT ANNUAL-WORTH COMPARISONS

In its simplest form, justification is provided by the mathematics of answering the question, "Will I make more money by following procedure A, or procedure B?"

Joseph Harrington, Jr.[†]

Dr. Harrington is credited with inventing the phrase *computer-integrated manufacturing (CIM),* whereby integration of all the functions within a manufacturing enterprise leads to a better way of producing a product. These functions include communications, design, production, assembly, marketing, and so on. Harrington did not envisage that all functions within the enterprise would have to be computerized, but the intervening years that have elapsed since the term CIM was coined have seen more and more computerization being implemented in manufacturing. Computer-controlled machining centers, commonly called *direct numerical control (DNC) machines,* may cost hundreds of thousands of dollars. Evaluation of these machines against older, more conventional processes will have to consider quality, productivity, equipment reliability, possible scheduling simplification, work in process reduction, and other potential benefits. Assuming a monetary value can be placed on all the factors that make up the decision process, how might the benefit and cost data be best presented to allow a careful and informed decision to be made? We saw, in Chap. 3, that present-worth evaluations are often preferred because of the relevancy of current timing to the decision maker. In some instances, as discussed also in Chap. 3, evaluation at a time in the future will sometimes be more logical. Many economic decisions can be assisted by determining

---

[†]Joseph Harrington, Jr., *Computer Integrated Manufacturing,* Krieger Publishing Company, Malabar, FL, reprint edition, 1979.

costs, expenditures, and net worth on the basis of annual or periodic timing. Manufacturing and other engineering alternative evaluations often just make more sense when viewed on an annual basis. The manufacturing manager, e.g., is often required to justify his or her operation on a monthly or yearly basis. Annual goals are frequently set for marketing and other people in the enterprise. But using a periodic base for economic decisions is not limited to engineering or manufacturing operations, as we shall see in the rest of this chapter.

Not only is it often meaningful to structure an investment solution in terms of annual payments, but also it can be a more convenient way to arrive at a present worth or rate of return (to be covered in Chap. 5). It will be shown that all three methods of analysis will indicate the same preference among engineering alternatives, though one might be more logical to utilize for a specific situation. For example, we will see that present-worth comparison of assets with unequal lives, as shown in Example 3.4, can be much easier to compute by first using an annual-worth comparison.

4.1   UTILIZATION OF EQUIVALENT ANNUAL-WORTH COMPARISON METHOD

With an annual-worth method, all the receipts and disbursements occurring over a period are converted to an equivalent uniform yearly amount.[†] It is a popular method because of the widespread inclination to view a year's gains and losses as a yardstick of progress. Cost accounting procedures, depreciation expenses, tax calculations, and other summary reports are annual. These yearly cost tabulations generally make the annual-worth method easier to apply and comprehend than the other comparison methods.

As mentioned earlier, equivalent annual-worth comparisons produce results compatible with present-worth and rate-of-return comparisons. For a set of common assumptions, a preference for an alternative exhibited by one method will be mirrored by the other two. Annual-worth calculations are frequently part of the computations required to develop present-worth and rate-of-return values, and parallel computations by different methods are useful for complementary comparisons that improve the clarity of an analysis.

The six conditions listed in Chap. 3 for basic present-worth comparisons also apply to basic annual-worth comparisons: cash flows and interest rates are known, cash flows are before taxes and in constant-value dollars, and comparisons include neither intangible considerations nor limits due to availability of financing. These restrictions are relaxed in later chapters.

[†]Equivalent uniform periodic amounts are not restricted to annual periods. The periods may be monthly, quarterly, and so on. A large number of engineering economic decisions are based on annual comparisons, and so the term *equivalent uniform yearly amount* is often used in this text, but the implication will be that the methodologies are just as applicable to other time periods.

4.1.1 Structure of a Capital Recovery Annuity

The cornerstone of annual-worth calculations is the capital recovery factor, which converts a lump sum to an equivalent annuity. This annuity usually represents an investment in an asset that is expected to generate a positive future cash flow, and the duration of the annuity is therefore the life of the asset. Since the cost of an asset is a cash outlay, the resulting annuity is a uniform series of negative payments. This negative cash flow is offset by the positive revenue produced by the asset in establishing the net equivalent annual worth of the investment.

The *capital recovery factor (A/P, i, N)* accounts for both the repayment of invested capital P and the interest earned on the unrecovered portion of the investment. Although payments A are uniform in size, the proportion of capital recovered and interest earned changes each period. The structure of an annuity, in which varying amounts from the equal payments are allocated to capital recovery and interest, is best revealed by examining a sample application.

Assume that an asset is purchased for $40,000. It has an expected life of 4 years and no salvage value at the end of its life. The purchaser intends to recover the $40,000 investment over 4 years *plus* the interest the $40,000 would have earned if it had been invested elsewhere. If an acceptable interest rate is 10 percent, the series of equal payments that will return the capital plus interest is computed as

$$\text{Equivalent annual payment } A = P(A/P, 10, 4)$$
$$= \$40,000(0.31547) = \$12,619$$

Every year the proportion of a payment allotted to capital recovery and interest changes because interest applies only on the amount of capital not yet recovered, and that amount changes each year. During year 1, before a payment is received, the $40,000 investment earns $40,000 \times 0.10 = \$4000$ interest. The first payment of $12,619 then reduces the unrecovered capital by $12,619 - \$4000 = \$8619$. During year 2, 10 percent interest is paid on $40,000 - \$8619 = \$31,381$, amounting to $3138. Therefore, of the second payment, $3138 is interest, and $12,619 - \$3138 = \$9481$ is allocated to capital recovery. The complete sequence of changing proportions is given in Table 4.1.

Anyone who has had a home mortgage or loan, or who has contemplated one, has probably been told that "You can reduce the total interest paid and the length of time it takes to pay off the mortgage by increasing the annual payments." If the $12,618.83 annual payment shown in Table 4.1 is considered to be a loan payment and is increased by 50 percent to $18,928.25, we get the capital (principal) and interest payments shown in Table 4.2. The final-period payment is less than $18,928.25 since only $9515.74 remains to fully recover the capital.

TABLE 4.1

Pattern of capital recovery and interest charges when capital recovery factor at $i = 10\%$ is applied to purchase of $40,000 asset with life of 4 years and no salvage value

End of period	Capital not recovered by end of period, $	Interest due on unrecovered capital, $	Amount of capital recovered, $	Period capital recovery charge, $
0	40,000.00			
1	31,381.17	4,000.00	8,618.83	12,618.83
2	21,900.45	3,138.12	9,480.72	12,618.83
3	11,471.67	2,190.05	10,428.79	12,618.83
4	0.00	1,147.17	11,471.67	12,618.83
		10,475.33	40,000.00	50,475.33

The total interest paid with the increase in annual payment is reduced from $10,475.33 to $7372.24, and the total amount paid over the four periods is reduced from $50,475.33 to $47,372.24. The time period over which the payments are made is reduced by 25 percent. Whether this type of reduction should be realistically considered is a function of the interest rate, what you can do with the money in the periods saved, and whether you have the money to increase the annual payments.

A more realistic loan case is given in Table 4.3, where computer-generated interest and capital (principal) payments are given for a loan that has a present value of $80,000 which is to be paid off in 48 equal quarterly (3-month) payments, at a quarterly interest rate of 3 percent. The equivalent quarterly equal payments were computed from

$$A = \$80,000(A/P, 3, 48)$$

TABLE 4.2

Pattern of capital recovery and interest charges if annual payment given in Table 4.1 is increased by 50%

End of period	Capital not recovered by end of period, $	Interest due on unrecovered capital, $	Amount of capital recovered, $	Actual period payment, $
0	40,000.00			
1	25,071.75	4,000.00	14,928.25	18,928.25
2	8,650.68	2,507.18	16,421.07	18,928.25
3	0.00	865.07	8,650.68	9,515.74
		7,372.24	40,000.00	47,372.24

TABLE 4.3

Loan payment data for $80,000 loan at quarterly 3 percent rate for 48 quarters

End of period	Capital not recovered by end of period, $	Interest due on unrecovered capital, $	Amount of capital recovered, $	Period capital recovery charge, $
0	80,000.00			
1	79,233.78	2,400.00	766.22	3,166.22
2	78,444.57	2,377.01	789.21	3,166.22
3	77,631.69	2,353.34	812.88	3,166.22
4	76,794.41	2,328.95	837.27	3,166.22
5	75,932.02	2,303.83	862.39	3,166.22
6	75,043.77	2,277.96	888.26	3,166.22
7	74,128.86	2,251.31	914.91	3,166.22
8	73,186.50	2,223.87	942.36	3,166.22
9	72,215.88	2,195.59	970.63	3,166.22
10	71,216.13	2,166.48	999.75	3,166.22
11	70,186.40	2,136.48	1,029.74	3,166.22
12	69,125.77	2,105.59	1,060.63	3,166.22
13	68,033.32	2,073.77	1,092.45	3,166.22
14	66,908.10	2,041.00	1,125.22	3,166.22
15	65,749.13	2,007.24	1,158.98	3,166.22
16	64,555.38	1,972.47	1,193.75	3,166.22
17	63,325.81	1,936.66	1,229.56	3,166.22
18	62,059.36	1,899.77	1,266.45	3,166.22
19	60,754.92	1,861.78	1,304.44	3,166.22
20	59,411.35	1,822.65	1,343.57	3,166.22
21	58,027.46	1,782.34	1,383.88	3,166.22
22	56,602.07	1,740.82	1,425.40	3,166.22
23	55,133.91	1,698.06	1,468.16	3,166.22
24	53,621.70	1,654.02	1,512.20	3,166.22
25	52,064.13	1,608.65	1,557.57	3,166.22
26	50,459.84	1,561.92	1,604.30	3,166.22
27	48,807.41	1,513.80	1,652.43	3,166.22
28	47,105.41	1,464.22	1,702.00	3,166.22
29	45,352.35	1,413.16	1,753.06	3,166.22
30	43,546.70	1,360.57	1,805.65	3,166.22
31	41,686.88	1,306.40	1,859.82	3,166.22
32	39,771.26	1,250.61	1,915.62	3,166.22
33	37,798.18	1,193.14	1,973.08	3,166.22
34	35,765.90	1,133.95	2,032.28	3,166.22
35	33,672.65	1,072.98	2,093.25	3,166.22
36	31,516.61	1,010.18	2,156.04	3,166.22
37	29,295.89	945.50	2,220.72	3,166.22
38	27,008.54	878.88	2,287.35	3,166.22
39	24,652.57	810.26	2,355.97	3,166.22
40	22,225.93	739.58	2,426.64	3,166.22

TABLE 4.3 *(Continued)*

End of period	Capital not recovered by end of period, $	Interest due on unrecovered capital, $	Amount of capital recovered, $	Period capital recovery charge, $
41	19,726.49	666.78	2,499.44	3,166.22
42	17,152.06	591.79	2,574.43	3,166.22
43	14,500.40	514.56	2,651.66	3,166.22
44	11,769.19	435.01	2,731.21	3,166.22
45	8,956.04	353.08	2,813.15	3,166.22
46	6,058.50	268.68	2,897.54	3,166.22
47	3,074.03	181.76	2,984.47	3,166.22
48	0.03	92.22	3,074.00	3,166.22
		71,978.70	79,999.98	151,978.58

Table 4.4 on page 152 shows the effect of doubling the quarterly payment. The total amount of interest paid is reduced by 69 percent ($71,979 to $22,075). The total amount of payments has the same absolute reduction, from $151,978 to $102,075, for a 49 percent reduction. The payout period is reduced from 48 to 17 time periods, a healthy decrease. So, if your interest rates are high and it is not feasible to refinance to a lower rate, the possibility of increasing the period payment might be beneficial.

The computer program CHEER will compute loan analyses, such as we have just seen. Just click Project on the main screen and then click Loan Analysis and insert the required data.

4.1.2 Capital Recovery Calculations

As indicated in Table 4.1, the sum of the four annuity payments is $50,475, of which $10,475 is interest. This tabular format, as was seen, can be used to trace the capital recovery. When only the amount of unrecovered capital at a certain time is sought, it can be determined directly from the present worth of the remaining payments:

$$\text{Unrecovered capital (year 3)} = A(P/A, \ 10, \ 1)$$
$$= \$12,618.83(0.90909) = \$11,471.65$$

$$\text{Unrecovered capital (year 2)} = A(P/A, \ 10, \ 2)$$
$$= \$12,618.83(1.73554) = \$21,900.48$$

$$\text{Recovered capital (by year 3)} = \$40,000 - \$11,471.65 = \$28,528.35$$

$$\text{Interest due (year 4)} = \$12,618.83 - \$11,471.65 = \$1147.18$$

$$\text{Recovered capital (by year 2)} = \$40,000 - \$21,900.48 = \$18,099.52$$

$$\text{Interest due (years 3 and 4)} = 2(\$12,618.83) - \$21,900.48$$
$$= \$3337.18$$

that the equivalent value of negative cash flow for disbursements is greater than the corresponding positive flow of receipts. Negative worths usually mean that an alternative is unacceptable. Exceptions occur when projects must be undertaken to satisfy certain requirements such as safety citations or building codes, or when a "do nothing" option is not viable. Then the objective is to identify the alternative with the least equivalent annual cost (negative cash flow). We will use the term *equivalent annual cost (EAC)* to designate comparisons involving only costs, and we will use the term *equivalent annual worth (EAW)* when costs and incomes (benefits) are both present.

It is often very difficult, and not worth the required study time, to discover the income derived from only one component in a complex system having many different components. For instance, the income produced by a copying machine is troublesome to derive exactly since its output is utilized by many people, often from different departments, working on many projects. In this type of situation, alternatives to satisfy the copying needs are evaluated on the basis of their relative costs, because each alternative capable of meeting the requirements of the system will produce the same income to the system. When it is apparent that only costs are involved in an evaluation, it is convenient to ignore the minus sign convention and let comparison figures represent the absolute value of costs. Several situations for applying equivalent annual-worth calculations are described in the examples that follow.

4.2.1 Consolidation of Cash Flows

What's it worth? is the decisive query in the appraisal of a proposal. It is difficult to ascertain what to expect from a proposal until the myriad receipts and disbursements associated with its conduct are collectively analyzed. Improvement programs are prime examples. Organizations regularly engage in programs to improve productivity, reduce accidents, raise quality, etc. Each is a worthwhile goal, expected to have positive rewards, but each has costs, too. Consolidating the various costs into a pattern that can be compared with potential rewards may take the form of a net annuity.

EXAMPLE 4.1

Equivalent Monthly Net Worth of Cash Flows

A consulting firm proposes to provide "self-inspection" training for clerks who work with insurance claims. The program lasts 1 year, costs $2000 per month, and professes to improve quality while reducing clerical time. A potential user of the program estimates that savings in the first month should amount to $800 and should increase by $400 per month for the rest of the year. However, operational confusion and work interference are expected to boost clerical costs by $1200 the first month, but this amount should subsequently decline in equal increments at the rate of $100 per month. If the required return on money is 12 percent compounded monthly and there is a stipulation that the program must pay for itself within 1 year, should the consultants be hired?

Solution

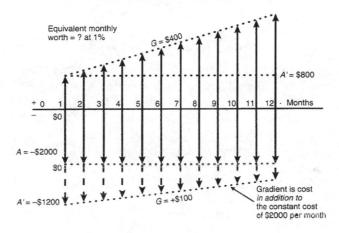

$$i = \frac{r}{m} = \frac{0.12}{12} = 0.01 \text{ per period}$$

$N = 12$ periods

Equivalent monthly worth = $800 + $400(A/G, 1, 12)
    of savings = $800 + $400(5.36815) = $2947

Equivalent monthly worth = -$2000 - [$1200 - $100(A/G, 1, 12)]
    of costs = -$3200 + $100(5.36815) = -$2663

Equivalent net monthly = $2947 - $2663 = $284
    cash flow

The program looks very promising because the equivalent monthly worth is positive during the first year, and savings generated by the training should continue into the future.

Gradient factors were utilized in Example 4.1 to convert uniformly varying cash flows to their equivalent constant worths. Recovery of capital is not an issue, since no property ownership is involved. The comparison is made directly on the basis of expected income versus outgo.

4.2.2 Recovery of Invested Capital

Will it pay off? is the question investors want answered. An adequate pay-off recovers the invested capital plus the desired rate of return. Since returns are spread over the life of the investment, it is convenient to convert capital recovery costs to the same annual pattern. The consequential result of combining uniform cost and revenue flows is a *positive, zero,* or *negative* series of payments that, respectively, categorizes the investment as gratifying, adequate, or insufficient.

EXAMPLE 4.2

Net Annual Worth of a Single Project

The purchase of a truck with an operator's platform on a telescoping hydraulic boom will reduce labor costs for sign installations by $15,000 per year. The price of the boom truck is $93,000, and its operating costs will exceed those of present equipment by $250 per month. The resale (salvage) value is expected to be $18,000 in 8 years. Should the boom truck be purchased when the current available interest rate is 7 percent?

Solution

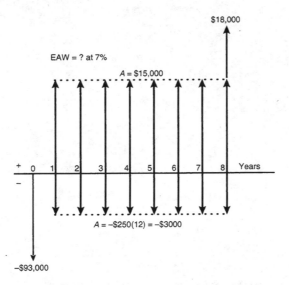

$$\text{EAW} = -\$93,000(A/P, 7, 8) + \$18,000(A/F, 7, 8) - \$3000 + \$15,000$$
$$= -\$93,000(0.16747) + \$18,000(0.09747) + \$12,000$$
$$= -\$1820$$

Equivalent annual-worth calculations indicate that the purchase and use of the boom truck will cause a loss equivalent to $1820 per year for 8 years, compared with other investments that could earn a 7 percent return.

The solution to Example 4.2 was developed from the accompanying cash flow diagram. The capital recovery factor leads to the same solution when capital recovery costs are registered negatively and the net annual savings are positive:

EAW = annual savings – capital recovery costs
   = $15,000 – $3000 – [(P – S)(A/P, 7, 8) + Si]
   = $12,000 – [($93,000 – $18,000)(0.16747) + $18,000(0.07)]
   = $12,000 – ($12,560 + $1260) = –$1820

4.2.3 Net Cash Flow Comparison

A third question is, Which one is better? If the criterion is strictly economics, the alternative with the highest net worth is preferred, if worth is measured by revenues; but when alternatives have only costs and no income, a low EAC is preferred.

EXAMPLE 4.3   **Comparison of Net Annual Worths**

A supplier of laboratory equipment estimates that profit from sales should increase by $20,000 per year if a mobile demonstration unit is built. A large unit with sleeping accommodations for the driver will cost $97,000, while a smaller unit without sleeping quarters will be $63,000. Salvage values for the large and small units after 5 years of use will be, respectively, $9700 and $3500. Lodging costs saved by the larger unit should amount to $11,000 annually, but its yearly transportation costs will exceed those of the smaller unit by $3100. With money at 9 percent, should a mobile demonstration unit be built? And if so, which size is preferable?

Solution

EAW of the large mobile demonstration unit:

Annual increase in profit	$20,000
Savings in lodging costs over smaller unit per year	11,000
Extra transportation costs over smaller unit per year	–3,100
Capital recovery cost:	
($97,000 – $9700)(A/P, 9, 5) + $9700i = $87,300(0.25709)	
+ $9700(0.09)	–23,317
Net AW =	$4,583

EAW of small mobile demonstration unit:

Annual increase in profit	$20,000
Capital recovery cost	
($63,000 – $3500)(A/P, 9, 5) + $3500i = $59,500(0.25709)	–15,612
+ $3500(0.09)	
Net AW =	$4,388

(b) Silo filtration:

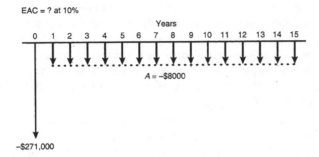

EAC = ? at 10%

Years

0 1 2 3 4 5 6 7 8 9 10 11 12 13 14 15

$A = -\$8000$

$-\$271,000$

$$EAC = \$271,000(A/P,\ 10,\ 15) + \$8000$$
$$= \$271,000(0.13147) + \$8000$$
$$= \$35,628 + \$8000 = \$43,628$$

(c) Upgrade kilns:

$$EAC = (\$380,000 + \$43,000)(A/P,\ 10,\ 15)$$
$$= \$423,000(0.13147) = \$55,612$$

In priority order, the equivalent annual costs show that putting filtration equipment on the silos is the lowest cost, upgrading the kilns is next, and enclosing the conveyors has the highest cost.

This problem would be ideal for an evaluation by a technique called *benefit/cost (B/C) analysis,* a topic covered in Chap. 8. Benefits will be a measure of pollution reduction, and maximizing the ratio of pollution reduction over cost to get that reduction seems to be more appropriate than just picking one alternative based on cost alone, since not all alternatives will reduce pollution by the same amount.

For Example 4.4, if the manager decided to make the analysis on a present-worth basis, all that has to be done is to multiply each of the alternative EAC values by $(P/A,\ 10,\ 15)$. For part (a),

Net present worth = ($60,268)(7.60608) = $458,403

For part (b),

Net present worth = $43,628(7.60608) = $331,838

For part (c),

Net present worth = $55,612(7.60608) = $422,989

4.3   CONSIDERATION OF ASSET LIFE

Translating cash flows to equivalent annuities is a mechanical process that becomes almost automatic with practice. Understanding the meaning of an economic comparison and being able to explain its significance to others are the critical skills. The discussion of economic asset life, as introduced in Chap. 3, is continued in this section to stress the importance of selecting an appropriate study period in EAW comparisons.

4.3.1   Definitions of Asset Life

In time-value mechanics, N is simply the number of compounding periods appropriate for the analysis of cash flows. And N takes on a special meaning when it represents the life of an asset that loses value as a function of use or time. The more frequently applied terms to describe the life of an asset are listed and defined as follows:

* *Ownership life* or *service life* is the period of time an asset is kept in service by the owner(s). Implied is a period of useful service from the time of purchase until disposal. Actually, under the vague expectation that it might somehow again prove useful, equipment is often retained beyond the point where it is capable of satisfying its intended function. A machine can have a physical life longer than its service life; the machine is still physically sound, but there is no useful function for it to perform.
* *Accounting life* is a life expectancy based primarily on bookkeeping and tax considerations. It may or may not correspond to the period of usefulness and economic desirability.
* *Economic life* is the time period that minimizes the asset's total equivalent annual cost or maximizes its equivalent net annual income. At the end of this period, the asset would be displaced by a more profitable replacement if service were still required. Economic life is also referred to as the *optimal replacement interval* and is the condition appropriate for many engineering economic studies.

Land is not subject to a specified life or to capital recovery, because it historically appreciates in value rather than depreciates with age. The cost of land ownership is the interest not received on funds invested in the property. As Mark Twain advised, "Buy land, they're not making it anymore."

4.3.2   Comparisons of Assets with Equal and Unequal Lives

Examples 4.5 and 4.6 are typical applications of EAC comparisons. The lease-or-buy question posed in Example 4.5 is raised with increasing regularity that corresponds to the rapid growth of leasing companies. It is now possible to lease almost any type of production equipment that is not custom-designed for narrowly specialized service. Important tax and inflation considerations involved in the lease-or-buy choice are discussed in Chap. 10.

EXAMPLE 4.5

Alternatives with Equal Annual Costs

A machine needed for 3 years can be purchased for $77,662 and sold at the end of the period for about $25,000. A comparable machine can be leased for $30,000 per year. If a firm expects a return of 20 percent on investments, should it buy or lease the machine when end-of-year payments are expected?

Solution

$$
\begin{aligned}
\text{Equivalent annual cost to buy} &= (\$77,662 - \$25,000)(A/P,\ 20,\ 3) \\
&\quad + \$25,000(0.20) \\
&= \$52,662(0.47473) + \$5000 \\
&= \$30,000
\end{aligned}
$$

$$\text{Annual cost to lease} = \$30,000$$

Since the results are the same for both leasing and buying, the decision will likely be affected by the existence or absence of other projects in need of funding. If there are none, then the $77,662 investment in the machine will return 20 percent, assuming that the salvage value estimates are reasonable.

The two alternatives in Example 4.5 are compared on the basis of their costs because the income resulting from their contribution is not available and it is believed that both are capable of producing that contribution. The question is not whether to get a machine. It is known that the machine is necessary, so the choice is to buy or lease it. In selecting between the alternatives with equal equivalent annual worths, recall that they are equal only after ownership of the machine has earned 20 percent on the capital invested in it.

EXAMPLE 4.6

Comparison of Assets with Unequal Lives

Two models of small machines perform the same function. Type 1 machine has a low initial cost of $9500, relatively high operating costs of $1900 per year more than those of the type 2 machine, and a short life of 4 years. The more expensive, type 2 machine costs $25,100 and can be kept in service economically for 8 years. The scrap value from either machine at the end of its life will barely cover its removal cost. Which is preferred when the minimum attractive rate of return is 8 percent?

Solution

Type 1 machine:

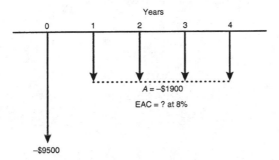

$$\text{EAC}_{\text{type 1}} = \$1900 + \$9500(A/P, 8, 4)$$
$$= \$1900 + \$9500(0.30192) = \$4768$$

Type 2 machine:

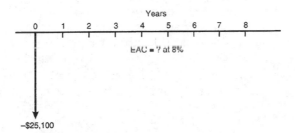

$$\text{EAC}_{\text{type 2}} = \$25,100(A/P, 8, 8) = \$25,100(0.17401) = \$4368$$

The type 2 machine has a lower annual cost for service during the next 8 years and is therefore preferred.

The machines described in Example 4.6 exhibit the common feature that more expensive models, designed to serve the same function as less expensive versions, are expected to operate more economically and/or last longer. (If a costlier machine also produces better-quality products, the benefits from improved quality must be included in the analysis to make the outcomes comparable.) The difficulty in comparing alternatives with unequal lives lies in accounting for the service provided during the period in which one outlasts the other.

The implied assumption in the solution to Example 4.6 is that two machines of type 1 will be purchased consecutively to provide the same length of service as one type 2 machine. The equivalent annual cost for 8 years of service from two type 1 machines is, of course, the same as calculated in the solution above:

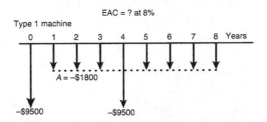

$$\begin{aligned} \text{EAC}_{\text{type 1}} &= \$9500(A/P, 8, 8) + \$9500(P/F, 8, 4)(A/P, 8, 8) + \$1900 \\ &= \$9500(0.17401) + \$9500(0.73503)(0.17401) + \$1900 \\ &= \$1653 + \$1215 + \$1900 = \$4768 \end{aligned}$$

which is the same as calculated earlier.

The repeated-projects assumption for evaluating assets with different lives is fairly reasonable and widely used. Unless reliable forecasts can be made about future operating conditions and the probability of technical advances, the assumption that today's conditions will exist in the future is plausible. With regard to possible inflationary effects on future costs, recall that in Chap. 3 we stated that we will assume that cash flows have had their actual dollars converted to constant dollars by using

$$\text{Constant dollars} = \text{actual dollars}\left[\frac{1}{(1 + f)^k}\right]$$

where f is the annual inflation rate as a fraction and k is the number of years into the future that the estimated cash transaction takes place, $k = 1, 2, \ldots, N$.

When *future* conditions can be estimated with confidence, excluding inflation, since we are working with constant dollars, these valuations are the data that should be used for equivalent annual-worth calculations. For instance, a confident prediction that current developmental work on the type 1 machine will produce refinements within 4 years to reduce operating costs to $400 above those of the type 2 machine while increasing the purchase price to $11,500 leads to a revised economic analysis:

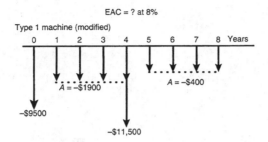

The annual worth is calculated by (1) translating the cash flow in the last 4 years to a present value at year 4 and discounting this value to year 0; (2) computing the present value of the first 4 years' cash flow; (3) adding the two present worths; and (4) converting the total to an 8-year annuity:

$$\begin{aligned} EAC_{\text{type 1 mod}} &= \{[\$400(P/A, 8, 4) + \$11,500] \; (P/F, 8, 4) \\ &\quad + \$1900(P/A, 8, 4) + \$9500\} \; (A/P, 8, 8) \\ &= \{[\$400(3.31213) + \$11,500] \; (0.73503) \\ &\quad + \$1900(3.31213) + \$9500\} \; (0.17401) \\ &= (\$9427 + \$15,793)(0.17401) = \$4389 \end{aligned}$$

The modified type 1 machine now has nearly the same equivalent annual cost as the type 2 model. If a decision maker has confidence in the forecasted data, the choice between types can go either way; but it will more likely swing to type 1 because the lower purchase price and shorter life mean that less capital is committed for a shorter period. This conservative philosophy provides some protection from unexpected developments. It was assumed in the comparison that the need for the machine would exist for 8 years. Many things can happen in 8 years to thwart the most carefully conceived plans: new designs, changing markets, successful competition, etc. The opportunity to reevaluate tactics in 4 years, as is possible with the type 1 machine, is a subtle but valued attribute.

4.3.3 Perpetual Life

Occasionally an asset is treated as if it will last forever. The assumption of infinite life in terms of capital recovery is slightly more reasonable than the physical interpretation. Nothing made by humans, even Egyptian pyramids or the Great Wall of China, lasts forever; but the difference between infinity and 100 years in the numerical value of the capital recovery factor is quite small:

$$(A/P, i, N) = \frac{i(1 + i)^N}{(1 + i)^N - 1}$$

And as N gets very large,

$$[(1 + i)^N - 1] \rightarrow (1 + i)^N$$

The limit of the capital recovery factor as N approaches infinity is

$$(A/P,\ i,\ N)_{N \rightarrow \infty} = i$$

Therefore, in an economic comparison involving an asset with an infinite life, *such as land,* the interest rate replaces the capital recovery factor. The human-made assets most closely approaching perpetual life are dams, tunnels, canals, aqueducts, and monuments. The nature of very-long-lived assets relegates them mostly to public projects, and there the trend has been to set a study period of 50 years or so in recognition of changing public needs and technological advances that generate new ways to fulfill the needs.

The similarity between the perpetual-life assumption for calculating equivalent annual worth and the capitalized cost method associated with present-worth models should be apparent. Both assume infinite life and therefore have very limited application. Note that the difference between capital recovery factors for $N = 50$ and $N = \infty$ is less than 1 percent for $i = 10$ percent and less than 10 percent for $i = 5$ percent; computations for "engineering estimates" are still possible.

4.4   USE OF A SINKING FUND

The sinking fund factor $(A/F,\ i,\ N)$ was discussed previously as an alternative means of calculating capital recovery costs:

$$(P - S)(A/P,\ i,\ N) + Si = P(A/P,\ i,\ N) - S(A/F,\ i,\ N)$$

As is clear in the equation, the sinking fund factor is applied to compute the annuity required to accumulate a certain future amount. Organizations are sometimes obligated by legislated or contractual agreements to establish a fund, separate from their internal operations, to accumulate a specified amount by a specified time. This accumulation is called a *sinking fund.*

Provision for a sinking fund requires that an organization set aside a portion of the income derived from sales or taxes each year in order to retire a bond issue (or, in some cases, an issue of preferred stock). Failure to meet the sinking fund payments forces the bond issue to be thrown into default, causing serious credit and credibility problems. The payments are a direct cash drain on the organization. That is the purpose of the sinking fund—to protect investors by enforcing an orderly retirement of debt from current income.

A debt can be retired by regular payments from the sinking fund or by letting money accumulate in the sinking fund until the debt is due and then paying it in full (plus interest). Periodic payments are associated with *callable bonds*. A call provision in a bond gives the issuing organization the right to pay off a bond before its maturity date. Funds reserved from income are allocated each year to retire a portion of the bond issue. Sinking fund payments thus utilized earn at the rate at which interest payments are avoided on the bonds retired.

When a sinking fund is established to accumulate sufficient money to meet the bond cost at maturity, annual payments are normally required to be invested in a savings institution. The interest rate for these "savings" typically is lower than the organization earns on its own capital, but the sinking fund is less an earning device than a way to ensure that funds will not be diverted to other ventures.

For example, a firm borrows $1 million at 9 percent simple interest because it believes that the amount borrowed can be utilized within the firm to earn 18 percent—double the borrowing rate. If $1 million is acquired by issuing 20-year bonds with the stipulation that a sinking fund is to be set up, the firm has to set aside a payment each year and put it in an external account. This account probably earns less than the 18 percent internally earned on investment funds, but it represents a very secure investment. Assuming that the account pays 6 percent annually compounded interest, we find that the annual payments into the sinking fund would be

$$A = \$1,000,000(A/F, 6, 20)$$
$$= \$1,000,000(0.02718) = \$27,180$$

to make total annual debt repayment on the principal plus interest of $27,180 + $1,000,000(0.09) = $117,180.

4.5

EQUIVALENT UNIFORM PAYMENTS WHEN INTEREST RATES VARY

Interest rates have fluctuated widely in recent years as a response to different degrees of inflation. Rates also vary according to the type and size of investment; larger investments are often awarded higher interest rates, and riskier investments demand higher returns. It is therefore occasionally appropriate to assign different interest rates to specific periods of cash flow.

Present and future worths of cash flows with changing interest rates are calculated by translating each transaction backward or forward in time according to the prevailing interest rate in each period of the transaction. For example, assume that a deposit of $5000 was made 4 years ago and a withdrawal of $2000 was made 2 years ago. The prevailing interest rate during the first year was 6 percent, and the rate was increased by 1 per-

TABLE 4.5

Calculation of future worth with varying interest rates

End of year	Deposit or withdrawal, $	i during year, %	Balance in account at end of year, $
0	+5000		
1		6	5000(F/P, 6, 1) = 5300
2	−2000	7	5300(F/P, 7, 1) − 2000 = 3671
3		8	3671(F/P, 8, 1) = 3965
4		9	3965(F/P, 9, 1) = 4321.50

cent each year. The amount in the account at the end of each year is shown in Table 4.5.

By the same approach, the present worth (PW) at time 0 of the cash flow is

$$PW = \$5000 - \$2000(P/F, 6, 1)(P/F, 7, 1) = \$3236.63$$

A uniform series of four payments equivalent to the given cash flow with changing interest rates is calculated as

$$PW = A(P/F, 6, 1) + A(P/F, 6, 1)(P/F, 7, 1) + A(P/F, 6, 1)(P/F, 7, 1) \times$$
$$(P/F, 8, 1) + A(P/F, 6, 1)(P/F, 7, 1)(P/F, 8, 1)(P/F, 9, 1)$$

Using the present worth of the cash flow calculated earlier, we find that

$$\$3236.63 = A[0.94340 + 0.94340(0.93458) + 0.94340(0.93458)(0.92593)$$
$$+ 0.94349(0.93458)(0.92593)(0.91743)]$$
$$= A(3.3904)$$

and

$$A = \frac{\$3236.63}{3.3904} = \$954.65$$

A corresponding calculation of a series of equal payments A from the future worth (FW) is

$$FW = A + A(F/P, 9, 1) + A(F/P, 8, 1)(F/P, 9, 1) + (F/P, 7, 1)$$
$$\times (F/P, 8, 1)(F/P, 9, 1)$$

which gives

$$A = \frac{\$4321.50}{1 + 1.09 + 1.08(1.09) + 1.07(1.08)(1.09)}$$
$$= \frac{\$4321.50}{4.5268}$$
$$= \$954.65$$

Thus, four year-end payments of $954.65 yield a future amount of $4321.50 when interest rates progress from 6 to 7 to 8 to 9 percent during the 4-year span, and the worth of this annuity is equivalent to a cash inflow of $5000 at time 0 and an outflow of –$2000 at the end of year 2.

4.6 ANNUITY CONTRACT FOR A GUARANTEED INCOME

To conclude this material on equivalent periodic analysis, we might do well to briefly talk about annuity contracts since all of us, sometime in the future, would probably like to retire with a guaranteed income. Annuities are often associated with retirement plans. In this context, an annuity implies a payment received each year according to a purchased contract. In practice, annuity payments are more likely to be made monthly to the receiver, or *annuitant*.

An annuity contract is essentially the reverse of a life insurance policy. In the latter, an insurance company pays a stipulated sum to heirs based on the amount of payments made during the policyholder's lifetime. In the classical annuity situation, an individual pays a stipulated sum, or number of payments, to a company and then receives regular income payments, starting at a designated date and continuing for life. Annuities of this form were used very early in recorded history; mortality tables for computing their values were compiled by Romans and have been found in Egypt and Babylon.

A vast variety of annuity contracts are available. A straight-life annuity is the classic pattern: Income payments terminate with the death of the annuitant. Since many people are reluctant to purchase such an annuity because they fear that they will die prematurely, causing their investment in the annuity to be wasted, companies offer plans that guarantee a refund to heirs under specified conditions, such as an unusually early death. Annuities may have variable rates that are linked to inflation indexes, gold prices, or foreign currencies. The purpose of indexing is to conserve the buying power of annuity income. As with any investment, the annuity buyer must balance risks against returns.

4.7   REVIEW EXERCISES AND DISCUSSIONS

EXERCISE 1

A hospital purchases a new piece of ultrasound equipment for $60,000. The hospital expects to use it for 4 years and then sell it to a small clinic for $20,000. Thus, the salvage value is expected to be $20,000. If the interest rate is 10 percent, develop a table that shows, by year, capital not recovered, interest due, capital recovered, and the annual capital recovery (ACR) charge. The observant reader will note that these are the same data evaluated in Table 4.1 with the first cost and salvage value both being $20,000 higher in this exercise; the total capital to be recovered is the same in both cases—$40,000.

SOLUTION 1

As we found in Sec. 4.1.2,

$$\text{EAC} = (P - S)(A/P, i, N) + Si$$
$$= (\$60,000 - \$20,000)(A/P, 10, 4) + \$20,000(0.1)$$
$$= \$40,000(0.31547) + \$2000 = \$14,619$$

The tabular computations, all in dollars, now mirror those we did to generate Table 4.1:

End of year	Capital not recovered	Interest due on unrecovered capital	Amount of capital recovered	Annual capital recovery charge (ACR)	Interest on unrecovered salvage (Si)	Total equivalent annual cost (Si + ACR)
0	60,000					
1	51,381	6,000	8,619	12,619	2,000	14,619
2	41,900	5,138	9,481	12,619	2,000	14,619
3	31,471	4,190	10,429	12,619	2,000	14,619
4	20,000	3,147	11,471	12,619	2,000	14,619
		18,475	40,000	50,476	8,000	58,476

For convenience, the tabular values of total annual cost given above have been separated into the annual capital recovery charge (which is exactly the same as when we had no salvage value in Table 4.1) and the $2000 per year that is locked into the expected salvage value. The reader must realize that we have, in effect, a loan of $60,000; the salvage value is not realized until after all payments have been made. Compared with the situation given in Table 4.1, we have $2000 additional per payment to cover the annual charge for the capital locked in the salvage value; $Si = \$20,000(0.1)$. We therefore have $8000 in total additional interest payments compared to the case in Table 4.1. Logically, the total annual cost will also increase by the same $2000.

When the time comes to recover the salvage value, we will probably find that the salvage value is a function of what the "market will bear" or pay. Sometimes, a contractual agreement with a vendor might specify exactly what the salvage value will be, possibly as a down payment on a replacement piece of equipment. Frequently, there is a measure of uncertainty in salvage values.

EXERCISE 2
An asset was purchased 5 years ago for $52,000. It was expected to have an economic life of 8 years, at which time its salvage value would be $4000. If the function that the asset was serving is no longer needed, for what price must it be sold now to recover the invested capital when $i = 12$ percent?

SOLUTION 2
The expected annual cost of the asset over its 8-year life was

$$\begin{aligned} \text{EAC} &= (P - S)(A/P,\ 12,\ 8) + S(0.12) \\ &= (\$52,000 - \$4000)(0.20130) + \$4000(0.12) \\ &= \$48,000(0.20130) + \$480 = \$10,142.40 \end{aligned}$$

The unrecovered capital at the end of the fifth year is the present worth of the last 3 years of the EAC annuity plus the discounted salvage value:

$$\begin{aligned} \text{Unrecovered capital (year 5)} &= \$10,142.40(P/A,\ 12,\ 3) + \$4000(P/F,\ 12,\ 3) \\ &= \$10,142.40(2.40188) + \$4000(0.71178) \\ &= \$24,361 + \$2847 = \$27,208 \end{aligned}$$

An alternative solution method provides the same result:

$$\begin{aligned} \text{Selling price (year 5)} &= \$48,000(A/P,\ 12,\ 8)(P/A,\ 12,\ 3) + \$4000 \\ &= \$23,208 + \$4000 = \$27,208 \end{aligned}$$

This sum is a possible price. Realistically, the market value for similar equipment at a similar stage in the asset's life will probably be a more reasonable estimate.

EXERCISE 3
A city maintenance crew has had experience with a conventional backhoe that suggests that its service life is 6 years. A newly designed machine costs 50 percent more than the conventional machine but is quieter in operation, which will make it more adaptable to residential neighborhoods. Both machines will have about the same operating costs, and salvage costs are expected to be negligible. What will the service life of the new backhoe have to be to make its cost comparable to that of the conventional machine at $i = 10$ percent?

SOLUTION 3
Since the machines will apparently have different lives, it is logical to attack the problem by using an annual-worth evaluation, assuming that replacement costs will be comparable to current costs.

First, we equate the two machines' annual worths:

$$\text{AW}_{\text{conv}} = \text{AW}_{\text{new}}$$

$$P_{\text{conv}}(A/P,\ 10,\ 6) = P_{\text{new}}(A/P,\ 10,\ N)$$

But we know that $P_{new} = 1.5 P_{conv}$; therefore,

$$P_{conv}(A/P, 10, 6) = 1.5 P_{conv} (A/P, 10, N)$$

Solving for $(A/P, 10, N)$, we get

$$\frac{1}{1.5} (A/P, 10, 6) = (A/P, 10, N)$$

$$0.667 (0.22961) = 0.1532 = (A/P, 10, N)$$

Interpolating in the tables, we find that N lies between 11 and 12 years:

$$N = 11 + \frac{0.15396 - 0.1532}{0.15396 - 0.14676}$$
$$= 11.1 \text{ years}$$

The life would have to be about double that of the conventional machine to justify the additional cost. A life of 12 years might be a lot to expect from such equipment. Possibly, the noise abatement might help justify the new equipment, especially if a worth could be assigned to it in terms of dollars. We discuss such decision theory types of problems in Chap. 15.

EXERCISE 4

In Example 3.4, we looked at a comparison of alternatives with unequal economic lives for a present-worth analysis. Specifically, we had assets A_1 and A_2. Asset A_2 has an initial cost of $3200 and an expected salvage value of $400 at the end of its expected 4-year life. Asset A_1 costs $900 less than A_2, has an economic life of 3 years, and has no salvage value; and its annual operating costs exceed those of A_2 by $250. The required rate of return is 15 percent. Example 3.4 asked for a PW determination of the better alternative by the repeated-projects method. This problem can be solved more efficiently by using an annual-worth comparison.

SOLUTION 4

$$\begin{aligned} AW_{A_1} &= -\$250 - \$2300(A/P, 15, 3) \\ &= -\$250 - \$2300(0.43798) = -\$1257 \end{aligned}$$

$$\begin{aligned} AW_{A_2} &= -\$3200(A/P, 15, 4) + \$400(A/F, 15, 4) \\ &= -\$3200(0.35027) + \$400(0.20027) = -\$1041 \end{aligned}$$

This says that A_2 has the lower equivalent *annual worth* and so should probably be chosen. Only three factors had to be looked up. The present-worth solution in Example 3.4 required six factors to be applied (one was applied twice), which gave a greater chance for error. If we really wanted a present-worth analysis, then each of the two solutions just found would be multiplied by $(P/A, 15, 12)$, since 12 is the common denominator for the two lives:

$$\text{PW}_{A_1} = -\$1257(5.42062) = -\$6816$$

$$\text{PW}_{A_2} = -\$1041(5.42062) = -\$5642$$

These are the same results we obtained in Chap. 3.

EXERCISE 5

A short concrete canal can be constructed as part of a flood control project; the placement of a large galvanized culvert will serve the some function. The cost of the canal, which will last indefinitely, is $75,000; and maintenance costs will average $400 per year. A culvert, which will have to be replaced every 30 years, will cost $40,000 and have an annual maintenance cost of $700. Salvage values are negligible for both alternatives, and the government interest rate is 6 percent. Which alternative has the lower equivalent annual cost?

SOLUTION 5

Annual-cost comparison of a canal with perpetual life and a culvert with an economic life of 30 years:

Canal

Annual maintenance	$400
Interest on investment − $75,000(0.06)	4500
Equivalent annual cost	$4900

Culvert

Annual maintenance	$700
Capital recovery = $40,000 $(A/P, 6, 30)$	
$\quad\quad\quad = \$40,000(0.07265)$	2906
Equivalent annual cost	$3606

The culvert has the advantage of a lower equivalent annual cost.

EXERCISE 6

Exercise 4 in Chap. 3 had data on a possible improvement. The exercise asked that CHEER be used to find the present worth of the alternative action. Use that same CHEER output to determine the EAW of the alternative, and verify that this is correct from the PW result.

SOLUTION 6

The CHEER summary output from the earlier exercise is repeated in Fig. 4.1. In addition to the original PW value, we can read the value of EAW directly: $7058.22. Using the original PW value, we can verify the EAW value:

$$\begin{aligned} \text{EAW} &= \text{PW}(A/P, 10, 5) \\ &= \$26,756.22(0.26380) = \$7058 \end{aligned}$$

which checks with the CHEER result.

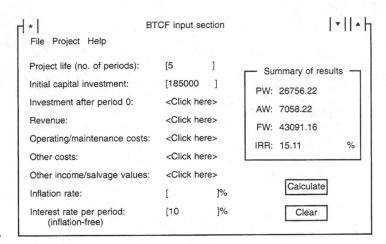

FIGURE 4.1
CHEER screen for finding annual worth.

4.8 PROBLEMS

4.1 You apply to your local bank for a loan of $15,000. The prevailing annual interest rate is 8 percent, and you are to pay off the loan in five equal end-of-year payments. Determine the total interest that you will pay over the 5-year period.

4.2 For the situation given in Prob. 4.1, calculate directly the recovered principal (capital) by the end of year 3.

4.3 A large gasoline station is required by the city to install vapor containment equipment on its gasoline pump nozzles and storage tank vents. The immediate conversion cost will be $180,000 with an estimated $600 per year for maintenance. It will be necessary to update the equipment every 3 years at a cost of $3500. The station pumps an average of 1 million gallons (3,785,400 liters) of gasoline per month. On an annual basis, what would be the price increase per gallon (liter) necessary to pay for the conversion over a 6-year period? Include the sixth year's update cost in your analysis, and assume an interest rate of 14 percent.

4.4 A grocery chain of four stores is evaluating whether to install video screens on all its grocery carts. These screens will display pricing and "specials" as the cart goes by the pertinent items. Cart location is sensed by ceiling sensors that trigger the appropriate information for the particular screen. The first cost of the equipment is $65,000 per store. Annual programming and screen information would be subcontracted at a total cost of $25,000 per year for the four stores. Because of the novelty, sales are expected to increase by $28,000 per store in the first year and then drop at a rate of $4500 per store per year for each subsequent year, that is, $28,000, $23,500, . . . , $10,000. The technological life of the system is 5 years. If a 12 percent return on investment is required, determine the minimum salvage value of the equipment that would be needed after the 5-year period, basing your analysis on the equivalent annual net worth of the project. Evaluate the result.

4.5 A company owns several gasoline stations in a major city. It is decided that a major television advertising campaign will greatly improve income. Initial development costs for the advertisements will be $120,000. Monthly television airing costs are quoted at $35,000 for the first month, decreasing by $500 per month thereafter during the period in which the ads will run, which is 18 months. Revenues are expected to increase by $40,000 in the first month and increase by $700 per month thereafter for 11 months more. The last 6 months of the study are expected to see a linear decline of $300 per month from the peak increase. Determine whether the campaign will be economically viable, using an equivalent monthly worth analysis. Assume a nominal annual interest rate of 12 percent with monthly compounding.

4.6 Megabitt Electronics is considering the purchase of a new programmable circuit tester in order to improve its product quality. The equipment has a first cost of $85,000, and the salvage value is predicted to be $6000 after a service life of 5 years. Maintenance and operating costs are expected to be $8000 the first year of operation and to increase by $1500 per year for each additional year of use. Using an interest rate of 10 percent, determine what annual savings must be obtained through the use of this equipment to make it economically justifiable.

4.7 A standby electric power generator was purchased 6 years ago for $8000. At that time it was expected that the equipment would be used for 15 years and would have a salvage value of 10 percent of the first cost. The generator is no longer needed and is to be sold for $2500. Using an interest rate of 15 percent, determine the difference between the anticipated and actual equivalent annual capital costs.

4.8 Granite Rock and Gravel Company is considering the feasibility of purchasing a piece of land for a small quarrying operation. The following cost estimates have been developed for evaluating the venture:

Cost of land	$2,000,000
Site clearing and road preparation	200,000
Annual operating costs:	
First year	400,000
Increase for each additional year of operation	50,000
Site cleanup prior to resale	100,000

The quarry will probably have a useful life of 10 years, and the reclaimed site should have a resale value of $1 million. Using an interest rate of 15 percent, determine the equivalent annual cost of this operation.

4.9 A company can purchase a piece of equipment for $20,000 and sell it for $4000 at the end of a 6-year service life, or it can lease the unit for the same period by making first-of-the-year payments of $3000. Compare the equivalent annual costs of the alternatives, using an interest rate of 15 percent.

4.10 Five years ago, a car owner bought an automobile for $13,000. Today, a trade-in of $1500 was allowed on the purchase of a new car. The old one had been driven 70,000 miles (112,651 kilometers). If the owner's other investments earn 6 percent annually, indicate the old car's cost per mile (kilometer) for capital recovery plus interest during the period of ownership.

4.11 Laser beams are to be used on a major construction project to ensure the exact alignment of components. Two types of laser alignment systems, with the costs shown below, are suitable for the project.

	IC system	UC system
First cost	$5000	$3200
Salvage value	1000	0
Annual operating cost	600	950
Additional taxes and insurance per year	180	0

If both systems have a life of 4 years and the minimum rate of return is 15 percent, which offers the lower equivalent annual cost?

4.12 For the situation given in Prob. 4.11, how much longer would the economic life of the IC system have to be in order to make the equivalent annual costs of the two systems equal?

4.13 Problem 3.26 required the present-worth evaluation of three robot options. Now perform that analysis, using an EAW basis.

4.14 Problem 3.28 asked for a present-worth evaluation of options with different lives. Now perform this analysis with an EAW basis, and comment on whether the annual basis is easier to compute.

4.15 Two methods of supplying water and sewage treatment for a housing development that is outside the districts where water and sewage disposal services are provided by the city are described by the accompanying cash flows for a 40-year study:

Years	Method 1	Method 2
0	–$350,000	–$735,000
1–9	–11,000/year	–8,000/year
10	–36,000	+95,000
11–19	–13,000/year	–13,000/year
20	–163,000	+87,000
21–29	–15,000/year	–15,000/year
30	–40,000	–90,000
31–40	–18,000/year	–15,000/year

Both methods have the same total cash flow without regard for interest (–$1,102,000), and both provide a comparable quality of service. At an interest rate of 8 percent, determine which method has the lower equivalent annual cost.

4.16 A bond issue for $125,000 has been passed by voters to buy six minibuses for a senior citizens' transportation service. It is anticipated that the revenue from the bus service will yield a rate of return of 7 percent on the investment. A provision in the bond issue was that a sinking fund be established through a local bank to accumulate enough money to recover the $125,000 in 6 years. The bond issue is to pay 8 percent simple interest (due in a lump sum at maturity), and the local bank pays annual interest of 6 percent.

  (a) What annual payment is required for the sinking fund at the bank?
  (b) What annual return is required to recover the capital invested plus profit?

4.17 A sheltered workshop requires a lift truck to handle pallets for a new contract. A lift truck can be purchased for $27,000. Annual insurance costs are 3 percent of the purchase price, payable on the first of each year. An equivalent truck can be rented for $1500 per month, payable at the end of each month. Operating costs are the same for both alternatives. For what minimum number of months must a purchased truck be used on the contract to make purchasing more attractive than leasing? Interest is 12 percent compounded monthly. (Assume that the purchased truck has no salvage value at any time.)

4.18 An old wooden bridge over a bay is in danger of collapse. The highway department is currently considering two alternatives to alleviate the situation and provide for expected increases in future traffic. One plan is a conventional steel bridge, and the other is a tunnel under the bay. The department is familiar with bridge construction and maintenance but has no experience with maintenance costs for tunnels. The following data have been developed for the bridge:

First cost	$17,000,000
Painting every 6 years	1,000,000
Deck resurfacing every 10 years	3,000,000
Structural overhaul at end of 15 years	4,000,000
Annual maintenance	300,000

The tunnel is expected to cost $24,000,000 and will require repaving every 10 years at a cost of $2,000,000. If both designs are expected to last 30 years with negligible salvage value, determine the maximum equivalent annual amount for maintenance that could be permitted for the tunnel while holding the total EAC to that of the bridge. Let $i = 8$ percent.

4.19 What is the present worth of the following cash flow with nonequal interest rates shown below?

End of year	0	1	2	3	4	5
Interest rate, %		7	7	9	10	8
Receipts, $	10,000		10,000		10,000	
Payments, $		3000		6000		11,000

4.20 Determine the future worth of the cash flow given in Prob. 4.19.

4.21 Determine the uniform series value A that is equivalent to the cash flow given in Prob. 4.19.

4.22 An electric utility company is looking at two alternatives for tree-trimming equipment. One is to subcontract to an independent maintenance company. The subcontractor's bid calls for $98,000 the first year with additional costs of $8000 per year for subsequent years. The utility company is considering buying equipment with a first cost of $220,000 and annual operating expenses of $65,000 per year. The equipment is expected to have a salvage value of $25,000 at the end of its useful life (to the utility company) of 5 years. Using an interest rate of 12 percent, evaluate the alternatives on an EAC basis.

4.23 The utility company in Prob. 4.22 now has different alternatives. The subcontractor agrees to the same bid but over a 6-year period instead of a 5-year period. The utility company now has a bid on equipment from another company. The equipment will be leased to the utility company for $65,000 per year for the first 3 years and $72,000 per year for the last 3 years, and annual operating expenses are estimated to be $45,000 per year. Evaluate these alternatives on an EAC basis, using the 12 percent interest rate.

4.24 An earth compactor costs $38,000 and has an economic life of 9 years. However, the purchaser needs it for only one project that will be completed in 3 years. At the end of the project, it can be sold for one-half its purchase price. What is the annual cost to the owner, if the required rate of return is 12 percent?

4.25 The athletic department of a university is proposing that a new general-purpose stadium be constructed on campus. A design utilizing a combination earth-work bowl with a steel upper deck and press box is being considered. The following cost estimates have been developed:

First cost of complete construction	$32,000,000
Paint steel structure every 6 years	2,000,000
Replace wooden seats every 10 years	4,000,000
Repave parking facilities and ramps every 12 years	3,000,000
Annual maintenance	1,500,000

Assuming a 60-year life and negligible salvage value, determine the minimum annual revenue that could justify the project, using a tax-free interest rate of 7 percent.

4.26 Two types of power converters, alpha and beta, are under consideration for a specific application. An economic comparison is to be made at an interest rate of 10 percent, and the following cost estimates have been obtained:

	Alpha	Beta
Purchase price	$10,000	$25,000
Estimated service life	5 years	9 years
Salvage value	$0	$5000
Annual operating cost	$2500	$1200

Determine the annual equivalent costs of the alternative systems.

4.27 For the power converters in Prob. 4.26, determine a salvage value for the beta system such that it would have an equivalent annual cost equal to that of the alpha system.

4.28 An asset is expected to depreciate in market value at a constant rate from its purchase price of $20,000 to a zero salvage value during its 8 years of physical life. Operating costs are expected to be $8000 for the first year and to increase at a 10 percent annual rate as the asset gets older. What is the annual cost of ownership, if the asset is replaced every 3 years? The required rate of return is 12 percent.

4.29 You have two alternatives for a loan for a home mortgage. The house you want is for sale at $138,000, but you can afford a down payment of $25,000. Company A offers you a loan for the balance at 7.5 percent annual interest to be compounded monthly. The loan is to be paid off in 15 years. Company B offers you a rate of 9 percent with the balance to be paid off in 20 years; compounding is also monthly. Evaluate the monthly payments for the two alternatives.

4.30 Suppose that company A in Prob. 4.29 will actually give you a loan for the full amount of the house price under the same conditions as given in Prob. 4.29, except that your annual interest rate will increase by 0.5 percent. You want to use $5000 of the original down payment for draperies for the new house. Would you consider the new financing possibilities if you could get a guaranteed return of 9 percent compounded annually by investing the rest of the down payment for 15 years?

4.31 An airline is evaluating a new reservations mainframe computer that is expected to have a technological life of 3 years. The first cost of the computer is $480,000 with operating costs expected to be $50,000 for the first year and $3000 per year additional for each year afterward. Salvage value is expected to be 10 percent of first cost. The computer supplier suggests that in 3 years a replacement computer will have first costs that are 10 percent less than those of the current machine. Also, operating costs are expected to have the same percentage of first cost and gradient cost reductions. The current computer system is expected to have an EAC over the next 3 years of $285,000. Evaluate the alternatives by the EAC method, using an interest rate of 15 percent. Assume that replacement will be either now or in 3 years.

4.32 A mining and excavating company uses a large number of light pickup trucks for crew transport and general utility duties. The trucks have a first cost of $19,000 and owing to the generally rugged use lose value at a geometric rate of approximately 30 percent per year. Operation and maintenance costs for two-shift use amount to $4000 for the first year and increase about $800 per year for each additional year of service. Current company policy is to keep the vehicles for 5 years before they are sold. The maintenance supervisor has suggested that they be sold 1 year earlier in order to reduce maintenance expenses. Using an interest rate of 12 percent, determine the equivalent annual-cost effect of implementing the supervisor's suggestion.

4.33 A frozen fish company is planning an expansion to a cold storage facility. Four alternative site design proposals are being considered at an interest rate of 15 percent. Plans A and B require the expenditure of $350,000 for land, and plans C and D require $425,000 for land. These real estate investments are assumed to be permanent. The buildings are expected to last 30 years, the compressors and related equipment will last 10 years before requiring replacement, and energy costs will increase throughout the building's life. Neither the buildings nor the equipment is expected to have any salvage value. With this information and the data provided on the next page, make an annual-cost comparison to determine which proposal is preferred.

	Proposal			
	A	**B**	**C**	**D**
Building and insulation	$600,000	$700,000	$400,000	$500,000
Compressors	100,000	135,000	85,000	70,000
Expected energy costs:				
First year	65,000	48,000	65,000	54,000
Increase for each additional year	3,000	2,000	3,000	2,000
Annual maintenance expense	20,000	15,000	50,000	40,000

RATE-OF-RETURN CALCULATIONS

No law can reduce the common rate of interest below the lowest ordinary market rate at the time when that law is made.

Adam Smith, *The Wealth of Nations, 1776*

The rate of return is the last of the discounted cash flow comparison methods we need to consider. A *minimum acceptable rate of return (MARR)* is the lowest level at which an independent alternative (or, as we will see, an incremental cash flow between two mutually exclusive alternatives) is still attractive. It varies among and within organizations. Although there are a wide variety of recommendations for determining this lowest level of acceptability, it is generally agreed that the level should be no lower—and most likely considerably higher—than the cost of capital. How much higher depends on the circumstances, objectives, and policies of the organization. The purpose of establishing a minimum acceptable rate of return is to ration capital to the most deserving proposals.

Calculation of an *internal rate of return (IRR)* will allow us to determine, under possible reinvestment constraints, whether an alternative meets the MARR value. The IRR analysis may begin with an equivalent annual-worth (EAW) (covered in Chap. 4), present-worth (PW), or future-worth (FW) (both PW and FW are covered in Chap. 3) formulation. By definition, *the internal rate of return of an investment is the rate of interest earned on the unrecovered balance of an investment where the terminal balance is zero.* Given that the present and future worths of a cash flow are equivalent when either is $0, the IRR computation frequently starts with the PW formulation of the cash flow, which is equal to FW = 0 through PW = $0[1/(1 + i)^N]$.

There is no way to avoid trial-and-error computations in *manually* calculating the IRR for complex formulations, but as we will see, the structure of the cash flow can offer clues about where to begin. The computer program (CHEER) that is ancillary to this text allows the IRR to be calculated directly, as do many spreadsheet functions available to the analyst (Excel, Quatro Pro, Lotus, Supercalc, etc.). The spreadsheet programs provided with this text use Quatro Pro and Excel functions.

As mentioned in Chap. 4, consistent results are obtained from EAW, PW, and FW comparisons. This will also be true with the incremental IRR computation, assuming it is applied correctly, as we will see in Sec. 5.5.

We will see that a cash flow pattern that reverses signs (from negative to positive, or vice versa) more than once may have a present-worth equation that is a polynomial in terms of the rate of return. In such cases we can have multiple roots $i*$, and we will not know right away whether one of these roots is the true IRR. Historically, one suggested way to eliminate all but one possibility for the IRR is to apply an external rate of return to a portion of the cash flow, in order to eliminate sign reversals. This external reinvestment rate is usually the MARR. Another historically suggested way, commonly called the *external rate-of-return (ERR) method,* to obtain just one root is to (1) apply an explicit interest rate i percent, probably equal to the MARR, in calculating the future worth of *receipts* and (2) equate this FW to the future worth of *expenditures* compounded at a yet unknown rate of return e'. The value of e' is then found, usually by a trial-and-error procedure, that results in FW = 0. Both methods recognize that the IRR should not be the rate of return used for *reinvestment,* although both methods have logical flaws. Examples will be given later to show how the approaches work. To avoid confusion with the true external rate of return (ERR), a term which will be used later, we will use the full name *historical external rate-of-return (HERR) method* instead of *external rate-of-return (ERR) method.*

A more logical approach is the *project balance method (PBM),* whereby an external rate of return is utilized when any *cash flow balance,* computed by using a potential IRR, is greater than zero. We will see in Sec. 5.3 that using the PBM or determining the rate of return simply by setting the PW equation to zero and solving for i is a function of the cash flow structure (type of investment) and whether the alternatives are independent (selection of one does not affect the selection of another) or mutually exclusive (selection of one alternative precludes the selection of another). Definitions and evaluation methodology will be delayed until Sec. 5.3.

5.1   RATES OF RETURN

The rate of return is a percentage that indicates the relative yield on different uses of capital. Since interest rates are well understood throughout the world of commerce, there should be little danger of misinterpreting rate-of-return figures.

As indicated in the introductory remarks, three rates of return appear frequently in engineering economy studies:

- The *minimum acceptable rate of return* (MARR) is the rate set by an organization to designate the lowest level of return that makes an investment acceptable.
- The *internal rate of return* (IRR) is the rate on the unrecovered balance of the investment in a situation where the terminal balance is zero.
- The *external rate of return* (ERR) is the rate of return that is possible to obtain for an investment under current economic conditions. For example, suppose that analysis of an investment shows that it will realize an IRR of 50 percent. Rationally, it is not reasonable to expect that we can invest in the external market and get that high a rate. In engineering economy studies, the external interest rate most often will be set to the MARR.

All three rates of return are discussed in the following sections.

5.2   **MINIMUM ACCEPTABLE RATE OF RETURN**

The minimum acceptable rate of return, also known as the *minimum attractive rate of return,* is a lower limit for investment acceptability set by organizations or individuals. It is a device designed to make the best possible use of a limited resource, i.e., money. Rates vary widely according to the type of organization, and they vary even within the organization. Historically, government agencies and regulated public utilities have utilized lower required rates of return than have competitive industrial enterprises. Within a given enterprise, the required rate may be different for various divisions or activities. These variations usually reflect the risk involved. For instance, the rate of return required for cost reduction proposals may be lower than that required for research and development projects in which there is less certainty about prospective cash flows.

There is a wealth of literature on the subject but little agreement. The components included in the selection of a before-tax MARR include an inflation-free rate for the cost of using capital and the risk profile of a particular venture. A MARR to be used with *constant* dollars, the assumption we have adopted, is an *inflation-free interest rate* that represents the earning power of capital when inflation effects have been removed. A MARR value that includes the effect of inflation is referred to as the *market interest rate.* Use of this rate will require that all cash flows be in *actual* dollars. It is generally accepted that the lower bound for a minimum required rate of return should be the *cost of capital.* The constitution of this cost is also subject to controversy. As will be discussed in Sec. 5.6, the cost of capital for competitive industries must reflect the expense of acquiring funds from various sources; and as will be discussed in Chap. 8, the cost of safe government bonds is a basis for the lower bound of interest rates used to evaluate public investments.

How much above the cost of capital to set the minimum attractive rate of return depends on an organization's circumstances and aspirations. A small company strapped for cash and burdened by a low credit rating will have a higher cost of capital and so must have a very attractive proposal before it can consider investing. Larger, established companies tend to view the rate as a realistic expectation of how much their capital can earn when it is invested. This MARR is a typical figure promised (and later substantiated) for a large number of high-quality investment proposals available to the firm; it is assumed that the proceeds earned from current projects can be reinvested at comparable rates in future proposals. The rate so derived is sometimes called the *opportunity cost of capital* because any proposal funded to earn a lower rate precludes the opportunity to earn the minimum attractive rate of return.

The purpose of establishing a minimum attractive rate of return higher than the cost of capital is to ration capital. It is rationed to *divisions of an organization* and to the *whole organization* as a function of time. The purpose is to avoid unproductive investments in marginal activities, perhaps favored for political reasons, and to conserve capital during periods when fewer attractive proposals are submitted. Rationing capital by setting higher MARRs is simplistically seen in Sec. 6.5, where we discuss funding a *subset* of independent proposals from the *capital-budgeting viewpoint*.

5.3 INTERNAL RATE OF RETURN

The IRR is the best-known and most widely used rate-of-return method. It is also known as the *true rate-of-return method* and the *discounted cash flow method*. The latter term is indicative of the way interest rates were interpreted in previous chapters; the internal rate of return, represented by i in the traditional interpretation of interest rates, is the rate of interest earned by an alternative investment on the unrecovered balance of an investment. (For example, Table 4.1 illustrated the pattern of capital recovery at an IRR = i of 10 percent.)

The internal rate of return can be calculated by equating the annual, present, or future worth of cash flow to zero and solving for the interest rate (IRR) that allows the equality. It should be added that solving for the interest rate in this manner results in a polynomial equation that is a function of i, which may result in multiple roots of the equation (i^*). In such cases the IRR may or may not be one of the equation roots. This will be clarified and exemplified in Sec. 5.3.1.

Although both the EAW and FW approaches are legitimate, the rate of return is often defined in terms of present worth, under the constraints of possible i^* roots, where the IRR is

- The interest rate at which the present worth of the cash flow of a project is zero, *or,* to restate this in another way:
- The rate which when employed in computing the present worth of all costs and present worths of all returns will make them equal

Because rate-of-return computations usually begin with a problem expressed in terms of present worth or annual worth, it is necessary to pay attention to the guidelines for the EAW and PW methods. In particular, mutually exclusive alternatives (where selection of one precludes selection of others) must be compared on the basis of equivalent outcomes. In the case of independent alternatives (the choice of one does not affect the choice of another, except for limited capital availability), all costs and benefits must be explicitly stated. As in the previous discussions of discounted cash flow, we initially investigate the rate-of-return methods without considering the effects of income taxes.

5.3.1 Calculation of IRR

Determining the IRR is a function of the type of investment (simple, pure, and mixed) and the characteristics of the alternatives (mutually exclusive or independent). If we have independent projects, we may fund combinations of the projects since an independent project does not affect the funding of another project (except for capital availability limitations which are very real in most situations analyzed by the engineering economist). The cash flows of several independent alternatives that are being considered as a group may be summed to form the group's composite cash flow. Analysis can then be performed on this composite cash flow. Where capital limitations are apparent in a department and several independent alternatives are competing for funding, combinations of alternatives may be formed where each combination's first costs have to be equal to or less than the capital available. In this case, mutually exclusive *combinations* will usually be realized, where selection of one group of independent alternatives will preclude the selection of another. This can be due to alternatives being in more than one group and/or capital limitations.

We will see that ranking alternatives according to their IRR values is not consistent with the PW, FW, or AW rankings. Mutually exclusive alternatives may be analyzed by *incremental IRR analysis,* and the results will be found to be completely consistent with the PW, FW, and AW methods. Incremental analysis assumes that we start with a satisfactory low-investment alternative. Analysis of a higher-investment alternative is then based on the differences between the cash flows of the second alternative and the acceptable alternative. These differences in cash flows are *incremental* cash flows. The cash flow of the second alternative is equal to the cash flow of the first alternative plus the incremental cash flows. Thus, if the *incremental* cash flow is acceptable when compared to the MARR, then the larger investment has to be a better investment than the first alternative, which was also acceptable. Otherwise, remove the larger investment from consideration. This type of evaluation is continued until all alternatives have been evaluated; one of the mutually exclusive alternatives is then determined to be the best investment. This will be exemplified later.

As mentioned earlier, there is a possibility that the PW equation may be a polynomial in terms of i such that multiple roots i^* of polynomial PW(i) may result. Often, multiple i^*'s are assumed to be multiple IRR values. This is misleading since there is really only one true IRR for an investment, and so we will need to determine which i^*, if any, is the investment IRR. Classifying investments into *simple* and *nonsimple* investments will tell us if just one i^* exists which, in turn, tells us that we have found the IRR when we have found i^*. An investment is simple if there is only one cash flow sign change (minus to plus) from period to period. A simple investment is as follows:

Time period	Cash flow, $	Sign change
0	−1000	
1	−200	
2	500	Yes (− to +)
3	500	
4	500	

There will only be one i^* if the investment is simple.

A *nonsimple investment* will have more than one sign change in the cash flow sequence:

Time period	Cash flow, $	Sign change
0	−1000	
1	200	Yes (− to +)
2	−500	Yes (+ to −)
3	500	Yes (− to +)
4	500	

There may be multiple i^* values if the investment is nonsimple.

The next step in the analysis will be to determine value(s) for i^*. We will see that this is usually done by trial and error if manually accomplished, or for very simple manual cases we can find i^* directly. Or we can use a spreadsheet program (with some possible reservations for multiple i^* values). Better yet, we can use CHEER which will guarantee the correct

IRR if there is a single root $i*$ and will give close approximate values if two values of $i*$ exist. All methods will be considered shortly.

Finally, if we have multiple $i*$ values (nonsimple investment), we will need to determine the true IRR. First, we determine whether the investment is *pure* or *mixed*. A *pure investment* occurs if the project cash flow balances, evaluated at $i*$, are all less than or equal to zero. We should now realize that a simple investment has to be a pure investment as will be exemplified very shortly. If any of the project cash balances are positive (and some are negative), we have a need to use an external interest rate for reinvestment. This is called a *mixed investment* since we will "externally" reinvest at the external rate (MARR) when balances are positive and we will invest "internally" at the IRR rate when balances are negative (or zero). We do not consider mixed investments until we get to Sec. 5.5. Now we are ready to determine IRR values for a simple investment.

5.3.2 Single, Simple Investment

The rate of return for a single, simple investment is determined by setting the present worth (or EAW) of receipts equal to the present worth (or EAW) of disbursements. Then an interest rate is sought that makes the discounted cash flows conform to the equality:

Find i so that

PW(receipts) = PW(disbursements)

The same relation obviously occurs when the discounted flows are subtracted from each other to equal zero:

Find i so that

PW(receipts) – PW(disbursements) = net PW = 0

For either PW formulation, the *manual* calculation of i is usually a trial-and-error procedure. We initially look at manually computing the IRR to foster understanding of the method, but it will be assumed that the analyst will use CHEER, a spreadsheet function, or a programmed calculator to determine the IRR values after the learning period.

When a single proposal is for a cost reduction project, the receipts take the form of net savings from the method of operation used before the cost reduction investment. In effect, we get an *incremental investment* that is the difference between the do-nothing case and the single investment.

EXAMPLE 5.1 **Income-Producing Proposal**

A parcel of land adjacent to a proposed freeway exit is deemed likely to increase in value. It can be purchased now for $80,000 and is expected to be worth $150,000 within 5 years. During that period it can be rented for pasture at $1500 per year. Annual taxes are presently $850 and will likely remain constant. What rate of return will be earned on the investment if the estimates are accurate?

Solution

The conditions of the proposal are depicted in a cash flow diagram.

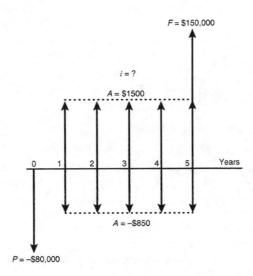

The income (positive cash flow) and disbursements (negative cash flow) can be equated according to their equivalent present worths:

$$PW_{inc} = PW_{disb}$$

or

$$\$150,000(P/F, i, 5) + \$1500(P/A, i, 5) = \$80,000 + \$850(P/A, i, 5)$$

or the positive and negative cash flows can be subtracted:

$$\$150,000(P/F, i, 5) - \$80,000 + \$1500(P/A, i, 5) - \$850(P/A, i, 5) = 0$$

which reduces to

$$\$150,000(P/F, i, 5) - \$80,000 + \$650(P/A, i, 5) = 0$$

The specific value of i, i^*, that conforms to the equation above is the rate of return on the remaining balance of the investment. As said earlier, manual computation usually requires the value to be determined by trial and error.

For a simple investment, a quick preliminary check to see whether the relation has a positive rate of return results from letting $i = 0$. At $i = 0$,

$$\$150,000 - \$80,000 + \$650(5) = \$70,000 + \$3250 = \$73,250$$

The positive value indicates that the investment will produce a positive rate of return because the total income is much greater than the outgo. The check also gives a very rough idea of how large the rate of return might be. For instance, the 72 rule suggests that a sum doubles in value every $72/i$ years. Since the \$80,000 initial investment results in almost twice as much income at the end of 5 years, i should be near $72/5 = 14.4$ percent.

Letting $i = 15$ percent as the first trial, we have

$$\$150,000(P/F,\ 15,\ 5) - \$80,000 + \$650(P/A,\ 15,\ 5) \overset{?}{=} 0$$

$$\$150,000(0.49718) - \$80,000 + \$650(3.35216) = -\$3244.10 < 0$$

The negative value indicates that the trial i used was too large. Now it is known that i lies between 0 and 15 percent.

Letting $i = 14$ percent gives

$$\$150,000(P/F,\ 14,\ 5) - \$80,000 + \$650(P/A,\ 14,\ 5) \overset{?}{=} 0$$

$$\$150,000(0.51937) - \$80,000 + \$650(3.43308) = \$137.00 > 0$$

which shows that the IRR lies between 14 and 15 percent (since we now have a positive PW and the previous PW was negative), but much closer to 14 percent. The approximate value of i is determined by linear interpolation:

i	14%	?	15%
PW	\$137.00	0	-\$3244.10

$$i^* = 14\% + \frac{(15 - 14)\ \%\ (\$137.00 - \$0)}{\$137.00 - (-\$3244.10)} = 14\% + \frac{137 \times 1\%}{3381.10} = 14.04\%$$

A characteristic worth noting in the previous calculations is that whenever the present worth turns out to be positive, the next trial should employ a higher interest rate to approach the desired zero outcome. Conversely, lowering the interest rate in the present-worth formulation increases the resulting outcome.

If the interest tables at the back of this text are used, a small degree of error is introduced by linear interpolation between interest table values that are not linearly related. To keep the error as small as possible, interpolations should be conducted between adjacent interest tables. The error is naturally less between lower-interest-rate tables, separated by 0.5 percent, than at increments of 10 percent for the largest interest rates. For the purposes of this book, interpolated rates of return computed to the nearest 0.1 percent are adequate. The slight error that may be thus introduced will very seldom influence the choice among alternatives; this error is probably much less significant than are actual deviations from the cash flows estimated in the comparisons.

The reader should be familiar with manually computing the IRR values. CHEER will also calculate IRR values, but it can be dangerous to blindly use programs without fully understanding what they are computing and how. Obviously, it makes a lot of sense to use a program to compute IRR values, thus obviating the need for the manual trial-and-error process. To demonstrate the program's use in this regard, Example 5.2 will use the program to solve Example 5.1.

EXAMPLE 5.2   **Using the Computer Program for Example 5.1**

Eventually, after mastering the basic concepts of rate of return, the user will want to use CHEER or some other automatic means to determine the IRR value. Details on using the computer program are given in App. B.

It will be assumed that the reader has been able to start the program according to App. B directions. The five stages in getting the IRR solution to Example 5.1 are given in Fig. 5.1.

1. Figure 5.1*a* shows the initial screen display. The user should access locations for data input by using a mouse or cursor manipulations (a mouse is much more convenient). The first two pieces of data to be input are the project life (5) and initial capital investment ($80,000). The initial screen display shows these two values having been input.

2. We have three more categories of data to input: annual taxes of $850 per year, annual rent (income) of $1500 per year, and a future worth of $150,000 after the 5-year period is over. We click for Revenue in the main screen, and the gross revenue input screen (Fig. 5.1*b*) comes up. Since we have a constant income per year, we can handle this through cash flow 1 only. The user inputs 1500 for the annual amount, 1 for the starting year, and 5 for the ending year. The option C is clicked to indicate that this is a constant income for each of the five periods. When the user is satisfied with the data input, OK is clicked. This returns the user to the initial screen.

3. Now we click to get the Operating/Maintenance Costs screen (Fig. 5.1*c*). The $850 annual tax value is a constant value per year, and so this is entered in the same manner as we entered the annual income. After we are satisfied with the data, we click OK to return to the main screen. We could have input the tax information by clicking for the

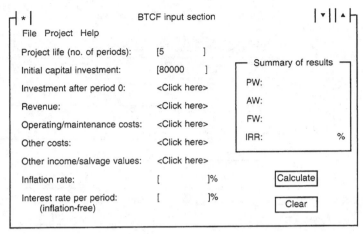

(a) Initial screen display entries

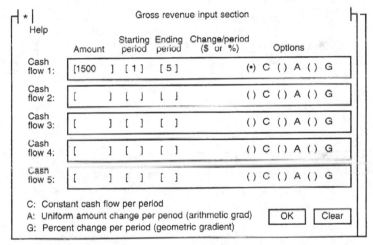

FIGURE 5.1
Initial CHEER example screen displays.

(b) Constant income entry screen

Other Costs menu in the main screen. This would have required five different values to be input even though the tax values would all be the same. The result would be the same either way, of course.

4. Finally, we input the future worth of $150,000 through the Other Income/Salvage Values screen request (Fig. 5.1d). We input 5 for the period and 150,000 for the worth value. We could have input the annual rent income of $1500 per year through this screen, but it was more convenient to accomplish this with the revenue screen.

5. After clicking OK on the last screen, we get the initial screen display once more. Now that we have all the data input, we can click the Calculate area and get the result shown in Fig. 5.1e. The IRR of 14.04 percent corresponds to the result we determined manually. Finally, once

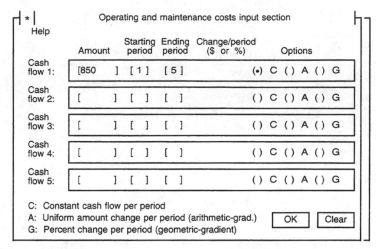

(c) Constant cost entries screen

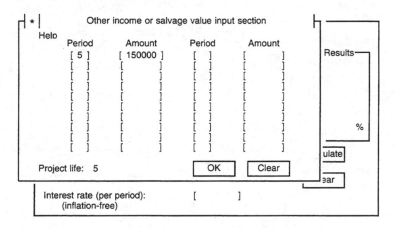

FIGURE 5.1
continued

(d) Future worth input screen

we are satisfied with the IRR result, we can click File on the initial screen and then click Print from the resulting menu to get the summary result in Fig. 5.1f.

A little practice using the program to compute IRR values will demonstrate the value of the computerized approach as contrasted to the trial-and-error manual approach.

EXAMPLE 5.3

Cost Reduction Proposal

Subassemblies for a model IV scope are purchased for $71 apiece. The annual demand is 350 units and is expected to continue for 3 years, at

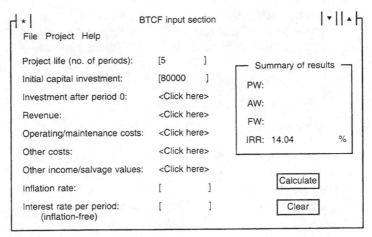

(e) Return to initial screen for IRR calculation

BEFORE-TAX CASH FLOW

Year	Capital investment	Gross revenue	O&M expenses	Other expenses	Sal val/ oth inc	Before-tax cash flow
0	-80000	0	0	0	0	-8000
1	0	1500	-850	0	0	650
2	0	1500	-850	0	0	650
3	0	1500	-850	0	0	650
4	0	1500	-850	0	0	650
5	0	1500	-850	0	150000	150650

FIGURE 5.1
continued

(f) Summary results screen

which time the model V scope now under development should be ready for manufacturing. With equipment purchased and installed for $21,000, the production costs to internally produce the subassemblies should be $18,500 for the first year and $12,250 in each of the last 2 years. The equipment will have no salvage value. Should the company make or buy the subassemblies?

Solution

This is an ideal problem for solution by CHEER. The objective of this text is to teach fundamentals, so this example will again stress manual solution to IRR problems even though in actual practice you will undoubtedly want to utilize the more efficient computer.

The savings expected in a cost reduction proposal are treated as income, and as in Example 5.1, we have an incremental analysis situation (do something versus do nothing). Initial calculations are as follows:

Present annual cost = 350($71) = $24,850

Net savings (year 1) = $24,850 − $18,500 = $6350

Net savings (years 2, 3) = $24,850 − $12,250 = $12,600

Assuming that the transactions occur at the end of each year, we can create the following cash flow diagram (which is seen to represent a single, simple investment):

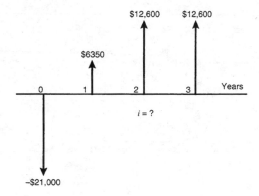

Now we can set up the present-worth equation in terms of the IRR (i):

PW = −$21,000 + $6350($P/F$, i, 1) + $12,600($P/F$, i, 2)
$\quad$ + $12,600($P/F$, i, 3) $\gtreqless$ 0

Trying successively higher rates of return, we find at i = 10 percent,

PW = −$21,000 + $6350(0.90909) + $12,600(0.82645)
$\quad$ + $12,600(0.75131)
$\quad$ = $4652.50 > 0

Similarly, using App. D tables, we find:

i = 15 percent$\qquad$PW = $2333.89

i = 20 percent$\qquad$PW = $ 333.21

i = 25 percent$\qquad$PW = −$1404.80

The PW with i = 25 percent is negative while the PW with i = 20 percent is positive. Therefore, we can interpolate to find the rate of return on the $21,000 investment:

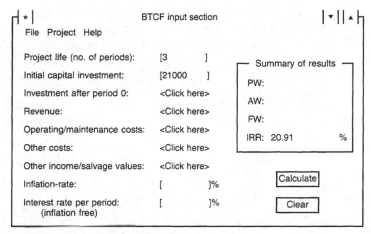

(a) Initial screen showing computed IRR

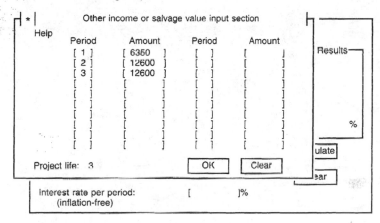

(b) Nonconstant incomes through "other income" screen

FIGURE 5.2
Computer solution
for Example 5.3.

$$IRR = 20\% + (25\% - 20\%) \frac{\$333.21 - \$0}{\$333.21 - (-\$1404.80)}$$

$$= 20\% + 0.96\% = 20.96\%$$

If CHEER had been utilized to directly determine the IRR value found in Example 5.3, we would find the IRR value much more easily than by the manual approach. Figure 5.2 shows the appropriate computer screens after solution. Figure 5.2b shows that the Other Income/Salvage Value screen was used rather than the Revenue screen used in Example 5.2. This is because we had three different values to input instead of the one constant-value input in Example 5.2. We could have used the Revenue screen to input $12,600 for periods 2 and 3 and the Other Income/Salvage Value screen for the $6350 value. This would give exactly the same results but would be a little cumbersome. The user can use the screens that seem best for a particular problem.

Figure 5.2*a* shows that the IRR value proves to be 20.91 percent as contrasted to the manually interpolated value of 20.96 percent. Logically, either one would give the same interpretation against a particular MARR value.

Figure 5.3 shows the computer program primary screen when Example 5.3 data were run with 15 percent, the first interest rate tried with the manual method. The IRR value is still computed, and, of course, this is still 20.91 percent (with roundoff error). Now, however, we have the PW, AW, and FW values computed since a specific interest rate was input. The PW was calculated to be $2333.85—a very minor change from the manual result. The insignificant difference is probably due to rounding errors in the appendix tables.

The answer to the make-or-buy question depends on how large a return the firm expects on its invested capital. For Example 5.3, we can see the conditions for accepting the proposal to manufacture the subassembly internally by plotting the present worth of the proposal as a function of interest. Several interest rates were tried before we interpolated between 20 and 25 percent using CHEER:

$$i = 10\% \qquad \text{PW} = \$4562.52$$

$$i = 15\% \qquad \text{PW} = \$2333.85$$

$$i = 20\% \qquad \text{PW} = \$333.33$$

$$i = 25\% \qquad \text{PW} = -\$1404.80$$

$$i^* = 20.91\% \qquad \text{PW} = -\$1.11 \approx \$0 \qquad \text{(IRR value)}$$

In addition, for $i = 0$ percent,

$$\text{PW}(0) = -\$21,000 + \$6350 + 2(\$12,600) = \$10,550$$

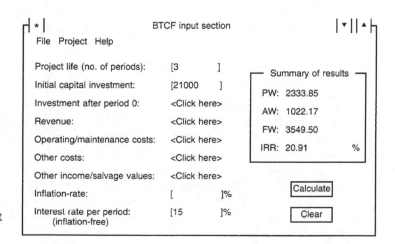

FIGURE 5.3
Computer solution when $i = 15$ percent in Example 5.3.

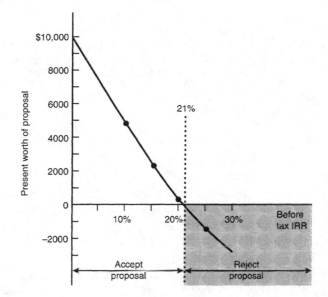

FIGURE 5.4
Present worth of cash flow for the proposal of Example 5.3 at different interest rates.

A plot of the PW(i) versus i is shown in Fig. 5.4. At any MARR value below 21 percent, the present worth of the proposal is positive and therefore acceptable. For a minimum attractive rate of return greater than 21 percent, the proposal exhibits a negative present worth and is therefore rejected.

5.3.3   Clues for IRR Calculations

Even though most analysts will use CHEER or spreadsheet functions to compute IRR values, we should comment on how we might possibly simplify the trial-and-error manual process, if only for completeness. There is really no way to avoid the trial-and-effort search procedure for manually determining the IRR in problems with complex cash flows, although an approach for simple problems will be mentioned shortly. A little preplanning may narrow the area of search.

The first maneuver to avoid unnecessary computations, if we have a simple investment, is to sum the cash flows. A negative total may indicate that the proposal being considered cannot meet even an $i = 0$ percent requirement, thereby eliminating it from further consideration whenever a positive IRR is required. This will happen only with the common simple investment case where we have investment at the beginning of the project followed by incomes. It is possible in unusual cases for PW(0 percent) to be negative while the PW for a higher interest rate is positive because of discounting the cash flow to the present. For example, consider the following cash flow:

End of period	0	1	2
Cash flow	−$100	+$250	−$156

Summing the cash values, we get PW(0 percent) = −$6. The present worth at an interest rate of 25 percent is

$$PW(25\%) = -\$100 + \$250(P/F, 25, 1) - \$156(P/F, 25, 2)$$
$$= -\$100 + \$250(0.8) - \$156(0.64) = \$0.16$$

Therefore an IRR is feasible, possibly close to 25 percent. Problem 5.30 will ask you to evaluate this further. This example has a cash flow that is a nonsimple, and as you will see in Prob. 5.30, there is more than one possibility for the IRR.

For the *simple investment,* the size of a positive net sum, with respect to the amount and length of investment, gives a rough suggestion of the rate of return. For instance, the net cash flow at $i = 0$ percent is $10,550 in Example 5.3, and the initial investment is $21,000 for 3 years. This 50 percent return on investment over 3 years suggests a substantial IRR.

A quick proximity fix on the IRR is possible for problems that have their major cash flows at the beginning and end of the study period, or those consisting largely of constant cash flow streams. When the salvage value is close to 100 percent of the first cost, the net annuity divided by the first cost gives a close approximation to i; that is, $A/P \simeq i$. Also, as demonstrated in Example 5.1, if most of the income is at year N and is about twice the initial outlay, then $i \simeq 72/N$.

The more variation in cash flows, the more difficult the guessing game gets. Sometimes irregular cash flows can be rounded to approximate an ordinary annuity, or individual transactions within short time intervals can be lumped together to allow gross preliminary calculations that suggest the vicinity of the IRR. For instance, in Example 5.3, the irregular receipts could be approximated by an average A of, say, $10,000. Then, $A/P = \$10,000/\$21,000 = 0.4761$. With this figure as an entry to an interest table for a capital recovery factor at $N = 3$, $(A/P, 20, 3) = 0.47473$ gives a good place to begin IRR trial computations. Of course, with the computer program, we do not have to worry about the trial-and-error procedure. To repeat what was said earlier, the computer program should be used for real problems, but the user should have a firm understanding of what is entailed in IRR calculations. Only by working with the trial-and-error manual process can this understanding be attained.

It is possible to determine the IRR directly for very simple situations. For example, the most simple situation might have

$$PW = -CI + FW(P/F, i, N) = 0$$

when searching for IRR (i), where CI = capital investment at time period 0 and FW = future worth at time period N. Rearranging terms gives

$$CI = FW(P/F, i, N)$$

$$\frac{CI}{FW} = (P/F, i, N) = \frac{1}{(1 + i)^N}$$

and

$$(1 + i)^N = \frac{FW}{CI}$$

If we take natural logarithms of both sides of the equation, we get

$$N \ln (1 + i) = \ln FW - \ln CI$$

and

$$\ln (1 + i) = \frac{\ln FW - \ln CI}{N}$$

For example, let FW = \$150, CI = \$100, and $N = 3$. Then

$$\ln (1 + i) = \frac{\ln 150 - \ln 100}{3} = \frac{5.01 - 4.61}{3} = 0.13$$

Finally, $1 + i = e^{0.13} = 1.14$, and

$$i^* = (1.14 - 1)(100\%) = 14\% = IRR$$

Unfortunately, the equation with i as an unknown is a polynomial with an order equal to the number of terms in the equation with i. This is an intractable situation for any problem of realistic complexity. Therefore, a trial-and-error procedure is often mandated.

A graphical approach can greatly simplify the problem, especially when it is used with a variety of IRR values in conjunction with the text's computer program to determine intermediate values of PW. Figure 5.6 will show such a graphical representation, and details for obtaining the graph are given later. Also, the computer program may be used directly to determine the solution for problems where only one IRR value exists.

5.4   **CONSISTENCY OF IRR WITH OTHER ECONOMIC COMPARISON METHODS**

The acceptability of alternative courses of action will be identical whether they are evaluated according to their annual worth, present worth, or

TABLE 5.1

Estimated cash flows (all costs) for alternative operating plans, $

Year	Plan *A*	Plan *B*	Plan *C*
0		30,000	25,000
1	20,000	15,000	12,000
2	20,000	15,000	12,000
3	20,000	15,000	12,000
4	20,000	15,000	12,000
5	20,000	15,000	37,000
6	20,000	15,000	12,000
7	20,000	15,000	12,000
8	20,000	15,000	12,000
9	20,000	15,000	12,000
10	20,000	15,000	12,000

incremental IRR. Ranking alternatives by individual IRR values will usually not be consistent with PW rankings as will be shown in Sec. 5.5.1. The important points to understand are the meaning of the measures of acceptability and the assumptions upon which they are based. Sample calculations applying all three comparison methods to the data given in Table 5.1 will reveal the consistency of results. They will also illustrate how the rate of return is calculated to compare investments when only the disbursements are known and how to interpret the outcomes.

Suppose that a certain function is currently being performed at an annual expense of $20,000. Three mutually exclusive alternatives are being considered. One alternative, plan *A,* is to leave the operation unchanged. In effect, this is the do-nothing alternative that is almost always present in a decision situation. A second alternative, plan *B,* is to invest in layout modifications that will allow the function to be performed at a reduced labor cost of $15,000. The expense of the renovations must be recovered in 10 years according to operating policy. Plan *C* is a proposal to install a labor-saving device that will cut the labor cost to $12,000. The device has a first cost of $25,000, will be worn out in 5 years, and has no salvage value. Table 5.1 is a year-by-year tabulation of the cash flow for the three plans. If the company's minimum acceptable rate of return is 8 percent, which plan offers the greatest economic benefit?

AW and PW comparisons

Using the already familiar procedures for computing the equivalent annual worth (cost) of a cash flow stream, we find that the annual cost for the current operating method, plan *A,* is read directly from the table:

EAC(plan *A*) = labor expense = $20,000

In plan B, the initial investment is spread over the 10-year study period and is added to the annual labor expense to get

EAC(plan B) = $30,000($A$/$P$, 8, 10) + $15,000
= $30,000(0.14903) + $15,000 = $19,471

Since the study period constitutes two cycles of the 5-year economic life of the labor-saving device in plan C, the annual cost will be the same over each 5-year period [assuming first costs have been corrected for inflation (constant dollars) and the technology is stable]:

EAC(plan C) = $25,000($A$/$P$, 8, 5) + $12,000
= $25,000(0.25046) + $12,000 = $18,262

Thus, plan C, with the lowest annual cost, is preferred. Compared with the currently existing plan A, an investment of $25,000 in a labor-saving device will yield a return of 8 percent per year plus the equivalent receipt of $20,000 – $18,262 = $1738 each year from savings in labor expense for 5 years.

The equivalent present worth (cost) of the three plans is calculated by simply multiplying each EAC by the uniform series present-worth factor (P/A, 8, 10) = 6.71008:

PW(plan A) = $20,000(6.71008) = $134,202

PW(plan B) = $19,471(6.71008) = $130,652

PW(plan C) = $18,262(6.71008) = $122,539

Since a lower present cost is preferred, plan C again gets the nod, as expected. This means that over a 10-year period when money is worth 8 percent, plan C is expected to cost $134,202 – $122,539 = $11,663 less in *today's dollars* to accomplish the same operation now being done under plan A. This total saving is, of course, the present worth of the annual gain beyond the 8 percent return calculated in the EAC comparison:

$1738($P$/$A$, 8, 10) = $1738(6.71008) = $11,662

IRR comparison

The data given in Table 5.1 provide examples of IRR comparisons that do not have natural cash flows which are positive (all values are costs). This is handled with *incremental* analysis as defined earlier. The positive cash flow stream is developed from the savings generated by each additional increment of investment. A more detailed discussion of incremental analysis is presented in Chap. 6, but it is sufficient here to understand that *each increment of capital expended must be justified in itself.*

Logically, we start with the smallest investment over the do-nothing alternative (plan A), which is the $25,000 outlay for the labor-saving device in plan C. The "earnings" from this investment are the annual reductions in labor expense: $20,000 – $12,000 = $8000. The incremental cash flow is seen to be a *simple* investment, so we do not have to be concerned with an external interest rate. By using the program CHEER, it is necessary to input only a first cost of $25,000 and a revenue of $8000 for each of years 1 through 5. The resultant IRR_{C-A} is 18.03 percent, indicating that plan C is preferred to plan A when the required rate of return is 8 percent. Why can we say this? From the way we compute incremental data it should be clear that

$$\text{Cash flow}(C) = \text{cash flow}(A) + \text{cash flow}(C - A)$$

Therefore, if the lowest investment plan is satisfactory (which we assume it is when we are dealing only with costs, as occurs with the do-nothing plan A), the next-lowest alternative has to be an even better alternative if the incremental cash flows satisfy the MARR since cash flow (C) will have the return from the increment $(C - A)$ plus the return from cash flow (A).

Although it is already known from the EAC and PW comparisons that plan C is preferred to plan B, it can be checked by determining the IRR for the $30,000 investment in plan B over the currently accepted plan C. The incremental cash flow $(B - C)$ has a $30,000 – $25,000 = $5000 incremental *investment* in B over C followed by incremental cost *increases* of $15,000 – $12,000 = $3000 per year with the exception of a net savings of $25,000 in year 5. The costs so far outweigh the savings in year 5 that the PW will be less than zero for any interest rate. Therefore, IRR_{B-C} is less than the MARR of 8 percent, and plan B is rejected. Plan C should be recommended.

5.5   IRR MISCONCEPTIONS

The consistency of AW and PW comparisons is above reproach, and both always agree with IRR evaluations when done correctly. Unfortunately, there are some misconceptions that should be clarified.

5.5.1   Ranking Alternatives by Individual IRR Values

The reader might wonder why incremental analysis was used in the previous example when it might seem that ranking individual alternative IRR values would be the way to go. Ranking alternatives on their individual IRR values can conflict with PW rankings. For example, suppose we have two projects with the cash flows indicated in Table 5.2. Both proposals require the same $1000 initial investment. The contrasting net annual returns are conspicuous; project X starts low and increases, whereas project Y has a high first-year flow followed by constant lower flows.

The two projects are first compared by their present worths when the minimum required rate of return is 10 percent:

TABLE 5.2

Cash flows for two mutually exclusive projects with 4-year lives and no salvage value

Project	End-of-Year Cash Flow, $				
	0	**1**	**2**	**3**	**4**
X	−1000	100	350	600	850
Y	−1000	1000	200	200	200

$$PW(X) = -\$1000 + [\$100 + \$250(A/G, 10, 4)] \, (P/A, 10, 4)$$
$$= -\$1000 + [\$100 + \$250(1.38117)] \, (3.16987)$$
$$= \$411.52$$

$$PW(Y) = -\$1000 + [\$1000 + \$200(P/A, 10, 3)] \, (P/F, 10, 1)$$
$$= -\$1000 + [\$1000 + \$200(2.48685)] \, (0.90909)$$
$$= \$361.24$$

This *ranks project X higher than project Y.*

When a comparison is made that uses individual IRRs, the rankings are reversed, as shown by the following calculations:

For project X:

$$PW = -\$1000 + [\$100 + \$250(A/G, i, 4)] \, (P/A, i, 4) \gtreqless 0$$

At $i = 20$ percent,

$$PW = -\$1000 + [\$100 + \$250(1.27422)] \, (2.58873) = \$83.53$$

and at $i = 25$ percent,

$$PW = -\$1000 + [\$100 + \$250(1.22493)] \, (2.36160) = -\$40.64$$

Interpolating for PW = 0, we get IRR(X) = 23.4 percent.

For project Y:

$$PW = -\$1000 + [\$1000 + \$200(P/A, i, 3)] \, [P/F, i, 1] \gtreqless 0$$

This results in IRR = 34.26 percent that *ranks project Y ahead of project X.*

The net present-worth profiles for the two projects are shown in Fig. 5.5. This shows that the present worth of X exceeds that of Y at $i = 10$ percent, and the internal rate of return is higher for Y than X when PW = 0. An *incremental* analysis is the way to handle the problem.

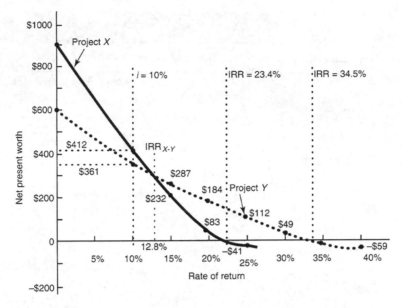

FIGURE 5.5
Relationship of net worth and different discount rates, showing how the rankings for two projects can change.

Using the original yearly data from Table 5.2, we can get year-by-year differences in X and Y cash flows. These are shown in Table 5.3. Now, using the data from Table 5.3, we can find the IRR that makes project X equivalent to project Y (use $X - Y$ column):

$$\text{PW} = -\$900 + \$150(P/F, i, 1) + \$400(P/F, i, 2) + \$650(P/F, i, 3) \stackrel{?}{=} 0$$

CHEER finds IRR_{X-Y} to be 12.8 percent, which is greater than the MARR of 10 percent, and so alternative X is acceptable. The IRR of 12.8 percent is called the *incremental rate of return,* and it makes project X equivalent to project Y. We see in Fig. 5.5 that the intersection of the present-worth

TABLE 5.3

Yearly differences in X and Y cash flows, \$

	Project		
Year	**X**	**Y**	**X – Y**
0	−1000	−1000	0
1	100	1000	−900
2	350	200	150
3	600	200	400
4	850	200	650

curves occurs at the IRR$_{X-Y}$ of 12.8 percent (PW$_{X-Y}$ = 0). This, of course, is the incremental rate of return we just calculated.

This intersection is the pivot point for selecting the superior alternative. Select X when the required rate of return is equal to or less than 12.8 percent, and select Y when the required rate is more than 12.8 percent but less than 35 percent. This selection rule is consistent with the PW comparison at i = 10 percent, which indicated a preference for X. A similar PW comparison at i = 14 percent indicates a preference for Y.

As another example to support the selection procedure, assume that an investment of $100 returns $200 at the end of 1 year; hence,

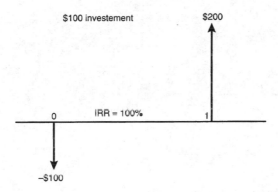

$$\text{PW(\$100 investment)} = -\$100 + \$200(P/F, i, 1)$$
$$= 0 \quad \text{at IRR} = 100\%$$

Let another investment of $1000 return $1500 in 1 year; hence,

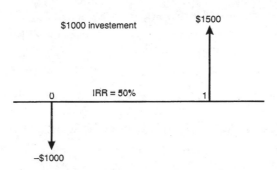

$$\text{PW(\$1000 investment)} = -\$1000 + \$1500(P/F, i, 1)$$
$$= 0 \quad \text{at IRR} = 50\%$$

Thus the $100 investment seems to be more attractive if it is ranked by the internal rates of return. However, if the MARR is only 10 percent,

$$\text{PW(\$100 investment)} = -\$100 + \$200(P/F, 10, 1) = \$81.82$$

and

$$\text{PW(\$1000 investment)} = -\$1000 + \$1500(P/F, 10, 1) = \$363.64$$

which seems to indicate a preference for the $1000 investment.

In actual fact, the reason that the $1000 investment is superior may be better understood by considering the IRR on the additional $900 increment of the investment:

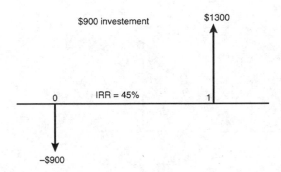

$$\text{PW(\$900 increment)} = -\$1000 - (-\$100) + (\$1500 - \$200)(P/F, i, 1)$$
$$= 0 \quad \text{at IRR}$$
$$= -\$900 + \$1300(P/F, 44.6, 1) = 2.78 \simeq 0$$

Thus, the additional $900 investment has an internal rate of return of 44.6 percent (found with CHEER), which well exceeds the minimum required rate of 10 percent, making it acceptable and confirming the preference shown by the previous present-worth comparison. This proves, by example, that mutually exclusive alternatives cannot be compared by their individual IRRs. The incremental approach must be used.

5.5.2 More Than One Possible Rate of Return (Nonsimple Investment)

When the cash flow or cumulative cash flow of a project switches from negative to positive (or the reverse) *more than once* (a *nonsimple investment*), the project may have more than one root of the present-worth equation $\text{PW}(i) = 0$. In such cases we have to determine which root is, in fact, the true IRR value. In a single project such situations will occur relatively rarely in practice, although they do occur. When incremental analysis is used to compare mutually exclusive alternatives, especially for projects with unequal lives, this becomes much more common.

EXAMPLE 5.4

Two Solutions for an IRR Evaluation

To introduce the multiple-root problem, consider a rather contrived single-project situation. One of the alternatives for improving an operation is to do nothing to it for 2 years and then spend $10,000 on improvements. If this course of action is followed, the immediate gain is $3000 (income) followed by 2 years of break-even operations. Thereafter, annual income should be $2000 per year for 4 years. What rate of return can be expected from following this course of delayed action?

Solution

End of year	Cash flow, $
0	+3,000
1	0
2	−10,000
3	2,000
4	2,000
5	2,000
6	2,000

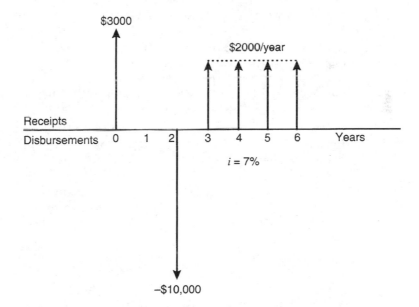

The cash flow suggests that there might be multiple roots for PW(i), i^*, since the cash flow reverses from positive to negative at year 2 and again reverses signs at year 3. Since a double sign reversal is not always accompanied by dual rates of return, trials can be conducted at arbitrarily

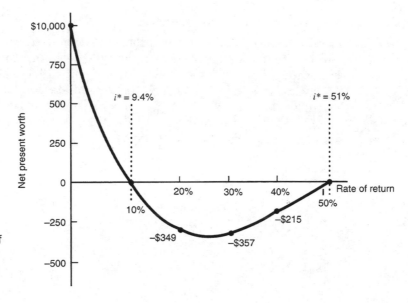

FIGURE 5.6

Net present worth of a proposal with multiple roots for PW (i) = 0.

selected interest rates to determine the general PW profile. Using the original data, summarized earlier, given on the cash flow diagram, we get

$$\text{PW} = \$3000 - \$10,000(P/F, i, 2) + \$2000(P/A, i, 4)(P/F, i, 2) \stackrel{?}{=} 0$$

Several interest rates were utilized with CHEER to give a profile of present worths over the discounting range of 0 to 51 percent, as shown in Fig. 5.6. We see that the proposal has an i^* of either 9.4 or 51 percent. Which, if either, of the two values is the correct IRR? As mentioned in the introduction to the IRR material, if we have a *mixed* investment case (where we have positive cash flow balances when the PW equation is evaluated at a root i^*), finding the correct IRR will be a function of how reinvestment of the positive cash flow accumulations is handled. If we assume that the IRR is the correct interest rate to use for reinvestment, then i^* will be the IRR value. In reality, this is not reasonable since reinvestment will be a function of external investment conditions; usually the MARR value is assumed since that is the desired minimum investment rate. For example, would it be reasonable that we could make an investment elsewhere that will return 51 percent, the highest of the i^* values shown in Fig. 5.6? We all wish that could be true. The true rate might be in the vicinity of 10 percent or so. In Sec. 5.5.5 we introduce the recommended method, the project balance method (PBM), to use in finding the true IRR. First we will look at two historical approaches that preceded the PBM method.

5.5.3 Explicit Investment Rate

One approximate answer to the IRR question in Example 5.3 is developed by applying an *explicit interest rate* to a limited portion of the cash flow that will disturb the total cash flow pattern as little as possible while eliminating one of the sign reversals. An explicit reinvestment rate is a designated interest percentage appropriate for a specific application. The *explicit reinvestment* rate may be the minimum attractive rate of return employed by the organization or a rate suggested by the PW profile. As an example, let us assume that the $3000 receipt at the beginning of year 1 is assumed to be invested at an explicit interest rate for 2 years. Under this assumption, one sign reversal is avoided (at year 2), and the modified cash flow diagram is as follows:

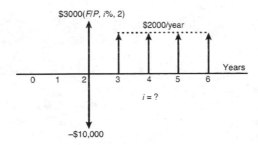

We see that by applying the explicit interest rate to a small portion of the cash flow we have transformed a nonsimple investment to a simple investment. Now we can modify the original present-worth equation:

$$PW = \$3000(F/P, i\%, 2) - \$10,000 + \$2000(P/A, i, 4) \stackrel{\geq}{=} 0$$

where $i\%$ is the explicit interest rate applied for 2 years. Let us determine the IRR for an explicit interest rate of 5 percent. This implies that only a 5 percent return can be confidently obtained on external investments. Investing the $3000 at 5 percent for 2 years will yield

$$FW(year\ 2) = \$3000(F/P, 5, 2) = \$3308$$

But at the beginning of year 2 we also have a $10,000 disbursement, and so the cash flow at the beginning of year 2 is

$$-\$10,000 + \$3308 = -\$6692$$

The cash flow over years 1 through 6 would now be as follows:

Year	0	1	2	3	4	5	6
Cash flow, $	0	0	−6692	2000	2000	2000	2000
Cumulative cash flow, $	—	—	−6692	−4692	−2692	−692	+1308

The IRR for the modified cash flow pattern is simply the interest rate that makes an initial investment of $6692 equivalent to a $2000 annual annuity for 4 years:

$$PW = -\$6692 + \$2000(P/A,\ i,\ 4) = 0 \qquad \text{at IRR}$$

$$(P/A,\ i,\ 4) = \frac{\$6692}{\$2000} = 3.3460$$

So, using the compound-interest tables, we have

$$IRR = 7\% + 1\% \left(\frac{3.38721 - 3.3460}{3.38721 - 3.31213} \right) = 7.5\%$$

The IRRs for a variety of explicit $i\%$ values are given in Table 5.4, and it is apparent that the proposal is attractive only when the explicit reinvestment rate is below 9.5 percent and above 50.9 percent, the same result as shown earlier in Fig. 5.6. It might be apparent that the text's computer program greatly simplifies the determination of the IRR values in Table 5.4. Using Table 5.4, we see that when funds can be invested externally at, say, 15 percent, there is no incentive to invest in a proposal that returns

TABLE 5.4

Different IRR percentages resulting from explicit reinvestment rates used on a limited portion of cash flow to convert dual rates of return to single IRR

Explicit reinvestment rate applied to $3000 payment for 2 years, %	IRR on net investment when explicit reinvestment rate is utilized, %
0	5.6
5	7.5
9.4	9.5
15	12.3
20	15.6
30	22.6
40	33.1
51	51.2
60	77.6

only 12.4 percent. If the external funding rate were 5 percent, as we used earlier, the IRR (7.5 percent) would be attractive.

The use of an explicit interest rate may seem like an artificial device to alleviate a mathematical difficulty, but the concept is both realistic and reasonable. Funds received from an ongoing project are indeed reinvested in new projects that have passed the MARR criterion. These funds then earn at least the required rate, but it would be unrealistic to expect them to earn an enormously higher rate, such as 51 percent suggested by the sample problem. However, if 51 percent were the actual external reinvestment rate, then the given cash flow pattern would also meet that criterion.

One major problem with the use of the explicit interest rate just described is the fact that where the rate is applied is somewhat arbitrary. Our contrived example worked correctly because the only positive cash flow value in the original situation occurred at time 0. Now we will look at a second historical reinvestment method (the HERR method) that applies the explicit interest rate to all positive cash flows. This has a major flaw, but historically it is the precursor for the project balance method, covered in Sec. 5.5.5.

5.5.4 Historical External Rate-of-Return Method

The occurrence of multiple i^* roots with the nonsimple investment return can be avoided by using the *historical external rate-of-return (HERR) method* where the main appeal is its pragmatic assumption that receipts are actually reinvested at a generally available interest rate. This rate is typically taken to be the MARR. The flaw is that this method does not base the reinvestment on project cash flow balances; it is based solely on project receipts.

An unknown rate of return e' is found by equating the future worth of receipts (positive cash flows) compounded at an explicit interest rate ($i\%$) to the future worth of disbursements (negative cash flows) compounded at c':

$$\text{FW(receipts compounded at } i\%) = \text{FW(disbursements compounded at } e')$$

When $i\%$ is the MARR and e' exceeds $i\%$, the investment is assumed to be attractive because it promises a yield greater than the lower limit of acceptability.

EXAMPLE 5.5

Example 5.4 Revisited with a HERR Evaluation

Evaluate the cash flow described in Example 5.4 when receipts are reinvested at the MARR of 15 percent.

Solution

Given $i\% = 15$ percent, the future worths of receipts and of disbursements are equated

$$\$3000(F/P, i\%, 6) + \$2000(F/A, i\%, 4) = \$10,000(F/P, e', 4)$$

from which

$$
\begin{aligned}
(F/P, e', 4) &= \frac{\$3000(2.31306) + \$2000(4.99338)}{\$10,000} \\
&= \frac{\$6939.18 + \$9986.76}{\$10,000} \\
&= 1.69259
\end{aligned}
$$

By interpolation, this produces an e' value of 14.1 percent. Since e' is less than the MARR, the investment is unacceptable under the HERR assumptions.

Now we will look at a technique where the external rate (MARR) is applied in a more systematic and logical manner.

5.5.5   Project Balance Method

An approach more logical than the traditional HERR methodology is the *project balance method (PBM)* that has the HERR method as a historical precedent but that applies the IRR and ERR (external investment rate, usually the MARR) to *cumulative cash balances* that include interest to date. Note that the acronymn *ERR* is now used correctly, which is why we renamed the external rate-of-return method the *historical* rate-of-return method. The PBM has evolved over many years, but Park[†] has nicely summarized the steps in the reinvestment problem [only needed if we have a nonsimple investment case—the cash flow sequence has more than one sign change (plus to minus or minus to plus) from period to period]:

1. Determine i^* (or multiple i^* values for the cash flow sequence). If there are multiple i^* values, it is suggested that the one closest to the MARR value be used in the subsequent analysis.
2. Determine the *current balance (CB)* for each period, using any of the determined i^* values. These we will call $\text{CB}(i^*)_t$, where t is the end of the period for which CB is being calculated.

[†]C. S. Park, *Contemporary Engineering Economics Text with $3\frac{1}{2}''$ disk*, © 1993, Addison-Wesley Publishing Company, Inc., Reprinted by permission of the publisher.

3. If all $CB(i*)_t$ are equal to or less than zero, receipts in all periods t are being used to pay off project investments and so are assumed to be used *internally;* thus $i*$ is the true IRR value.

4. If any $CB(i*)_t$ is positive and some are negative (so this is not pure borrowing), then the IRR is still not known. The MARR or other acceptable external rate of return will be applied to the positive $CB(IRR/ERR)_t$, which is funds in excess of those being applied to the project's investment; and $i*$ will be applied to the negative $CB(IRR/ERR)_t$. We do know that we have a mixed investment—both internal and external investment.

5. Iterate through the periods with an assumed IRR and the explicit external interest rate. Apply the IRR to negative balances and the explicit rate to positive balances. If $CB(IRR/ERR)_N$ is equal to zero, we have the truc IRR value which should be used in project evaluations.

As an example, let us apply this process to the original Example 5.4 data, which had the following cash flow sequence:

End of period	Cash flow, $
0	3,000
1	0
2	−10,000
3	2,000
4	2,000
5	2,000
6	2,000

As with the last two solutions, let us assume that the MARR is 15 percent. Also, suppose we just use an arbitrary first estimate for the IRR, close to the MARR, that is, 13 percent.

End of period	Cash flow, $	Current balance $CB(IRR/MARR)_t$[†], $	Comments
0	3,000	3,000	$CB_0 > 0$ (use MARR for $t = 1$)
1	0	$3{,}000(1 + MARR)^1 = 3{,}450$	$CB_1 > 0$ (use MARR for $t = 2$)
2	−10,000	$3{,}450(1 + MARR)^1 - 10{,}000 = -6{,}032.5$	$CB_2 < 0$ (use IRR for $t = 3$)
3	2,000	$-6{,}032.5(1 + IRR)^1 + 2{,}000 = -4{,}816.73$	All subsequent $CB_t \leq 0$, so
4	2,000	$-4{,}816.73(1 + IRR)^1 + 2{,}000 = -3{,}442.9$	IRR is used
5	2,000	$-3{,}442.9(1 + IRR)^1 + 2{,}000 = -1{,}890.48$	
6	2,000	$-1{,}890.48(1 + IRR)^1 + 2{,}000 = -136.25$	

[†]Since we used MARR as the specific value for ERR.

$$i = 3\% + (4\% - 3\%) \frac{\$32.36 - \$0}{\$32.36 - (-\$113.28)} = 3.2\%$$

which means that the bond purchased for $780 will earn 6.4 percent compounded semiannually.

EXERCISE 2

Use the computer program available with this text to solve directly for the bond return in Exercise 1.

SOLUTION 2

The solution to this exercise is given in the three screen displays of Fig. 5.10. The income data are given in Fig. 5.10a and b. First, we input the $20 per-period income through the Gross Revenue screen. The $1000 face value of the bond after

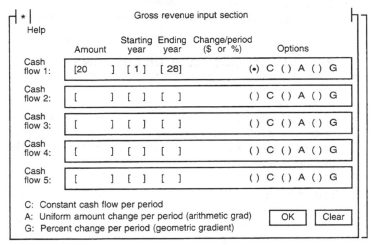

(a) $20 per period entered through gross revenue screen

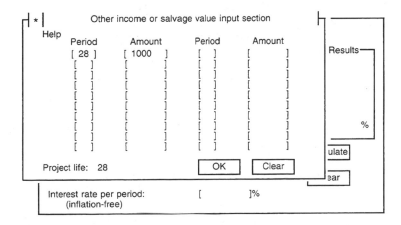

FIGURE 5.10
Computer solution
for Exercise 2.

(b) $1000 face value entered through "other income" screen

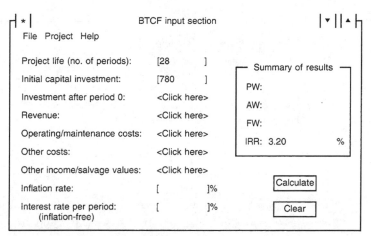

FIGURE 5.10
continued

(c) Initial entry data and IRR solution for Exercise 2. Note: The IRR cannot be computed until all the cost and income data have been input (previous two screens). Because CHEER accomplishes some data entry error checking, the value N has to be input through this initial screen before any cost or income data screens can be used.

28 periods is input through the Other Income/Salvage Value screen. Last, Fig. 5.10c gives the initial data—the project life is 28 periods, and the initial capital investment is $780 ($760 purchase price plus $20 commission). As can be seen on this screen, the calculated IRR is 3.20 percent, which is the value we tediously computed in Exercise 1.

EXERCISE 3

An old hotel was recently damaged by a fire. Since it has a desirable location in the old part of the city that is currently being rejuvenated by an urban-renewal project, it will be rebuilt and renovated as either a showroom and office building or a modern apartment building. Estimated receipts and disbursements for the 30-year life of the refurbished structure are shown below.

	Offices	**Apartments**
First cost of renovation	$340,000	$490,000
Increase in salvage value from renovation	120,000	190,000
Annual receipts	212,000	251,200
Annual disbursements	59,100	88,000
Present value of fire-damaged building	485,000	485,000
Expected salvage value of fire-damaged building after 30 years	266,000	266,000

If the required rate of return is 12 percent, which renovation plan is preferable?

SOLUTION 3

Investigating first the lowest-cost alternative, we check to see whether an office building will be profitable at $i = 0$.

$$PW = -\underbrace{\frac{(\$485{,}000 + \$340{,}000)}{P = -\$825{,}000}} + \underbrace{\frac{\$120{,}000 + \$266{,}000(1)}{S = \$386{,}000}}$$
$$+ \underbrace{\frac{(\$212{,}000 - \$59{,}000)(30)}{A = \$152{,}900}}$$
$$= \$4{,}148{,}000$$

Knowing a positive cash flow exists, we find a rough estimate of the IRR evident from the more significant flows of P and A:

$$(A/P,\ i,\ 30) \simeq A/P \simeq \frac{\$152{,}900}{\$825{,}000} \simeq 0.1853$$

which falls between the 15 and 20 percent interest tables. Then, by trial and error,

$$PW = -\$825{,}000 + \$386{,}000(P/F,\ i,\ 30) + \$152{,}900(P/A,\ i,\ 30) \stackrel{?}{=} 0$$

At IRR = 15 percent,

$$PW = -\$825{,}000 + \$386{,}000(0.01510) + \$152{,}900(6.56598)$$
$$= \$184{,}721 > 0$$

At IRR = 20 percent,

$$PW = -\$825{,}000 + \$386{,}000(0.00421) + \$152{,}900(4.97894)$$
$$= -\$62{,}095 > 0$$

Interpolation for PW = 0 gives IRR = 18.7 percent. If we had used the computer program, we would have obtained IRR = 18.5 percent. The slight discrepancy is due to interpolating over a 5 percent range in the tables (15 percent to 20 percent).

The conversion of the fire-damaged hotel to a showroom and office building is thus an acceptable alternative; the 18.7 percent IRR is greater than the required 12 percent.

Now we will check to see whether the additional expenditures and incomes for the apartment complex are justified. The alternative plan to convert to an apartment house has incremental additional values of

First cost:	$490,000 – $340,000 = $150,000
Salvage value:	$190,000 – $120,000 = $70,000
Net annual returns:	$251,200 – $88,000 – $152,900 = $10,300

The incremental rate of return is calculated as

$$PW = -\$150{,}000 + \$70{,}000(P/F,\ i,\ 30) + \$10{,}300(P/A,\ i,\ 30) \stackrel{?}{=} 0$$

At IRR = 6 percent,

$$PW = -\$150{,}000 + \$70{,}000(0.17411) + \$10{,}300(13.76483)$$
$$= \$3965$$

At IRR = 7 percent,

$$PW = -\$150,000 + \$70,000(0.13137) + \$10,300(12.40904)$$
$$= -\$12,991$$

Interpolating between 6 and 7 percent, we find

$$IRR = 6\% + (1\%)\left[\frac{\$3965 - 0}{\$3965 - (-\$12,991)}\right]$$
$$= 6.2\%$$

The computer value for IRR will also be found to be 6.2 percent.

The IRR value's being lower than the required 12 percent rate disqualifies the additional investment needed to proceed from the office plan to the apartment plan. This assumes that the additional capital could earn at least the required 12 percent.

Note that the apartment plan still has a total IRR greater than the minimum required 12 percent:

$$PW = -(\$490,000 + \$485,000) + (\$190,000 + \$266,000)(P/F, i, 30)$$
$$+ (\$251,200 - \$88,000)(P/A, i, 30) \stackrel{?}{=} 0$$

CHEER calculates the IRR value to be 16.66 percent. This tells us that if the apartment complex were the only alternative considered, then it would be viable. Since we had two alternatives, the 16.7 percent return is not viable since the costs and revenues additional to the office complex figures will return only 6.2 percent, which does not meet the required MARR of 12 percent. The results are summarized below:

	Office plan	→	**increment**	→	**Apartment plan**
First cost, $	825,000		150,000		975,000
Salvage value, $	386,000		70,000		456,000
Annual returns, $	152,900		10,300		163,200
Rate of return, %	18.5	→	6.2	→	16.7

EXERCISE 4

Expected cash flows for a strip-mining project are estimated as shown in the cash flow diagram.

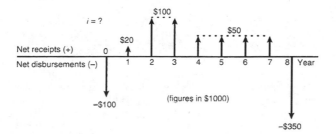

A start-up cost is incurred immediately. Then income exceeds outlays for the next 7 years. During the eighth year the major cost is for landscape improvement. Does the strip-mining project appear to be a profitable investment?

SOLUTION 4
The cash flow pattern has a sign change (minus to plus) at period 1 and another change at period 8 (plus to minus):

Year	0	1	2	3	4	5	6	7	8
Cash flow, $1000	−100	20	100	100	50	50	50	50	−350

This pattern suggests dual rates of return. The suspicion of dual interest rates is confirmed by calculations to find i^* based on

$$\begin{aligned}
PW = & -\$100{,}000 + \$20{,}000(P/F, i, 1) + \$100{,}000(P/F, i, 2) \\
& + \$100{,}000(P/F, i, 3) + \$50{,}000(P/A, i, 4)(P/F, i, 3) \\
& - \$350{,}000(P/F, i, 8) \\
& \overset{?}{=} 0
\end{aligned}$$

CHEER was used in the trial-and-error procedure to find the IRR values. The income and disbursement data were set up in the various entry screens, and CHEER estimated values to be 50 and 4 percent (within 2 percent) automatically. Various interest rates were then tried with CHEER, first around 4 percent and then 50 percent, to find the i^* that resulted in getting PW $\neq$ 0. Values of 3.1 and 48.2 percent resulted. We will see in Exercise 6 how the project balance reinvestment method will find one true IRR value.

EXERCISE 5
Calculate the e' value, using the HERR method for the cash flow in Example 5.3 when i = MARR = 20 percent.

SOLUTION 5
Given receipts (savings) of $6350, $12,600, and $12,600 at the end of years 1, 2, and 3, respectively, and an initial disbursement (investment) of $21,000 at time 0, the future worths of the positive and negative cash flows are equated:

$$\$6350(F/P, 20, 2) + \$12{,}600(F/P, 20, 1) + \$12{,}600 = \$21{,}000(F/P, e', 3)$$

from which

$$(F/P, e', 3) = \frac{\$6350(1.4400) + \$12{,}600(1.200) + \$12{,}600}{\$21{,}000} = 1.7554$$

Scanning the appendix tables for an $(F/P, e', 3)$ value equal to 1.7544, we see that it has to lie between 20 percent (1.72800) and 25 percent (1.95313). Interpolation gives an interest rate of 20.1 percent. This makes the project barely acceptable when MARR = 20 percent. Remember, though, that the HERR method does not consider all positive cash *balances*. This is the fallacy of the method.

EXERCISE 6

Apply the project balance method (PBM) to the data of Exercise 4. Use a MARR value of 20 percent as the external implicit rate. Start with the IRR values of 3.1 and 48.2 percent realized in Exercise 4.

SOLUTION 6

Checking the CB($i*$)$_t$ values, we get, using the spreadsheet program given in App. C, Example 6.[†]

Period	Cash flow, $	CB(3.1/3.1)$_t$, $	CB(48.2/48.2)$_t$, $
0	−100	−100.00	−100.00
1	20	−83.10	−128.20
2	100	14.32	−89.99
3	100	114.77	−33.37
4	50	168.33	0.55
5	50	223.54	50.81
6	50	280.47	125.30
7	50	339.17	235.70
8	−350	−0.32	−0.69

Both IRRs give some current balances greater than zero (and some less), so it follows that use of an external investment rate should be considered. Note that only one of the $i*$ values needs to be evaluated; both were shown to give an additional example of the results for the reader to check.

Now we set MARR = 20 percent and run the spreadsheet program with various potential IRR values until CB$_8$(IRR/20) ≃ 0 (or we try to manually tackle the trial-and-error process). Finally we get, for IRR = 38.5 percent,

Period	CB(38.5/20), $
0	−100.00
1	−118.50
2	−64.12
3	11.19
4	63.43
5	126.11
6	201.34
7	291.60
8	−0.07

[†]Note that, for this situation only, we set the MARR in the program to $i*$ since we are checking for positive balances with just $i*$.

We see that the i^* values of 3.1% and 48.2% found in Exercise 4 differ considerably from the true IRR value. Since IRR = 38.5 percent is far greater than the MARR of 20 percent, we have a potentially good investment.

5.8   PROBLEMS

5.1 Sometimes objects of art are respectable investments. In 1975 a marble bust of Benjamin Franklin, from which the engraving was made for $100 bills, was auctioned for $310,000. It was sculpted in France in 1778 by Jean-Antoine Houden. In 1939 the same bust sold for $30,000. What rate of return was earned by the collector who owned the statue from 1939 to 1975?

5.2 A $5000 bond matures in 10 years and pays 2.5 percent interest twice a year. If the bond sold for $5050, what is the actual investment rate?

5.3 A construction firm can lease a crane required on a project for 3 years for $180,000 payable now, with maintenance included. The alternative is to buy a crane for $240,000 and sell it at the end of 3 years for $100,000. Annual maintenance costs are expected to be $5000 the first 2 years and $10,000 the third year (payable at the end of each year). At what interest rate would the two alternatives be equivalent?

5.4 Additional parking space for a factory can be either rented for $15,000 per year on a 10-year lease or purchased for $160,000. The rental fees are payable in advance at the beginning of each year. Taxes and maintenance fees will be paid by the lessee. The land should be worth at least $95,000 after 10 years. What rate of return will be earned from purchase of the lot?

5.5 Proposal 1 has an initial cost of $1500 and a positive cash flow that returns $200 the first year and increases by $200 each of the following years until the end of the 5-year study period. Proposal 2 also has a 5-year life and an initial cost of $1500. Its positive cash flow is constant at $200 for the last 4 years. It also has another receipt in year 1. All receipts occur at the end of the year.
    (*a*)   What is the rate of return on proposal 1?
    (*b*)   If the two proposals are equally attractive at i = 15 percent annually, how large must proposal 2's unknown receipt be in period 1?

5.6 In 1994 a small apartment building was purchased for $200,000. Receipts from rent have averaged $30,200 a year; taxes, maintenance, and repair costs have totaled $8620 annually. The owner intends to hold the property until she retires in 2004. If at that time the property sells for $200,000, what rate of return will be obtained on the investment?

5.7 Stock in a corporation was purchased 10 years ago for $80 per share. For the first 6 years, the stock paid annual dividends of $11 per share and the market price climbed to $120. However, for the past 4 years, annual dividends have been only $5 per share and the price of the stock has dropped to $100.
    (*a*)   What rate of return would have been obtained by an investor who sold the stock at the end of the first 6 years?
    (*b*)   What rate of return would be obtained if an investor purchased the stock 4 years ago and sold it today?

    (*c*) What rate of return would be obtained by an investor who purchased the stock 10 years ago and sold it today?

5.8 A company can purchase a new central computer for $17,500 or can lease it for 3 years with annual payments of $8400. Determine at what interest rate the leasing and purchasing costs would be equivalent
    (*a*) If lease payments were due at the first of each year
    (*b*) If lease payments were due at the end of each year

5.9 Determine the annual effective interest rate at which the lease and purchase costs in Prob. 5.8 would be equivalent if a payment of $700 were due at the first of each month over the 3-year period instead of $8400 annually.

5.10 An investor has an opportunity to purchase a commercial rental property for $300,000. The current occupants have signed a 10-year lease at a constant annual rent of $48,000. Maintenance costs and taxes on the structure are currently $12,000 and are expected to increase at a rate of $1500 per year over the 10-year period. Assuming that the property can be sold for at least the purchase price when the current lease expires, determine the investor's minimum expected rate of return.

5.11 A student renting an unfurnished apartment has decided to purchase some furniture from Fred's Fine Furniture. The total purchase price of the three-room set is $495. However, after a down payment of $95, Fred will finance the balance through a 2-year series of end-of-month payments of $19.98. Determine the nominal and effective annual rates of interest paid by the student.

5.12 A bookstore is considering expanding its facilities. The first costs are estimated to be $50,000 with additional maintenance and operating expenses of $15,000 per year. Additional income is anticipated to be $25,000 for the first year with a $2000-per-year gradient for subsequent years. The store's MARR value is 12 percent. Determine if the investment should be pursued, using an evaluation period of 5 years. Afterward, try an evaluation period of 10 years and comment on the results.

5.13 Two alternative investment proposals are under consideration for a vacant lot owned by Urban Development Corporation. Plan *A* would require an immediate investment of $120,000 and a first-year expenditure for property taxes, maintenance, and insurance of $4000, with this amount expected to increase at a rate of $1000 per year. Plan *B* would have a first cost of $170,000 and total first-year expenses of $9000, with an increase of $1000 per year. The economic life of each project is forecast to be 10 years; and at the end of this time, only the facilities from plan *B* with a value of $50,000 are expected to be salvaged. During the life of the project, the facility in plan *A* is expected to produce $34,000 annually, whereas plan *B* is expected to produce $42,000.
    (*a*) Determine the rate of return of each plan.
    (*b*) Determine the rate of return of the additional investment required in plan *B* compared with plan *A*.
    (*c*) Which plan should Urban Development select if the company uses a MARR of 12 percent?
    (*d*) If applicable, use the PBM with a MARR of 12 percent to determine which plan to recommend.

5.14 Two mutually exclusive programs are being considered for funding. Projected cash flows are as follows:

| | Cash flow, $ | |
End of Year	Program *A*	Program *B*
0	−10,000	−15,000
1	3,000	5,000
2	5,000	5,000
3	2,000	5,000
4	4,000	5,000

Determine which program to recommend, assuming a MARR of 12 percent.

5.15 Two mutually exclusive projects are being considered: Project X requires $500 now and results in a return amounting to a one-time-only profit of $1000 in 5 years from now. Project Y also requires $500 now, but will return $170 per year for each of the next 5 years. Given a MARR of 14 percent, which project should be adopted?

5.16 In the next chapter we will see that through capital budgeting we might allow one department to fund two independent projects or several projects when the total expenditure does not exceed some budgeted amount. Suppose that the two projects in the previous problem are independent and your department can fund up to two projects if the capital outlay does not exceed $1000. What would you suggest if the MARR is 17 percent?

5.17 The cash flow for a project is shown below:

End of year	0	1	2	3	4	5
Cash flow, $	3000	1000	−5000	−5000	2000	5000

The first two payments (in thousands of dollars) represent advance payments for distribution rights on a motion picture. The next 2 years show a negative cash flow from production costs, and the last 2 years are net receipts from the finished picture. If advance payments can be invested at the external interest rate of 7 percent until period 2, what rate of return can be expected from the project?

5.18 Determine the e' rate with the HERR method for the project given in Prob. 5.17, assuming an explicit interest rate of 7 percent is feasible.

5.19 Use the project balance method to find the IRR with the same situation given in Prob. 5.18; the external rate is still 7 percent.

5.20 This problem is a variant of Prob. 2.39: A new piece of materials handling equipment costs $20,000 and is expected to save $7500 in the first year of operation. Maintenance and operating cost increases are expected to reduce the net savings by $500 per year for each additional year until the equipment is worn out at the end of 8 years. Evaluate the purchase against a MARR of 25 percent.

5.21 A bioengineering research laboratory has a patent that it is considering leasing for 10 years at $40,000 for the first year with increments of $4000 per year (arithmetic gradient) for the following 9 years. The accounting office says the company has $250,000 in development investment costs that are considered to be a first cost. Is the lease reasonable if the laboratory's MARR is 20 percent?

5.22 Suppose the research laboratory in Prob. 5.21 now has a firm MARR of 25 percent. The company it is negotiating with will not consider a first-year lease cost that is more than $30,000 due to uncertainty in the potential effectiveness of the patented process. The other company will, however, allow an increase in the arithmetic gradient that was originally proposed to be $4000 per year. What is the minimum gradient that the laboratory should consider?

5.23 Alberta Oil has paid $300,000 for a producing oil well. Field engineers estimate that net receipts will be $120,000 for the first year of operation with a reduction of 15 percent per year in the following years (geometric gradient). It plans to sell the well after 5 years for $80,000. How does this seem financially if their MARR is 20 percent?

5.24 Suppose that Alberta Oil, from Prob. 5.23, now has a MARR of 25 percent. What is the minimum salvage value that it should realize in 5 years to make its investment viable?

5.25 This problem is a variant of Prob. 3.18: A company is considering the purchase of a new piece of testing equipment that is expected to produce $8000 additional profit during the first year of operation; this amount will probably decrease by $500 per year for each additional year of ownership. The equipment costs $20,000 and will have an estimated salvage value of $3000 after 8 years of use. How does the proposal match up against a MARR of 18 percent?

5.26 Rotor Turbine Engine Company needs a new automated gear production machine. It has two bids with associated estimated data:

	Company *A*	Company *B*
Initial cost	$85,000	$110,000
Estimated net income for:		
Year 1	45,000	61,000
Year 2	40,000	53,000
Year 3	30,000	44,000
Estimated salvage value	15,000	21,000

The net income estimates include subcontracting necessary to offset different productivity levels. Determine which company to recommend, if any, given a MARR of 12 percent.

5.27 Suppose for the bids given in Prob. 5.26 that the salvage value for company *B* drops to $0. Does this change your recommendation from that for Prob. 5.26?

5.28 Owing to perennial complaints from students and faculty about the lack of parking spaces on campus, a parking garage on university-owned property is being considered. Since there are no university funds available for the project, it will have to pay for itself from parking fees over a 15-year period. A 10 percent minimum rate of return is deemed reasonable for consideration of how large the structure should be. Based on the income and cost data shown below, determine how many levels should be built.

Number of levels	Cumulative construction costs, $	Annual operating cost, $	Income per year, $
1	600,000	35,000	100,000
2	2,200,000	60,000	350,000
3	3,600,000	80,000	570,000
4	4,800,000	95,000	810,000

5.29 A business property can be purchased today for $90,000; the expected resale value after 20 years is $60,000. If annual rental income is $11,800 and expenses are $4700, what before-tax rate of return will be earned by purchasing the property?

5.30 A cash flow pattern shows an income of $250 at the end of year 1 between expenditures of $100 now and $156 at the end of year 2.
  (a) Calculate the roots i^* for PW$(i) = 0$ by trial and error and/or with an appropriate program.
  (b) We looked at a way to directly solve IRR simple problems earlier in this chapter. It is possible to do the same thing for this problem. Write the PW equation for the cash flows in terms of the $(P/F, i, N)$ factors $1/(1 + i)^N$. Now set the PW equation to zero and multiply both sides by $(1 + i)^2$. Gather terms to form a quadratic equation. You should be able to solve the quadratic equation directly for i. Logically, you should get the same results as you did in part (a).
  (c) What is the true IRR value, given MARR = 18 percent?

5.31 Assume that the MARR of 18 percent can be earned on positive cash balances for Prob. 5.30. Use the project balance reinvestment method to determine the cumulative equation to set the FW to zero, as in part (c), but leave the internal rate as i. You should be able to solve directly for the IRR value instead of by trial and error.

5.32 The owner of a truck-weighing and lumber-scaling station has agreed to lease the facility for 15 years at $8000 per year under an agreement that the scales and other equipment will be overhauled and repaired by the owner at the end of the eighth year at a cost not to exceed $150,000. The lease payments occur at the end of each year.
  (a) What potential rate(s) of return i^* will the owner receive for the station lease with the equipment repair agreement?
  (b) After negotiations on the above lease, caused by concern that the equipment needed overhauling before 8 years, it was agreed that the owner would pay up to $90,000 for repairs at the end of year 4 instead of making the repairs at the end of year 8. What rate(s) of return i^* will the owner receive under the revised agreement?
  (c) Check the revised agreement to see if it is acceptable at a MARR of 20 percent.

5.33 An interesting article about the reasons why Continental Oil Company switched in 1955 to the discounted-cash method for evaluating investments was written by John G. McLean, then vice president for international and financial operations.[†] One of the applications described was a water-flood project that exhibited dual rates of return.

The problem was to determine the profitability of acquiring a small oil-producing property in which the primary reserves were nearly exhausted. The owner of the property would receive a royalty of 12½ percent on all oil produced from the property, and the company would agree to water-flood the reservoir at an expected cost of $2.5 million. The injection of water into a reservoir is a method of *secondary recovery* that often increases the total amount of oil recovered after the free-flowing oil supply has diminished.

Estimated cash flows for the 10-year project are as follows:

Present worth of secondary oil recovery project at different discount rates (cash flows in $1000)

Year	Cash flow	Present worth of cash flow at:						
		10%	20%	28%	30%	40%	49%	50%
1	200	182	167	156	154	143	134	133
2	100	83	69	61	59	51	45	44
3	50	38	29	24	23	18	15	15
4	−1800	−1229	−868	−671	−630	−469	−365	−356
5	600	373	241	175	162	112	82	79
6	500	282	167	114	104	66	46	44
7	400	205	112	71	64	38	24	23
8	300	140	70	41	37	20	12	12
9	200	85	39	21	19	10	5	5
10	100	39	16	8	7	3	2	2
	650	198	42	0	−2	−8	0	1

The primary reserve of oil yields returns the first 3 years. The water flood is then expected to boost the company's income to $700,000 in the fourth year while it invests $2.5 million, for a net outlay of $1,800,000 that year. Thereafter, income decreases annually by $100,000. The present worths of the yearly cash flows are indicated for different discount rates. At $i = 28$ percent and $i = 49$ percent, the present worth of the cash flow is zero. Between these rates the present worth of the venture is negative.

Instead of settling for two rates of return, assume that the cash flows from the first 3 years can actually be reinvested at an annual interest rate of only 15 percent. What is the IRR on the resulting net investment, when this portion of the total is reinvested at the external 15 percent rate? How would you explain your solution to a group of investors not very familiar with discounted cash flow analysis?

5.34 Determine the PBM solution for the IRR for the cash flow given in Prob. 5.33, using the external rate of return equal to 15 percent.

[†]J. G. McLean, "How to Evaluate New Capital Investments," *Harvard Business Review,* vol. 36, no. 6, pp. 59–69, 1958.

CHAPTER 6

STRUCTURAL ANALYSIS OF ALTERNATIVES

If you will not hear reason, she will surely wrap your knuckles.

Benjamin Franklin,
Poor Richard's Almanack, 1757

Franklin tells us that we need to listen to reason, possibly through a structured analysis in our context, or we will have significant problems. We need to determine the one alternative out of many that is best to accept. Logic and reason lead to the correct decision, and now we will evolve logical processes with which to analyze alternatives.

From previous chapters we know that alternatives can be compared according to their present worths (PWs), equivalent annual worths (EAWs), and internal rates of return (IRRs). The selection of a preferred proposal from a set of alternatives depends on the structure of the set, where the structure is one of independent or dependent alternatives:

- *Independent alternatives* occur in a set when the acceptance of one alternative has no effect on the acceptance of any other alternative in the set. Such a situation occurs when we have unlimited capital and several alternatives are available that can be chosen in any combination. Stock investment might be such an example for a wealthy individual.
- *Dependent alternatives* arise when alternatives are related in a way that influences the selection process. For instance, having to choose between two machines to replace an existing machine forces only one to be feasible. Such a dependency is between *mutually exclusive* alternatives. A second dependency is forced when an alternative can be selected only if another alternative has already been selected. Such a relationship will be classified as *contingency-dependent*.

6.1   **DEVELOPMENT OF ALTERNATIVES**

An *alternative* in engineering economics is an investment possibility. It is a single undertaking with a distinguishable cash flow. Alternatives vary from doing nothing, leaving the existing cash flow intact, to very elaborate and lengthy projects. To make informed engineering economic decisions, it is necessary to understand both the composition of an alternative and its structural relationship to other investment options.

6.1.1   Identifying Alternatives

Many people besides engineers develop and evaluate investment alternatives. However, few other professions are so intimately and regularly involved with selecting the optimum device or best way to do a particular operation. Further, the operation usually has long-term consequences. That is why it is important for engineers, and others engaged in similar decision situations, to be competent economic analysts.

Analysis starts with the identification of alternatives. A need to do something originates from asking, What must be done? What can be done? What should be done? A general idea for an undertaking evolves into a family of alternatives through further questioning of the feasibility of alternative solutions and of how to do them and when. Answers to these questions may suggest several ways to accomplish the same mission or other missions that deserve attention.

Perhaps the most bothersome question in the search for alternatives is, How many is enough? Decision making can be paralyzed by a continuing search for a still-better option. At the other extreme, acting on the first option that comes to mind may ensure a fast decision but seldom a wise one. The governing objective is to develop a set of alternatives large enough to include the best possible solution. Earlier, a balance was suggested in Example 1.2, where the cost of a less-than-ideal solution was weighed against the cost of making a more optimal decision. We should not forget this possibility when we are looking at our "optimal" possibilities.

6.1.2   Defining Alternatives

From previous discussions of comparison methods we know that the basic data required for an economic analysis are the timing and amount of cash flows. These come from an understanding of the present situation and future situations. Besides the current minimum acceptable rate of return (MARR) and today's cost commitments, knowledge is needed about future objectives, resources, and operational constraints.

Proposals for investments typically exceed available funding. Some proposals can be sliced from the list of alternatives owing to their excessive size. Others may be suspect owing to their assumptions about future resources, especially when their attraction stems from unproven technology or questionable cost estimates. Part of this uncertainty can be handled by techniques presented in Chaps. 11, 13, and 14 (sensitivity analysis and risk analysis), but for now all the data will be considered reliable. Therefore, cash flows will be treated as certain to occur as estimated, and financial relations among alternatives will be assumed to be known.

<table>
<tr><td>**6.2**</td><td>**CLASSIFICATION OF ALTERNATIVES**</td></tr>
</table>

The role of the engineering economist was defined early in this text to include the identification of alternatives and analysis of their worth. Since then, alternative courses of action have been evaluated for many different situations. Alternatives that share certain features can be grouped to facilitate analysis. As indicated earlier, we can classify alternatives into dependent and independent categories.

An *independent alternative* is not affected by the selection of another alternative. Each proposal is evaluated on its merit and is approved if it meets the criteria of acceptability. Comparisons of independent investment proposals are designed to determine which proposals satisfy a minimum level of economic value. All those that surpass the minimum level may be implemented as long as sufficient capital is available. For example, if the proposals in Table 6.1 are independent and the criterion of acceptability is a return of at least 5 percent on any investment, proposals *N, W,* and *S* would be satisfactory investments because they possess positive net present worths at the required interest rate, meaning that the respective IRR values will exceed the MARR requirement.

Since alternatives may be independent, it follows that they can also be dependent. There are two classifications for dependent alternatives: *mutu-*

TABLE 6.1

Cash flows for proposals having equal lives and no salvage value

Proposal	Investment, $	Life, years	Net annual cash flow, $	Net PW[†] (at $i = 5\%$), $
N	−1000	5	+300	+299
E	−2000	5	+400	−268
W	−3000	5	+900	+896
S	−4000	5	+1000	+329

[†]PW(5) = −$1000 + $300*(P/A,* 5, 5)

ally exclusive dependent and *contingency-dependent*. Alternatives are *mutually exclusive* when the selection of one eliminates the opportunity to accept any of the others. Most of the comparisons made in previous chapters were among mutually exclusive alternatives. Operational problems normally fit into this category, because a single course of action is sought to solve a particular, often urgent, problem. When the best solution is determined, the problem is theoretically solved by implementing the indicated course of action.

Multiple alternatives are often associated with levels of development for the same asset or activity. Each level is an alternative, and the purpose of the analysis is to select the most promising level. For instance, the proposals in Table 6.1 would be considered mutually exclusive if they represented different sizes of the same design (e.g., diameters of pipe or thicknesses of insulation) or incremental levels of resource application (e.g., number of crews assigned or number of units ordered).

There are many ways in which we can evaluate mutually exclusive alternatives, assuming each can be funded by the current availability of capital. We have already seen most of these approaches in previous chapters. Net present worth and the corresponding future worth immediately come to mind. Because management frequently bases budgets on annual costs and savings, the net annual-worth approach is commonly utilized. Another common means to handle mutually exclusive alternatives is through IRR incremental analysis.

The *contingency-dependent* alternatives arise when individual investment opportunities are linked to other alternatives through legal, administrative, political, or physical requirements. Then the acceptance of one alternative depends on the simultaneous acceptance of one or more related alternatives. Cash flows are also affected by relational factors, as in a flood control proposal where the benefits of a levee of a given height depend on the acceptance of proposed dams on the headwaters of the river. Contingency-dependent analysis can be accomplished by combining the dependent alternatives into one alternative. For example, assume that proposal *W* from Table 6.1 could be implemented only if proposal *E* were also funded (perhaps a public swimming pool can be considered only if a public park is developed). This linkage simply consolidates two investments into one alternative with an initial cost of $2000 + $3000 = $5000, which is expected to earn $400 + $900 = $1300 annually. The evaluation then proceeds with *E* and *W* being treated as an individual alternative. The end effect of relational considerations is a listing of grouped, internally contingent-dependent alternatives, with some of or all the groups being mutually exclusive. If *W* is contingent on *E* but *N* and *S* are independent, we get the following alternatives: *E, E + W, N,* and *S,* where *E* and *E + W* are mutually exclusive. An impetus for investigating relational connections is to avoid the selection of a course of action that cannot be implemented without additional commitment of resources.

6.3   IRR ANALYSIS OF MUTUALLY EXCLUSIVE ALTERNATIVES

The aim of a cash flow analysis is to put all competing alternatives into a comparable investment perspective. It acts as a screen. The alternative with the most promising future from one evaluation is then pitted against winners of other evaluations where intangible and financial considerations become critical. No organization has sufficient capital to fund all conceivable worthwhile proposals within its province. Care must be taken in all evaluations to ensure correct and consistent selections. These are two logical-sounding selection criteria that sometimes lead to inaccurate conclusions:

- Select the alternative that offers the highest rate of return on total investment.
- Select the alternative with the largest investment that meets the minimum required rate of return.

Example 6.1 will show samples of both types of mistakes. The first criterion may bypass alternatives that earn lower rates of return which are still higher than other options available. The second criterion could lead to a larger investment than is desirable, which prevents a portion of the funds from earning higher returns available through substitute investments. A decision procedure to avoid inaccurate selections is the flowchart in Fig. 6.1. The procedure implicitly assumes that any size investment is possible although, as will be seen shortly, the flowchart may be modified slightly to take care of capital constraints that occur at the *operational* level where the economic decision is being made. For example, a limit on the capital to expend for an automated machine is frequently made by the manufacturing manager. This is not in conflict with the statement made in Chap. 5 that the MARR value is developed in order to ration capital. That decision will be at a higher level than the budgeted manufacturing department. Whether the selected proposal is actually funded is a financial decision that relates available capital to all types of investment proposals and their effect on the funding organization. The IRR comparison rates the alternatives as inputs to the final decision process.

Step 4 in Fig. 6.1 might need a little explanation, although this was a point that was briefly made in Chap. 5. If the lowest investment alternative (say X) satisfies the MARR ($\text{IRR}_X \geq \text{MARR}$), then X is a satisfactory alternative. If we now consider the *incremental* cash flows for the next-lowest investment, say Y, the cash flow for Y is

Cash flow$_Y$ = cash flow$_X$ + cash flow$_{Y-X}$

Therefore, when the incremental return on the cash flow $X \rightarrow Y$ satisfies the MARR, we have the previous satisfactory investment in X *plus* the incremental investment to Y that satisfies the MARR. Therefore Y is acceptable

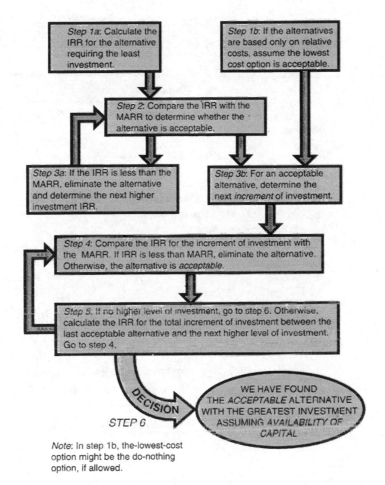

FIGURE 6.1

Process for evaluating mutually exclusive alternatives when a MARR is required.

Note: In step 1b, the-lowest-cost option might be the do-nothing option, if allowed.

at the MARR. This can then be generalized for all subsequent incremental analyses for the remaining alternatives.

EXAMPLE 6.1

Comparison of Several Mutually Exclusive Alternatives

Four designs for a product with their associated revenue and cost estimates have been presented to top management for a decision. A 10-year study period was used. A minimum rate of return of 10 percent before taxes—a rate expected from other investments with similar risk—is required. Based on the projected cash flows in Table 6.2, which of the four designs appears the most attractive?

Solution

The alternatives are already arranged in order of increasing investment requirements in Table 6.2. Table 6.3 gives related incremental values which we will use in the analysis. The annual net returns in Table 6.3 are

TABLE 6.2

Ten-year cash flows, $

	Design *A*	Design *B*	Design *C*	Design *D*
Initial investment	170,000	260,000	300,000	330,000
Annual receipts	114,000	120,000	130,000	147,000
Annual disbursements	70,000	71,000	64,000	79,000

calculated by subtracting the annual disbursements from the annual receipts for each alternative and then obtaining the differences between alternatives. For example,

$$\text{Annual net return of increment } A \to B = \$120,000 - \$71,000$$
$$- (\$114,000 - \$70,000)$$
$$= \$5000$$

We will utilize the flowchart steps given in Fig. 6.1 to determine the best alternative.

Step 1a. Calculate the IRR for design *A* (which is the increment from "do nothing" to design *A*). A *simple* investment results:

$$-\$170,000 + (\$114,000 - \$70,000)(P/A, i, 10) \doteq 0$$

and

$$(P/A, i, 10) = \frac{\$170,000}{\$44,000} = 3.8636$$

We could interpolate in the tables at the back of this book or use CHEER to give us the results directly. CHEER gives a rate of return of 22.5 percent.

TABLE 6.3

Related incremental values, $

	$A \to B$	$A \to C$	$C \to D$
Additional investment	90,000	130,000	30,000
Annual net return	5,000	22,000	2,000

Step 2. Design A is an acceptable alternative because IRR = 22.5 percent, which is greater than the 10 percent required (MARR).

Step 3b. The increment of investment from design A to design B is $260,000 – $170,000 = $90,000, and the net annual returns are $5000.

Step 4. These annual returns will obviously not pay back the investment in 10 years since $5000(10) is less than $90,000. For illustrative purposes, we can find the incremental IRR by

$$PW = -\$90,000 + \$5000(P/A, i, 10) \stackrel{?}{=} 0$$

This results in $i = -10$ percent, which is less than any feasible MARR.

Step 5. Design C is evaluated by comparing it with the last acceptable alternative, which in this case is design A. Then the incremental comparison $A \rightarrow C$ progresses as

$$-\$300,000 - (-\$170,000) + [\$130,000 - \$64,000 - (\$114,000 - \\ \$70,000)] \, (P/A, i, 10) \stackrel{?}{=} 0$$

CHEER helps us to find the IRR value of 10.9 percent.

Step 4. With its rate of return greater than 10 percent on the indicated extra increment of investment, design C becomes an acceptable alternative.

Step 5. The additional investment for design $C \rightarrow$ design D is $30,000, and the incremental annual net return is $2000. As with design $A \rightarrow$ design B, the *simple* investment returns cannot pay for themselves since $2000(10) is less than $30,000.

Step 6. Choose design C. This, of course, assumes that $300,000 is available for investment.

If the economic decision situation has capital limited at the operational level, as is often the case, the first part of step 5 in Fig. 6.1 can be modified to say, "If no higher level of investment, or sufficient additional capital is not available, go to step 6."

The rate of return on *total capital* for design C is found by

$$-\$300,000 + (\$130,000 - \$64,000)(P/A, i, 10) \stackrel{?}{=} 0$$

CHEER finds the IRR value to be 17.7 percent.

The return on *total* investment (not incremental investment) is given in Table 6.4 along with incremental results.

Earlier, we listed two mistakes that are commonly made in picking alternatives. Now we can clarify the statement with examples. One type of mistake would have been to select design A, which has the greatest rate of return on total investment, as the preferred alternative. This

TABLE 6.4

IRR relationships for Example 6.1

Design	Total investment, $	Annual return, $	IRR on total investment, %	Incremental IRR, %
A	170,000	44,000	22.5	
				$A \to B$: (−)
B	260,000	49,000	13.5	
				$A \to C$: 10.92%
C	300,000	66,000	17.7	
				$C \to D$: (−)
D	330,000	68,000	15.9	

choice would prevent the additional investment of $300,000 − $170,000 = $130,000 in design *C,* which returns 10.92 percent. Since 10.92 percent is higher than the 10 percent expected from other investments with similar risks, a loss of about 1 percent on $130,000 would occur. This can be clarified as follows:

Invest $170,000 in design A (and invest the increment that would have been invested in design *C* at the MARR = 10 percent). The annual return would be

$$\underset{\substack{\text{design } A, \\ \text{Table 6.4}}}{\$44,000} + \underset{\substack{\text{investment in } C \\ - \text{ investment in } A}}{(\$130,000)(A/P, 10, 10)} = \$65,157$$

Invest $300,000 in design C. The annual return is $66,000 (Table 6.4) and the net annual benefit for design *C* is $66,000 − $65,157 = $843.

Now, let's return to the original statement we were considering: If we invested in design *C,* we would have a return of 10.92 percent on the investment increment of $130,000 instead of 10 percent. Using CHEER, we find that

$130,000 at 10 percent will return $21,157 per year

$130,000 at 10.92 percent will return $22,000 per year

The difference in returns is $843, which of course equals the net annual benefit we just found for design *C* over design *A.*

Even though we determined the maximum investment alternative with the incremental procedure, it is prudent to keep in mind the high returns possible through an investment in design *A* in case (1) there is insufficient capital to fund design C or (2) there is another independent opportunity for investing \$130,000 at an IRR greater than 10.92 percent.

The second type of error that was mentioned earlier relative to selecting alternatives involved selecting the largest investment that still meets the 10 percent rate-of-return requirement. The unsatisfactory IRR for the extra investment in design D over design C was apparent in the incremental analysis. Therefore, putting \$330,000 − \$300,000 = \$30,000 into design D forces this amount of capital to earn less than the 10 percent it could receive if invested elsewhere.

6.4 COMPATIBILITY OF IRR INCREMENTAL ANALYSIS WITH OTHER MEASURES

We are not restricted to evaluating mutually exclusive alternatives with the IRR incremental approach. In fact, in certain circumstances it is feasible to compare the total investment IRR of a single alternative with the MARR, even though it seems to be a violation of the incremental IRR criterion. We have to remember that a do-nothing alternative and a do-something alternative comparison is the same as the total investment analysis for the do-something case. Therefore, in this situation, the incremental IRR equals the IRR on the total investment, thus satisfying the incremental analysis procedure.

Now the question is, How does the incremental investment IRR approach match up to other criteria that we have seen in earlier chapters? The answer is that we could have substituted present worth, equivalent annual worth, or future worth for IRR in the flowchart of Fig. 6.1. Instead of evaluating against the MARR value, we would have said that any alternative would be acceptable if the measurement criterion were positive. Or, we could simply do the evaluation based on the PW (or EAW or FW) of total investments instead of incremental values.

EXAMPLE 6.2   **Compatibility of PW and Incremental IRR Analysis**

Given the same data for a selection between mutually exclusive alternatives, present worth and equivalent annual-worth methods agree with the choice indicated by the rate-of-return method, as long as the *IRR* is applied to *increments* instead of to the whole investment. The present worths of the four projects described in Example 6.1 are shown in Table 6.5.

Comparing Table 6.5 with Table 6.4 confirms that PW calculations based on total investment point to the same selection as IRR calculations for *incremental* investments. Both indicate a preference for design C. The supplementary calculation of the present worths of incremental investments also agrees with the IRR results:

TABLE 6.5

Present worths of designs from Example 6.1 when MARR is 10%

Design	Investment, $ Total	Investment, $ Increment	Annual return, $ Total	Annual return, $ Increment[†]	PW at 10%, $ Total	PW at 10%, $ Increment[‡]
A	170,000		44,000		100,361	
		90,000		5,000		−59,277
B	260,000		49,000		41,084	
		40,000		17,000		64,457
C	300,000		66,000		105,541	
		30,000		2,000		−17,711
D	330,000		68,000		87,831	

[†]Difference between adjacent values; AR_{A-B}: $49,000 − $44,000 = $5000.
[‡]PW_{B-C} = −$40,000 + $17,000(P/A, 10, 10) = $64,457

$$PW(C) = PW(A) + PW(A \rightarrow B) + PW(A \rightarrow C)$$
$$\$105,541 = \$100,361 - \$59,277 + \$64,457$$

From Table 6.5 we see that the incremental PW(A → B) is negative, confirming B's unacceptability. Combining PW(A → B) with PW(B → C) produces a net positive gain that corresponds to IRR(A → C) > MARR, indicating the acceptability of design C. Thus the $90,000 + $40,000 = $130,000 investment increment that affords design C over design A earns 10 percent plus a present sum of $105,541 − $100,361 = $5180. Or equivalently, it earns an internal rate of return greater than the required 10 percent, one that equals 10.92 percent. This increment is preferable to investing $130,000 in another investment that will earn only the minimum acceptable rate of return of 10 percent.

Finally, it should be apparent that the EAW and FW values would have to correspond, from a decision point of view, to the PW relationship and to the incremental IRR analysis, since

$$EAW = (PW) \, (A/P, 10, 10)$$
$$= (PW) \, (0.16275)$$

and

$$FW = (PW) \, (F/P, 10, 10)$$
$$= (PW) \, (2.59374)$$

Table 6.6 summarizes the results.

TABLE 6.6

PW, EAW, and FW results for total investment (at 10%), $

Design	PW	EAW	FW
A	100,361	16,334	260,310
B	41,084	6,686	106,561
C	105,541	17,177	273,746
D	87,831	14,295	227,811

6.5   ANALYSIS OF INDEPENDENT ALTERNATIVES

The demarcation between dependent and independent alternatives gets fuzzy at times. Recall the plans for different product designs we had in Example 6.1. When only one new product design is sought, the four product proposals are certainly mutually exclusive. Similarly, four plans for remodeling an office are surely mutually exclusive. The best product proposal and the best office plan appear to be completely independent of each other. Yet both contribute to the profit status of the organization.

The product proposal is for a new product that will bring in revenue in excess of costs in order to increase profit, and the office plan is designed to produce improved working conditions that will lower costs to increase profit. At least tangentially, both plans are related through their contribution to the firm's financial standing and by their reliance for initial funding on the firm's capital. In effect, they may be mutually exclusive.

It is seldom worthwhile to trace tenuous links that may relate various investment proposals, particularly during initial comparison screenings. Diligent detective work could probably uncover links between any and all alternatives, but their effect on early economic comparisons would be negligible. Most mutually exclusive options are clearly evident via coinciding functions; and conditional dependencies are conspicuous by physical relations, such as the condition for adding a second floor to a building is that of constructing the first floor. Such obvious relations are natural and necessary recognitions for most economic evaluations. The question of how to finance the alternatives may or may not enter the initial comparisons.

Independent proposals can be collected in various combinations and evaluated as grouped to determine how well each combination meets the investment objectives. The groups selected depend on the conditions set for the evaluation. For instance, one division of a firm might be allowed to fund two proposals while other divisions are allowed to fund only one. Then each combination would include two proposals from the favored division with one from each of the other divisions. This is a classical capital budgeting problem and, in this case, probably one that is suboptimal.

TABLE 6.7

Cash flows for four independent proposals that have passed a screening based on a MARR of 10%

| Proposal | First cost, $ | End-of-year-cash flow, $ | | | IRR, % | PW(10%), $ |
		Year 1	Year 2	Year 3		
1	−300	130	130	130	14.4	23.29
2	−500	210	210	210	12.5	22.24
3	−600	250	250	250	12.0	21.71
4	−1500	628	628	628	12.3	61.74

Optimization techniques can be adapted to make systematic selections from numerous combinations. Such methods are beyond the scope of this text. We will introduce the simplest problem of selecting a subgroup of proposals from a larger set of proposals because of capital limitations.

6.5.1 Capital budgeting viewpoint

Determining a subset of eligible independent proposals for funding may be accomplished by using a capital budgeting approach.[†] Suppose we have four independent proposals that have been requested for funding and a limit on available capital of $2300. Data on the proposals are given in Table 6.7. Newnan shows that independent proposals competing for funding should be picked according to their IRR values—monotonically from highest to lowest. If we rank by IRR, we get the following results:

Proposal	IRR, %	Proposal first cost, $	Cumulative first costs, $
1	14.4	300	300
2	12.5	500	800
4	12.3	1500	2300
3	12.0	600	2900

With a $2300 capital limitation, we see that the combination of proposals 1, 2, and 4 should be funded.

If we look back at Table 6.7, we see that ranking on present-worth values (computed at the specified MARR of 10 percent) may not give the same results—it does in this case since we have so few proposals to pick from,

---

[†]D. G. Newnan, *Engineering Economic Analysis*, 3d ed., Engineering Press, Inc., San Jose, Calif., 1988.

but this is by chance. Proposal 4 has the highest present-worth result but the third-highest IRR value while proposal 1 has the highest IRR with the second-highest present worth. Basically, what we have done in this little exercise is to set a MARR to *ration capital*. In effect, we have set the MARR at 12.3 percent (the IRR of the last proposal selected).

We can see that ranking by IRR values is correct when we are determining the *group rate of return (GRR)* by computing a weighted average of the IRR values of the selected proposals, where weighting is by the proposals' first costs:

$$\text{GRR} = \frac{\$300(0.144) + \$500(0.125) + \$1500(0.123)}{\$300 + \$500 + \$1500} = 12.62\%$$

This is the same as that found by adding the grouped cash flows:

$$\begin{aligned} \text{PW(group)} &= -(\$300 + \$500 + \$1500) + (\$130 + \$210 + \$628) \\ &\quad \times (P/A, i, 3) = 0 \\ &= -\$2300 + \$968(P/A, i, 3) \overset{?}{=} 0 \end{aligned}$$

CHEER determines i to be 12.63 percent.

From the weighted rate of return we see the need to assign proposals by the highest IRR values. If we replace one of the three proposals with one that has a lower IRR than 12.3 percent, the grouped IRR has to be reduced. Ranking by PW values will not necessarily give the same result.

There are still potential problems in selecting proposals in this manner. What if a proposal had the second-highest IRR value and a first cost of $1000 when the capital availability was $1000? If the highest IRR proposal has a first cost of $100 and there are several other proposals with relatively low IRR values that also have first costs of $100, then our ranking process would preclude the $1000 investment from consideration. Also, what happens if our combination of proposals leaves a large sum of capital unfunded? It is assumed that proposal first costs are not too dissimilar and that there is a fairly large group to pick from. In reality, we would have to use a fairly complex algorithm for proposal selection; we have just given a simple method to exemplify the process.

6.5.2 Ranking by PW/first-cost ratio

Given a specified MARR value, Newnan[†] suggests that proposals be ranked on the basis of

$$\text{Ranking ratio} = \frac{\text{proposal PW(MARR)}}{\text{proposal first cost}}$$

[†]Ibid.

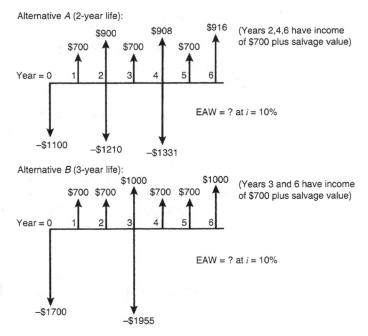

FIGURE 6.3

Cyclic cash flow over 6-year life with estimated increases in future purchase and salvage values (MARR = 10 percent).

CHEER determines the IRR value to be 21.9 percent, which exceeds the MARR value of 10 percent. Therefore, alternative A is a good investment.

Now, what is the incremental IRR when we go from alternative A to alternative B? The incremental costs and incomes for $B - A$ are

Year 0   −$1700 − (−$1100) = −$600
Year 1 $700 − $700 = $0
Year 2 $700 − (−$1210) − $900 = +$1010
Year 3   −$1955 + $1000 − $700 = −$1655
Year 4 $700 − (−$1331) − $900 = +$1123
Year 5 $700 − $700 = 0
Year 6 $1018 − $916 = +$102

This is a nonsimple investment since we have more than one sign change between adjacent cash flows. We need to see if we have multiple roots i^* for the present-worth equation. It turns out that CHEER gives a message indicating that a feasible IRR could not be found. Several interest rates were tried with CHEER to observe the effect on the present worth. It turned out that all present worths were negative. Finally, the project balance method (PBM) was tried with a MARR of 10 percent, and the following results were realized at IRR = 0.7599 percent:

End of period	Cash flow (CF), \$	Current balance (CB), \$	Calculation
0	−600	−600	$CB_0 = CF_0$
1	0	−604.56	$CB_1 = CB_0(1.007599) + CF_1$
2	1010	400.85	$CB_2 = CB_1(1.007599) + CF_2$
3	−1655	−1214.07	$CB_3 = CB_2(1.1) + CF_3$
4	1123	−100.30	$CB_4 = CB_3(1.007599) + CF_4$
5	0	−101.06	$CB_5 = CB_4(1.007599) + CF_5$
6	102	$0.17 \approx 0$	$CB_6 = CB_5(1.007599) + CF_6$

So, with a MARR of 10 percent, the IRR is less than 1 percent, and alternative *B* will not be considered further.

Of course, this is only an academic example, and we could have had numbers that reversed which alternative had the better EAW value. The point is that if you have unequal lives for your alternatives, any attempt at removing a time bias has to be accomplished by using good data.

6.7 **REINVESTMENT-DEPENDENT ALTERNATIVES**

An investment made today could allow special investment opportunities in the future that would not otherwise be available. Such an investment is *reinvestment-dependent*. If one or more alternatives in a set of mutually exclusive proposals are reinvestment-dependent, the special reinvestment opportunities must be included in the analysis.

The PW and incremental IRR methods described in this chapter are sufficient when future investments are independent of current investments. In this case, *current* proposals are accepted or rejected on the basis of the cash flows they generate, and future investments are evaluated according to their cash flows. Reinvestment dependence can also be ignored when future investments are expected to earn less than the MARR, because such future investments would be rejected owing to their negative PW.

Reinvestment dependence typically results from a current investment that permits a higher rate of return to be earned on reinvested receipts or allows the investment of new capital at a higher rate than would otherwise be possible. For instance, the purchase of a computer might yield an IRR of 30 percent *and* provide the opportunity for future purchases of peripheral equipment that would return 40 percent on subsequent investments; the latter investments would not be possible without the former.

Analysis of reinvestment-dependent alternatives is conducted by (1) estimating the rate of return applicable to future cash flows from reinvestments and additional capital investments; (2) determining the amount, timing, and future worth of the dependent cash flows; and (3) discounting the FW back to the present at the MARR. The study period during which funds can be reinvested must be the same for all alternatives and no less than the longest life of any proposal in the mutually exclusive set. The preferred alternative is the investment plan with the maximum net present value.

To illustrate a comparison involving possibilities for reinvestment dependence, we assume that the three investments in Table 6.9 are mutually exclusive. Investment A provides no special reinvestment opportunities. For investment B the annual receipts are reinvested each year at IRR = 20 percent. Proposal C recaptures its original investment plus interest in 1 year and permits another investment at year 2 equal to twice the original investment, to earn a 30 percent rate of return. Reinvestment opportunities are continued over a 4-year study period. The MARR is 10 percent.

Since receipts from proposal A are assumed to be invested at the MARR,

$$PW(A) = -\$1000 + \$400(P/A, 10, 4) = \$268$$

Of course, the same PW(A) results from FW(A) discounted back to time 0:

$$PW(A) = [-\$1000(F/P, 10, 4) + \$400(F/A, 10, 4)]\,(P/F, 10, 4)$$
$$= \$392(0.68301) = \$268$$

TABLE 6.9

Cash flow and other data for three proposals; B and C allow reinvestment while A does not

	End of year	Alternative A	Alternative B	Alternative C
	0	−$1000	−$1000	−$1000
	1	400	600[†]	1100[‡]
	2	400	600[†]	−2000[§]
	3	400	0	0
	4	400	0	0
Reinvestment rate		MARR	20%	30%
PW at IRR = 10% (ignoring reinvestments)		268	41	0[¶]
FW (reinvested receipts)		0	1901	4844
PW at IRR = 10% (including reinvestments)		268	298	656

[†]Receipts reinvested at 20 percent.
[‡]Receipt from original investment will return MARR for next 3 years.
[§]New capital invested at 30 percent.
[¶]Based only on original $1000 investment.

The two $600 receipts in proposal B can be reinvested at 20 percent as soon as they are received, and therefore they have a future worth in 4 years of

$$\text{FW(reinvestments)} = \$600(F/P, 20, 3) + \$600(F/P, 20, 2) = \$1901$$

Discounting the future worth back to time 0 at MARR = 10 percent then makes the cash flows of the alternatives comparable:

$$\text{PW}(B) = -\$1000 + \$1901(P/F, 10, 4) = \$298$$

In proposal C, the $1100 capital recovery payment is assumed to earn only the MARR of 10 percent when reinvested, but the original investment allows a new $2000 investment to earn 30 percent for 2 years. The terminal value of the two investments is

$$\text{FW(reinvestment)} = \$1100(F/P, 10, 3) + \$2000(F/P, 30, 2) = \$4844$$

The present worth of proposal C is calculated by discounting the future worth at 10 percent for 4 years and subtracting the present worths of the $1000 and $2000 outlays:

$$\text{PW}(C) = -\$1000 - \$2000(P/F, 10, 2) + \$4844(P/F, 10, 4) = \$656$$

Outcomes of PW comparisons with and without reinvestment are shown in Table 6.9. The change in preference between alternatives resulting from opportunities for reinvestment amply demonstrates the importance of recognizing the existence of reinvestment-dependent options and accommodating dependent cash flows in the analysis.

6.8   SUPPLEMENTARY CONSIDERATIONS

We have seen some approaches to tackling the challenging problem of finding which alternative is the best for our situation. We have made many assumptions, some stated and others implied. Later topics will allow us to relax these assumptions. Consider the following examples.

- *Taxation.* In all the materials to this point, we have ignored taxation. If we borrow money to invest in an alternative or if we have a profit, then our operation will be subject to federal and provincial income taxes and possible shelters against taxes. In the worst case, the total effective taxation rate might be close to 50 percent. The engineering economic analysis could be greatly biased by the elimination of taxes. This topic is covered in Chap. 9.

- *Inflation*. Inflation was introduced earlier, and it was assumed that all cash flows are in constant dollars in that inflation effects have been damped out. Chapter 10 is completely devoted to the problems with inflation and will clarify further consideration of the effects of inflation.
- *Sensitivity analysis*. After we have completed our analysis to the best of our ability, we might want to see how estimates that were used in supplying analysis data affect the outcomes. In other words, how *sensitive*, e.g., are the PW results to the salvage value estimate that was really an informed guess? We might find that a wide range of salvage values does not significantly affect our results. If so, then the PW values are not sensitive to salvage values and we should not spend a large amount of cost and effort in trying to refine the salvage value estimates. Chapter 11 will discuss sensitivity analysis and introduce us to that capability in CHEER.
- *Risk analysis*. As will be discussed in Chap. 13, the outcome of any economic decision is usually subject to an environment of uncontrollable influence. In our analyses to this point, we have assumed that cash flow is known with certainty. The shorter the time span of the analysis period, the closer we are to being certain of our cash flow estimates. For those situations where risk is a reality, simulation of the situation under varying circumstances might be warranted to see the worst or best possible outcomes so that an informed decision could be made. CHEER, the program ancillary to this text, allows simulations to be run to give us the best information possible when we make a recommendation.

6.9   USE ALL THE DATA!

As with any engineering text, the material could be covered completely, and yet, when the reader reports to work, the first engineering economy problem encountered probably will not fit exactly the material presented. We can provide only a foundation for approaching problems; it is up to the engineer to use intuition, common sense, and other attributes in adapting to the new problem. We now look at a situation that calls for marginal analysis for a problem that deviates from those we have visited so far. The aim is to show that using all your *good* data is imperative to get a good solution.

Many decision situations involve mutually independent proposals that have alternatives which become mutually exclusive when resources are limited. Since these situations are usually settled by marginal analysis—the examination of each additional activity increment—proposals can be displayed graphically to show the relation of alternatives and their relative acceptabilities.

Suppose three government departments have indicated a desire to hire engineering students on a part-time basis: highway (H), motor vehicle (MV), and internal management (IM) departments. All have forwarded

TABLE 6.10

Gross margin (expected value of savings) from hiring[†]

Department	Number of student positions	Gross margin, $
H	1	2100
	2	3700
	3	5000
	4	6100
MV	1	1800
	2	2600
	3	5500
IM	1	500
	2	3800

[†]Not listed but implied is the possibility that none of the positions will be filled.

their requests to the executive department, stating the number of students wanted and the savings expected from hiring them to work on specific problems that would otherwise not be addressed. The proposals are shown in Table 6.10, where *gross margin* is the expected value of savings (or benefits) prorated by month for each project the students might work on. This figure does not include the labor cost of hiring a student.

Employment proposals from the respective departments are independent alternatives for funding by the executive department, but the number of positions that can be filled in each department is mutually exclusive.

The incremental relations of positions within each department are shown in the three parts of Fig. 6.4. Indicated in each part by a dashed line

FIGURE 6.4
Graphs of employment alternatives.

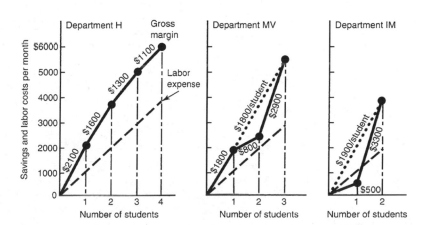

is the monthly cost of employment, which amounts to $1000 per student. Consideration of this employment expense leads to the elimination of unqualified alternatives, such as having only one student in department IM; apparently the combination of two students working together will produce collective savings of $3800, or is $1900 apiece, but one student working alone can generate savings of only $500. The skip over the unacceptable $500 alternative to the acceptable $3800 margin for two positions is indicated by a dotted line labeled with the incremental savings, $1900 per student when two are employed.

If the executive department can budget enough to fill only one position, it should go to department H, where the gross margin from hiring one student is highest—$2100. But if two students can be hired and management decides they should both go to one department, then they should both be assigned to department IM, where their average gross margin is $1900. When three students can be hired, one should go to H and the other two to IM for a total gross margin of $5900, which amounts to $1967 per person.

This example shows the importance of having a complete array of alternatives available for analysis. If each department had gone through a preselection process to submit only its best plan, as frequently happens in decentralized organizations, a less-than-optimal allocation would result whenever three or more positions were filled, based on the given data. A preselection policy may cause suboptimization when resources are limited.

6.10 REVIEW EXERCISES AND DISCUSSIONS

EXERCISE 1
Data for three alternative investment plans are as follows:

Alternative	Investment, $	Salvage value, $	Life, years	Annual net cash flow, $
X	6,000	0	3	2,600
Y	12,000	3,000	6	2,500
Z	18,000	0	6	4,000

When the minimum attractive rate of return is 10 percent, which alternative(s) should be selected under each of the following decision conditions?

(a) Individual alternatives are mutually exclusive.
(b) Individual alternatives are independent.

SOLUTION 1

Since alternative X will last one-half the time of the other two alternatives, we need to have two 3-year cycles for X and one cycle of 6 years for alternatives Y and Z:

$$PW(X) = -\$6000 - \$6000(P/F, 10, 3) + \$2600(P/A, 10, 6)$$
$$= -\$6000 - \$6000(0.75131) + \$2600(4.35526) = \$815.82$$

$$PW(Y) = -\$12,000 + \$2500(P/A, 10, 6) + \$3000(P/F, 10, 6)$$
$$= -\$12,000 + \$2500(4.35526) + \$3000(0.564487)$$
$$= \$581.61$$

$$PW(Z) = -\$18,000 + \$4000(P/A, 10, 6)$$
$$= -\$18,000 + \$4000(4.35526) = -\$578.96$$

a. Mutually exclusive alternatives. Alternative Z will not be considered due to the negative PW, meaning we cannot meet the desired interest rate of 10 percent. When both X and Y investments are compared over a 6-year period, with the implicit assumption that a second investment in X can be made at the end of 3 years at the original cost in constant dollars, X is preferred.

Of course, we could have evaluated the noncyclic data with the EAW criterion since it was assumed that the $6000 investment cost for X would not change in year 4:

$$EAW_X = -\$6000(A/P, 10, 3) + \$2600 = -\$6000(0.40211) + \$2600$$
$$= \$187.34$$

$$EAW_Y = -\$12,000(A/P, 10, 6) + \$2500 + \$3000(A/F, 10, 6)$$
$$= -\$12,000(0.22961) + \$2500 + \$3000(0.12961)$$
$$= \$133.51$$

Again, X is preferred, as expected.

Computing the present worths from the annual worths, we get

$$PW_X = \$187.34(P/A, 10, 6) = \$187.34(4.35526) = \$815.91$$

$$PW_Y = \$133.51(P/A, 10, 6) = \$133.51(4.35526) = \$581.47$$

Needless to say, these match the original present-worth values computed except for minor rounding differences.

b. Under the assumption that funds are available for all alternatives that meet the minimum attractive rate of return, investments in X and Y are indicated by their positive present worths. Both satisfy the 10 percent return criterion.

EXERCISE 2

The five investment proposals shown below have been investigated carefully and are deemed to be equally safe. An investor will be satisfied if a minimum before-tax return of 9 percent is realized.

Proposal	Investment, $	Life, years	Salvage value, $	Net annual cash flow, $
Alpha	30,000	5	0	7,500
Beta	60,000	5	10,000	13,755
Gamma	20,000	5	0	5,000
Delta	40,000	5	10,000	10,000
Epsilon	30,000	5	5,000	7,500

Using EAW calculations, answer the following:

(a) Which proposal is preferred if only one can be selected?
(b) How much should be invested if the proposals are independent and if unlimited capital is available?
(c) Which proposals should be utilized if an investor wishes to allocate exactly $60,000 of investment capital and if any funds not put into one or more of the proposals will be used to purchase bonds paying annual dividends of $7\frac{1}{2}$ percent on the amount invested?

SOLUTION 2
The annual worth of each proposal is calculated as follows:

$$EAW(alpha) = \$7500 - \$30,000(A/P, 9, 5)$$
$$= \$7500 - \$30,000(0.25709) = -\$213$$

$$EAW(beta) = \$13,755 + (-\$60,000 + \$10,000)(A/P, 9, 5) + (-\$10,000)(0.09)$$
$$= \$13,755 - \$50,000(0.25709) - \$900 = 0$$

$$EAW(gamma) = \$5000 - \$20,000(A/P, 9, 5)$$
$$= \$5000 - \$20,000(0.25709) = -\$142$$

$$EAW(delta) = \$10,000 - (\$40,000 - \$10,000)(A/P, 9, 5) - \$10,000(0.09)$$
$$= \$10,000 - \$30,000(0.25709) - \$900 = \$1387$$

$$EAW(epsilon) = \$7500 - (\$30,000 - \$5000)(A/P, 9, 5) - \$5000(0.09)$$
$$= \$7500 - \$25,000(0.25709) = \$625$$

(a) If only one proposal can be accepted, delta is preferred because it has the largest net annual worth on the capital invested.

(b) With unlimited capital, delta and epsilon are obvious selections, owing to their positive net annual worths (AWs). Beta should also be accepted, even with its zero annual worth, because the $60,000 invested will still earn 9 percent; any positive AW indicates a return *equal to or greater than* the minimum attractive rate of 9 percent. Therefore, $60,000 + $40,000 + $30,000 = $130,000 should be invested from the unlimited treasury.

(c) An investment capital limitation of $60,000 allows three logical choices:

1. Invest the full amount in beta where it will earn exactly 9 percent.
2. Invest in delta ($40,000) plus gamma ($20,000) to earn 9 percent plus $1387 − $142 = $1245.

3. Invest in delta plus a $20,000 bond. This combination is obviously superior to the similar combination of epsilon plus a $30,000 bond. Annual returns from the bond are $0.075 \times \$20,000 = \$1500$.

$$
\begin{array}{ccccc}
\text{EAW} = \$1387 & - & \$20{,}000(A/P,\,9,\,5) & + & \$20{,}000(A/F,\,9,\,5) & + & \$1500 \\
\text{delta} & & \text{bond} & & \text{bond} & & \text{bond} \\
\text{return} & & \text{investment} & & \text{redemtpion} & & \text{dividend}
\end{array}
$$

$$= \$1387 - \$20{,}000(0.25709) + \$20{,}000(0.16709) + \$1500$$

$$= \$1087$$

Thus the EAW of the $60,000 investment in delta plus the bond is better than the $60,000 beta investment proposal, but less rewarding than investing in delta and gamma.

EXERCISE 3

Table 6.2 gave four mutually exclusive design alternatives to be evaluated. The flowchart procedure outlined in Fig. 6.1 was used in determining the best alternative under the incremental IRR criterion. Show that this same incremental analysis procedure will work with the PW criterion.

SOLUTION

The solution follows the steps in the flowchart.

Step 1a. Calculate PW for design A (the increment from do nothing to design A). From Table 6.5 we see that PW = $100,361.

Step 2. Since we have a positive PW, design A is a satisfactory alternative.

Step 3b. The increment of investment from design A to design B is $90,000, and the incremental annual returns are $5000.

Step 4.

$$\text{PW}_{A \to B} = -\$90{,}000 + \$5000(P/A,\,10,\,10)$$
$$= -\$90{,}000 + \$5000(6.14457) = -\$59{,}277$$

Design B is not viable.

Step 5. The increment is now evaluated to design C from the previously accepted alternative, design A.

$$\text{PW}_{A \to C} = -\$130{,}000 + \$22{,}000(P/A,\,10,\,10)$$
$$= -\$130{,}000 + \$22{,}000(6.14457) = \$5181$$

Step 4. Since the PW is positive, design C is acceptable.

Step 5. Evaluate design $C \to$ design D:

$$\text{PW}_{C \to D} = -\$30{,}000 + \$2000(P/A,\,10,\,10)$$
$$= -\$30{,}000 + \$2000(6.14457) = -\$17{,}711$$

Since the PW is negative, reject alternative D.

Step 6. Accept design C.

Needless to say, the procedure mirrors the results we got by using the incremental IRR criterion. Also, it makes more sense to perform the PW (or EAW or FW) analysis on total investment per alternative than on incremental values.

EXERCISE 4

Table 6.8 showed 15 feasible groups of proposals where each proposal was independent of the others. Apply the incremental IRR criterion to determine the best alternative when we have a $2300 total capital constraint.

SOLUTION

CHEER will be used to determine the IRR values. First, the group cash flows are summarized from Table 6.8 as follows, by ranking the groups from minimum first costs through maximum:

Group	Proposals	First costs, $	Annual receipts (years 1, 2, 3), $
1	1	−300	130
2	2	−500	210
4	3	−600	250
3	1, 2	−800	340
5	1, 3	−900	380
6	2, 3	−1100	460
7	1, 2, 3	−1400	590
8	4	−1500	628
9	1, 4	−1800	758
10	2, 4	−2000	838
12	3, 4	−2100	878
11	1, 2, 4	−2300	968

The incremental cash flow IRR values are computed as follows:

From group x	To group y	Incremental present worth (x to y), $	CHEER IRR, %	Decision based on MARR of 10%
0	1	$-300 + 130(P/A, i, 3)$	14.36	Accept group 1
1	2	$-200 + 80(P/A, i, 3)$	9.71	Keep group 1
1	4	$-300 + 120(P/A, i, 3)$	9.71	Keep group 1
1	3	$-500 + 210(P/A, i, 3)$	12.51	Accept group 3
3	5	$-100 + 40(P/A, i, 3)$	9.67	Keep group 3
3	6	$-300 + 120(P/A, i, 3)$	9.71	Keep group 3
3	7	$-600 + 250(P/A, i, 3)$	12.05	Accept group 7
7	8	$-100 + 38(P/A, i, 3)$	6.89	Keep group 7
7	9	$-400 + 168(P/A, i, 3)$	12.51	Accept group 9
9	10	$-200 + 80(P/A, i, 3)$	9.71	Keep group 9
9	12	$-300 + 120(P/A, i, 3)$	9.71	Keep group 9
9	11	$-500 + 210(P/A, i, 3)$	12.51	Accept group 11

Fund group 11 (proposals 1, 2, and 4) which, as expected, is the same decision made by using the present-worth criterion.

EXERCISE 5

Often alternatives are based on only relative costs. A company has to install a new air conditioning system, or a hospital has to retrofit the rest rooms. Suppose that a hospital needs a copy machine for the accounting department for internal use. The accounting department has been sharing a machine with another department, but the load has become so great due to government reporting requirements that a separate machine seems justified. Evaluations are to be based on 3-year lives before replacement will be required. Three bids are received—two for a new machine and one for a reconditioned model. Operation and maintenance costs, as well as future trade in values, will be a function of the machine bought, warranties, and so on. The industrial engineering department comes up with the following data:

	Initial cost, $	Operating/maintenance cost, $			Trade-in value, $
		Year 1	Year 2	Year 3	
Bid A (new machine)	−12,000	−3,100	−3,300	−4,000	3,500
Bid B (new machine)	−10,500	−3,500	−3,800	−4,500	2,500
Bid C (reconditioned)	−5,000	−5,000	−5,300	−6,000	600

Which bid would you recommend be accepted, given a MARR of 10 percent?

SOLUTION

Let's use the incremental IRR approach to solve this problem; the methodology is outlined in Fig. 6.1. The approach says that when we have alternatives that have only costs in the cash flow, we start with that alternative with the lowest first cost and assume that it is satisfactory (assuming that the do-nothing alternative is not plausible). There are incomes from salvage values, but these are very small compared with the costs. The smallest investment would be for the reconditioned machine. The incremental data in going from bid C to bid B, the next-lowest investment, are as follows:

	Initial cost, $	Operating/maintenance cost, $			Trade-in value, $
		Year 1	Year 2	Year 3	
Increment C → B	−5,500	1500	1500	1500	1900

CHEER determined that the IRR for this simple incremental reinvestment is 6.9 percent, which is not acceptable since the MARR is 10 percent.

Now we have to determine the incremental return from C to A:

	Initial cost, $	Operating/maintenance cost, $			Trade-in value, $
		Year 1	Year 2	Year 3	
Increment $C \rightarrow A$	−7000	1900	2000	2000	2900

Again, we have a simple incremental investment, and CHEER computes an incremental IRR of 10.4 percent which is reasonable. Therefore, bid A should be picked.

6.11 PROBLEMS

6.1 A spare-parts service department for a construction equipment supplier must be established in Yukon to meet contractual commitments. The firm has eliminated the option of building a new field office because it expects to conduct business in Yukon for only the next 10 years; so an existing structure will be purchased. At best, the field office will meet expenses and make a small profit contribution. Only three structures that are available for purchase meet the space needs and have the desired location. A major portion of the investment will likely be recovered by appreciation in land values. A minimum acceptable rate of return of 15 percent before taxes is expected on such investments. What rate of return will be earned by each increment of investment from the anticipated cash flows shown? Which investment would you recommend?

	Site 1	Site 2	Site 3
Purchase price	$140,000	$190,000	$220,000
Resale value	125,000	155,000	175,000
Net annual revenue	24,000	31,000	41,000

6.2 Evaluate the following plans, using the incremental IRR approach, and select the preferable alternative. The minimum acceptable rate of return is 6 percent.

	Plan 1	Plan 2	Plan 3
First cost, $	70,000	59,000	100,000
Salvage value, $	6,000	4,000	7,500
Economic life, years	8	8	8
Annual receipts, $	32,000	30,000	51,000
Annual disbursements, $	18,000	23,000	35,000

6.3 A temporary water line is required to supplement the water supply at a plant until city water becomes available in a new industrial area. Three alternative pipe sizes with associated pumping facilities will satisfy the water requirements:

	Pipe size		
	14 inches **(35.6 centimeters)**	**16 inches** **(40.6 centimeters)**	**18 inches** **(45.7 centimeters)**
First cost, $	18,000	25,000	34,000
Annual pumping cost, $	6,400	4,400	2,800

The pipeline and pumping stations will be in the same location for all three alternatives. The planning period is 5 years, and pipe can be recovered at the end of the period. It is expected to yield 40 percent of its first cost when recovered, and the cost of recovery will be $2000 regardless of pipe size. Recommend an alternative if a 9 percent return before taxes is desired.

6.4 The cyclic cash flow data shown in Fig. 6.3 had investment and salvage values that had noninflationary changes. Summary results were given in the related text material: $EAW_A = \$107.66$ and $EAW_B = \$65.38$. Show that these values are correct.

6.5 Three mutually exclusive investments to be compared by the rate-of-return method are described below. The MARR is 9 percent.

	Alternatives		
	X	**Y**	**Z**
First cost, $	20,000	16,000	10,000
Annual expense, $	5,000	3,000	4,000
Annual income, $	11,500	11,500	7,000
Economic life, years	4	2	4

(a) Which alternative has the highest overall IRR, and what is it?
(b) Recommend an alternative, and justify your recommendation.
(c) Suppose that first costs are expected to increase at 4 percent per year due to technological instability. How will this affect your decision?

6.6 Four requests for expenditures are given:

Proposal	First cost, $	Net annual savings, $
Maintenance	50,000	20,000
Production	73,000	31,000
Purchasing	82,000	35,000
Computer	93,000	38,900

All proposals have a life of 3 years, and the minimum acceptable rate of return is 12 percent.
(a) Which proposal(s) should be accepted if they are independent?
(b) Which proposal should be accepted if they are mutually exclusive?

6.7 Autocon Company is evaluating three robots for use in assembly operations (only one robot will be purchased). These data are associated with the robots:

	Robot *A*	Robot *B*	Robot *C*
First cost, $	55,000	58,000	53,000
Operating and maintenance costs, $	3000/year	4500/year	4000/year
Expected income, $	26,000/year	30,000/year	24,000/year
Salvage value, $	4000	6000	4000

Assuming a technological life of 3 years and a MARR of 12 percent, evaluate the robots by using the incremental IRR approach.

6.8 Suppose the technological life for robots *A* and *C* in Prob. 6.7 is 3 years while that for robot *B* is reduced to 2 years. Also, robot first costs are supposed to increase at a rate of $500 per year for the next several years. Reevaluate your recommendation in Prob. 6.7, given that salvage values will stay at the rates quoted in Prob. 6.7.

6.9 A seafood company is planning an expansion to a cold storage facility. Three alternative site-design proposals are being considered that use a MARR of 10 percent. Plans *A* and *B* require an expenditure of $350,000 for land which will retain its value in 10 years, while plan *C* requires $425,000 for land which will also retain its value in 10 years. The estimated income increase due to facility availability is annualized at $248,000 per year. The company requires that a life of 10 years be used for the analysis. Data, all in dollars, associated with the project are as follows:

	Proposal *A*	Proposal *B*	Proposal *C*
Building and installation	600,000	700,000	400,000
Compressors	100,000	135,000	85,000
Expected energy costs:			
First year	65,000	48,000	65,000
Increase for each additional year	3,000	2,000	3,500
Annual maintenance costs	20,000	15,000	50,000
Estimated salvage value	35,000	43,000	18,000

Evaluate which proposal to recommend using the EAW criterion.

6.10 Evaluate the alternatives in Prob. 6.9 by using the IRR criterion.

6.11 An estimating service for contractors plans to provide an additional service for its customers. Besides the normal routine for making estimates, an additional follow-up service will be offered to review the records of each project and analyze actual versus estimated costs. Based on the expected workload for the next 3 years, the proposal could be conducted by

(a) One secretary and a clerk with total direct and indirect wages of $28,000 per year, using hand-operated equipment with an initial cost of $2800

(b) One secretary with total annual wages of $15,000, using computerized equipment that is priced at $16,000 and has maintenance costs of $300 per month

(c) Subcontracting part of the work at a monthly cost of $1400 and hiring a part-time secretary for $10,000 per year

Evaluate the proposals, assuming a 3-year life and no salvage values. An 8 percent minimum rate of return is required. Use the EAC criterion in your analysis.

6.12 Based on the data in Exercise 2 and the investment conditions in part (c) (where the investment capital is limited to $60,000), explain the following characteristics of the solution:

(a) The reasoning that eliminated the epsilon proposal without recourse to calculations when it is compared with the delta proposal as part of the $60,000 investment in a proposal plus a bond

(b) The reason why the annual worth of delta plus a $20,000 bond paying $7\frac{1}{2}$ percent interest is less than the AW of the delta proposal alone

6.13 A firm finds that it will be necessary to air-condition a rather large area for its computers and data processing equipment. An engineering study revealed that the more money spent on insulating the walls and ceiling area, the less money required for the air-conditioning unit. The engineer's estimates, all in dollars, are as follows:

	Alternative			
	1	2	3	4
First cost of insulation	35,000	45,000	60,000	80,000
First cost of air conditioning	52,000	45,000	38,000	32,000
Annual power cost	6,500	5,100	4,100	3,500

The study also estimated that (1) the insulating material would have a life of 20 years with zero salvage value and (2) the air-conditioning equipment would have a life of 10 years with no salvage value. Taxes and insurance are expected to be 2 percent of the first cost per year. Which alternative should be selected if the firm requires a 15 percent rate of return before taxes and a PW evaluation is used? Assume that any replacement costs will remain the same as the current value.

6.14 This problem is the same as Prob. 6.13 except that you are asked to evaluate the effect of air conditioning first costs increasing at 4 percent per year.

6.15 Advanced Product Engineering Group has developed a list of potential, mutually exclusive project proposals as possible new investments. All have a 10-year life and no salvage value. Using IRR calculations and the data shown below, determine which project, if any, should be accepted. Use MARR = 10 percent.

Project	First cost, $	Annual cash flow (positive), $
A	100,000	16,980
B	85,000	14,500
C	25,000	3,200
D	43,000	6,700
E	79,000	12,300
F	13,000	1,800
G	112,000	17,800

6.16 Assume that the projects given in Prob. 6.15 are independent projects. If management said you could have up to $80,000 to spend on projects, which would you pick, assuming a MARR of 10 percent has to be satisfied?

6.17 Suppose that a city has three proposals for funding with the following data:

Proposal	First cost, $	Annual cash flow (positive), $
Park	54,000	15,000
Swimming pool	32,000	12,000
Recreation center	50,000	16,000

All investments have to be evaluated over 5-year lives, and the MARR is 10 percent. The last two proposals are independent of each other, but each is contingent-dependent on the park's being constructed. If there is unlimited funding available (for a city?), which proposal(s) would you recommend be funded?

6.18 Assume that the maximum amount that can be spent on the proposals in Prob. 6.17 is $105,000. What proposals would you now recommend?

6.19 Four alternative investment proposals are being evaluated:

Proposal	Initial investment, $	IRR for proposal, %	Incremental IRR, %, when compared with proposal		
			A	B	C
A	120,000	20.5			
B	168,000	17	11		
C	205,000	18.5	18	21	
D	248,000	16.5	13	16	13

(a) If the proposals are mutually exclusive, which one should be selected if the MARR is 15 percent?

(b) If the proposals are independent, which should be selected if the MARR is 15 percent?

(c) If the proposals are independent, what is the highest rate of return that can be gained when investment capital is limited to $300,000 and any funds not allocated to the given proposals can be invested at 15 percent?

6.20 The think-tank group at Imagineering Inc. has recently come up with six proposals for consideration. Each project has an estimated life of 10 years with no salvage value. Their potential impacts in dollars are given below:

	Project					
	A	**B**	**C**	**D**	**E**	**F**
Required capital	8000	4000	1000	3000	1500	9000
Annual cash flow	1100	800	200	715	250	1400

(a) Assuming Imagineering Inc. has unlimited capital and the projects are independent, which projects should be accepted? The MARR is 15 percent.
(b) Given that Imagineering has only $10,000 of investment capital available, determine which of the independent alternatives should be selected.
(c) Assuming that the projects are mutually exclusive, determine which, if any, of the proposals should be accepted.

6.21 Cash flows from five investment proposals are itemized below. All investment opportunities are evaluated by using a 15 percent rate of return and are based on a 5-year period.

Proposal	Investment, $	Cash flow, $, in year				
		1	**2**	**3**	**4**	**5**
A	−15,000	4,500	4,500	4,500	4,500	4,500
B	−25,000	12,000	10,000	8,000	6,000	4,000
C	−20,000	2,000	4,000	6,000	8,000	10,000
D	−30,000	0	0	15,000	15,000	15,000
E	−10,000	4,500	4,500	−2,500	4,500	7,500

(a) If the proposals are mutually exclusive, which is the best investment based on its present worth?
(b) If investment capital is limited to $30,000 and the proposals are independent, which proposals should be accepted?

6.22 A half-dozen cost reduction proposals have been forwarded by the industrial engineering department. A 20 percent rate of return is expected, and all equipment investments are to be written off in 5 years with no salvage value.

Proposal	Equipment cost, $	Net annual savings, $
Combine	28,000	8,800
Rearrange	64,000	23,000
Modify	18,500	8,000
Eliminate	19,500	9,200
Improve	39,000	15,000
Safer	31,500	9,800

(a) Which proposal should be selected if only one can be accepted?
(b) Which proposals should be selected if all proposals are independent and there is effectively unlimited capital available for cost reduction projects?

6.23 Four mutually exclusive alternatives are being considered. They are listed in order of increasing first costs in the following table, where the rate of return for the overall investment in each and the incremental IRR for every increment are given. All the alternatives have the same lives and comparable intangible values. A MARR of 12 percent is specified.

Alternative	IRR on overall alternative, %	IRR, %, on increments of investment compared with alternative		
		1	2	3
1	1			
2	7	20		
3	12	15	12	
4	16	21	19	17

(a) If one of the alternatives *must* be implemented, which one should be selected?
(b) What would you recommend if none of the alternatives is mandatory (do nothing is an acceptable alternative) and there are insufficient funds for alternative 4.

6.24 Three independent proposals have passed a preliminary screening to confirm that all are acceptable at a minimum IRR of 15 percent. Each one has an economic life of 4 years. The cash flows are given in the following table, with the salvage values included in the final year's income:

Proposal	First cost, $	End-of-year cash flows, $			
		1	2	3	4
A	17,000	10,000	8,000	6,000	4,000
B	23,000	3,800	6,800	9,800	12,800
C	20,400	8,000	8,000	8,000	8,000

Which combination of proposals should be selected if sufficient capital is available to fund any choice, as long as the rate of return is 20 percent or greater? Why?

6.25 A public utility board is considering an addition to the existing pumping system. Alternative designs are being studied at two sites, and the following cost estimates have been developed (only one system will be installed):

Site	Design	Equipment cost, $	Annual operations and maintenance expense, $
Annex 1	A	3,000,000	560,000
	B	3,400,000	475,000
Annex 2	C	3,900,000	380,000
	D	4,750,000	190,000

The Annex 1 site will require an expenditure of $2,800,000 for land and right-of-way easements, and the Annex 2 plans would require $3,350,000. The land will represent a permanent investment, whereas the equipment will require replacement at a 30-year interval.

(a) Determine which of the mutually exclusive proposals should be selected through a rate-of-return comparison based on a MARR of 7 percent.

(b) Determine the capitalized cost of each alternative, using an interest rate of 7 percent.

6.26 Clinker Creek Coal Company is considering the purchase of new pumps for use in the open-pit mine. Occasionally, excess rainfall causes minor flooding which reduces production while pumping is being carried out. Several alternatives are to be considered on a before-tax annual-cost basis with an interest rate of 20 percent. The service life of the pumps is assumed to be 10 years, and the portable piping and other equipment are expected to last 5 years with no salvage value for any of the items.

	Type of pump			
	Two-cylinder	**Four-cylinder**	**Diesel**	**Electric**
Pump first cost, $	20,000	30,000	50,000	75,000
Piping and auxiliary equipment, $	10,000	10,000	20,000	20,000
Annual energy and maintenance, $	7,000	6,000	5,000	4,000
Annual expected cost of lost production while pumping, $	30,000	25,000	20,000	12,000

Determine which of the pumping systems should be selected.

6.27 Two mutually exclusive proposals have the following cash flows in dollars:

Year	Proposal J	Proposal K
0	−100,000	−100,000
1	60,000	60,000
2	50,000	15,000
3	40,000	60,000
4	30,000	0
5	0	0

All receipts from proposals J and K can be reinvested at 20 percent for J and 25 percent for K, respectively. The reinvestment rates are expected to continue throughout the 5-year comparison period. The minimum acceptable rate of return for all investments is 15 percent.

(a) What is the PW of each proposal when reinvestment opportunities are ignored?

(b) What are the PWs when receipts are reinvested at the given rates?

6.28 A dispatcher has four crews available to service three routes. As indicated in the table below, the gross margin on each route depends on the number of crews allocated to it. (Gross margin as used here implies weekly revenue before crew costs are deducted.)

Number of crews	Weekly gross margin, $		
	Route A	Route B	Route C
1	9,000	1,300	7,100
2	14,000	9,100	12,500
3	16,500	11,000	14,400

(a) Draw a graph for each route, and determine how many crews should be allocated to each when crew costs are $2800 per week.

(b) If additional crews can be hired and trained to service the routes, each at a cost of $3000 per week, to which routes should they be assigned?

6.29 Consider the air-conditioning problem given in Prob. 6.13. Use the incremental IRR approach for cost-only alternative selection as given in the right-hand branch of Fig. 6.1 in determining the alternative to recommend.

6.30 Review Exercise 5 gave CHEER values for incremental IRR computations. Manually determine if these results are numerically correct—set up the equation and try the CHEER IRR values.

6.31 A new model of a machine can be bought now for $2 million and its estimated resale value after 3 years of use is $1.75 million. The estimated O&M costs of this model amount to $0.01 million/year (end of year payments). Instead of paying $2 million now, an installment plan is available which requires $0.833 million/year for three years (end of year payments). Assume that sales taxes (i.e., goods and services tax (GST) and provincial sales tax (PST)) are not applicable to both payment options. Find the internal rate of return if the new model machine is bought for $2 million at the outset as opposed to the yearly payment (installment) option.

REPLACEMENT ANALYSIS

When it is not necessary to change, it is necessary not to change.
Lucius Cary; speech to the House of Commons, 22 November 1641

The introductory quotation could start an interesting philosophical discussion in a group of practicing engineering economists. For example, should a construction firm trade in its pickup trucks on a cyclic basis, or should the firm operate them "until they drop"? An economic model can be built to show that it may be less costly, from a systems point of view, to trade in the trucks on a cyclic basis even though they do not apparently need to be replaced. We will take a look at this situation in Sec. 7.5.

Should we convert from a traditional manufacturing process to an automated approach that uses a robot and manufacturing cell approach, even though the current process seems to be profitable? In the early 1960s, with the advent of computer process control, cement plants all across Canada and the United States started to convert from a process where an expert operator could "sense" when changes needed to be made in a kiln control operation to one where a control computer emulated the expert's logic in making changes. In fact, this can be considered one of the first examples of computer expert systems where the expertise of people was transformed to a logic flow process that the computer could follow. The reason for the mass movement to computer control in the cement industry related to staying competitive in a field where profits were somewhat marginal and dependent on keeping the kiln processes operating on a 24-hour basis. If one company had an economic edge through computer control, all the companies would need that edge. Many similar examples could be cited, including paper manufacturing, where sensing the quality of the paper as it was being produced was difficult to automate.

We have all been faced with the decision of whether to replace a consumer product or repair the existing device. Automobiles immediately come to mind. Rising repair costs suggest that the repair/replace decision might be changing characteristics with electronic products. Table 7.1 lists some relative replace/repair information for electronic products that exemplifies this situation.

This chapter will present focused procedures to assist in the replacement analysis process. While some of these procedures could well assist in some decisions we face as home or automobile owners, the aim is primarily to assist in making industrial replacement decisions. Existing assets may be replaced because of deteriorating performance, obsolescence, or inadequate capacity.

Replacement analyses based on before-tax cash flow assume that tax effects of replacement plans are identical. However, should asset disposal

TABLE 7.1[†]

Repair or replace?

Home electronic item	Average repair bill, $	Components worth repairing	Components not worth repairing
Television set	100–150 (31-inch [79 centimeters] and larger); and projection: 200–400	Power supply; tuner problems; fly-back transformer arcs or cracks	New picture tube
Videocassette recorder	85	Replace belts, idler; fix bent cassette basket; clean heads	Replace head assembly
Camcorder	150–200	Replace belts, idlers; clean heads; fix bent cassette basket	Replace lens assembly
Microwave	50–75	Replace interlock switch on door	Replace control panel
Audio CD player	80–100	Alignment; jammed mechanism or slipped belt; fix switches or motors	Replace laser

[†]*The Arizona Republic,* February 12, 1994. (Sources: Arizona State Electronics Association, local service dealers.)

tax effects of replacement plans be relevant for their evaluation, concepts and methodologies covered in Chapter 9 should be used in support of decision making.

7.1   REPLACEMENT STUDIES

Replacement refers to a broad concept embracing the selection of similar but new assets to replace existing assets and the evaluation of entirely different ways to perform an asset's function. For instance, old trucks could be replaced with new models that operate similarly but have advanced features that improve performance. The trucks could also be replaced with a conveyor system, an overhead crane, a subcontract for hauling, or even manual labor, if any of these methods serves the needed function at a lower total cost.

Replacement decisions are critically important to a firm. A hasty decision to "get rid of that junk" because a machine is temporarily malfunctioning, or a decision to faddishly buy the latest model because "we take pride in being very modern," can be a serious drain on operating capital. A firm hard pressed for operating funds may go to the other extreme by adopting a policy that postpones replacements until there is no other way to continue production. A policy of postponement places a firm in the dangerous position of becoming noncompetitive. Reliance on inefficient equipment and processes that lead to higher long-run operating costs or low quality, while competitors enjoy declining costs and better quality gained from modern machinery, is a delaying action that eventually must be paid for, perhaps in bankruptcy. Engineers bear responsibility to recognize when an asset is no longer employed efficiently, what replacements should be considered, and when replacement is economically feasible.

A replacement decision is a choice between the present asset, sometimes called the *defender,* and currently available replacement alternatives, sometimes called *challengers.* The defender may or may not be at the end of its economic life. An asset is *retired* when its owner disposes of it, but it may still serve other owners as second-hand equipment before it is scrapped. Unsatisfactory performance and inability to meet current capacity needs are the main causes of retirement. The challenger may or may not perform the function of the defender in the same way.

Replacement studies are usually made as equivalent annual-cost (EAC) calculations to take advantage of data traditionally collected as annual charges: maintenance costs, operating expenses, salaries, inflation, depreciation, taxes, etc. The last three topics will be developed in later chapters.

7.1.1   Current Salvage Value of the Defender

The salvage value of an asset being evaluated for replacement is the cost of keeping it in service. That is, the best estimate of the defender's worth is the capital cost of the no-change alternative, which is usually taken to be its market value at the time of the study. This "cost" is called an *opportunity cost* since by keeping the defender we are forgoing the "opportunity" to receive its current value when we replace it by a challenger. The decision-making process employed is called the *outsider viewpoint* in that an outsider would look at the defender and challenger as two ways to satisfy a need. The outsider would expect to pay the current market value for the defender.

An alternative procedure considers the defender's salvage value as a receipt (positive cash flow) that offsets part of the purchase price (negative cash flow) of each challenger. Then the net differences between the cash flows of the defender and each challenger are compared. To illustrate the two approaches, consider the choice between a defender that has a current market value of $5000 and a challenger that can be purchased for $7500. Both have a service life of 3 years with no salvage value expected at the end of that time. Their operating costs are shown in Table 7.2.

TABLE 7.2

Costs for alternatives D and C, $

Year	Defender D	Challenger C	Difference $D - C$
0	5000	7500	−2500
1	1700	500	1200
2	2000	1100	900
3	2500	1300	1200

Operating costs typically increase as an asset gets older. Since the defender has already provided prior service, its annual costs are usually higher than the challenger's. Also, the first-year operating cost for a challenger may be very low when a warranty is issued by the seller.

If the market value of the defender is considered to be the capital cost of its continued service with the MARR at 12 percent, then the equivalent annual cost is

$$EAC(D) = [\$5000 + \$1700(P/F, 12, 1) + \$2000(P/F, 12, 2) \\ + \$2500(P/F, 12, 3)] \, (A/P, 12, 3) \\ = (\$5000 + \$4892)(0.41635) = \$4119$$

The equivalent annual cost of the $7500 challenger that reduces the yearly operating costs is

$$EAC(C) = [\$7500 + \$500(P/F, 12, 1) + \$1100(P/F, 12, 2) \\ + \$1300(P/F, 12, 3)] \, (A/P, 12, 3) \\ = (\$7500 + \$2249)(0.41635) = \$4059$$

which indicates that it should replace the defender. A present-worth (PW) comparison would show the same preference, of course, by indicating a lower present worth of costs over the 3-year period for the challenger:

$$PW(D) = \$9893 \quad \text{and} \quad PW(C) = \$9749$$

The other way to make the comparison is to subtract the market value of the defender from the first cost of the challenger ($7500 − $5000 = $2500) to establish the net purchase price. Then the differences in annual operating costs are determined as the savings (positive cash flow) associated with the replacement. Using the differences $D - C$ from Table 7.2 gives

$$\begin{aligned} EAW(D - C) &= [-\$2500 + \$1200(P/F, 12, 1) + \$900(P/F, 12, 2) \\ &\quad + \$1200(P/F, 12, 3)](A/P, 12, 3) \\ &= (\$2500 + \$2643)(0.41635) = \$60 \end{aligned}$$

Since identical cost estimates were used and the asset lives were the same, the equivalent annual worth (EAW) of replacing the defender equals the difference between the previously calculated EACs:

$$EAC(D) - EAC(C) = \$4119 - \$4059 = \$60$$

It is important to remember that in the recommended procedure of calculating an EAC for *each* alternative, the defender's salvage value at replacement time cannot be both a capital cost for continuance of the defender *and* a reduction in the challenger's purchase price. If the challenger is purchased, then the latter will reflect the actual cash flow if the net cost (market price − market salvage value) is used. The former is required when we are determining the most economical time for replacement of an asset when the challenger and defender have different expected lengths of useful service (see Sec. 7.1.2).

EXAMPLE 7.1   **Inflated Salvage Value of a Defender**

A second challenger competes with the defender described in Table 7.2. This challenger (CX) has a purchase price of $9000, but $6000 is offered for the defender as a trade-in and the seller guarantees that operating costs will be no more than $800 per year. Should the offer be accepted when the required rate of return is 12 percent and no salvage value is expected at the end of challenger CX's 3-year life?

Solution

It is not unusual for a vendor to offer more than the market value for a used asset, to make the sale; the seller hopes to obtain a steady buyer and likely has accounted for the discount with an inflated selling price. Therefore, *the difference between a known market value and a seller's higher offer is treated as a reduction in the challenger's purchase price.* The discount of $6000 − $5000 = $1000 is applied to the $9000 first cost of challenger CX, reducing its effective purchase price to $8000. Then with the yearly $800 operating cost,

$$\text{EAC(CX)} = (\$9000 - \$1000)(A/P,\ 12,\ 3) + \$800$$
$$= \$8000(0.41635) + \$800 = \$4131$$

This value is compared with EAC(D) based on the defender's real market value ($5000) and EAC($C$) of the first challenger's actual purchase price; the new challenger is rejected because its EAC(CX) is higher, even with the purchase-price discount included.

7.1.2 Defender and Challengers with Unequal Lives

Ways to make comparisons of assets having unequal lives were introduced in earlier chapters. There are two basic methods: study period and repeated life. The former is applicable when an asset is required for only a specified period, and the latter is appropriate when the asset is needed indefinitely. In both cases the most economical time for the replacement to occur should be checked.

The duration of a *study period* is set by the period of known need for an asset's service. When this period is less than or equal to the remaining service life of the defender, and the challengers have longer lives, the salvage values at the time of service termination must be estimated. These salvage values are then inserted for S in the equivalent annual capital-cost formula $\text{EAC} = (P - S)(A/P,\ i,\ N) + Si$, where N is the number of years in the period. It may be necessary to check several termination points to secure the lowest total EAC (sum of equivalent capital and operating costs), because the replacement can take place during any year of the study period or not at all.

When a known service need extends beyond the defender's remaining service life, it is usually assumed that the defender will be replaced by the best challenger. This policy applies to both the original defender and replacement of the original challenger, if the study period is longer than the challenger's life. In some studies it may be feasible to anticipate that a better challenger will become available later in the period; then future replacement plans will include this best-possible challenger. The cash flow of each alternative during a study period thus includes the original capital cost, net purchase price of repeated (or best available) replacements, salvage value at the termination of the study period, and annual operating costs.

A *repeated-life* analysis is based on the assumptions that an asset is replaced with an identical asset and that there is a continuing requirement for its services. Identical replacement, often called *like-for-like replacement,* is a reasonable assumption for a challenger, but unrealistic for the defender. A defender is typically an older piece of equipment exhibiting decreasing efficiency, and it is doubtful that an identical piece could be found, even if it were desired. However, a repeated-life comparison is still appropriate for the continuous-service case because it indicates whether a challenger promises a lower EAC than the existing asset. If so, the next question addresses when to make the replacement.

Consider the defender described in Table 7.2 and a challenger with a first cost of $12,000, salvage value of $2000 at the end of its 5-year economic life, and annual operating costs of $700. Services provided by the equipment will be needed indefinitely. When the MARR = 12 percent, repeated identical replacements of the challenger lead to

$$\text{EAC(challenger)} = (\$12,000 - \$2000)(A/P, 12, 5) + \$2000(0.12) + \$700$$
$$= \$2774 + \$240 + \$700 = \$3714$$

Since this equivalent annual cost is significantly lower than the previously calculated EAC(defender) = $4119, replacement is advisable. The rationale for this decision is that keeping the defender for 3 years costs the equivalent of $4119 per year, *after which it will be replaced by the minimum-cost replacement*; the best current challenger will be that minimum-cost replacement unless there is reason to believe that an even better challenger will become available in 3 years.

Given a challenger with a lower EAC than the defender and no expectation of a better challenger in the foreseeable future, the remaining question addresses when to make the replacement. In most cases, the annual costs for the defender will increase in successive years, so it is not necessarily the case that replacement would be made immediately, although we need to be careful not to make this a universal truism. For example, if the plan is to overhaul the defender in year 1, the cost for that year will probably be higher than those for the next few years, after which costs will start to climb. In cases like this, it is necessary to find the minimum EAC life for the defender, to compare with the challenger, and to replace *now* if

$$\min \text{EAC}_{\text{def}} > \min \text{EAC}_{\text{chal}}$$

A year-by-year check will then be needed beyond the minimum EAC life.

The replacement normally takes place when the cost of 1 more year's service by the defender exceeds the equivalent annual cost of the challenger. As just indicated, an exception occurs in the rare instance when a defender's market value does not progressively decline with age or its operating costs do not progressively increase.

exchange: (1) computers shrank in size and cost, to enable construction of robots, and (2) wage inflation raised the cost of labor to a level that made the use of robots feasible. A $100,000 robot may be an economically acceptable replacement for a human worker who earns only $7 an hour, because the robot can work three shifts a day without breaks or vacations and can produce consistently high quality. However, a robot is far less flexible than a person, being unable to solve unknown problems, innovate, and self-adjust, except in research laboratory cases.

A robot replacement study may result from a *problem-pull condition* or a *technology-push situation*. The former attempts to correct a known difficulty, and the latter is an experiment with promising technology. Solving production problems with piecemeal robotics is unlikely to yield maximum savings because each introduction is an independent occasion. Comparably, installing a robot only because it is fashionable is hardly justifiable. An analysis should incorporate conventional cash flow categories plus reasonable estimates of difficult-to-quantify factors such as quality benefits and losses owing to inflexibility. Problem solutions can then pull in appropriate technology to push financially responsible modernization.

7.3.2 The Lease/Buy Decision

In an earlier example we suggested that a challenger for a copier replacement might be a leased piece of equipment. Even though leasing will be covered more thoroughly in Chap. 10 when we discuss inflation, it is appropriate to make a few comments regarding leasing as a replacement alternative.

An equipment lease is a condition whereby one party—the lessor who owns the equipment—conveys use of that equipment to another—the lessee—in exchange for periodic rental payments.[†]

Leasing contracts can be structured to meet virtually any needs of the lessee, but the decision to buy or lease is strictly an economic one. We should follow the procedures covered in this book so far. A prime reason for leasing is that it can be a way to avoid large initial capital outlays. Another leasing advantage, as given by Cudworth, is that a company can match its equipment cost not only to optimize its cash flow but also to match use of the equipment to the practical life of the equipment.

Lease or buy your car? *Money* magazine reports[‡] that, historically, leasing a car nearly always costs more than buying one. With car dealers becoming more competitive, this might not always be the case. Consider the example given in Table 7.3. Is leasing cheaper than cash? It seems too

---

[†]E. F. Cudworth, *Equipment Leasing Partnerships*, Probus Publishing Company, Chicago, 1989.
[‡]J. Edgerton, "When It's Cheaper to Lease than Buy." Table on the next page reprinted from the March 1994 issue of *Money* by special permission; copyright 1994, Time, Inc.

TABLE 7.3

Pay cash, finance, or lease?

	Cash, $	Financing, $	Leasing, $
Initial payment	27,980[b]	2,798[b]	887[d]
Sales tax (6%)	1,679	1,679	0[e]
Total initial cash outlay	29,659	4,477	887
Monthly payment	0	778	437
Total payments over 36 months	0	28,008	15,295[f]
Total cash outlay	29,659	32,485	16,182
Lost interest on payments[a]	0	1,696	953
Lost interest on initial costs[a]	3,775	570	113
Cash outlay plus lost interest	33,434	34,751	17,247
Resale value	−12,298[c]	−12,298[c]	−450[g]
Total cost	21,136	22,453	16,798

[a]Assumes investment return of 4%.
[b]Assumes the price is 10% over the dealer's cost.
[c]Assumes 41% residual value.
[d]Includes first payment plus security deposit.
[e]Sales tax included in payments.
[f]35 additional payments, since the first payment is made at time of leasing.
[g]Refund of deposit.
Sources: Money, March 1994 from Chart Software, automotive lease consultants.

good to be true. It will be interesting to look at the situation from the lessor's point of view.

It is assumed that the lessor has the following cost and income structure:

- Initial automobile cost is same as dealer cost:

$$\frac{\$27,980}{1.1} = \$25,436$$

- Monthly income to lessor is $437 less sales tax = $437/1.06 = $412.26.
- Salvage value is same as to customer, $12,298.
- The last monthly payment is received at the *beginning* of month 36 since the initial payment at time 0 included the first payment.

Figure 7.1 shows the cash flow diagram from the lessor's point of view. Figure 7.2 shows the determination of the internal rate of return (IRR) for the lessor. The present-worth calculations were found from

$$PW = -\$25,436 + \$862.26 + \$412.26(P/A,\ i/12,\ 35)$$
$$+ (\$12,298 - \$450)(P/F,\ i/12,\ 36)$$

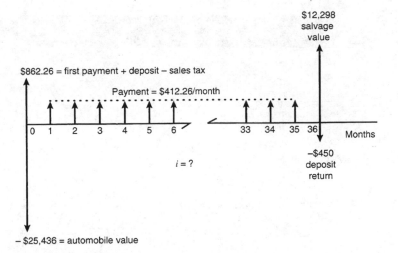

FIGURE 7.1
Lessor's view of
lease contract.

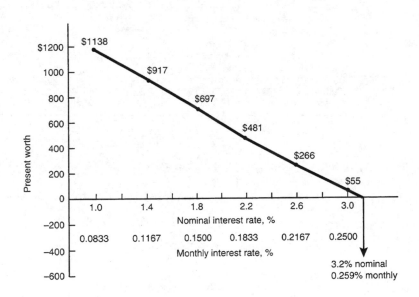

FIGURE 7.2
IRR for lessor.

The monthly IRR is 0.259 percent, which gives an annual effective rate of

$$\text{Effective rate} = 1.00259^{12} - 1 = 3.20\%$$

This is a very low return on investment, and if the cost and income assumptions are correct, it would concern the lessor as to whether a profit really would be made even though the assumed salvage value may be rather low for the lessee.

7.4   REPLACEMENT DUE TO INADEQUACY

When current operating conditions change, an older asset occasionally lacks the capacity to meet new requirements. Sometimes a similar asset can be purchased to supplement the old asset, as in the case of placing a new generator alongside an old one to meet new power demands. New layouts, building additions, and design changes are examples of possible modifications to increase capacity.

Alternatives or supplements to an existing asset are usually compared with a challenging new asset that may perform an equivalent function in an entirely different manner. Replacing a wood stove with an oil furnace, e.g., provides an entirely different way to heat a home. Even though a challenger is deemed a desirable replacement, the defender may still have value as usable equipment. In such cases it can be sold or retained for standby purposes. Also, secondary uses may be found for assets replaced from their primary function; the wood stove replaced by an oil furnace might be used as an incinerator.

EXAMPLE 7.5   **Upgrading versus Demolition and Replacement**

A small bridge leading to a proposed industrial park has a load limit of 10,000 pounds (4536 kilograms). A manufacturing firm will lease a building site in the park if the capacity of the bridge is raised to 60,000 pounds (27,216 kilograms). The developers of the land have two alternatives. They can reinforce the old bridge, or they can tear it out and fill in the low area, leaving a culvert to carry away surface water.

The present bridge has no realizable salvage value. Reinforcement would cost $30,000 and should provide adequate access for 10 years without any major additional work. The salvage value from added materials could be $2000 in 10 years.

A culvert-and-fill approach to the park would cost $60,000 and should meet all requirements for the next 25 years. There would be no salvage value. In addition, it will cost $2000 to remove the old bridge. Maintenance costs are expected to be $2200 per year less than upkeep for a bridge.

Annual property taxes and insurance on the improvements will be 1 percent of the first cost. The required return on investments is 8 percent before taxes. If the developer feels that a new approach to the park is required, which alternative should be selected?

Solution

Since a replacement for the old bridge is definitely necessary, there is no distinct defender-challenger relationship. The lower-initial-cost alternative—reinforcement—would best fit the role of defender. Its equivalent annual cost is the sum of capital recovery, extra maintenance costs, and taxes plus insurance.

Equivalent annual cost of reinforcing the bridge:
Additional maintenance costs are $2200. Capital recovery is

$$(P - S)(A/P, 8, 10) + S(0.08) = (\$30{,}000 - \$2000)(0.14903)$$
$$+ \$2000(0.08)$$
$$= \$4333$$

Taxes and insurance are

$$\$30{,}000(0.01) = \$300$$

$$EAC_{\text{bridge reinf}} = \$2200 + \$4333 + \$300 = \$6833$$

Equivalent annual cost of the culvert and fill:
Capital recovery is

$$P(A/P, 8, 25) = (\$60{,}000 + \$2000)(0.09368) = \$5808$$

Taxes and insurance are

$$\$60{,}000(0.01) = \$600$$

$$EAC_{\text{cul/fil}} = \$5808 + \$600 = \$6408$$

From strictly a cost viewpoint, the culvert-and-fill method has a clear advantage of $6833 − $6408 = $425 per year. Other management considerations could influence the final choice. For instance, the developers might be willing to forgo the annual $425 benefit in order to be allowed an opportunity to change plans in 10 years when the reinforced bridge will again need a replacement study. They might be short of capital at present or have other possible investments with a greater potential rate of return than that earned on the extra increment of investment ($62,000 − $30,000 = $32,000) required for the culvert and fill. (Note that the extra increment earns 8 percent *plus* $425 a year.)

7.5   **ECONOMIC LIFE FOR CYCLIC REPLACEMENTS**

Many mechanical items used in service agencies and manufacturing are replaced by essentially the same machine when the original one wears out. Informal rules may be used to establish cyclic replacement times. One government department replaces a car whenever it exceeds 104,605 kilometers of use or 5 years of service, or when the cumulative maintenance cost equals the purchase price. Such replacement rules recognize that automobiles, trucks, typewriters, and similar machines become less efficient and accumulate higher and higher repair bills as they age. Conversely, the longer

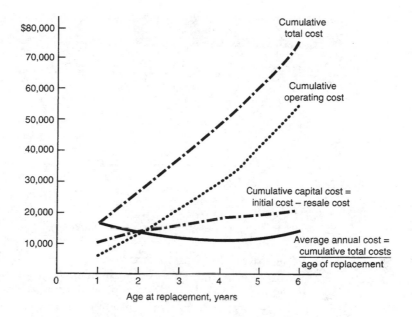

FIGURE 7.3
Cost pattern for
asset as it ages.

they are kept in operation, the lower will be their average annual capital cost because the purchase price is spread over more years. The sum of these two types of cost is the total cost of providing the machines' services. As shown in Fig. 7.3, total lifetime cost continues to increase with age, but average annual cost passes through a minimum.

Before we get into details on cyclic replacements, it will be beneficial to formalize a few relevant terms:

- *Economic life*[†] is the period of time over which a prudent owner will retain an existing facility to minimize costs.
- *Physical life*[†] is the period of time after which an asset can no longer be repaired or refurbished so that it can perform a useful function.
- *Service life*[‡] is the period of time after which an asset cannot perform its intended function without a major overhaul. Such an overhaul is an investment for which a new economic life has to be determined.
- *Useful life* is the length of time an asset might reasonably be expected to be useful in the production of income.

7.5.1 Assumption of Zero Interest Rate

The objective of a cyclic replacement study is to determine the pattern of replacement that will minimize the average annual cost. Data for future

---

[†]H. J. Lang and D. N. Merino, *The Selection Process for Capital Projects,* John Wiley & Sons, Inc., New York, 1993.
[‡]Cudworth, op. cit.

TABLE 7.4

Truck cost data, $

	Year					
	1	**2**	**3**	**4**	**5**	**6**
Operating cost	6,100	6,800	7,800	9,300	11,400	14,600
Resale value	15,000	12,000	9,300	7,100	5,400	4,300

costs must be estimated, but cost figures for most assets that are used enough to warrant a cyclic replacement study are available from internal or suppliers' records. Simplifying assumptions made to introduce the calculation procedure include a replacement price that remains constant and no interest charges for the use of capital. This latter assumption may seem very strange to the reader, but this is done primarily to demonstrate the procedure for finding the so-called optimum cycle time. We will remove the assumption of no interest rate after we have seen how to approach the problem. In general, relaxing these assumptions does not affect the optimum cycle time very much unless there are dramatic changes in price or exceptionally high interest rates.

Calculations to determine the minimum-cost age follow an iterative routine in which the capital cost (decrease in salvage value to a certain age) is added to the accumulated operating cost (maintenance plus use expenses) for that same period. Each sum is divided by the relevant age to give an average cost for that replacement interval.

The data in Fig. 7.3 are for a city delivery service that owns a fleet of small delivery trucks for store-to-home deliveries. The purchase price per truck is $25,000, and the anticipated schedule of future operating costs and salvage values is given in Table 7.4. These costs are inputs to the tabular solution method which reveals, through Table 7.5, that trading in the trucks every 4 years for new ones is the minimum-cost replacement cycle. As mentioned earlier, cost data from Table 7.5 were the values graphed in Fig. 7.3.

7.5.2 Cyclic Replacement Analysis with Nonzero Interest Rate

Logically, the previous analysis should have been done with a nonzero interest rate. Now that we have seen the basic process to follow, we can add the interest. Essentially the same procedure for calculating the minimum-cost replacement age can be used when interest charges are included. This calculation determines the *economic life* of an asset subject to cyclic replacement—its *least-cost replacement interval*.

TABLE 7.5

Cycle time iterative results

End of year	Cumulative[†] capital costs, $	Cumulative[‡] operating costs, $	Cumulative[§] total costs, $	Average[¶] total costs per year, $
1	10,000	6,100	16,100	16,100
2	13,000	12,900	25,900	12,950
3	15,700	20,700	36,400	12,133
4	17,900	30,000	47,900	11,975
5	19,600	41,400	61,000	12,200
6	20,700	56,000	76,700	12,783

[†]Capital cost ($25,000) − resale value from Table 7.4.
[‡]Values from Table 7.4 accumulated by year.
[§]Sum of second and third columns.
[¶]Fourth column divided by first column.

Data from Table 7.4 will again be utilized to illustrate the discounted cash flow approach. We set the MARR at 10 percent and assume that each year is the economic life N of the asset. Using that N, we calculate the equivalent annual cost of owning the asset for N years:

$$EAC = \text{capital recovery} + \text{equivalent annual operating cost}$$
$$= (P - S)(A/P, i, N) + Si + FW(\text{operating costs for } N \text{ years})$$
$$\times (A/F, i, N)$$

The annual cost for 1 year of ownership when $i = 10$ percent is

$$EAC_{N=1} = (\$25,000 - \$15,000)(A/P, 10, 1) + \$15,000(0.10)$$
$$+ \$6100(A/F, 10, 1)$$
$$= \$10,000(1.10) + \$1500 + \$6100(1.0000) = \$18,600$$

Similarly, for 2 years of ownership:

$$EAC_{N=2} = (\$25,000 - \$12,000)(A/P, 10, 2) + \$12,000(0.10)$$
$$+ [\$6100(F/P, 10, 1) + \$6800](A/F, 10, 2)$$
$$= \$13,000(0.57619) + \$1200 + [\$6100(1.10) + \$6800](0.47619)$$
$$= \$7490 + \$1200 + \$6433 = \$15,123$$

For 3 years we get

$$EAC_{N=3} = (\$25,000 - \$9300)(A/P, 10, 3) + \$9300(0.10) + [\$6100$$
$$\times (F/P, 10, 2) + \$6800(F/P, 10, 1) + \$7800](A/F, 10, 3)$$
$$= \$15,700(0.40211) + \$930 + [\$6100(1.21) + \$6800(1.1)$$
$$+ \$7800](0.30211) = \$14,090$$

TABLE 7.6

Summary of EAC$_{10\% \text{ MARR}}$ and average annual costs at 0%

Asset life, years	EAC$_{10\% \text{ MARR}}$, $	Average annual costs of 0% interest, $
1	18,600	16,100
2	15,124	12,950
3	14,090	12,133
4	13,732	11,975
5	13,745	12,200
6	14,068	12,783

The same procedure can be followed to determine the EAC values for years 4 through 6. The results are summarized in Table 7.6.

Table 7.6 indicates that the economic life of the truck and the minimum-cost replacement period are 4 years. Note that equivalent annual capital costs decline as the ownership period increases, and at the same time, the equivalent annual operating costs increase owing to deteriorating performance. The pattern of changes in capital and operating costs should be checked periodically, when like-for-like replacements are in effect, to confirm that the economic life remains the same.

The reader should be warned that the economic life at 0 percent interest will not always equal the economic life with interest greater than 0 percent. Problem 7.31 will ask for solution of the previous example, whose results were summarized in Table 7.6, when the interest rate increases from 10 to 15 percent. It will be found that the economic life increases from 4 to 5 years.

Inflation and taxes, two factors that could have a significant effect on the replacement decision, are covered in Chaps. 9 and 10.

7.6   PRECAUTIONS FOR REPLACEMENT STUDIES

The value of a replacement study, like other economic evaluations, is directly proportional to the validity of the data. Some costs have greater effect in a comparison than others. Replacement decisions are very sensitive to recurring cash flows, especially operating costs. Unfortunately, operating expenses are more difficult to extrapolate into the future than are other periodic cash flows such as taxes and insurance.

A conservative approach when estimates are highly uncertain is to give every advantage to the defender. This is accomplished by assuming that the present differential between the operating costs of the defender and of the challenger will remain constant during the study period and that there are no capital recovery costs for the defender. If a challenger still looks good under these handicaps, it is truly a valid contender.

Salvage values are necessarily subject to question because they occur at the most distant point in a replacement study. The basic principle is to use the best *current* estimate of the future, regardless of previous estimates. Appraisals may change from one study to the next, owing to price fluctuations, availability, and needs. An often-neglected cost associated with salvage is the expense of getting an old asset ready for the new purchaser. These expenses could include dismantling, overhaul, painting, crating, cartage, and repairs to the area vacated by the disposed asset. When such costs exceed the disposal price, the salvage value is a loss and is treated as a minus quantity (S is negative) in capital recovery calculations.

Another commonly ignored cost is the expense associated with putting a new asset in operating order. Special wiring, piping, guardrails, foundations, and other facilities may be needed before new equipment can operate. Radically different or complex equipment often requires more "debugging" than is provided by the supplier. In a replacement study these one-time operational-type costs should be treated as capital costs.

The bridge replacement example given earlier demonstrated a case in which there was no choice about making a replacement study. More commonly an asset performs its intended function without obvious financial loss. If an acceptable challenger goes unnoticed, the accumulated yearly losses from failing to recognize the need for a replacement can be substantial. One clue to the replaceability of an asset is its economic life. As an asset nears the end of its original life estimation, it becomes a more likely candidate for a replacement study. Other clues include an awareness of new developments that could lead to asset obsolescence and the deterioration of performance, as indicated by rejection rates or frequent repairs. Since machines age less obviously than humans and cannot complain about their frailties, it is an engineering function to diagnose infirmities and prepare remedies.

7.7   **REVIEW EXERCISES AND DISCUSSIONS**

EXERCISE 1

A grinder was purchased 3 years ago for $40,000. It has provided adequate service, but an improved version is now available for $35,000 that will reduce operating costs and cut inspection expenses. Costs and salvage values for the two machines are shown below. Costs that are the same for either machine are not included. Also, the operating costs for the challenger are very low due to warranted equipment. Should a replacement be made if the required rate of return is 15 percent and the services of a grinder will be needed for only 4 more years?

	Defender D		Challenger C	
Year	Operating cost, $	Salvage value, $	Operating cost, $	Salvage value, $
0		12,000		35,000
1	3,400	7,000	200	30,000
2	3,900	4,000	1,000	27,000
3	4,600	2,500	1,200	24,000
4	5,600	1,000	1,500	20,000
5			2,000	17,000
6			2,600	15,000

SOLUTION 1

The first calculation determines the EAC when replacement is made immediately. This allows consideration of only the first 4 years of the challenger's 6-year economic life. Its salvage value after 4 years is $20,000. The defender's current salvage value of $12,000 is its market worth now; the original purchase price of $40,000 has no bearing on the replacement decision.

$$EAC(D) = [\$12,000 + \$3400(P/F, 15, 1) + \$3900(P/F, 15, 2) + \$4600$$
$$\times (P/F, 15, 3) + \$5600(P/F, 15, 4) - \$1000(P/F, 15, 4)](A/P, 15, 4)$$
$$= \$23,560(0.35027) = \$8252$$

$$EAC(C) = (\$35,000 - \$20,000)(A/P, 15, 4) + \$20,000(0.15) + [\$200(P/F, 15, 1)$$
$$+ \$1000(P/F, 15, 2) + \$1200(P/F, 15, 3) + \$1500(P/F, 15, 4)]$$
$$\times (A/P, 15, 4)$$
$$= \$17,577(0.35027) + \$3000 = \$9157$$

Logically, a replacement should not be made now. So we should look at all EAC combinations for later replacement:

- Replace at beginning of year 2—EAC over years 2 through 4.
- Replace at beginning of year 3—EAC over years 3 and 4.
- Replace at beginning of year 4—EAC over just year 4.

Table 7.7 summarizes the results of these computations. To exemplify the calculations, we look at the equations for replacing at the beginning of year 3 with EAC computations over years 3 and 4.

Defender:

$$EAC(D)_{years\ 3,\ 4} = (\$4000 - \$1000)(A/P, 15, 2) + (\$1000)(0.15)$$
$$+ [\$4600(P/F, 15, 1) + \$5600(P/F, 15, 2)](A/P, 15, 2)$$
$$= \$3000(0.61512) + \$150 + [\$4600(0.86957)$$
$$+ \$5600(0.75614)](0.61512)$$
$$= \$7061$$

TABLE 7.7

EAC values depending on when defender is replaced

Period of remaining service	EAC(*D*), $	EAC(*C*), $
Years 2, 3, and 4	7,399	9,170
Years 3 and 4	7,061	9,543
Year 4 only	7,475	10,450

This assumes that the salvage value at the end of year 2 will really be $4000 and that the estimate of salvage value at the end of year 4 is still valid. The analyst will need to reevaluate estimates in about a year or so, before the grinder is replaced. The computation made now is for planning purposes only, although some computer numerically controlled equipment requires a lead time of over 1 year due to demand and supply.

Challenger:

$$EAC(C)_{\text{years 3, 4}} = (\$35,000 - \$27,000)(A/P, 15, 2) + \$27,000(0.15)$$
$$+ [\$200(P/F, 15, 1) + \$1000(P/F, 15, 2)](A/P, 15, 2)$$
$$= \$8000(0.61512) + \$27,000(0.15) + [\$200(0.86957)$$
$$+ \$1000(0.75614)](0.61512)$$
$$= \$9543$$

This computation assumes that the price quoted for the grinder will still be the purchase price 2 years later. As stated for the defender, the analyst will need to update these figures and recalculate in about 1 year.

Assuming that the data are as good as possible at this time, Table 7.7 shows that the challenger, even with the reduced purchase price and possibly unreasonably low operating costs, should never be considered as a replacement for the defending grinder.

EXERCISE 2

The headquarters building owned by a rapidly growing but still small company is not large enough for current needs. A search for bigger quarters revealed only two alternatives that provide sufficient room, enough parking, and the desired appearance and location. (*a*) One can be leased for $144,000 per year, and (*b*) the other can be purchased for $800,000, including a $150,000 cost for land.

The study period for the comparison is 30 years, and the desired rate of return on investments before income taxes is 12 percent. It is believed that land values will not decrease over the ownership period, but the value of a structure will decline to 10 percent of the present value ($650,000 for buy and $600,000 for remodel) in 30 years. Property taxes are 4 percent and rising. For comparison purposes, annual tax payments should be uniformly close to 5 percent of the purchase price.

The present headquarters building is already paid for and is now valued at $300,000. The land under it is appraised at $60,000. An engineer suggests that consideration be given to (*c*) remodeling the present structure. The engineer estimates that an expenditure of $300,000 will provide the necessary room and improve the appearance to make it comparable to the other alternatives. However, the remodeling will occupy part of the existing parking lot. An adjacent privately owned parking lot can be leased for 30 years under an agreement that the first year's rent of $9000 will increase by $500 each year. If upkeep costs are the same for all three alternatives, which one is preferable?

SOLUTION 2
The cash flow diagrams for this case are given in Fig. 7.4.
(a) Leasing:

$$EAC(\text{lease}) = \$144,000$$

(b) Equivalent annual cost for buying. Capital recovery is

$$[P + \text{land} - (0.1P + \text{land})](A/P, 12, 30) + (0.1P + \text{land})(0.12)$$
$$= (\$800,000 - \$215,000)(0.12414)$$
$$+ (\$65,000 + \$150,000)(0.12)$$
$$= \$98,422$$

$$\text{Taxes} = \$800,000(0.05) = \$40,000$$

$$EAC(\text{buy}) = \$98,422 + \$40,000 = \$138,422$$

(c) Equivalent annual cost of remodeling includes the following:
Parking lot rent:

$$A' + G(A/G, 12, 30) = \$9000 + \$500(7.29742) = \$12,649$$

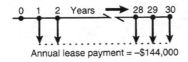

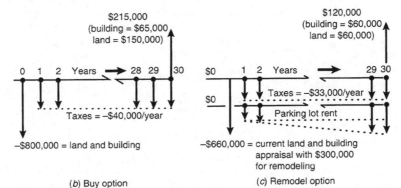

FIGURE 7.4
Cash flow diagrams
of headquarters
building options.

Capital recovery:

$$(\$660,000 - \$120,000)(A/P, 12, 30) + \$120,000(0.12)$$
$$= \$540,000(0.12414) + \$120,000(0.12)$$
$$= \$81,436$$

$$\text{Taxes} = \$660,000(0.05) = \$33,000$$

$$\text{EAC(remodeling)} = \$12,649 + \$81,436 + \$33,000 = \$127,085$$

Remodeling the presently occupied building is the preferred course of action. Note that the only capital recovery on land value is for interest on the amount invested in land, since the salvage value equals the investment value. Also, the already-paid-for value of the present headquarters building is included in the capital recovery charge.

EXERCISE 3

An electronic games producer cannot keep up with the demand for a particular line of product. A form of mass production is used that is primarily labor-intensive. This creates a very expensive production process that is also relatively inflexible as far as product changeover is concerned. The competition has completely automated its facility with the result that if nothing is done, this operation may well go out of business and at best, profits will plummet. As a result, management has made an irrevocable decision to automate the process. The industrial and manufacturing engineers have evaluated the costs of a new production system.

The managers have agreed that the production system should be one that has robot-controlled workstations. Movement between workstations will be handled by transfer mechanisms that are very expensive but that can be programmed to sense the type of product coming down the line, to allow optimum handling of each different product. After considerable analysis, they have decided that the production facility will be one of two possibilities, as shown in Fig. 7.5. In addition to the robot stations and transfer mechanisms being completely automated, the inspection station is an automated facility with one supervising operator.

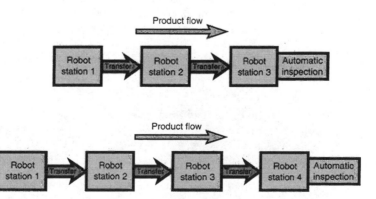

FIGURE 7.5
Schematic of robot-controlled production system.

These data are associated with the two new line possibilities:

Three robot stations and two transfer mechanisms:
Implemented cost of robot station: $215,000 per station
Transfer mechanism installed cost: $85,000 per mechanism
Operating costs for the line: $165,000 for the first year with a 5 percent
    increase per year thereafter
Cost of inspection station installed: $21,000
Line production capacity: 24,000 units per year
Maintenance costs per year: $5000 for each of first 2 years (due to maintenance
    agreements) followed by $15,000 for each of years 3 through 5
Estimated salvage value of line after 5 years: $33,400

Four robot stations and three transfer mechanisms:
Implemented cost of robot station: $185,000 per station
Transfer mechanism installed cost: $85,000 per mechanism
Operating costs for the line: $240,000 for first year with 5 percent increase per
    year thereafter
Cost of inspection station installed: $21,000
Line production capacity: 30,000 units per year
Maintenance costs per year: $6500 for each of first 2 years followed by $17,000
    for each of years 3 through 5
Estimated salvage value of line after 5 years: $40,600

Because of the volatile nature of the business, management wants the evaluation over a 5-year period.

Given that the market share that the plant can expect is up to 30,000 units per year and that the market price per unit is about $21.67 and is expected to stay fairly constant for the next 5 years, which line configuration do you recommend based on an economic evaluation? Your company's MARR is 13 percent.

SOLUTION 3

The difference in cost for a robot station in a three-robot line and one in a four-robot line is due to the complexity of the station, since the smaller line will have more operations per station. Also, the robot complexity affects the number of units that can be produced per year. This is a function of production cycle time, where cycle time is the length of time a unit of product can be worked on in a station. For example, if we have a total of 4000 hours per year on a two-shift basis for the three-robot line, and if the line is 95 percent available (preventive maintenance and preparation are done on the third shift), the *cycle time (CT)* is

$$CT = \frac{(4000 \text{ hours})(60 \text{ minutes per hour})(0.95)}{24{,}000 \text{ units per year}}$$

$$= 9.5 \text{ minutes}$$

This says that a unit of production has up to 9.5 minutes in each station for work prior to being moved to the next station. This is quite a long cycle time; automobile lines will produce a car with a cycle time in the vicinity of 1.5 to 3 minutes. Also, maintenance costs in the first 2 years are low due to equipment warranties.

A logical way to analyze the two "challengers" is to determine their equivalent annual worths. The term *challenger* was put in quotation marks because we do not really have a defender; management has decreed that a new system will be installed due to the competitive obsolescence of the new equipment.

Three robots and two transfer mechanisms:
If the current equipment had a salvage value greater than zero, we would have subtracted that from the capital costs; since it is zero, we do not have to consider it. Also, if the removal of the current equipment cost more than the salvage value, we would have had to add the difference to the first costs of the system being considered.

The equivalent annual worth is

$$
\begin{aligned}
\text{EAW} &= \text{annual income} - \text{capital costs} + \text{salvage value} - \text{operating costs} \\
&\quad - \text{maintenance costs} \\
&= 24,000 \text{ units}(\$21.67) \\
&\quad - [\$215,000(3) + \$85,000(2) + \$21,000](A/P, \ 13, \ 5) \\
&\quad + \$33,440(A/F, \ 13, \ 5) \\
&\quad - \$165,000\left[\left\{1 - \frac{(0.05)^5}{(0.13)^5}\right\}/(0.13 - 0.05)\right](A/P, \ 13, \ 5) \\
&\quad - [\$5000(P/A, \ 13, \ 2) + \$15,000(P/A, \ 13, \ 3)(P/F, \ 13, \ 2)](A/P, \ 13, \ 5) \\
&= \$520,080 - \$836,000(0.28431) + \$33,440(0.15431) \\
&\quad - \$165,000(3.8411)(0.28431) \\
&\quad - [\$5000(1.66810) + \$15,000(2.36115)\,(0.78315)](0.28431) \\
&= \$97,029
\end{aligned}
$$

Four robots and three transfer mechanisms:
The calculation for this alternative is handled in exactly the same manner as just shown for the three-robot line. The calculations will not be repeated here, but one of the problems in the next section will ask the reader to verify the solution:

$$
\text{EAW} = \$93,397
$$

The three-robot system is preferred.

This can be further exemplified by performing an internal rate-of-return analysis. Recall from Chap. 6 that we would calculate the rate of return for the system with the lowest first cost and then evaluate the *incremental rate of return* in going from that system (the three-robot case) to the four-robot situation.

The incremental data are as follows:

- Income per year: $650,000 - $520,080 = $130,020
- First cost: $1,016,000 - $836,000 = $180,000
- Salvage value: $40,640 - $33,440 = $7200
- Maintenance costs per year: $6500 - $5000 for each of years 1 and 2 and $17,000 - $15,000 for each of years 3 through 5
- Operating costs per year: $240,000 - $165,000 for first year with 5 percent geometric gradient additional for years 2 through 5

CHEER, the program ancillary to this text, was used to compute the IRR values for the three-robot case and for the incremental case:

IRR for three-robot line: 29.9 percent
IRR for incremental case: 9.9 percent

As expected, the investment *beyond* the three-robot case will not satisfy the 13 percent MARR. The additional capital would be better spent on an investment that management feels will return the minimum amount required. Of course, the engineering economist makes only a recommendation to management. Other considerations, such as maintaining a maximum market share, might factor into management's decision. Strictly from the economic analysis, the four-robot case should not be considered.

One additional point needs to be made. Costs that are not tied to specific projects or operations but are related to the operation of the plant as a whole have to be recovered in some manner. The plant's data processing functions, utility costs, sales department operations, etc., all have costs that have to be realized when profit determination is made. These costs are classified as overhead or burden, and the cost accounting department determines the overhead rate based on the previous year's operations. The MARR value related to sales is the value that the engineering economist obtains from cost accounting when making an analysis. This value includes the overhead factor and profit function. Thus, in the last exercise, we assumed income based on product price multiplied by production volume. The MARR ensures a satisfactory profit and absorption of overhead costs.

7.8   PROBLEMS

7.1   At the end of one-half of its expected economic life, a 4-year-old machine has a book value of $5800 from its original cost of $9200. Estimated operating costs for the next year will amount to $6000. An equipment dealer will allow $3600 if the machine is traded in now and $2800 if it is traded in 1 year later. The dealer proposes the purchase of a new machine to perform the same function; it will cost $14,000 installed. This machine will have an estimated operating cost of $4500 per year and a salvage value of $3000 at the end of 4 years. Is it profitable to replace the existing machine now if the minimum return on investments is 15 percent before taxes?

7.2   Machine A was installed 4 years ago at a total cost of $10,500. At that time it was estimated to have a life of 10 years and a salvage value of $1000. Annual operating costs, excluding depreciation and interest charges, have held relatively constant at $2600. The successful marketing of a new product has doubled the demand for parts made by machine A. The new demand can be met by purchasing an identical machine which now costs $12,000 installed. The economic life and operating costs for the second machine A will be the same as originally estimated for the first machine A. The salvage value for the second A-type machine will be $1600.

Machine B, a different type, costs $19,500 installed but has twice the capacity of machine A. Its annual operating costs will be about $3300, which should be relatively constant throughout its 10-year economic life. The salvage value is expected to be $2500. The present machine can be used as a trade-in on new machine B, which the vendor says is worth $3000.

Compare the two alternatives on the basis of equivalent annual cost when the interest rate is 10 percent.

7.3 A small construction firm's front loader is working fairly well but is only expected to last for 2 more years. An offer of $3500 has been made for it by a small township. A new machine has a first cost of $18,500 and should last for 8 years. The annual savings in operation and maintenance are expected to be $1500 per year over those of the current machine. The current machine will have zero salvage value in 2 years. What is the minimum salvage value required for the new machine that will barely allow it to be selected? A MARR of 15 percent is required.

7.4 A firm purchased a pump and motor for $1925 installed. It was soon discovered that the pump had been improperly selected for the required head and discharge. As a result, the power bill for operating the pump will be $900 for 1 year.

A new pump, suited to the requirements, is available for $2450 installed, with a guarantee that power costs will not exceed $500 annually. The original pump and motor can be sold for $375.

Assume an 8-year study period with zero salvage value for both pumps at the end of the period. The firm uses a minimum attractive rate of return of 12 percent before taxes. Based on present-worth calculations, should the pump be replaced?

7.5 Machine 1 will do a required operation adequately; it can be delivered immediately at a price of $11,250. Its operating costs are $9500 annually, and it will have no realizable salvage value at the end of its 5-year economic life. This machine is being compared with another presently available machine; machine 2 has a first cost of $30,000, annual operating costs of $6500, and a salvage value of $3000 in 10 years.

A much-improved machine 3 performs the same function as do the other two contenders; it has a first cost of $14,500 with an expected salvage value of $4250 after 5 years. Its major advantage is a lower operating cost of $5000 per year. The only drawback is that machine 3 is so much in demand that there is a 2-year wait for delivery. Since the firm cannot delay acquiring one of the machines, it must choose between the currently available alternatives 1 and 2. It uses a 15 percent rate of return before taxes for economic comparisons.

  (a) Compare the alternatives, using the repeated-projects method of analysis.
  (b) Compare the alternatives, using a 10-year study period.
  (c) Compare the alternatives, using the best-possible-replacement approach.

7.6 Assume that your present car could be sold to a used-car dealer for $1500. It will probably keep running for 2 more years, at which time it will have a scrap value of $400. Operating costs next year are expected to be $2800 and will likely be $3250 the following year. Its resale value will decrease by $500 during the coming year.

The lowest-priced new car that you can find costs $11,500. If you buy it, you plan to keep it for 6 years, at which time it will have a market value of $2000. The car dealer has offered you $1750 for your old car as a trade-in on the new one and claims that your operating costs should drop to $1800 the first year and should increase by about $350 in each of the following years. Your annual interest rate is 11 percent.

(a)   What is the equivalent annual cost of the challenger?

(b)   What are the equivalent annual costs for your old car?

7.7   Assume that a friend of yours is thinking about buying a new car. Her presently owned car can be sold for $1600 or can provide adequate service for 2 more years at an operating cost of $1500 next year and $1700 the year afterward. She has been offered $2500 for her car as a trade-in on a demonstrator model that has a purchase price of $10,500. The demonstrator is expected to have an economic life of 6 years, with operating costs of $1200 the first year that increase by $300 per year thereafter, and a salvage value in 6 years of $800. The value of her car in 2 years will be the $400. An 8 percent interest charge is appropriate. Assuming that she will need a car indefinitely, what advice can you offer based on equivalent annual costs?

7.8   Using a 10 percent minimum acceptable rate of return, calculate the present worth of the costs for the two alternatives described below, based on a best-possible-replacement policy, when the need for the equipment is expected to continue indefinitely.

The present equipment could be sold now for $5000, but in 3 years it will have no salvage value owing to radically improved equipment expected to be available then; it will cost $1000 to remove the old equipment in 3 years. This alternative (A) has annual expenses of $3300.

A greatly improved version of the equipment that is to be introduced in 3 years will have annual operating costs of $1900, a first cost of $10,000, and a salvage value of $2000 at the end of its 3-year life.

A presently available replacement has a price of $14,500 and a salvage value of $1000 at the end of its 6-year economic life. This alternative (B) has operating costs of $2800 per year.

7.9   A small retail business is housed in a structure built 8 years ago and is heated by a central gas furnace. Current heating costs average $1200 per month, and the furnace is in need of an overhaul, including replacement of the fan motor and filter system. Cost of this work, which is expected to be $3600, will improve the furnace efficiency by approximately 10 percent. The furnace could also be replaced by either of two new units. The first is a modified version of the current system, which would cost $8500 and is expected to reduce energy costs by 25 percent. The second is a pulse-jet system costing $11,000 and providing a 35 percent saving. All three systems would be expected to last 10 years with no maintenance costs other than routine cleaning and filter replacement. At the end of that time, the current system would have no salvage value and the new systems would each probably be worth about 15 percent of the purchase price. The current system now has a salvage value of $500 which could be applied as a trade-in. Using a MARR of 20 percent, determine which alternative should be selected.

7.10   A question has arisen with respect to whether it is more economical to replace a forklift truck or to rebore the engine and completely rebuild the present one. The original cost of the present truck 5 years ago was $12,000. To rebore the engine and completely rebuild the truck will extend its life another 5 years and will cost $7500. A new forklift truck of the same capacity will have a first cost of $15,000 and an estimated life of 10 years. Fuel and lubricants for the rebuilt truck will be about $6000 per year. Similar costs for the new truck will be about 15 percent less. Repairs for the new truck are expected to be about $600 per year less than those for the rebuilt truck. Neither unit will have any realizable value when retired. State your assumptions and determine the equivalent present worths of the two alternatives, using an interest rate of 12 percent.

7.11 A necessary function can be performed by any of the assets described by the accompanying data:

Alternative	First cost, $	Life, years	Salvage value, $	Annual cost, $
1	8500	6	1100	1100
2	4500	3	800	1200
3	3000	3	0	1300

When investment funds are expected to earn 12 percent annually, what is the equivalent annual cost of the alternatives according to the repeated-life method?

7.12 Table 7.6 summarized the EAC values for a variety of life (N) situations in order to determine a cyclic replacement policy. The computations were not given for N values of 4 through 6, only the final results. Verify the correctness of these three tabular results.

7.13 Table 7.3 gave an automobile leasing plan that returns 3.20 percent effective interest for the lessor. Assuming that all the relative data stay the same while the annual lease payment increases, determine what the lease payment would have to be in order to allow an effective annual interest rate of 11 percent return for the lessor.

7.14 A new delivery truck has a sticker price of $18,395, but the dealer will sell it for $17,700 cash if there is no trade-in. A 3-year-old van can be traded for $6000 on the new truck purchased at the sticker price or sold to a used-car dealer for $5700. The resale value of the van is expected to decrease annually by 40 percent of the previous year's value. Operating costs for the van will be $3100 next year and will increase each following year by $900.

A new truck is expected to have operating costs of $2500 per year for the next 2 years; these costs will then increase by $450 each year. After 6 years a truck can likely be sold for 10 percent of its sticker price. It is the policy to retire trucks and vans after 6 years of service and to earn 8 percent annually on invested funds.

Assuming the price of a new truck will not increase in the next few years, when should the van be replaced?

7.15 A specialized sewage treatment pump has an initial cost of $10,000 and first-year operating and maintenance expenses of $4000. These annual costs are expected to increase yearly at a geometric gradient rate of 6 percent, but the salvage value of the pump is dependent on material recovery only and will remain constant at $500 regardless of how long it remains in service. Assuming a tax-free interest rate of 8 percent, determine how long the pump should be retained in service before replacement if a pump has a maximum life of 4 years.

7.16 Two years ago an automated testing machine was installed to monitor product quality. The equipment cost $25,000 and is capable of testing 400 units per day at a total operation and maintenance cost of $0.26 per unit. Product sales have now increased to the point that it is necessary to increase production to 700 units per day, and the company must choose between replacing the current equipment or buying an additional machine of the same type. A larger machine with a capacity of 800 units per shift would cost $45,000 and have operating and maintenance costs of $0.22 per unit. A new 400-unit-per-shift machine would cost $27,000 and have inspection costs identical to those of the existing equipment. It is expected that the testing equipment will be required for 5 more years, at which time the salvage value will be approximately equal to 10 percent of the first cost. An equipment supplier has offered a $10,000 trade-in for the existing equipment on the high-capacity unit. Assuming the company continues on a single-shift 250 day/year operation, determine which alternative should be selected, using a MARR of 20 percent.

7.17 A mechanical testing machine with an initial cost of $11,000 closely follows the cost pattern shown below:

Year	Operating cost, $	Salvage value, $
1	3700	8500
2	3950	7600
3	4200	6400
4	4700	5000
5	5400	3600
6	6300	2200
7	7200	800

Using 0 percent interest rate (to get a preliminary evaluation) and assuming that replacement equipment will follow the same cost pattern, determine the economic life.

7.18 Determine the replacement interval for the data in Prob. 7.17 if a MARR of 10 percent is required. Which result would you feel more comfortable in, the one from Prob. 7.17 or the one from this problem?

7.19 A new type of testing machine to perform the same function as depicted in Prob. 7.17 is now available at a purchase price of $16,500. The new machine costs more, but it has twice the capacity of the older models. A company plans to replace four of the older types with the new design. The four candidates for replacement are now 2 years old. They will be replaced when the expected cost of keeping them in service 1 more year is greater than the average annual cost for new machines of comparable capacity. The expected cost pattern for the new type of testing machine is as follows (a maximum life of 4 years will be considered in the analysis):

Year	Operating cost, $	Salvage value, $
1	7,200	13,000
2	7,900	10,500
3	8,700	8,500
4	9,900	6,500

When should the replacement occur if no interest is charged?

7.20 Redo Prob. 7.19, using an interest rate of 10 percent.

7.21 Uptown Urban Transit District is considering the purchase of new articulated buses for use in expanding service to suburban areas. The new units have a first cost of $205,000 and are expected to have a service life of 6 years. Maintenance and operating costs are estimated at $80,000 for the first year of use and will probably increase at an arithmetic rate of $4000 per year thereafter. The projected intermediate salvage values are as follows:

End of year	1	2	3	4	5	6
Salvage value, $	160,000	120,000	75,000	30,000	15,000	10,000

Determine when replacement should occur if interest is charged at a rate of 15 percent annually.

7.22 Assume that the transit district has purchased several of the buses described in Prob. 7.21 and has used them for 3 years. A new model with comparable service characteristics is made available on a lease basis for a cost of $120,000 per year including all maintenance and operating expenses. Should the existing buses be sold and replaced by a lease agreement? If so, when should the change be made?

7.23 Three years ago, Dynamic Mechanics purchased a desktop testing machine for $7000, and since that time, the resale or salvage value has been decreasing at a linear rate of $1000 per year. Maintenance and operating costs were $1600 the first year and have been increasing at a rate of $500 per year for each additional year of service. No exact projections are available, but it appears that both trends should continue for at least the next 3 years. At the end of that time, the equipment could be replaced by another unit with similar cost patterns. However, a new machine with a service life of 10 years is now available for a purchase price of $12,000 and no salvage value. A factory maintenance plan is also available at a fixed cost of $1500 per year on a contract basis.

Using a before-tax MARR of 25 percent, determine what replacement policy Dynamic Mechanics should follow with regard to this equipment. Assume that a need for this type of machine will exist for at least 10 years more.

7.24 A major hospital plans to replace the outpatient x-ray facility. The existing equipment has a current market value of $8500 that will decrease at 40 percent per year over the next 3 years. The hospital administrator, in conjunction with the supervisor of the outpatient unit, decides that the equipment has to be replaced within that time (3 years). The sole supplier of the equipment gives the following replacement bid: $43,000 first cost with a trade-in allowance of $10,000 given for the current equipment. If the new equipment is purchased later, its trade-in allowance will be the true market value. Operating costs are expected to give $2500 per year savings over the current equipment (which are $8500 per year). Salvage value is expected to be $12,000 after 5 years. Also, all costs for the new equipment are expected to increase geometrically at 10 percent per year after the first year (the salvage value is expected to be about the same, regardless of when the equipment is purchased). The trade-in value of the hospital's old equipment will revert to the hospital's estimates after the first year. Should replacement of the equipment be made sometime in the next 3 years? If yes, when? A MARR of 10 percent is required.

7.25 Tip Top Testers, Inc. (TTT, Inc.) is considering the purchase of a new testing machine. The following cost estimates have been obtained:

Purchase price of equipment = $115,000

Market values are estimated to be:

End of year	1	2	3	4	5
Market value, $	85,000	60,000	48,000	39,000	30,000

The expected service life is 5 years. Operating expenses will be $18,000 the first year, increasing by a geometric gradient of 4 percent per year each following year.
- (a) When MARR = 10 percent, determine the EAC of owning and operating the equipment over the expected service life.
- (b) Assume TTT, Inc. has purchased the tester described above and used it for 3 years. A new model is now available at a cost of $140,000 that includes installation charges. This unit is expected to have a negligible salvage value after an 8-year life, and operating expenses are expected to be a constant $16,000 per year. Should the new equipment be purchased now if the old machine can be sold at its market value, if the need for a tester will continue indefinitely, and if the MARR is still 10 percent?

7.26 A factory uses 11 machines of identical design. Each one costs $15,000. In operation, maintenance costs are $3000 the first year and increase arithmetically by $400 each year thereafter. Since the machines are of special design, they have no salvage value at any time. The MARR is 10 percent. What is the economic life for cyclic replacement of the machines?

7.27 Shortcircuit Co. is considering the purchase of a newly developed Sparksalot chip tester. The following data have been provided by the manufacturing engineering group for a cost evaluation: The purchase price of the equipment is $45,000 plus $5000 for installation. The maximum life is 5 years, with the following intermediate salvage values: year 1, $30,000; year 2, $20,000; year 3, $15,000; year 4, $11,000; year 5, $8000; and year 6, $6000. Operating expenses will be $20,000 for year 1, with an annual increase of $4000 in future years.

Based on a required rate of return of 20 percent and an assumption of cyclic replacement, determine the economic life of the tester.

7.28 An engineering college is considering replacing 15 workstations which are on a STAR network. These workstations have a total salvage value of $8500 (from a junior college bid). The existing system could last for another 3 years with a system update that will cost $4500 immediately. Also, after the update, the current system will have the following associated data:

Year	Salvage value, $	Operating and maintenance costs, $
1	7000	13,000
2	3500	18,000
3	1000	23,000

The new workstations will cost $8000 each, and implementation for all the computers will be $1500. The technological life of the new equipment is 5 years, and salvage values decrease from the first cost by 28 percent per year. Operating costs will be $4000 for each of the first 2 years (due to warranty agreements) and will be $8000, $10,000, and $13,000 for years 3 through 5, respectively. What replacement plan would you recommend with a MARR of 8 percent?

7.29 List 10 factors that should be considered in an economic analysis of a proposed robot installation. For which ones would data be relatively easy to obtain, of uncertain accuracy, or difficult to quantify? For example, the first cost of a robot is readily available, its salvage value is uncertain, and the monetary worth of experience gained from employing a robot is difficult to estimate. Now name 10 more factors.

7.30 Review Exercise 3 evaluated two automated lines that were candidates to replace a current line which is now obsolete due to competitive obsolescence. Cost computations were shown for the three-robot line but not for the four-robot line. Verify that the results given for the four-robot line are correct.

7.31 In Sec. 7.5.2 we considered a cyclic replacement problem using an interest rate (the results are summarized in Table 7.6). In that example, a replacement period of 4 years was obtained with 0 percent interest as well as 10 percent. For the same problem use an interest rate of 15 percent and interpret your results.

ANALYSIS OF PUBLIC PROJECTS

Public men are bees working in a glass hive; and curious spectators enjoy themselves in watching every secret movement, as if it were a study in natural history.

Henry Ward Beecher, *Proverbs from Plymouth Pulpit,* 1887

The public and industrial sectors of the North American economies interact as mutually supportive, but occasionally contradictory, forces. Government functions to facilitate the operation of a free-enterprise system may thwart or make difficult certain actions deemed advantageous by particular industrial subsystems. Despite claims that "government is best which governs least," the private sector simply does not have the means to provide all the necessary social goods and services. Government activities regulate and support the legal framework of the marketplace, establish and collect taxes for the redistribution of income, and allocate resources to programs and projects believed beneficial to society. Ideally, these activities will mirror the disposition of the citizenry with reasonable accuracy, while not completely satisfying the loudly vocal minorities calling either for no government or for government solutions to all the perceived ills of society. The diversity of public sector activities designed to serve so many interests complicates the evaluation of their effectiveness.

The engineering economist may well feel perplexed when facing the analysis of a complex public project. The identification of factors to be considered, quantified, and combined in the analysis can be very extensive. A major difference between the public and private sectors, when it comes to analysis of projects, can be the fact that a benefit to one segment of the public sector may well be a disbenefit to another group. For example, routing a freeway around a small town will benefit travelers, but the economic effect on local retail businesses could be disastrous. Similarly, construction of the English Channel tunnel, which opened to the public in November

1994, will be a boon to vacationers, but existing hydrofoil ferries will certainly lose customers. On the other hand, it is generally assumed that economic decisions made by private business management for the "good of the company" are for the benefit of all concerned. In actual fact, the benefit may be for only a segment of the employees; layoffs are a disbenefit to those affected. The net result relates to the overall profit picture, which is how most private sector operations are measured. The concept of profit is not so readily apparent in the public sector.

There is a growing trend towards public-private partnerships in developing projects. A major resource development project is that of the Hibernia Oil Field,[†] located offshore about 315 kilometers southeast of St. John's, Newfoundland, Canada on the Grand Banks. Discovered in 1979, it has estimated recoverable reserves of 615 million barrels. A consortium—consisting of Mobil Canada, Chevron, Petro Canada, Murphy Oil, and the Canadian government—is investing in the Hibernia Oil Field; and a specially formed operating company, the Hibernia Management and Development Company, is developing the project on behalf of the consortium. A concrete gravity base structure to be located in 80 meters of water is the first large offshore concrete platform to be built in North America.

A second example of public-private partnership is Highway 407, a new multi-lane urban toll highway under construction across the top of Metropolitan Toronto.[‡] This major east-west toll highway is intended to improve transportation access for Metropolitan Toronto and surrounding regions and ease congestion. Various segments are expected to open in the 1996–1998 period. An Ontario-based consortium, the Canadian Highways International Corporation, was selected as the private sector partner for the Highway 407 Project. A provincial Crown agency, the Ontario Transportation Capital Corporation, was formed to raise the required financing. The innovative plan is for the capital cost to be paid back over time by using toll revenues instead of government funds. This 69 kilometer highway, with an estimated cost of $928 million, will be one of the first completely electronic non-stop toll highways to become operational in the world.

A third example of public-private cooperation in developing major projects is that of the Northumberland Strait Crossing.[§] The government of Canada signed an agreement with Strait Crossing Inc. on October 7, 1993, to finance, build, and operate a 13 kilometer bridge in the Northumberland Strait, between Prince Edward Island and New Brunswick. The total cost

---

[†]George C. Hoff and Elomor Radoslar, "Concrete Production for the Hibernia Platform," Proceedings, 1995 Annual Conference of the Canadian Society for Civil Engineering, Ottawa, V.III, pp. 693–716.
[‡]David P. Garner and Peep Korgemagi, "Ontario's Highway 407 Project," Proceedings, 1995 Annual Conference of the Canadian Society for Civil Engineering, Ottawa, V.III, pp. 97–106.
[§]Public Works and Government Services Canada, "Northumberland Strait Crossing Project, A Link to the Future," May 26, 1995 (Internet).

is $840 million (in 1992 dollars), borne entirely by the private sector. The expected completion date is Spring 1997. According to the agreement, the company was responsible for raising the necessary capital to finance the project. Two basic sources of revenue are the government of Canada's 35 annual payments of $41.9 million (1992 dollars), and bridge tolls. The payment from the federal government is less than the overall cost to the government for the existing Marine Atlantic ferry system, which is to be replaced by the bridge. In addition to saving money for the federal government, the project was to generate tangible benefits to the regional economy.

Approximately 2,675 person years of construction employment will be created by this project. Following its completion, the bridge is likely to contribute additional long-term benefits including: ease of access to PEI; over $10 million per year of savings for the PEI transportation industry; an increase in visitors of up to 25 percent; better product delivery scheduling for the fisheries and agriculture sectors; technology transfer to regional businesses and workers; a more highly skilled Atlantic Canada work force; the creation of a heavy industrial, deep water port in PEI; and more accurate predictability of delivery for goods from every industrial sector including agriculture, fisheries, and manufacturing.

Although approximately 420 permanent Marine Atlantic employees will lose their jobs once the bridge becomes operational, a comprehensive work force adjustment strategy was developed. It includes employment in bridge operation and maintenance, a negotiated severance package, and retraining and relocation assistance where necessary.

The most common way to approach public project evaluation is by *benefit/cost analysis*. Often, this approach is called *cost-benefit analysis,* but the two approaches are the same. The basic measure for accepting project consideration is a benefit/cost (B/C) ratio that is greater than 1 or, equivalently, a positive net difference between benefit and cost. Incremental B/C ratios should also exceed 1 for added increments of investment. As we will see, $B/C > 1$ is a standard of minimum approval, but it is not an effective ranking criterion. Discounting procedures, computational practices, and capital-rationing considerations are essentially the same as for the private sector.

As just stated, the benefit/cost factor is usually the ratio of benefits B to costs C, denoted by B/C. Another representation can be $B - C$. If benefits and costs are in present-worth (PW) monetary terms, it follows that

$$PW = B - C$$

will be maximized when the difference between benefits and costs is maximized. We could then rank alternatives according to their $B - C$ values. This is not true for the B/C ratios, which is why we just stated that B/C is not an effective *ranking* criterion.

Benefit/cost analysis is not restricted to public project analysis, although that will be the framework for this chapter. The methodology can be yet another tool available to the analyst. As a private sector example, suppose that a company is planning to allow certain technical workers to operate from their homes. The company will provide computers and modems as well as ancillary supplies to the selected workers. The benefits to the company should include improved effectiveness of the workers who do not have to make a tiring drive to and from work every day. Negative benefits might accrue from not having face-to-face interaction every day with workers. Some quantification of these benefits will be needed. The cost aspects should be fairly straightforward. A different ratio might be presented to the workers: Benefits will still include the nontravel benefits (which will now include a cost benefit to the workers) but might also include home-parenting possibilities. Costs to the worker will include additional utility costs and possibly some supply purchasing.

The St. Clair River International Tunnel is a real-world example of a private sector investment project. Following extensive studies, CN North America engineers recommended that a new tunnel, capable of handling double stack containers as well as all other oversize rail traffic, should be built linking Sarnia and Port Huron. Completed in 1995 at a cost of $210 million dollars (1994 dollars), this new tunnel replaces an existing tunnel 27 meters away. Given the increasing trade between Canada and the U.S. as a result of the North American Free Trade Agreement (NAFTA), the St. Clair Tunnel has strategic importance in providing a direct route between Montreal, Toronto, and Chicago. Benefits to CN North America include reduced transit times, improved service, and improved efficiency. Environmental benefits are expected as well. Since a substantial portion of new freight traffic will be diverted from motor carriers and loads will be moved on double stack container cars, savings of fuel and emission reduction are among the environmental benefits.[†]

Conceptually, a public project analysis considers the worthiness of shifting resources from the private sector to the public sector and the extent to which a public project should be pursued when its benefits exceed its costs. Many factors besides a benefit/cost analysis influence the final decision about funding public projects, and weaknesses of benefit/cost analyses as traditionally conducted have cast doubts on the resulting ratings; but the analytical procedures still invite credibility and objectivity in appraisals of public expenditures.

A second method for evaluating public projects is by *cost-effectiveness analysis*. This is really no different from conventional benefit/cost analysis in that cost-effectiveness analysis can be a one-sided benefit/cost study when the analysis is based on a specified level of cost or a determined level of benefit. For example, given a certain cost outlay approval for a specific

---

[†]Bernie Martin and Ata M. Khan, "Environmental Issues of the New Intermodal Tunnel, Canada/U.S.," Proceedings, 1996 Annual Conference of the Canadian Society for Civil Engineering, Edmonton, pp. 119–128.

should be based on economic efficiency principles.[†] For example, a future high speed ground transportation system (i.e., a 300 km/hour high speed rail or 450 km/hour magnetically levitated vehicle—maglev) intended for the Toronto–Ottawa–Montreal corridor, should be evaluated on the basis of benefits vs. costs.[‡]

The use of the social cost-benefit approach to appraising highway investments, establishing road pricing, and road cost allocation decision making was recently highlighted by the British Columbia Ministry of Transportation and Highways. This policy reflects the need to ration shrinking budgets for investments, given the ever growing demand for public funds. It is recognized that the same cost-benefit analysis framework could be used as a pragmatic base for determining full road-price and cost allocation to road users.[§]

Even for relatively small-scale projects, the benefit/cost approach is frequently used to support investment decisions. For example, the economic feasibility of reserved lanes for high occupancy vehicles on the approach to Victoria Bridge, Montreal was investigated by a study team for the Quebec Ministry of Transportation. The Victoria Bridge, as one of the five links between the Island of Montreal and the South Shore, serves heavy commuter traffic. The reserved lanes are intended to improve traffic flow and reduce congestion by reducing the number of vehicles. Alternatives, including the do-nothing alternative, were screened by using criteria for high occupancy vehicle (HOV) lanes such as safety, travel time savings, and fuel conservation. Incremental benefit/cost ratios were studied and benefits were examined. The benefit/cost analysis was used in establishing the economic feasibility of the project and finding the best alternative.[¶]

In the United States, the Rivers and Harbour Act of 1902 stipulated that a board of engineers must report on the merits of river and harbour projects of the Army Corps of Engineers. The reports were to include the amount of commerce benefited with respect to the estimated cost. A later act required a statement of local benefits to facilitate sharing of project costs with local interests that would benefit from the project. Government participation in public projects was extended by the U.S. Flood Control Act of 1936, which justified improvements to waterways for flood control *"if the*

[†]Royal Commission on National Passenger Transportation, Directions: The Final Report, Government of Canada, Ottawa, 1992.

[‡]A.M. Khan, "Maglev vs. High Speed Rail in the Quebec City–Windsor Corridor: A Comparison of Costs and Revenues," Proceedings of the International Conference on High Speed Ground Transportation Systems, edited by V.A. Bondada and Roger L. Wayson, American Society of Civil Engineers (ASCE), New York 1992, pp. 166–175.

[§]Peter Bein, "Cost-Benefit Basis of Highway Investment Appraisal and Road Pricing," Proceedings, Canadian Transportation Research Forum 29th Annual Meeting, Victoria, B.C. May 15–18, 1994, pp. 743–757.

[¶]Brenda Wong and Dominique Lord, "Feasibility for a Reserves HOV Lane for the Approach of the Victoria Bridge during the Morning Peak Period," 1994 Annual Meeting of the Canadian Transportation Research Forum, pp. 872–892.

benefits to whomsoever they may accrue are in excess of the estimated costs." In the 1940s this principle was expanded to justify other projects or programs for social welfare, and it is now an accepted measure of desirability of projects at the federal, state, and local levels of government.

More recently, B/C analysis gained considerable credibility in the U.S.A. when President Ronald Reagan, on February 17, 1981, signed Executive Order 12291 that formally made B/C analysis a control element in his administration's policy.[†] From then on, proponents of a regulation would have to demonstrate that the *benefits* from its adoption would outweigh the *costs*.

8.1.1 Benefit/Cost Criteria

In comparing benefit B to cost C, several different perspectives are reasonable, which partially explains why B/C analysis does not select an alternative; it develops information that can be used as the basis for a decision. Consider the simplified data in Table 8.1 that describe the alternatives for a small flood control project. The current average annual damage from flooding is $200,000. Three feasible options are available to reduce the damages; each larger investment of public funds provides greater protection.

The three projects and the do-nothing alternative are mutually exclusive. Data for selecting the most attractive alternative are shown in Table 8.2, where the figures are in thousands of dollars.

The following criteria indicate possible different preferences among the alternatives:

[†]Campen, op. cit.

TABLE 8.1

Annual costs and benefits from different levels of investment in small flood control project

Alternative	Equivalent annual cost of project, $	Average annual flood damage, $	Annual benefit, $
A No flood control	0	200,000	0
B Construction of levees	40,000	130,000	70,000
C Small reservoir	120,000	40,000	160,000
D Large reservoir	160,000	10,000	190,000

TABLE 8.2

Total and incremental benefit/cost values for data in Table 8.1

Alternative	Annual benefit B, $	Annual cost C, $	Total		Incremental			
			B/C	B − C, $	ΔB, $	ΔC, $	ΔB/ΔC	ΔB − ΔC, $
A	0	0	0	0				
					70	40	1.75	30
B	70	40	1.75	30				
					90	80	1.125	10
C	160	120	1.33	40				
					30	40	0.75	−10
D	190	160	1.19	30				

- *Minimum investment:* Choose alternative **A**. If funds are severely limited, this may be the only possible choice.
- *Maximum benefit:* Choose alternative **D**. Flooding would occur only during extremely wet seasons.
- *Aspiration level:* This depends on the threshold set for the cost or benefit. If, e.g., the aspiration level is to reduce flood damage by at least 75 percent, then alternative **C** should be chosen because it meets the aspiration with a lower cost than does alternative **D**. Similarly, an annual-cost threshold of $100,000 indicates a preference for alternative **B**.
- *Maximum advantage of benefits over cost B − C:* Choose alternative **C**.
- *Highest B/C ratio:* Choose alternative **B**.
- *Largest investment that has a benefit/cost ratio greater than 1.0:* Choose alternative **D**.
- *Maximum incremental advantage of benefit over cost ΔB − ΔC:* Choose alternative **B**.
- *Maximum incremental benefit/cost ratio ΔB/ΔC:* Choose alternative **B**.
- *Largest investment that has an incremental B/C ratio greater than 1.0:* Choose alternative **C**.

Even though all criteria give an indication of *politically beneficial* possibilities that, for good or bad, can be a prime consideration in public project funding, only those relating to benefits minus costs consistently maximize the present worth.

A liberal interpretation of the wording of the 1936 Flood Control Act (U.S.A.) suggests that the highest investment in which benefits exceed costs is the most desirable. A more realistic interpretation is that the act sets a lower limit on acceptability, with respect to both total project amount and the incremental amounts in multilevel alternatives. By the latter interpretation, alternative **D** is rejected because of its negative $\Delta B - \Delta C$

component, and its $\Delta B/\Delta C$ ratio is less than 1.0 (given **C** is funded, additional funding for alternative **D** is not justified). Then alternatives **B** and **C** are both acceptable, so other considerations should enter into the final choice. These considerations include the availability of investment funds, capital-rationing criteria, and the special features of social merit and economic objectives that affect most public projects.

8.1.2 Benefit/Cost Comparisons

The mechanics of benefit/cost comparisons are straightforward and simple—deceptively so; the determination of costs and benefits for alternatives, as will be seen in Secs. 8.2 and 8.3, are usually not straightforward and simple. The basic formulas are

$$B/C = \frac{\text{present worth of benefits}}{\text{present worth of costs}} \tag{8.1}$$

$$= \frac{\text{equivalent annual benefits}}{\text{equivalent annual costs}} \tag{8.2}$$

and

$$\text{Present value of net benefit } B - C = \text{PW(benefits)} - \text{PW(costs)} \tag{8.3}$$

where, according to Circular A-94 (1972) from the Office of Management and Budget, Executive Office of the President (U.S.A.), the present worth of benefits is the discounted *constant*-dollar value of goods and services expected to result from a project or program for each of the years it is in effect. Estimates may reflect changes in the *relative* prices, when there is a reasonable basis for estimating such changes, but should not include any forecast change in the general price level during the planning period. The present worth of costs is the discounted annual value in *constant* dollars of resources, goods, and services required to establish and carry out a project or program. All economic costs, including acquisition, possession, and operating costs, must be included whether or not they are actually paid by the government. Such costs, *not* generally involving a direct payment by the government, include imputed market values of public property and state and local property taxes forgone.

If we are concerned solely with maximizing PW, we maximize formula (8.3). It will be found that ratios are frequently used in practice even though the worth must be evaluated by Eq. (8.3) or by using *incremental* ratios. One possible advantage of using Eqs. (8.1) and (8.2) is that they could allow alternatives with nonmonetary factors to be considered in the final evaluation. To repeat what was stated in the introductory remarks, B/C ratios are not *effective ranking values*. Consider the following data:

Alternative	B	C	B/C	B − C	ΔB	ΔC	ΔB/ΔC	ΔB − ΔC
X₁	4	2	2	2				
					3	2	1.5	1
X₂	7	4	1.75	3				

Although X_1 has a higher B/C value than does X_2, the incremental ratio for the extra benefit and cost exceeds 1.0, making X_2 an acceptable alternative. If it can be assumed that sufficient capital is available to fund only one alternative, then X_2 is selected because it provides greater benefits. However, when the total costs for projects exceed the resources allocated to the proposing agency, capital-budgeting procedures are required and intangible effects may influence the selection.

EXAMPLE 8.1   **Incremental Benefit/Cost Evaluation**

A number of small earthen dams are contemplated for the headwaters of a drainage system. Four tributaries originate in a national forest and flow together to form a river that passes through private lands. Each year there is some flooding, and every few years a major inundation occurs. Construction of one or more dams will ease the threat of high water. Dams on all the tributaries would largely eliminate the chance of a major flood.

In addition to the damage to private lands, floods ruin fire and logging roads in the forest. Other benefits from the dams include the value of the impounded water for fire protection and recreational use. The following benefit and cost estimates have been developed for the only topologically feasible combinations of dams:

Dam sites	Construction costs, $	Annual maintenance and operation, $	Annual flood benefits, $	Annual fire benefits, $	Annual recreation benefits, $
1	1,200,000	20,000	200,000	20,000	30,000
1 and 2	1,500,000	35,000	190,000	40,000	30,000
1, 2, and 3	2,700,000	50,000	280,000	60,000	60,000
1, 2, 3, and 4	3,500,000	60,000	300,000	70,000	70,000

A 40-year life and no salvage value are assumed for earthwork dams. An interest rate of 4 percent is deemed appropriate for the investment. This rate reflects the low risk involved and is in line with the historical interest rate for bonds issued by the federal agency to finance public projects. On the basis of B/C ratios, which of the four alternatives should be selected?

Solution

A B/C ratio based on equivalent annual values for each alternative is calculated from

$$B/C = \frac{\text{annual flood and fire savings} + \text{recreation benefits}}{\text{equivalent annual construction costs} + \text{maintenance cost}}$$

Equivalent annual construction cost = (initial construction cost)
$$\times (A/P, 4, 40)$$
$$= \text{(initial construction cost)}$$
$$\times (0.05052)$$

Benefit and cost data are as follows:

Dam sites	Annual benefits, $	Annual cost, $	Increments of Benefit, $	Cost, $	Total B/C ratio
1	250,000	80,624			3.10
			10,000	30,156	
1 and 2	260,000	110,780			2.35
			140,000	75,624	
1, 2, and 3	400,000	186,404			2.15
			40,000	50,416	
1, 2, 3, and 4	440,000	236,820			1.86

For an accurate evaluation, the requirement that annual benefits equal annual costs should be applied to each separable increment of project costs. This is exactly analogous to the incremental IRR analysis we studied in Chap. 6. In fact, if we substitute the B/C ratio for IRR in the flowchart of Fig. 6.1, we have the current procedure.

First, site 1 is compared with the no-action alternative to yield a total B/C ratio = incremental B/C ratio = 3.10, which qualifies it as an acceptable alternative. If this were not acceptable, we would check the next alternative, sites 1 and 2, with the no-action alternative to see whether we can get started.

Now we check site 1 against the next-lowest annual-cost option, that of sites 1 and 2. The *incremental* B/C ratio is $10,000/$30,156 = 0.33. Since this is less than 1, the alternative of sites 1 and 2 is not feasible even though the total B/C ratio is 2.35. The additional benefits and costs over site 1 just do not pay for themselves.

Next we check sites 1, 2, and 3 against the last satisfactory option, which in our case is the site 1 option. We find the incremental B/C ratio from

$$\frac{\$400,000 - \$250,000}{\$186,404 - \$80,624} = 1.42$$

The alternative of sites 1, 2, and 3 is satisfactory.

Last, we check the incremental B/C ratio for the last alternative (sites 1, 2, 3, and 4) against the most recent satisfactory alternative (sites 1, 2, and 3):

$$\text{Incremental } B/C = \frac{\$40,000}{\$50,416} = 0.79$$

The last alternative (sites 1, 2, 3, and 4) is not satisfactory, and therefore preference is indicated for the third alternative—dams at sites 1, 2, and 3.

Without an incremental analysis, the last alternative (four dams) might have been selected, because it does possess a B/C ratio greater than 1.0 and offers the greatest total benefits. Another mistake would be to eliminate all other alternatives because the dam at site 1 has a larger benefit/cost ratio than do the other options. The reasoning errors behind such conclusions are the same as those examined for incremental rates of return (Chap. 6). The conclusion to accept the three-dam alternative on the basis of the given data would also result from a rate-of-return or present-worth evaluation.

It is interesting to note the *sensitivity* of the selection to changes in the data. As is asked in Prob. 8.20, to use a required interest rate of 8 percent instead of 4 percent would change the choice to the first alternative (one dam) because all the added benefit and cost increments would produce B/C ratios smaller than unity. Including only the flood control benefits would also make site 1 the only alternative with an acceptable B/C ratio. The number of spillover benefits to include in an analysis and the monetary rating given to less tangible benefits can significantly influence decisions; this topic will be briefly addressed in Sec. 8.6.1.

8.1.3 Irregularities in B/C Comparisons

No investment criterion seems to be able to escape all theoretical objections. The benefit/cost criterion has been subjected to considerable criticism because of its oversimplification of complex inputs, susceptibility to misinterpretation, and potential for misuse. Many objections are forced by social and political entities, often difficult for the engineer to consider. Historically, a few of these objections are as follows:

Lack of assistance in setting priorities

A B/C ratio, by itself, includes the cost and benefit of a particular project but no indication of how valuable the benefit is, compared with other projects, or the relative amount of resources involved.[†] As an extreme

[†]Discussed in A. Maass, "Benefit-Cost Analysis: Its Relevance to Public Decisions," *Quarterly Journal of Economics,* vol. 80, no. 2, pp. 208–226, 1966.

example, two projects could have the same B/C ratio and have costs of $1 million and $1 billion. The billion-dollar project might have long-range consequences for the improvement of the environment in a sparsely populated region whereas the million-dollar project would serve a critical inner-city need. Eventually, both projects might serve the same number of people, but the smaller project might have far greater immediate benefits for the taxpayers who are funding it. A third $100,000 project, with the same B/C ratio as the other two, could be to preserve a site that will be destroyed if it is not subsidized immediately. If there are not enough resources available to undertake all three projects, the B/C ratios themselves are of little help in setting priorities.

Equal benefit to all

A related social objection is that the B/C standard *assumes* that benefits are equally valuable to the rich and to the poor. *Conceptually,* public funds are expended to equalize opportunities among the citizenry. A project to push a new freeway through a densely populated low-cost-housing neighborhood would thus use money partially drawn from the poor to force them to relocate to make room for an expressway that would benefit mainly wealthier suburban commuters.

The argument against the two criticisms just leveled is that the B/C criterion was not designed to rank projects; it sets only a *minimum* level of acceptability and does not pretend to identify the source of investment funds. Its use as a guide to decision makers is poignantly described in a compendium of papers submitted to the Subcommittee on Priorities and Economy in the Government of the U.S. Congress:[†]

> If benefit-cost analysis is to be implemented and used to its fullest potential, renewed efforts must be made by policy makers in both the executive and legislative branches of government. The economics profession has made significant advances in the level of sophistication of their analyses which should aid this task, but one thing is clear—benefit-cost analysis does not make decisions. Analysis can provide an important and helpful tool for making decisions, but it is no more than a tool. Problems involving social policy and value judgments must be considered and weighed in conjunction with the results of benefit-cost analysis and the final decision made by the human policymaker.

Variations due to formula inputs

Possible misuse of the B/C ratio comes about from interpretation of how to handle benefits and disbenefits, although the use of $B - C$ instead of B/C will eliminate any possibility of error. The numerator of the B/C ratio is usually taken to mean the *net benefit*—the sum of all benefits minus all disbenefits. As an example, tolls and other fees are typically treated as disbenefits for a toll road evaluation while reduced travel time

---

[†]*Benefit-Cost Analysis of Federal Programs,* Government Printing Office, Washington, 1973.

and additional use are considered as benefits. If the disbenefits were treated as costs in the denominator, the ratio would obviously change. For instance, if the present worth of a benefit is 10, a disbenefit is 3, and the cost is 5, then

$$B/C = \frac{10 - 3}{5} = 1.40$$

But if the disbenefit is counted as a cost, then

$$B/C = \frac{10}{5 + 3} = 1.25$$

This variation presents no difficulty when we remember that the purpose of the $B/C > 1$ criterion is simply to distinguish between acceptable and unacceptable alternatives and is not intended as a ranking indicator. Of course, if all ratios are less than 1 and one value has to be picked (a do-nothing alternative is not viable), then a B/C ratio less than 1 might have to be accepted. There is no way in which shifting of disbenefits from the numerator to the denominator can cause a B/C ratio to change from greater than 1 to less than 1. Equivalently, the new present value (benefit minus disbenefit minus cost) must be the same regardless of the order of subtractions:

$$(B - C)_1 = 7 - 5 = 2$$

$$(B - C)_2 = 10 - 8 = 2$$

Nor will an incremental analysis indicate any difference in the *absolute* acceptability of alternatives owing to the location of disbenefits in the B/C ratio. Two alternatives are evaluated below, first by subtracting disbenefits from benefits and then by adding them to costs. In both cases, even though the values of the ratios differ, the extra increment of investment is found to be acceptable according to the $\Delta B / \Delta C > 1$ standard:

Present worth of benefit B, disbenefit D and cost C				Computations where disbenefits subtracted from benefits $B' = B - D$				Computations where disbenefits added to costs $C' = C + D$			
B	D	C	B – D – C	B'/C	$\Delta B'$	ΔC	$\Delta B'/\Delta C$	B/C'	ΔB	$\Delta C'$	$\Delta B/\Delta C'$
X 10	3	5	10 – 3 – 5 = 2	$\frac{7}{5}$ = 1.4				$\frac{10}{8}$ = 1.25			
					9 – 7 = 2	6 – 5 = 1	$\frac{2}{1}$ = 2		13 – 10 = 3	10–8 = 2	$\frac{3}{2}$= 1.5
Y 13	4	6	13 – 4 – 6 = 3	$\frac{9}{6}$ = 1.5				$\frac{13}{10}$ = 1.3			

8.2   QUANTIFICATION OF PROJECT COSTS AND BENEFITS

Costs for all resources required to achieve the stated objectives of a project should be included in the analysis. Each alternative in multilevel proposals should be self-contained in terms of cost to avoid double-counting or overlapping expenses. A few cost considerations have particular significance to benefit/cost analyses:

- Imputed costs of existing assets employed on a project should be included when there are alternative uses for the assets. For instance, land and facilities desired for use in another project besides the one being analyzed would be treated in both projects as costs based on fair market values. Neglecting such costs would be similar to building houses on inherited land and then basing the selling price of the homes on only the construction costs because the land was free.
- Preliminary costs of investigation and technical services required to get a project started are part of the project's budget. Once the project is underway, interest charges during the construction period before earnings begin are applicable expenditures. Management costs, whether incurred by the sponsoring agency or contributed by the beneficiaries, are part of the total project cost.
- *Spillover costs*, which constitute all significant adverse effects caused by the construction and operation of a project, are expressed in terms of market prices regardless of whether actual outlays for compensation are made. For instance, an irrigation project could reduce the quality of water downstream from the area to be serviced; the additional treatment facilities necessary to restore the quality of water or provisions for water from another source would be costs to the irrigation project.

Public projects are typically conceived to provide a certain benefit or family of benefits. Many of the difficulties of quantifying these benefits have already been discussed. The nature of some social benefits often precludes their measurement by direct market pricing, because there is no market in the private sector that offers the benefits. Recreational benefits are a good example of *derived values*. Factors affecting recreational values include the number and distribution of the population in the project area; socioeconomic characteristics including disposable income, occupation, education, age, and mobility of the relevant population; and the population's leisure time and recreational habits as indicated by trends in hunting and fishing license sales, sales of recreational equipment, and total demand. Such factors suggest the potential participation rate but do not put dollar amounts on the value of the participation.

To facilitate valuation, two types of recreation days are recognized, where a *recreation day* is defined as a unit of use consisting of a visit of one individual to a recreational development during a reasonable portion of a 24-hour period:

Type of recreation day	Value of 1 day's use, $
General This type of activity attracts the majority of outdoor recreationists and requires the development of convenient access and maintenance of adequate facilities (e.g., swimming, picnicking, studying nature, tent and trailer camping, canoeing)	7.50–40.00
Specialized For this type of outdoor activity, opportunities are limited and intensity of use is low, and often they involve a large personal expense by the user (e.g., cold-water fishing, big-game hunting, wilderness pack trips)	20.00–175.00

Indications of the values that users put on such experiences can be obtained from charges for similar activities in the private sector, time and cost of travel required to partake in an activity, cost of alternative uses of the facilities, and questionnaires about how much a user would be willing to pay for various experiences. A suggested composite value for 1 visitor day to any area is simply the gross national product per day divided by the total population.

Some attributes of a public project are *intangible*. In the 1940s, aesthetic values were considered of immeasurable worth, so any cost that made them available to the public was acceptable. This line of reasoning meant that every project that promised aesthetic values automatically had a B/C ratio of at least 1.0. An equivalent conclusion results from placing an infinite value on irreplaceable assets such as wilderness areas.

A more systematic approach to the valuation of intangible characteristics defines categories of attributes and employs a subjective rating system to rank the quality of different projects. Formal environmental quality evaluation procedures have been developed to compare intangible benefits and disbenefits for alternative water- and land-use plans. The procedure starts with the identification of the environmental resources involved in a proposed project. Resources include open spaces, stream systems, beaches, wilderness areas, historical and cultural features, and ecological systems. These resources are then evaluated according to the following criteria:

- *Quantity.* Specific environmental features are enumerated and measured in units such as hectares of wilderness; kilometers of white water; areas of lakes; and numbers of waterfalls, animals, scenic attractions, and significant sites.
- *Quality.* The desirability of an environmental feature is rated by assigning a number from 1 to 10 after the features have been compared with known or projected conditions at other locations.
- *Human influence.* Subjective 1-to-10 ratings are made to indicate the degree to which people would use the resource identified; the degree to

which it is protected for continued use; and the degree to which it contributes to education, scientific knowledge, and human enjoyment.

- *Uniqueness.* A 1-to-10 rating measures the frequency of occurrence of a specific resource in the project relative to its occurrence elsewhere.
- *Significance.* Irreversible damage to a resource is rated on a 1-to-10 scale that indicates the magnitude of adverse effects on the environment. The rating reflects the scarcity of supply of a resource and the capability of its return to its original or natural state after the proposed project is implemented.

The ratings for intangible benefits are typically reported as an appendix to the monetary comparisons. A narrative may accompany the presentation of intangible considerations to explain how the ratings were developed, to discuss opposing views, and to provide supplementary information.

Now let's change our area of application to demonstrate the complexity of determining and quantifying project benefits; we will look at a unique Air Force problem.

EXAMPLE 8.2

Determining Benefits of Simulation in Fighter Pilot Training[†]

We have probably all seen television programs, such as the Public Broadcasting System's *Nova* series, describing the advantages for airline pilot training and retraining through the use of physical cockpit simulators. While the costs of such simulators are enormous, many benefits are apparent.

- Reduced day-to-day operational wear and tear on aircraft
- Reduced fuel expenses
- Elimination of possible training injuries
- Elimination of possible plane damage from accidents
- Simplified training scheduling possibilities; flight takeoff and landings not affected by actual weather conditions
- Ability to simulate highly dangerous emergency situations that are not really feasible in an actual airplane from a planned point of view (e.g., wind sheer)

Even these few benefits would tax our abilities for quantification. Reduced fuel use and operational wear and tear could be fairly simple, in terms of dollars, but how would we handle the cost of possible death or injuries? Now we add to this the use of simulators for fighter pilots flying

[†]Appreciation is expressed to W. Moor for permission to utilize information from W. C. Moor and D. E. Andrews, *Benefits Estimation for Simulation Systems Used for Aircrew Training in a Multiship Environment,* AL/HR-TR-1993-0158, Air Force Materiel Command, Brooks AFB, Texas, November 1993.

multiairplane missions. How much more complex would this situation be when compared with conventional airline flying? How might alternative simulator bids be evaluated by the Canadian Armed Forces or the U.S. Air Force?

Solution

What would be the basis for benefits computation in a situation such as this? In the field of economics, one method for benefits computation is called the *cost savings method.*[†] Schmid argues that in transportation, e.g., if we want to evaluate cost savings in substituting one mode of transportation for another (say, barge navigation for railroad freight), then the relative price paid for shipping a certain volume of goods by each method will be a feasible measure. *Time* worth has to be considered as a cost since one mode of transportation (barge) will undoubtedly be much slower than the other.

Moor suggests that the *cost savings method* may not be sufficient for the simulator analysis. A more logical approach might be to use the economic *intermediate-good method.* This approach computes changes in cost for providing the service with or without the project under consideration being considered. Schmid[‡] suggests an example that relates to education and training. The lifetime net incomes of people with and without a given level of education are compared. All other factors affecting income are held constant.

In evaluating the replacement of fighter aircraft hours with simulator hours, a degree of combat-readiness, or *utility,* is needed. This is similar to the utility/cost approach we will look at in Review Exercise 4. The *isoutility* curve shown in Fig. 8.1 describes the tradeoff between simulator training hours (currently in use) and aircraft hours. If we reduce, e.g., the annual aircraft hours per pilot by 50, the utility curve shows us that we might have to increase the simulator hours by 100 to get the same training level. In evaluating a simulator bid, it is necessary to evaluate cost savings over a range of simulator and fighter hours that will allow satisfaction of the desired utility requirement.

The next step, which is too extensive to be covered in detail at this time, is to select *performance areas* for a simulator. Typically it would include night tactics, visual lookout, multiple-plane maneuvers, all-weather employment including radar capabilities, and so on. Once these areas have been selected, it is necessary to determine the utilization characteristics needed for each. Training experts were heavily used to evaluate the timing of this training for mission-ready pilots. This evaluation is a measure of the continuity of training need and the necessity of using a simulator to meet this need.

[†]Schmid, op. cit.
[‡]Schmid, op. cit.

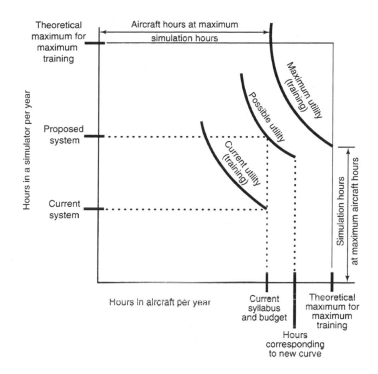

FIGURE 8.1
Isoutility curve for pilot training (from W. C. Moor, "A method for comparison of alternative multi-ship aircraft simulation systems utilizing benefit estimation," Research and Development Laboratories, Culver City, California, 1992).

Now we are ready to get back to the emphasis under consideration, that of quantifying benefits. A few of the costs developed in the report, from which benefits were derived, are these:

- *Aircraft shadow cost.* A shadow cost occurs when the actual cost, say, of an airplane, is not sufficient to present all the factors needed in an analysis. In this study, it was decided that the appropriate value to start with was the marginal cost of flying. This cost had been predetermined by the Air Force: shadow cost of aircraft = $5000 per flying hour.

- *Pilot cost.* The possibility of a pilot's incurring an accident that leads to death or injury is very real when she or he is flying a real airplane. Training in a nonflying simulator would reduce this possibility to a minute value. Therefore, a benefit is computed as the cost of pilot training multiplied by the probability of death and/or injury per flying hour. A 1987 cost of training a pilot, adjusted for inflation, was multiplied by a rough probability of pilot death while flying, resulting in pilot cost = $182 per flying hour.

- *Aircraft cost.* The cost due to the loss of an aircraft is computed in a manner similar to that of pilot cost. This uses the inflation-corrected cost of replacement multiplied by a probability of loss. This should include damage and total-loss possibilities, but in this study only total-loss data were conveniently available: Aircraft cost = $1232 per flying hour.

a densely populated city highway, which one should be selected to reduce annual *head-on* collisions? The construction and maintenance costs therefore have to be weighed against accident rates. If the *cost* of such an accident is available, then the problem could be tackled as a true B/C application. In fact, such an example has been given by Frost.[†] We will hypothesize a similar example.

Suppose we have decided that the type of barrier will be the most expensive possible (reinforced concrete). Construction of the barrier along a 5-kilometer stretch of highway has been estimated to cost $220,000 per kilometer with annual maintenance costs of $6000 per kilometer. (We assume that costs will not significantly increase over time; if they did, we would use our knowledge gleaned from earlier chapters to handle normal annual-cost increases.) Data and computations needed for benefit/cost analysis include

- Traffic volume (in million kilometers traveled per year) forecasts A for the next 5, 10, or possibly 15 years
- Annual accident rates B per 100 million kilometers of travel
- Number of accidents per kilometer expected C—compute $C = AB/100$.
- Dollar values D of a head-on collision
- Potential annual savings per kilometer CD

Now, taking the equivalent uniform annual construction and maintenance costs, we can form the benefit/cost values over the forecasted time horizon. Present-worth values can be obtained through the appropriate discount rate. This analysis can also be accomplished for the other options, and suggestions on interpretation can be offered to the decision maker.

Now, suppose we decide to use *cost-effectiveness analysis* instead of the benefit/cost approach. We need to get data such as those just considered but possibly not as complex. Such data might be as given in Table 8.3. In computing the values for total equivalent annual uniform costs, a 10-year study period was assumed. For the concrete barrier, this value would be

$$\text{EAC} = \$30,000 + \$1,110,000(A/P, 6, 10)$$
$$= \$30,000 + \$1,110,000(0.13587)$$
$$= \$180,816$$

According to Fleischer,[‡] there are only three conditions under which the ranking of cost-effectiveness ratios is appropriate:

- Effectiveness of all alternatives is the same, so rank by decreasing costs.
- Costs for all alternatives are equal, so rank by decreasing effectiveness.

[†]Ibid.
[‡]G. A. Fleischer, *Engineering Economy—Capital Allocation Theory.* (Boston: PWS Publishing Company, 1984.)

TABLE 8.3

Cost-effectiveness data for barrier construction (5-kilometer section)

Alternative	First costs, $	Annual maintenance, $	Annual uniform costs C at 6%, $	Annual reduced number of accidents A	Cost-effectiveness ratio C/A, $
Concrete barrier	1,110,000	30,000	180,816	85	2127
Wire-mesh barrier	680,000	40,000	122,392	63	1943
Landscaped median (land available)	540,000	20,000	103,370	41	2521

- For any pair of alternatives, if both the cost and the effectiveness of one dominate the other (lower cost *and* higher effectiveness), then eliminate the dominated alternative.

None of these conditions occurs for our example, so we would consider criteria such as given in Sec. 8.1.1 for benefit/cost evaluations. For example, if we had a maximum (threshold) of $150,000, on a uniform equivalent annual cost basis, for barrier construction and maintenance, then the wire barrier would be logical. Since accidents can be a very emotional issue, the city council might throw political caution to the wind and adopt the concrete barrier due to the maximization of accident reduction.

Some economists tend to downgrade the value of cost-effectiveness analysis when contrasting the technique to benefit/cost analysis. Hopefully, the simple highway barrier example has shown how the problem could be approached by both methods. The choice of method will often be a function of data availability. There is no doubt that both approaches have significant *benefit,* and both can be very *effective* (puns intended).

8.5 THE DISCOUNT RATE QUESTION

The engineering economist will, in general, not be involved with setting government interest rates. However, the knowledge of what goes into such rates should be one of the analyst's tools. For this reason, we will spend just a little time discussing this important question.

The appropriate interest rate to use in evaluating public investments is a voluminously debated issue. Although numerous suggestions have been forwarded, none has been awarded complete acceptance. In Canada, the Treasury Board of the government of Canada establishes social discount rates for government-funded projects on the basis of financial markets as well as government bond rates. These social discount rates are usually communicated to interested agencies. The Office of Management and Budget

(U.S.A.) has required federal agencies to use a real discount rate of 10 percent unless a special rate is set by law or as a result of a formula or guidelines required by law.[†] An exception is made for evaluating water and related resources projects where the Water Resources Council (U.S.A.) annually issues the discount rate to be used in evaluating federal water projects. Row et al. say this was $7\frac{3}{8}$ percent for the 1981 fiscal year, and the USDA Forest Service adopted a recommendation to use a 4 percent discount rate in long-term land and resource planning use about the same time period.

The effect of the discounting rate on benefit/cost ratios for projects with different lives is shown in Fig. 8.3. The five curves represent B/C ratios at different discount rates for an initial investment of $1 that returns a total of $2 in equal installments over N years. Therefore, at a 0 percent discount rate and $N = 10$,

$$B/C = \frac{(\$2/10)(P/A,\ 0,\ 10)}{\$1} = \frac{0.2(10)}{1} = 2$$

but at $i = 10$ percent for 10 years,

$$\begin{aligned} B/C &= \frac{(\$2/10)(P/A,\ 10,\ 10)}{\$1} \\ &= \frac{0.2(6.1445)}{1} = \frac{1.23}{1} = 1.23 \end{aligned}$$

[†]C. Row, H. F. Kaiser, and J. Sessions, "Discount Rate for Long-Term Forest Investments", *Journal of Forestry,* vol. 79, no. 6, pp. 367–369, June 1981.

FIGURE 8.3

Graph of benefit/cost ratios at five discount rates for different project lives of a proposal to invest $1 in order to receive $2 in equal installments prorated over the project's life.

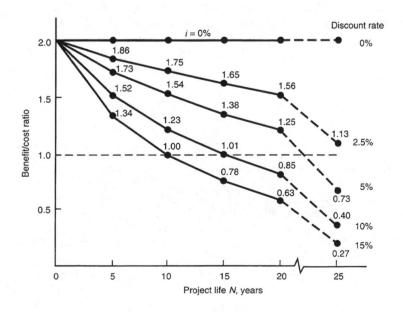

Figure 8.3 is given to demonstrate a point. Realistically, with an inflation-free rate, we would never expect to see rates as high as 10 or 15 percent.

8.5.1 Range of Discount Rates

The government borrowing rate is an obvious measure of financing costs for public projects. It is akin to the *cost-of-capital* concept by which a minimum attractive rate of return (MARR) is determined for investments in the private sector. The cost of capital to the government can also be taken as a minimum discount rate for public projects. The interest rate for government borrowing depends on the level (federal, provincial, or local), tax exemption privileges offered, current economic conditions, and length of the loan. Since government bonds are generally considered to be risk-free, any public project should promise a minimum return that is at least equal to the bond rate. Otherwise, the resources that could be used to fund projects should be applied to debt repayment instead.

The rates of return expected in the private sector are higher than the interest rates on government bonds. This is a reasonable condition, because a firm would invest in risk-free government bonds if it did not expect larger returns from industrial investments. In the opinion of W. A. Baumol, "The correct discount rate [for public projects] is the percentage rate of return that the resources would otherwise provide in the public sector."[†] His view recognizes the opportunity cost to general welfare that occurs when resources are used to produce benefits smaller than could have been obtained if the resources were applied elsewhere. Specifically, a public project that barely exceeds $B/C = 1$ when evaluated at a low discount rate would, if carried out, produce fewer benefits than could have been obtained by leaving the amount invested in the private sector.

An argument against charging higher rates for public projects is that certain socially desirable programs would never meet higher evaluation standards but are nonetheless worthwhile. This line of reasoning emphasizes the responsibility of the present population to ensure adequate living conditions for future generations. Since most people are more concerned with satisfying their current needs and wants than with saving for the future, proponents of low discount rates say only government action can enforce investments for future benefits and this transfer of resources necessarily yields a lower return than do resources used for current consumption.

Counterarguments question the legitimacy of allowing a few policy makers to decide what is best for general welfare, especially when their allocations appear to contradict public preferences shown in a free market. It is generally agreed that no generation has the right to completely con-

---

[†]W. A. Baumol, "On the Appropriate Discount Rate for the Evaluation of Public Projects," in H. H. Hinrichs and G. M. Taylor, eds., *Program Budgeting and Benefit-Cost Analysis,* Goodyear, Pacific Palisades, CA, 1969.

- Sturdiness of construction (As just mentioned, a disbenefit might be accidents where the vehicles run into the barrier!)
- Height of the barrier
- Attractiveness of the barrier (A landscaped median might help give a parklike atmosphere that could attract business.)

(c) Evaluate each factor's contribution (in terms of percentage) to each alternative's goals—another difficult number to come up with. For the concrete barrier, Fig. 8.6 shows that the experts decided that sturdy construction should contribute to 60 percent of potential death reductions while barrier height could have a 40 percent contribution. Barrier attractiveness is not expected to contribute to death reduction and so receives a 0 percent value. For each goal, such as death reduction, the sum of factor contributions has to be 100 percent.

(d) Rate each factor (determined in step b) on a scale of 1 to 10 as regards contribution to the goals or criteria (specified in step a) as they relate to the alternative in question. For the concrete-barrier alternative, as seen in Fig. 8.6, our experts decide that sturdy construction deserves the highest rating (10) for death reduction and for major-injury reduction, but assign lower ratings for the remaining three goals. So the percentage values in step c are assigned in the vertical columns by goal while the factors of step d are assigned horizontally, across goals.

(e) Multiply each rating by the percentage contribution (step c result by step d result).

(f) Sum the values found in step e to give a total for each goal (criterion).

(g) Multiply the totals in step f by the corresponding weighting assigned in step b to form a subutility function value for each goal (criterion).

(h) Sum all the values in step g for each goal (criterion) to form the utility function for the alternative in question.

(i) Form the utility/cost ratio for the alternative by dividing the alternative's utility function from step h by its cost.

(j) Repeat these steps for all alternatives under consideration.

Calculations for the three alternatives are given in Figs. 8.6 through 8.8. Obviously, a ratio of less than 1 is not a problem in this type of analysis; we are concerned with only the relative values of the ratios for the alternatives. The wire-mesh barrier has the highest utility value of all three possibilities, and that would probably be the one to recommend, though we cannot mathematically rank the values since none of the three criteria given in Sec. 8.4 are met.

Remember that we attached some rather odd criteria to the accident and death possibilities: business effect and barrier appearance. The wire-mesh barrier might be more pleasing in appearance and, to stretch a point, might not detract from customers' enjoyment while getting to business as much as the concrete barrier. The landscaped median logically would be more advantageous to businesses and would be aesthetically pleasing, two related attributes. Effect on head-on collisions would not be as significant as with the other two alternatives, as has been proved with freeways with medians rather than barriers. Of course, ratings and percentages assigned are very subjective and will play a major role in the decision, a task not to be taken lightly! Factor assessment and assigning ratings and percentages is discussed in Chap. 15.

Goals / Factors	Death Reduction 60%		Major-injury reduction 20%		Minor-injury reduction 5%		Barrier appearance 5%		Business effect 10%		Total 100%
Sturdy Construction	10	60	10	60	8	50	2	5	0	0	
	10×60=600		10×60=600		8×50=400		2×5=10		0×0=0		
Barrier height	10	40	5	40	5	50	6	10	2	5	
	10×40=400		5×40=200		5×50=250		6×10=60		2×5=10		
Barrier attractiveness	0	0	0	0	0	0	10	85	8	95	
	0×0=0		0×0=0		0×0=0		10×85=850		8×95=760		
Total:	1000		800		650		920		770		Utility sum = 91,550
Subutility	1,000×60=60,000		800×20=16,000		650×5=3,250		920×5=4,600		770×10=7,700		Utility/cost = $\frac{91,550}{180,816}$ = 0.51

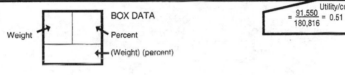

BOX DATA

Weight → ← Percent

← (Weight) (percent)

FIGURE 8.6
Concrete barrier ($180,816).

Goals / Factors	Death Reduction 60%		Major-injury reduction 20%		Minor-injury reduction 5%		Barrier appearance 5%		Business effect 10%		Total 100%
Sturdy Construction	10	80	8	80	8	50	5	5	0	0	
	10×80=800		8×80=640		8×50=400		5×5=25		0×0=0		
Barrier height	8	20	5	20	5	50	8	5	2	5	
	8×20=160		5×20=100		5×50=250		8×5=40		2×5=10		
Barrier attractiveness	0	0	0	0	0	0	8	90	7	95	
	0×0=0		0×0=0		0×0=0		8×90=720		7×95=665		
Total:	960		740		650		785		675		Utility sum = 86,325
Subutility	960×60=57,600		740×20=14,800		650×5=3,250		785×5=3,925		675×10=6,750		Utility/cost = $\frac{86,325}{122,392}$ = 0.71

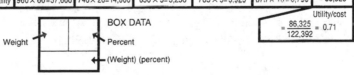

BOX DATA

Weight → ← Percent

← (Weight) (percent)

FIGURE 8.7
Wire-mesh barrier ($122,392).

Goals / Factors	Death Reduction 60%		Major injury reduction 20%		Minor injury reduction 5%		Barrier appearance 5%		Business effect 10%		Total 100%
Sturdy Construction	5	50	6	50	4	50	2	10	3	10	
	5×50 = 250		6×50 = 300		4×50 = 200		2×10 = 20		3×10 = 30		
Barrier height	3	50	4	50	4	50	4	20	5	10	
	3×50 = 150		4×50 = 200		4×50 = 200		4×20 = 80		5×10 = 50		
Barrier attractiveness	0	0	0	0	0	0	10	70	6	80	
	0×0 = 0		0×0 = 0		0×0 = 0		10×70 = 700		6×80 = 480		
Total:	400		500		400		800		560		Utility sum = 45,600
Subutility	400× 60 = 24,000		500× 20 = 10,000		400× 5 = 2,000		800 × 5 = 4,000		560 × 10 = 5,600		

BOX DATA

Weight → ← Percent

← (Weight) (percent)

$$= \frac{45,600}{103,370} = 0.44$$

Utility/cost

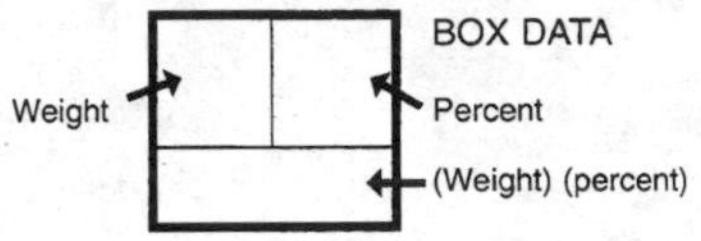

FIGURE 8.8
Median landscape
($103,370).

EXERCISE 5

Consider a freeway project that proposes a new four-lane highway leading from the downtown core of a city to a major arterial bypass in the suburbs. What factors besides the construction requirements could be considered in the total project cost?

SOLUTION 5

Benefit/cost analyses for some major highway construction projects consume hundreds of pages. Here are a few of the considerations:

- Air pollution from traffic flow
- Expenditures for traffic control
- Accident frequency and severity in the past and forecasts for the future
- Parking expectations in affected areas
- Time and cost consequences of congestion, before and after construction
- Shift of business competition
- Accessibility of outlying jobs to central-city poor
- Changes in property values due to accessibility
- Relocation of dwellings in the highway path; associated disruption of neighborhoods
- Detractions in scenic views and noise levels
- Temporary effects of construction: wages, prices of materials, living costs, employment, etc.

We all have seen cases where detractions from scenic views and noise levels have been alleviated by building landscaped noise barriers between the freeway and adjacent neighborhoods. The Squaw Peak Freeway in Phoenix, Arizona, attracted considerable national attention in the early 1990s when art competitions were held to allow locally attractive sculptures to be placed on such barriers. Unfortunately, neighborhood appreciation of the art was not nearly as positive as the appreciation by the competition judges.

8.8   PROBLEMS

8.1 Seven mutually exclusive proposals are to be compared by using the benefit/cost criterion. Each project has an expected life of 50 years with negligible salvage value and is to be evaluated with a tax-free interest rate of 10 percent. Data for the projects, in dollars, are as follows:

	Proposal						
	A	**B**	**C**	**D**	**E**	**F**	**G**
Initial cost	150	200	850	95	500	65	310
Annual maintenance cost	8	10	50	10	20	3	5
Estimated annual benefits	24	30	130	18	80	11	64

(a) Rank-order the proposals based on increasing first cost, and calculate the B/C ratios and $B - C$ values, treating annual maintenance as a cost.
(b) Calculate the B/C ratios and $B - C$ values, treating annual maintenance as a disbenefit.
(c) Determine which alternative will be selected if funds are severely limited.
(d) Indicate which alternative will be selected if the sole criterion is the largest available benefit.
(e) Decide which alternative would be selected if the sole criterion were the largest net benefit.
(f) Develop an incremental B/C ratio analysis, and select the appropriate alternative. Use your values from part a.
(g) Determine which alternative will be selected if an incremental rate-of-return analysis with MARR equal to 10 percent is employed. Use your data from part b.

8.2 Several alternative projects involving water supply systems are under consideration by a public utility board. The following data, in dollars, have been summarized for your consideration:

	Project				
	A	**B**	**C**	**D**	**E**
First cost	2000	100	700	1200	500
Annual operating cost	70	4	60	100	30
Annual recreation benefits	150	0	55	170	25
Annual increase in agricultural production	200	30	50	160	90

All costs are given in thousands of dollars, and negligible salvage values are assumed at the end of a 50-year life. Since annual operating costs are to be paid from area property tax revenues, they are treated as a disbenefit. Use a tax-free interest rate of 7 percent.

(a) Which projects should be selected if the alternatives are independent?

(b) Which project should be selected if the alternatives are mutually exclusive?

(c) Which of the mutually exclusive projects should be selected if a rate-of-return analysis is used?

8.3 The Provincial Department of Transportation pays Happy Ferry Company to transport cars across a bay that effectively splits the largest city in the province. Happy Ferry Company has submitted a bid of $5 million per year (to be paid to them by the province) for 15 years to provide the service since their current contract will run out shortly. The benefit associated with the ferry in time savings, gasoline consumption, etc., is estimated at $3 per car. A low-level bridge can be constructed that will increase the user benefits to $4.50 per car, mainly due to the reduced time needed to cross the bay. The low-level bridge will have a first cost of $30 million and annual maintenance charges of $1.8 million. A second bridge design will cost $37 million to implement with $2.5 million annual maintenance costs. The user benefits are estimated at $5.60 per car with the second bridge design. Assuming no other costs or salvage values, and given a 15-year bridge life, use an 8 percent interest rate and the assumption that 2 million cars per year will use either a ferry or a bridge in determining which alternative to recommend.

8.4 For the situation given in Prob. 8.3, develop a benefit/cost analysis of the proposals with the same interest rate, but assume that annual traffic will increase at a rate of 2 percent per year after the first year's volume of 2 million cars.

8.5 Usage fees were not considered in Prob. 8.4. Suppose that a toll fee of $1.50 per vehicle is to be charged for use of either bridge. Also the state has decided that it should receive a fee of $1.00 per vehicle, to be collected by Happy Ferry. Answer the same question posed in Prob. 8.4.

8.6 A major intersection has been the scene of numerous property damage and some personal-injury accidents over the past 3 years. With a single traffic light and no protected turning lanes, vehicles are delayed an average of 0.4 minute each trip through the area. A redesigned intersection with advanced left turns and lane control devices is expected to increase the delay to 0.7 minute but should decrease the number of accidents from 80 to 30 per year.

The average cost per accident is expected to remain constant at $5000, and maintenance costs associated with the new design are forecast to increase by a constant $12,000 over the existing system's annual maintenance costs. The new system, which is expected to have a total first cost of $300,000, will probably remain effective for the next 10 years. The estimated average user cost per vehicle delayed in route is $11 per hour, and average annual traffic count totals nearly 2 million vehicles. Determine the benefit/cost ratio for this proposal, using a tax-free interest rate of 8 percent.

8.7 Assume that the city council wants a utility/cost ratio developed for the traffic light situation in Prob. 8.6. The goals (criteria) specified for the new system are to reduce pedestrian injuries, vehicle damage, and vehicle occupant injuries. It has been decided that three factors should be evaluated for their effect on the goals: ergonomics (easy-to-read signals and signs), aesthetics (appearance), and pedestrian convenience. Assuming that the system costs will be as given in Prob. 8.6, determine a logical utility/cost index. This is an open-ended question. You have to specify and justify needed ratings and percentages.

8.8 Consider again the situation given in Prob. 8.6. In addition to the alternative specified in that problem (alternative **A**), we now have two more alternatives.

Alternative **B** is a cheaper-first-cost system, $265,000, with expected maintenance costs of $17,200 per year above the current system costs. The intersection delay is expected to increase 0.8 minute over the current system, and the number of accidents per year is expected to decrease to 35.

Alternative **C** is a more expensive system with a first cost of $320,000 and expected annual maintenance costs of $12,500 above the current costs. Intersection delay times are expected to increase by 0.55 minute over the current delay time per vehicle, and the number of accidents is expected to drop to 25.

Assuming an evaluation period of 10 years for all alternatives, perform a cost-effectiveness analysis for the three alternatives and recommend an option. Use an 8 percent interest rate in your analysis.

8.9 Perform a benefit/cost analysis for the three alternatives analyzed in Prob. 8.8 (alternative **A**'s B/C ratio was found in Prob. 8.6).

8.10 Two projects from each of four departments have been submitted for evaluation. The projects from each department are mutually exclusive. Associated data are as follows:

Department	Project	Benefit, $	Cost, $
A	A_1	100,000	70,000
	A_2	112,000	80,000
B	B_1	70,000	55,000
	B_2	76,000	60,000
C	C_1	160,000	100,000
	C_2	184,000	120,000
D	D_1	110,000	75,000
	D_2	122,000	85,000

(a)   Which projects should be funded according to the B/C ratio criterion if one project must be selected from each department?
(b)   Which projects should be funded if only $300,000 is available?

8.11 A 2.2-mile (3.54-kilometer) stretch of highway is known locally as "Fog Hollow." In an attempt to reduce accidents, the shoulders along Fog Hollow could be widened at a cost of $221,000 per mile ($130,488 per kilometer), and large electric warning signs could be installed at both ends of the dangerous stretch. The signs would be controlled by a computer hooked to sensing devices to display recommended speeds for various fog conditions. The fog warning signs could be installed for $185,000 and would have annual maintenance costs of $8000 during their 10-year life.

If the average accident cost in Fog Hollow amounts to $5800, how many accidents per year would have to be avoided by the project to make it acceptable for a 20-year study period? The discount rate used for such projects is 7 percent. *Hint:* Determine the minimum benefit value that would allow the project to be viable. Accidents avoided per year will be treated as a benefit.

8.12 Assume that the accident rate is cut by 29 cars per year for the situation described in Prob. 8.11. Determine the cost-effectiveness ratio.

8.13 A province-sponsored forest protective association is evaluating alternative routes for a new road into a formerly inaccessible region. Different routes for the road provide different benefits, as indicated in the following table:

Route	Construction cost, $	Annual savings in fire damage, $	Recreational benefits, $	Timber access benefit, $	Annual maintenance cost, $
A	285,000	8000	6500	1000	4500
B	310,000	8000	7500	1000	5800
C	425,000	9200	8000	2800	5200

The roads are assumed to have an economic life of 50 years; the interest rate normally required is 3 percent per year.
  (a) According to a B/C ratio comparison, which route should be selected?
  (b) Would the choice be different if the interest rate were doubled?
  (c) Would the choice in part a be different if annual maintenance costs were not included?

8.14 The Dry Springs Flood Control District has applied for a federal grant to eliminate a persistent flooding problem. Three alternative projects are being considered, and the following data, in dollars, have been collected.

	Plan 1	Plan 2	Plan 3
First cost	23,000,000	50,000,000	35,000,000
Average annual reduction in flood damage	1,300,000	2,800,000	1,800,000
Annual irrigation benefits	350,000	600,000	450,000
Annual recreation benefits	150,000	375,000	280,000
Annual operating and maintenance costs	210,000	400,000	285,000

A social discount rate of 6 percent is recommended. The life of each plan is estimated at 50 years, and no salvage value is expected.

Determine the benefit/cost ratios for each alternative, and suggest a course of action. Disbenefits will be treated normally—as costs in the denominator.

8.15 Repeat Prob. 8.14 except do your analysis on $B - C$ values.

8.16 Three proposals have been submitted for developing a recreational facility along a scenic highway:

1. Build a picnic ground with 25 picnic sites, each including a table, parking space, and charcoal grill.
2. Build a picnic and camping facility with 20 picnic sites and 10 campsites.
3. Build a picnic, camping, and cabin facility with 15 picnic sites, 10 campsites, and 5 cabins.

The expected demand per site, first cost, and annual maintenance cost for each type of site are as follows: In addition, the estimated value to the public per visit (above charges) is given for each type of facility.

Type of unit	Expected visits per year per unit	First cost per unit, $	Annual maintenance cost per unit, $	Perceived value per visit, $
Picnic site	800	6,500	350	1.50
Campsite	250	10,000	450	4.50
Cabin site	300	22,500	750	18.50

Based on a 10-year study with no residual value anticipated after 10 years and a discount rate of 5 percent, determine which proposal, if any, should be accepted.

8.17 Develop a cost-effectiveness index for each alternative in Prob. 8.16; effectiveness is the number of visits to a site. Do your conclusions match those of Prob. 8.16? Comment on this.

8.18 The provincial transportation department has collected data for a proposal to construct an overpass and extra lanes at a busy, dangerous highway intersection. Estimated land acquisition, demolition, and construction costs in dollars are as follows:

Land and demolition	875,000
Additional lanes [0.6 mile (0.966 kilometer)]	1,550,000
Overpass construction	2,740,000
Average annual maintenance during 30-year life of project	145,000

Improved safety is the primary benefit expected from the project. A road count revealed that 12,000 vehicles per day pass through the intersection. An average of 2.4 fatalities per year occurred at the present usage rate. Usage is expected to rise to 15,000 vehicles per day by the time improvements are completed, and accidents would be expected to rise commensurately. For every fatal accident there are 19 nonfatal accidents (with injuries) and 160 property damage accidents. Settlements for fatal, nonfatal, and property damage accidents are calculated, respectively, at $180,000, $25,000, and $3200. The improved intersection is expected to reduce all accidents by 90 percent.

Expenses associated with patrolling, maintaining the traffic signals, and directing traffic at the intersection are currently $51,000 per year; these would be eliminated by the project. Now 21 percent of the vehicles using the intersection must stop, with an average wait of 0.8 minute. The average cost of a stop for a vehicle's operation is estimated at $0.10, and waiting time is assumed to be worth $4.20 per hour. When the overpass is in operation, all stops will be avoided, but 40 percent of the vehicles will have an added travel distance of 0.2 mile (0.322 kilometer). A vehicle operating cost of $0.24 per mile ($0.112 per kilometer) is assigned as an average value.

The overpass will reduce pollution. This reduction is valued at $155,000 per year. Annual taxes forgone from property condemned for the expansion amount to $10,500. The discount rate for the study is 6 percent.

(a) What is the benefit/cost ratio based on only the primary benefit of improved safety and only the building costs?

(b) What is the B/C ratio based on secondary benefits and the building cost?

(c) What is the total B/C ratio?

(d) What other factors might be considered in the project?

8.19 Assume that you are asked to develop a cost-effectiveness index for the project presented in Prob. 8.18.

(a) Develop an effectiveness value based on only deaths and injuries. Suggest a weighting scheme to merge the two goals.

(b) Develop the cost-effectiveness index.

8.20 In Sec. 8.1.2 we evaluated dam sites, using the incremental B/C ratio approach. Instead of the 4 percent interest rate used there, use a 7 percent rate and determine the effect, if any, on the preferred alternative. Comment on your results. If the 7 percent rate shows no change in the decision, determine at what interest rate the decision would be changed.

8.21 A dam on the Spring River is being evaluated. A 50-year life and a 7 percent discount rate are to be used. Dollar estimates have been obtained for the following benefits and costs:

Flood losses prevented in the project area	900,000/year
Flood losses reduced in downstream rivers	800,000/year
Increases in property values along Spring River (present worth of values)	1,000,000
Annual income from electric power produced	3,200,000
Construction of dam and access roads	25,000,000
Cost of powerhouse and transmission facilities	10,000,000
Interest costs during construction	2,000,000
Annual operating and maintenance costs	100,000

Assume that construction costs occur at time 0 but that the benefits do not begin until the start of year 5 and interest charges during production are prorated evenly over the 4-year period.

    (a) What is the benefit/cost ratio?

    (b) Assume that opponents of the dam are questioning the study on the basis that no costs were included for the destruction of a popular recreational area that would be inundated by the dam's reservoir. All the land is federally owned, but a very popular park that features mineral-water springs will be inundated. What value would have to be placed on this park and associated recreational areas to make the project unacceptable? Could a reasonable case be developed to abandon the project? What other benefits and disbenefits might be considered?

8.22 Two alternative routes for a new expressway are being evaluated. One follows the valley along a river, and the other takes a shortcut through a range of hills. The only access and egress for either route will be at the beginning and end of the freeway.

The river route is 10 miles (16.09 kilometers) long and has a first cost of $14,250,000. Its annual cost of maintenance will be $9500 per mile ($5903 per kilometer), and a major overhaul will be required every 10 years at a cost of $2,500,000.

The hilly route will be 3 miles (1.86 kilometers) shorter than the river route, but it will cost $19 million. Annual maintenance costs will be $15,000 per mile ($9321 per kilometer), and the major overhaul and surfacing every 10 years will cost $1,800,000.

Traffic on either expressway is predicted to average 6000 vehicles per day, onefourth of which will be commercial traffic. The anticipated average speed on either route is 50 miles per hour (80.5 kilometers per hour). Time is valued at $14 per hour for commercial traffic and $5 per hour for other vehicles. The average operating costs for commercial and noncommercial traffic are, respectively, $0.95 and $0.23 per mile ($0.5903 and $0.1429 per kilometer) for the river route and $1.05 and $0.25 ($0.653 and $0.155 per kilometer) on the steeper hilly route.

Compare the alternative routes according to an incremental benefit/cost ratio based on a 30-year life and a discount rate of 7 percent.

8.23 In recent years many cities have constructed large municipal stadiums. A case in point is Maricopa County, home of the greater Phoenix area, where a county sales tax was approved in 1994 to partially pay for a major league baseball stadium, assuming that a franchise was awarded to Phoenix within a 12-month period. The sales pitch to get voter approval for funding often appeals to civic pride and implies that the stadium would be a self-supporting enterprise as well as an attraction for visitors, whose purchases would increase revenues for many merchants. After completion, some stadium projects failed to meet advertised expectations and caused difficulties that the voters had not anticipated.

Disregarding misjudgments of construction costs, which far exceeded original estimates in many cases, and inaccuracies that overestimated the income that would be received from promotions booked into a stadium, discuss what disbenefits and spillover costs could have been logically anticipated and accounted for in a thorough benefit/cost analysis. List 10 considerations, and discuss how values could be obtained for the factors involved.

8.24 Assume that a modest-size city park with which you are familiar is the end product of a public project. That is, a project produced the present park based on an accepted benefit/cost analysis. Further assume that the land became available for the park because a school on the site burned down, and since there was sufficient classroom space available in nearby schools, the city decided not to rebuild the facility. Instead, the city decided that the land would be used for other city purposes or sold, to add money to the city's treasury. One proposal for the land was to build the park that now exists. Based on the information given above, list the benefit and cost categories that should have been included in the evaluation of the park project.

8.25 Consider the section on consumers' surplus. A public good is represented by a linear demand schedule ranging from equilibrium at $1 for the first unit available to $0 when 1 million units are available. The current level of availability and consumption is 300,000 units.

(a) What is the dollar volume (total demand cost based on the last unit's cost for all units of current consumption)?

(b) What is the dollar volume of the current consumers' surplus?

(c) If a public project can decrease the cost to $0.40 per unit, what additional total benefit does it produce?

(d) What would the consumers' surplus be if the project were carried out?

(e) What is the dollar volume of consumption after the project is completed?

8.26 A public good has a linear demand function such that the first unit available is valued at $100,000, but when 50,000 units are available, the per-unit value drops to $2.

(a) What is the consumers' surplus when the demand is 30,000 units?

(b) What would be the change in consumers' surplus if a project increased demand from 30,000 to 50,000 units?

8.27 As one part of a model program to demonstrate ways to rehabilitate a decaying portion of a city, a proposal has been made to provide swimming facilities for residents of the model area. This can be accomplished by constructing swimming pools in small parks or by busing individuals to a nearby lake. Pertinent data are listed below:

- Population in the 5-square-mile (12.95-square-kilometer) area that might take part in the swimming program is 35,000.
- Average daily use for a pool could vary from 1 to 5 percent of the population living within $1\frac{1}{2}$ miles (2.41 kilometers) of a pool.
- Minimum standard for the surface area of water per swimmer is 20 square feet (1.86 square meters).
- A standard swimming pool has 7000 square feet (650.3 square meters) of water surface and requires 2 acres (8094 square meters) of land (part of the land serves also as a small park). Construction costs including equipment would be $400,000. Operating costs, including lifeguard wages, would be $70,000 during the swimming season. The life of a pool is 15 years.
- The swimming season lasts 100 days each year.
- Land prices in the area are $160,000 per acre ($39.54 per square meter). Taxes forgone on land acquired by the government would average $3600 per acre per year ($0.89 per square meter per year). Demolition and relocation expenses would amount to $140,000 per acre ($34.60 per square meter).
- School buses could be used during the swimming season at a cost of $210 per bus per day, including drivers' wages.

- Four round trips could be made each day per bus during the swimming season to carry swimmers from the model area to a nearby lake. A bus can carry 70 people. The same number of people is expected to participate in the swimming program if either the pools are constructed or busing is provided.
- Extra lifeguards and operating expenses at the city park on the lake to handle an influx of additional swimmers would be $400 per day. Sufficient space is available at the lake to accommodate any foreseeable use level.
- A recreation leader would be hired for each 100 people expected to take part in the busing arrangement. A recreation leader would cost the program $50 per day, including fringe benefits. Four administrators would receive $8000 each during the season if busing is used.
- A $1 admission fee is charged for pools in other parts of the city, and the same charge is reasonable for round-trip bus fare to the lake.

Analyze the swimming program based on a 10 percent discount rate. *Possible assumptions will negate the feasibility for one unique solution.*

    (a)   What is the equivalent annual cost per swimmer per day under each plan? Assume that no fees are paid for swimming. State your assumptions (i.e., pool usage?).

    (b)   Assuming that a $1 fee per day is charged to each swimmer, calculate the amount of additional benefits for the swimming pools that would have to be counted to allow them to pass the $B/C > 1$ criterion. Discuss the benefits in terms of consumers' surplus, spillover effects, and derived or intangible benefits.

    (c)   Conduct a sensitivity analysis. Is there any combination of readily quantifiable factors that can provide a $B/C > 1$ for the swimming pools? State your assumptions. *Hint:* Sensitivity analysis implies that key factors in a study are evaluated over a range of the factors' costs and/or benefits. So you can see whether a decision will change over the factors' ranges and then make the decision accordingly.

    (d)   Based on your calculations above, what decision would you make, if you were the government policy maker who had to decide whether a summer swimming program should be part of the model-city rehabilitation demonstration? Write a short summary supporting your conclusions.

8.28 A provincially funded university currently has a main campus and a smaller west-side branch campus in the greater Toronto area. Money was appropriated by the government of Ontario in 1994 for development of an east-side branch campus. Future plans call for other branch campuses to possibly be developed. Suggest some of the benefit/cost considerations that would need to be weighed in making a decision, first, to develop a branch campus and, second, where to locate that branch campus if a decision is made for such an entity.

8.29 The Canadian Department of Defence has been forced to downsize, with regard to both facilities and personnel. Suppose that a major air force base, located in your home province, is scheduled for closure 3 years from now. The province and city in which the base is located are charged with developing a plan for base usage once it has been abandoned by the military.

- Suggest five possible uses for such a military base that would benefit the province and city populace.
- With some justification, develop goals (criteria) that will assist officials to pick the two best uses for the former base. Develop weights (percentages) that add to 100 percent for the goals.
- Develop factors that relate to the goals, as you would in a cost utilization study. Logically, not all the factors will be used in evaluating goals. Assign a rating from 0 to 10 for each factor-goal combination. Also, within each goal, assign a weighting (percentage) to each factor that shows your feeling for the factors' relation to the goal. The weightings have to sum to 100 percent, but some factors might have a rating and weighting of 0.
- Develop the utility factor that will be used in the utility/cost ratio for an alternative.
- Assume costs to the province and city for each alternative.

Using the utility/cost approach, hypothesize how you would decide which two uses you would recommend for the base.

8.30 If you were charged to come up with a procedure for determining the uses of an abandoned military base, as in Prob. 8.29, which technique from this chapter would you feel most comfortable recommending? Fully justify your choice and the reasoning behind your picking it.

DEPRECIATION AND INCOME TAX CONSIDERATIONS

The power to tax involves the power to destroy.

John Marshall
United States Supreme Court, 1819

The power to tax is not the power to destroy while this Court sits.

Oliver Wendell Holmes, Jr.
United States Supreme Court, 1928

I f, indeed, "the name of the game is business and the score is kept with money," then the rules are set by government, the scorekeepers are accountants, and the referee is the tax collector. An engineering economist acts as the coach or play planner.

Provisions for recovering capital invested in income-producing assets are made by charging depreciation against current income. These depreciation charges and the regular operating expenses are deductible from gross income in determining taxable income. The type of depreciation method used for tax purposes affects the timing and amount of tax payments, which in turn affect the after-tax worth of proposals.

Depreciation charges are not actual cash flows and the true decrease in market value of an asset may not correspond to the allowable deductions. Tables and formulas approved by Revenue Canada for use in Canada establish the pattern of depreciation. In Canada, substantial changes in depreciation accounting came into effect in 1981.

---

†Selected material from the First Canadian Edition (1986) and the Supplement (1994) are included in this chapter. The authors appreciate the expert contributions of W. C. Moor and T. M. West to the U.S. income tax regulations and depreciation practices. A condensed description of these subjects is provided in Extension 9A.

Depreciation charges are introduced in accounting records in order to recover capital invested for production assets and to make deductions from current income allowed by tax laws for tax calculations. The *straight-line* and *declining-balance* methods are the two most commonly used depreciation methods. The straight-line method is designed to account for uniform depreciation, while the declining-balance method is an accelerated method intended to allow higher depreciation charges earlier in the write-off period. The accelerated charges allowed by tax regulations decrease the time value of taxes.

Well-defined rules for depreciation accounting for income tax calculation purposes are set by Revenue Canada in accordance with the laws passed by Parliament. The tax deduction allowed by regulations for depreciation of an asset is the *capital cost allowance (CCA)*.

Taxes play a major role in any profit-seeking venture of individuals and corporations. That is, *property, sales, excise*, and/or *income taxes* affect net income and rate of return. Various types of taxation and their levels of taxation serve as instruments used by governments to pursue their *fiscal policies*. Frequent changes in tax *surcharges* and *investment tax credits* are a reflection of the dynamic nature of fiscal policy. Likewise, changes are commonplace in regulations on *capital gains and losses, carry amounts forward* and *backward*, and capital cost allowance (CCA).

Effective income tax rates represent total corporate tax liability. A knowledge of these is essential for after-tax economic evaluations. For the determination of *taxable income,* all the applicable special tax provisions and charges for depreciation and/or interest are applied to the before-tax cash flow. Next, the effective income tax rate is applied to before-tax cash flow in order to calculate tax payable. From this, the *after-tax cash flow* for the year is computed. Frequently, a tabular format is used for these calculations, which provides information equivalent to a cash flow diagram. The calculation of after-tax data can form the basis of economic comparisons.

An after-tax analysis determines the *actual cash flow* expected from a proposal. Such an analysis may reveal the relative effect of taxes on proposals—providing information that is not a part of a before-tax comparison. For example, one proposal that qualifies for an investment tax credit would become more attractive than a comparable alternative that does not qualify for the tax credit. However, after-tax comparisons are more complicated than before-tax comparisons since tax laws are very complex. Although detailed tax information can be obtained with expert assistance, attention to basic tax provisions provides an adequate evaluation for most engineering economics problems.

According to Benjamin Franklin "in this world nothing is certain but death and taxes." He might have added a further observation that attention to both increases your chances of survival and prosperity.

9.1   DEPRECIATION†

Depreciation means a decrease in worth. Most assets are worth less as they age. Newly purchased production assets have advantages of possessing the latest technical improvements and operating with less chance of breakdown or need for repair. Except for possible antique value, production equipment gradually becomes less valuable through wear. This lessening in value is recognized in accounting practices as an expense of operating. Instead of charging the full purchase price of a new asset as a one-time expense, the outlay is spread over the life of the asset in accounting records. This approach does not represent the actual cash flow for a particular asset; but for all assets taken collectively, it provides a realistic representation of capital consumption.

Very seldom is a depreciation fund actually established to accumulate money earmarked for the replacement of a specific asset. Instead, *depreciation reserves* are used to fund the most attractive proposals put forward to improve operations, some of which are to replace worn-out and obsolete assets. Recovered capital is thus reinvested in a general way to maintain a company's physical plant and to pursue new ventures.

EXAMPLE 9.1

Where Did the Money Go?

Sandy worked for several years as a general handyman in construction. He inherited $100,000 and decided to start a landscaping service. Combining his inheritance with an $80,000 loan, he bought a used tractor, truck, and hauling rig. Business was good. A gross income of $125,000 per year covered annual operating and loan repayment expenses of $62,000. The rest he spent personally. After 5 years of good living, Sandy found that the loan was repaid but the equipment was worn out. Because he had made no provisions to compensate for the loss in value, he was left with almost worthless assets and no money to renew them. What did he do wrong?

Solution

Sandy got off to a good start by investing his inheritance in productive assets, but he failed to conserve his capital base, apparently not realizing that depreciation was occurring. He should have known that his investment was, in effect, a prepayment of operating costs that had to be recovered from the revenues they helped create. By not charging for the use of his inherited capital, Sandy forfeited income tax deductions, probably

---

†Expressions such as *depreciation reserve* and *capital recovery* are commonly used by accountants and are very descriptive of entries in a firm's book of accounts. These terms do not refer to the cash flows utilized in an economic analysis, but are so commonly used and are so descriptive in application that they will be used in this chapter.

underpriced his services, and tricked himself into believing he had more money to spend than his landscaping service actually produced.

9.1.1 Causes of Declining Value

Assets depreciate in value for several reasons. Their decreasing worth may be attributed to any of the following conditions:

- *Physical depreciation.* The everyday wear and tear of operation gradually lessens the physical ability of an asset to perform its intended function. A good maintenance program retards the rate of decline but seldom maintains the precision expected from a new machine. In addition to normal wear, accidental physical damage can impair ability. Wear and tear is an obvious cost of production.
- *Functional depreciation.* Demands made on an asset may increase beyond its capacity to produce. A central heating plant unable to meet the increased heat demands of a new building addition no longer serves its intended function. At the other extreme, the demand for services may cease to exist, such as with a machine that produces a product no longer in demand.
- *Technological depreciation.* Newly developed means of accomplishing a function may make the present means uneconomical. Steam locomotives lost value rapidly as railroads turned to diesel power. Current product styling, new materials, improved safety, and better quality at lower cost from new developments make old designs obsolete. Since the changes in needs and obsolescence cannot be accurately anticipated, their direct effect is on replacement decisions more than on tax deductions.
- *Sudden failure.* This refers to sudden or catastrophic loss in value due to technological characteristics inherent in the asset. However, this does include loss due to accident or misuse. Light bulbs burn out as a natural consequence of use and with little loss in operating efficiency up to the point of failure. Generally this category of asset includes items used in large numbers with relatively small cost per item.
- *Depletion.* Consumption of an exhaustible natural resource to produce products or services is termed *depletion*. Removal of oil, timber, rock, or minerals from a site decreases the value of the holding. This decrease is compensated for by a proportionate reduction in earnings derived from the resource. Theoretically, the depletion charge per unit of resource removed is

$$\text{Depletion rate (\$/unit)} = \frac{\text{Present value of resource}}{\text{Remaining units of resource}}$$

Allowances for depletion vary with the type of resource. Highest allowances are theoretically allowed for the resources that require the greatest expenditures for discovery and development. (See Review Exercise 1.)

- *Monetary depreciation.* A change in price levels is a subtle but troublesome cause of decreases in the value of owned assets. Customary accounting practices relate depreciation to the original price of an asset, not to its replacement. If prices rise during the life of an asset, then a comparable replacement becomes more expensive. This means that the capital recovered will be insufficient to provide an adequate substitute for the worn-out asset. It also suggests that the selling price of the product being produced by the asset does not accurately reflect the cost of production. Because the depreciation is actually happening to the invested capital representing the asset, instead of to the asset itself, monetary depreciation is very difficult to accommodate. It cannot be charged as an operating expense for tax purposes.

9.1.2 Canadian Vocabulary of Depreciation Accounting

According to Revenue Canada,[†‡] corporations and individuals engaged in professional activity can claim depreciation on assets that are used for earning income. Depreciable assets could be such items as machinery or equipment, software, real estate other than land, patents, copyright, etc. Land is not considered depreciable.

In Canada, businesses calculate depreciation for reporting the state of finances to their shareholders and for submitting income tax to Revenue Canada. The first type of calculation, called book depreciation, is intended to show the value of an asset. The methodology that has been used over the years is frequently straight line. However, Revenue Canada requires the use of declining-balance method as well as straight-line method for tax purposes.

Under the Canadian tax regulations, businesses can claim depreciation using very specific guidelines. Businesses are allowed to deduct part of the capital cost of specified depreciable property from income earned during the year. This depreciation deduction is called *capital cost allowance (CCA).* The CCA is the way in which the government allows a business to recover (expense) money invested in fixed assets that have to be replaced after a few years. The CCA allowance is applied to the *undepreciated capital cost (UCC)* or book value. The sum of tax savings in present worth due to CCA allowance is called *CCA Tax Shield.* Section 9.3.2 contains further details on this topic.

Depreciable assets (property) are arranged into classes and used in conjunction with the declining-balance or straight-line method of calculating depreciation. For the application of the capital cost allowance (CCA), depreciable property or assets are grouped into specific classes. For prop-

---

[†]Revenue Canada, *Income Tax Act, Capital Cost Allowance—General Comments, Interpretation Bulletin, IT-285R2,* March 1994.
[‡]Revenue Canada, T2 Corporation Income Tax Guide, 1994.

erty or assets within each class, the same method and rate of depreciation is applicable.

For assets to be eligible for depreciation, Revenue Canada has defined conditions in terms of *"available for use."* That is, a business cannot claim capital cost allowance until the property or asset becomes available for use. These conditions are described in detail in Section 9.3.2.2.

Since November 12, 1981, Canadian tax regulations do not allow a full year's depreciation during the first year. According to current tax regulations, only one-half of the normally allowable depreciation may be claimed. *This half-year rule (convention)* was designed in order to prevent a significant advantage to businesses or individuals who could purchase property before their year-end and claim a full year of depreciation or capital cost expense. For further details see Section 9.3.2.4.

If the income from the disposition of a depreciable property or asset is higher than its capital cost, a *capital gain* results. Tax on capital gain has to be paid at a rate specified by regulations. If a business sells off a depreciable property or asset with a positive undepreciated capital cost (UCC) or book value and there is no property left in that class at the end of the taxation year, it is referred to as a *terminal loss* and treated as an expense for that year. Should a business dispose of a depreciable property for more than its book value, recaptured depreciation referred to as *recaptured capital cost allowance* is to be applied. That is, the CCA recapture occurs when the proceeds from disposition of an asset are higher than the undepreciated value of the asset. Recaptured CCA must be declared as a business income. On the other hand, if the proceeds from disposition of a property or asset are lower than the undepreciated capital cost, a *tax shield adjustment* can be claimed. The present worth of the tax shield adjustment is an after-tax income.

9.2 BASIC METHODS OF COMPUTING DEPRECIATION CHARGES

In Canada, the *straight-line* (SL) and the *declining-balance* (DB) methods are the two basic procedures for estimating depreciation charges for financial reporting to the shareholders. These methods are described here without a number of additional features that have been added by tax regulations (e.g., half-year rule discussed in Section 9.3.2.4).

These methods require input information about an asset's basis, useful life, and salvage value expected at the end of its useful life. Different annual depreciation charges result from the application of each method.

The SL and DB methods are illustrated by reference to the problem data given in Section 9.2.1 for Examples 9.2 to 9.4. The symbols used in the development of formulas are:

P = purchase price (unadjusted basis) of asset

S = salvage value or future value at the end of asset's useful (tax) life

N = useful (tax) life of asset

n = number of years of depreciation or use from time of purchase

$DC(n)$ = annual charge for depreciation in year n

$BV(n)$ = book value shown on accounting records at the end of year n (adjusted basis); $(BV(0) = P)$

The basis for depreciation is the same as that used for figuring the gain on a sale. The original basis is usually the purchase price, but this may be increased by installation charges and other one-time costs required to bring the item into use.

9.2.1 Straight-Line Method

Straight-line depreciation is the simplest method to apply and the most widely used. The annual depreciation is constant. The *book value* (BV) is the difference between the purchase price and the product of the number of years of use and the annual depreciation charge DC:

$$DC(n) = \frac{P - S}{N}$$

$$BV(n) = P - \frac{n}{N}(P - S)$$

We will use a single set of data for Examples 9.2 through 9.4. Small computers purchased by a public utility cost $7000 each. Past records indicate that they should have a useful life of 5 years, after which they will be disposed of, with no salvage value. The company currently has a cost of capital of 7 percent. Determine, for Examples 9.2 and 9.3:

(a) The depreciation charge during year 1
(b) The depreciation charge during year 2
(c) The depreciation reserve accumulated by the end of year 3
(d) The book value of the computers at the end of year 3

EXAMPLE 9.2

Straight-Line Depreciation Applied to the Basic Data

Solution

(a) and (b) Since the annual depreciation cost is constant, the charges for both the first and second years are

$$DC(1) = DC(2) = \frac{P - S}{N} = \frac{\$7000}{5} = \$1400 \text{ per year}$$

(*c*) The depreciation reserve at the end of the third year is the sum of the annual depreciation charges for the first 3 years and is equal to 3($1400) = $4200.

(*d*) The book value at the end of the third year is

$$BV(3) = \$7000 - \left(3\,\frac{\$7000}{5}\right)$$

$$= \$7000 - \$4200 = \$2800$$

or, with the book value considered as the difference between the purchase price and the amount accumulated in the depreciation reserve,

$$BV(3) = \$7000 - 3(\$1400) = \$2800$$

9.2.2 Declining-Balance Method

The declining-balance method is a means of amortizing an asset at an accelerated rate early in its life, with corresponding lower annual charges near the end of service.

For the beginning of each depreciation period or tax year, the book value has to be determined. Next, a constant depreciation rate is applied to the book value for that period. Since the book value or undepreciated balance declines each year, the depreciation charge also decreases:

$$BV(n) = P(1 - \text{depreciation rate})^n$$

$$DC(n) = BV(n - 1)(\text{depreciation rate})$$

Another form of this method uses the basic equation

$$DC(n) = \frac{R}{N}\,[BV(n - 1)]$$

where R may be determined by the analyst. It may be seen that, if R has a value greater than 1, the first year's depreciation charge will be greater than the corresponding charge for straight-line depreciation. Hence the "acceleration" of depreciation early in the asset's life.

An important point with this method is that when the analyst determines a value for R, the salvage value must be greater than zero. It can be shown that the value of R is calculated by[†]:

[†] J. A. White, M. H. Agee, and K. E. Case, *Principles of Engineering Economic Analysis,* 3e, John Wiley & Sons, Inc., 1989.

$$R = 1 - (S/P)^{1/N}$$

which requires a positive value for S in order to be feasible. This constant rate is applied to the book value $[\text{BV}(n - 1)]$ for each depreciation period. Since the undepreciated balance decreases each year, the depreciation charge also decreases, and

$$\begin{aligned}
\text{BV}(n) &= P(1 - R)^n \\
&= P(1 - [(S/P)^{1/N}])^n \\
&= P(S/P)^{n/N}
\end{aligned}$$

A much more widely used version of the declining-balance method is based on a depreciation rate which does not depend on the S/P ratio. Under certain circumstances a rate is allowed that is twice as great as would be proper under the straight-line method. Under other circumstances, the rate is limited to 1.5 times that of the straight-line method.
When the maximum rate is used,

$$\text{Depreciation rate}_{\max} = R = \frac{200\%}{N}$$

This is called the *double-declining-balance method* of depreciation. It has the same characteristics as does the declining-balance method. If the depreciation rate for the declining-balance as well as the double-declining method is the same, then these methods are identical.

EXAMPLE 9.3

Declining and Double-Declining-Balance Depreciation Applied to the Data of Example 9.2

Recall from Example 9.2 that $P = \$7,000$, $S = \$0$ and $N = 5$ years. Find, as in Example 9.2: DC(1), DC(2), depreciation reserve at the end of year 3, and BV(3). Use a depreciation rate of 40 percent for declining-balance method. For the double-declining method, use the depreciation rate$_{\max}$.

Solution

(a) Given that depreciation rate = 40% = 0.4 and depreciation rate$_{\max}$ = R = 200%/5 = 40% = 0.4, the solution is identical according to these methods.

$$\text{DC}(1) = [\text{BV}(0)](0.4) = P(0.4) = \$7,000(0.4) = \$2,800$$

(b) DC(2) = $[(\text{BV}(1)](0.4) = (\$7,000 - \$2,800)(0.4) = \$1,680$
(c) The depreciation reserve at the end of year 3 is:

$$\begin{aligned}
\text{DC}(1) &+ \text{DC}(2) + [\text{BV}(2)](0.4) \\
&= \$2,800 + \$1,680 + (\$7,000 - \$2,800 - \$1,680)(0.4) \\
&= \$4,480 + \$1,008 = \$5,488
\end{aligned}$$

(d) BV(3) = P − depreciation reserve

$$= \$7{,}000 - \$5{,}488 = \$1{,}512$$

or BV(3) = $P(1 - R)^3$

$$= \$7{,}000(0.6)^3 = \$1{,}512$$

A difficulty may arise with the use of declining-balance depreciation because the salvage value is not included in the calculation of depreciation charges. Continuing Example 9.3 to determine the book value at the end of year 5, we find that

$$\text{BV}(5) = P(1 - R)^N = \$7{,}000(0.6)^5 = \$544$$

which is well above the anticipated salvage value of $0.

It is not uncommon for the book value calculated by double-declining-balance depreciation to exceed the asset's value at the end of its life. This situation always occurs when $S = 0$. For financial reporting to shareholders, a switch can be made to straight-line depreciation. In the case of depreciation accounting for tax purposes, for a given asset, Revenue Canada specifies the depreciation rate as well as the method. Therefore a switch to another method is not allowed.

The preferred time to switch is the one that provides a favorable depreciation result (see Table 9.1). The time to switch from double-declining-balance to straight-line depreciation is when the straight-line depreciation charge on the undepreciated portion of the asset's value exceeds the double-declining-balance allowance. The undepreciated portion is the difference between the asset's book value in a given year and its salvage value: straight-line DC = $[\text{BV}(n) - S]/(N - n)$. The procedure is demonstrated in Example 9.4. For property with a useful life of 3 years or longer, a salvage value less than 10 percent of basis may be ignored. This is called the "ten percent rule."

EXAMPLE 9.4

Switch from Double-Declining-Balance to Straight-Line Depreciation

An asset has a first cost of $7000, a 5-year useful life, and no salvage value. Determine an accelerated depreciation schedule in which BV(N) = 0.

Solution

Applying the double-declining-balance method, as was done for the same P and N values in Example 9.3, we know that

$$\text{BV}(5) = \$7000(0.6)^5 = \$544$$

TABLE 9.1

Depreciation pattern for switch from DDB method to SL method. Switch takes place at end of year 3 when SL depreciation charge exceeds DDB charge

End of year	DDB depreciation charges, $	Book value with DDB, $	SL depreciation on undepreciated balance, $	Book value, DDB → SL, $
0		7000		7000
1	2800	4200	7000/5 = 1400	4200
2	1680	2520	4200/4 = 1050	2520
3	1008	1512	2520/3 = 840	1512
4	605	907	1512/2 = 756	756
5	363	544	756	0

which is higher than the zero salvage value. Therefore, a switch to the straight-line (SL) method is advisable to get the ending book value down to zero. The pattern of depreciation charges and book values resulting from the DDB method and the composite method of starting with DDB and switching to SL (DD → SL) is shown in Table 9.1.

At the end of year 2, the book value resulting from DDB depreciation is $2520, which equals the undepreciated balance because $S = 0$. Then the SL charges for the last 3 years would be ($2520 − 0)/3 = $840

Since this annual charge is less than the DDB charge for year 3 ($1008), accelerated depreciation is continued another year. Then BV(3) = $1512 and the SL depreciation charge for each of the last 2 years is $1512/2 = $756. This is larger than the DDB depreciation charge for year 4 ($605) and signals the time to switch.

Figure 9.1 on page 374 shows the book values resulting from the three methods of depreciation discussed in examples 9.2, 9.3, and 9.4.

9.3 DEPRECIATION ACCOUNTING PRACTICE IN CANADA

Businesses in Canada report depreciation for two purposes. In their financial reports to shareholders, information on depreciation of assets is presented. The second use for depreciation information is for the preparation of the balance sheet and income tax statement for submission to Revenue Canada for paying taxes. The method used for the calculation of depreciation may differ, depending upon the purpose. The capital cost allowance to be reported as a part of tax returns has to be calculated according to Canadian tax regulations.

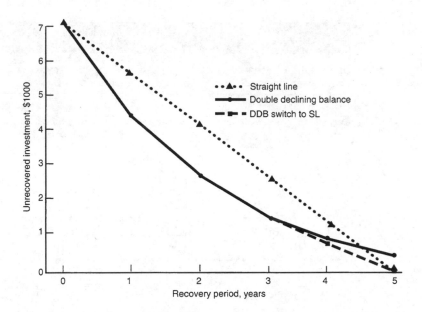

FIGURE 9.1
Book values of a
$7000 asset.

9.3.1 Depreciation for Financial Reporting to Shareholders

The depreciation methods that are used widely are the straight-line method, the declining-balance method, and the sum-of-years'-digits method. In general, Canadian firms apply the straight-line depreciation method for their annual and quarterly reports to shareholders. As noted earlier, the straight-line and the declining-balance methods of depreciation form the basis of Canadian tax laws on depreciation. In some instances, a company may report depreciation on a particular type of equipment according to the straight-line method, in spite of the fact that for tax purposes the CCA is usually claimed on a declining-balance method basis.

The various types of depreciation methods—straight-line and accelerated methods have different conceptual bases for depreciation of assets. The choice of method may reflect a company's view of the actual pattern of service provided by the asset and loss in its value. On the other hand, tradition and ease of computations may play a role.

9.3.2 Capital Cost Allowance: Revenue Canada Regulations

The capital cost allowance or depreciation is considered for tax purposes as a deductible expense of doing business. The essential features of the depreciation allowance are described here. However, it should be pointed out that the taxation rules governing the depreciation deductions are elaborate and complex. Therefore, for more details, Revenue Canada publications should be consulted.

Over the years, the Canadian government has used the income tax laws as an instrument to encourage corporations to invest in new productive assets. Specifically, the depreciation allowance (capital cost allowance) and the investment tax credit are the two mechanisms to encourage capital investment. [See Section 9.6.4 for investment tax credit.]

The Canadian tax regulations permit businesses to depreciate their assets according to very specific guidelines provided. These guidelines are intended to ensure that businesses will collectively use consistent depreciation methods and values for taxation purposes. Also, the depreciation guidelines and the investment tax credits are intended to encourage business to invest in certain types of assets in certain regions of the country.

Under the Canadian tax law individuals or businesses can deduct part of the capital cost of certain depreciable assets from their income earned during that year. This depreciation deduction is referred to as a *capital cost allowance (CCA)*. The depreciation guidelines provided by Revenue Canada are known as the capital cost allowance system. The capital cost usually includes the complete cost of a given property or asset. Normally, capital cost may include cost items such as the legal expense for purchase of an asset, engineering fees associated with a project, and all costs associated with acquiring, installing, and starting the asset.

According to the capital cost allowance system, depreciable property or assets are grouped into specified classes. Within each class, assets have to use the same method and rate of depreciation. (See Tables 9.2 and 9.3.) Businesses or individuals can claim deductions up to the maximum allowable for each class. Specific methods to be used for determining the maximum expense (capital cost allowance) are declining-balance and straight-line depreciation.

For example, in the case of furniture and refrigeration equipment (designated as class 8) depreciation is determined by using a declining-balance rate of 20 percent. This implies that at the year-end, 20 percent of the undepreciated capital cost of all the equipment in this class can be used to determine the maximum depreciation (or maximum capital cost allowance) that may be claimed for the year.

Corporations may deduct an allowance for mining and mineral processing. This is the *depletion allowance*. For a corporation to claim a depletion allowance, the corporation has to show the continuity of the earned depletion base, defined under Regulation 1205(1). This information is to be identified as Schedule T2S(12) in the top right-hand corner of the page.

According to the 1994 *T2 Corporation Income Tax Guide,* expenditures made by corporations after 1989 no longer increase the earned depletion base. On the other hand, corporations can continue to deduct depletion allowances until the earned depletion base is exhausted. For further information on depletion allowance, consult Revenue Canada Regulations 1201 to 1209, and 1212 (Section 65).

9.3.2.1 Depreciable Property

Depreciation can be claimed for property that is used in income-producing activities in trade or business. Such a property should have a definite service life of more than one year. Properties that are tangible can be depreciated if these are subject to wear and tear, to decay or decline from natural causes, to exhaustion, and to obsolescence. Examples of depreciable property include buildings, machinery, equipment, and vehicles. Inventories are regarded as depreciable property since these are held primarily for sale to customers in the ordinary course of business. Land is not a depreciable property.

Assets such as patents, copyrights, franchises, and trademarks that are intangible and have a limited period of usefulness can be depreciated. The owner has the responsibility to prove the value of the intangibles for tax purposes. Intangible property may be depreciated by using the straight-line depreciation method. The use of other methods is not permitted.

Although the focus of this discussion is on depreciation within firms, individuals may also depreciate assets provided that these satisfy the above noted conditions. For example if an individual uses a vehicle for business purposes, depreciation can be claimed proportional to the vehicle's use for business purposes.

For the calculation of depreciation, an asset's initial purchase price or cost has to be known. This initial cost generally includes the actual cost of the asset and all the other incidental expenses, such as freight, site preparation, installation, legal fees associated with the purchase of the asset, etc. Tax regulations permit that the capital cost includes the complete cost of a given property or asset. Normally costs such as legal expenses for purchase of an asset, engineering fees associated with a project, and all costs incurred in acquiring, installing, and starting the asset can be included.

The capital cost is used for calculating depreciation allowances, capital gains or losses in the event that the asset is sold or salvaged.

Useful Life and Salvage Value

Every asset has a useful life in terms of a period of time over which the asset may continue to serve its intended purpose. A number of factors affect useful life, including advances in related technology, age when purchased, asset's use, maintainability, obsolescence, physical deterioration, and so forth.

For depreciation purposes, the useful life of an asset need not be the same as the economic life. Although the tax regulations do not directly specify the useful life of an asset, it is regarded as the period over which the asset may reasonably be expected to be useful in the production of income.

The salvage value of an asset is its worth at the end of its life. It is the monetary value that is received as a result of sale, trade-in, or salvage. For economic analyses, the salvage value of an asset at the end of its service life must be estimated. Should this estimate be different than the undepreciated capital cost (called book value), an adjustment has to be made. Likewise, at the time of disposal of the asset, when the actual salvage value is known, the exact tax effects can be calculated.

9.3.2.2 Available for Use Rule

This rule indicates that an individual or a business cannot claim the capital cost allowance (depreciation expense) until the property or asset becomes *available for use*. In effect this rule establishes the earliest taxation year in which a corporation can claim CCA for depreciable property if acquired after 1989.

A *property other than a building* or a structure is considered to be available for use at the earliest of several dates. Examples of these dates are:

- when the firm can put the property to use for either producing a saleable product or a service (i.e., when the asset is used by the firm for the first time to earn income)
- the outset of the first taxation year that starts at least 358 days after the taxation year during which the property was acquired
- immediately prior to the disposal of the property or asset by the firm.

A *building* is regarded as available for use on the earliest of the following dates:

- when the firm uses all or a substantial part of the building for its intended purpose
- when the building is completed
- the outset of the first taxation year that starts at least 358 days following the taxation year during which the corporation acquired the property
- immediately prior to the disposal of the property by the corporation, or
- when the corporation acquires a replacement property for another that was disposed of on an involuntary basis (for example, expropriation) that was either acquired before 1990 or had already become available for use.

In the case of a building or structure, the *available for use* rule implies the earliest of the following dates:

- when the building or structure is actually used for it's intended purpose
- when construction of the building or structure is complete
- immediately prior to the disposal of the building or structure by the firm.

9.3.2.3 Capital Cost Allowance Classes and Rates

The *capital cost allowance (CCA)* system is the only allowable tax deductible depreciation expense in Canada. It is applicable to both corporations and individuals. The Canadian tax law allows a corporation to deduct a part of the capital cost of certain depreciable property from income it earned during the year from a business property.

The depreciable property is grouped into prescribed classes under the Part XI (Schedule II) of the Income Tax Regulations. Schedule T2S(8) of the Regulations contains a complete list of these prescribed classes. A partial list and description of the most common capital cost allowance (CCA) classes is shown in Table 9.2 (declining-balance classes) and Table 9.3 (straight-line classes).

The tax regulations prescribe a maximum CCA rate for each class. This rate is applied to the undepreciated capital cost of the class at year end in order to find the maximum CCA that the corporation is allowed to claim. That is, the corporation can deduct any amount up to the maximum rate that is allowed for the year.

9.3.2.4 Half-Year Rule

Canadian tax regulations (Subsection 1100-2) were modified in 1981 in order to limit the depreciation or capital cost allowance claims in the taxation year of acquisition of most depreciable property. This regulation became effective on November 12, 1981 in order to prevent individuals or businesses, who could purchase property before their year-end, from receiving a full year of depreciation or capital cost expense.

Therefore, instead of getting a full year's depreciation during the first year, the tax regulations treat the asset as if it were owned for one-half year, regardless of when it was actually put into service. Therefore for year 1, a corporation gets one-half of the normally allowable depreciation. For example, for Class 8, classified as 20 percent CCA, 10 percent for year 1 is allowed.

The half-year rule is applicable to most depreciable property. However, there are several classes of assets that are exempt. These include:

- Some class 12 assets such as computer software (i.e., not system software) certified feature film, motion picture, or videotape used for a television commercial message;
- Class 14 patents, concessions or licenses, franchises;
- Class 15 assets used for cutting and removing merchantable timber.

Several 50 percent rules apply to classes 13, 24, 27, 29, and 34. For a description of classes 13, 15, 24, 27, 29 and 34, see Schedule II of the Income Tax Regulations.

The subject of capital cost allowance in terms of categorization of assets and the application of the half-year rule can be very confusing even to an expert in the taxation field. For example, computer software as a class 10 asset has a 30 percent declining balance for system software, and under class 12 has a 100 percent declining balance for all other software.

TABLE 9.2

Capital cost allowance, declining-balance classes and rates[†‡]

Class number	Description	CCA rate
1	Most buildings made of brick, stone, or cement acquired after 1987, including their component parts such as electric wiring, lighting fixtures, plumbing, heating and cooling equipment, elevators, and escalators	4%
3	Most buildings made of brick, stone, or cement acquired before 1988, including their component parts as listed in class 1 above	5%
6	Buildings made of frame, log, stucco on frame, galvanized iron or corrugated metal that are used in the business of farming or fishing, or that have no footings below ground; fences and most greenhouses	10%
7	Canoes, boats, and most other vessels, including their furniture, fittings, or equipment	15%
8	Property that is not included in any other class such as furniture, calculators and cash registers, photocopy and fax machines, printers, display fixtures, refrigeration equipment, machinery, tools costing more than $200, and outdoor advertising billboards and greenhouses with rigid frames and plastic covers acquired after 1987	20%
9	Aircrafts, including furniture, fittings, or equipment attached, and their spare parts	25%
10	Automobiles (except taxis and others used for lease or rent), vans, wagons, trucks, buses, tractors, and trailers, drive-in theatres, general-purpose electronic software, and timber cutting and removing equipment	30%
10.1	Passenger vehicles costing more than $24,000 ($20,000 if acquired before September 1989)—for passenger vehicles acquired after 1990, the $24,000 cost does not include either GST or any provincial sale tax	30%
16	Automobiles for lease or rent, taxicabs, and coin-operated video games. Certain tractors and large trucks acquired after December 6, 1991, that are used to haul freight and that weigh more than 11,788 kilograms	40%
17	Roads, sidewalks, parking-lot or storage areas, telephone, telegraph or non-electronic data communication switching equipment	8%
38	Most power-operated movable equipment acquired after 1987 used for moving, excavating, placing, compacting earth, rock, concrete, or asphalt	30%
39	Machinery and equipment acquired after 1987 that is used in Canada primarily to manufacture and process goods for sale or lease	25%
43	Manufacturing and processing machinery and equipment acquired after February 25, 1992, described in class 39 above	30%
44	Patents, and licenses to use patents for a limited or unlimited period, that the corporation acquired after April 26, 1993. However, you can elect not to include such property in class 44 by attaching a letter to the return for the year the corporation acquired the property. In the letter, indicate the property you do not want to include in class 44.	25%

[†]Revenue Canada, *T2 Corporation Income Tax Guide*, 1994.
[‡]CCH Canada Limited, *Preparing Your Corporation Tax Returns*, Don Mills, Ontario, 1994.
Source: Revenue Canada *1994 T2 Corporation Income Tax Guide*. For more information, see CCH Canadian Limited, *Preparing Your Corporation Tax Returns*, Don Mills, Ontario.

TABLE 9.3

Capital cost allowance, straight-line classes[††]

Class number	Description	CCA rate
12	Chinaware, cutlery, linen, uniforms, dies, jigs, moulds or lasts, computer software (except systems software), cutting or shaping parts of a machine, certain property used for earning rental income such as apparel or costumes, and videotape cassettes; certain property costing less than $200 such as kitchen utensils, tools, and medical or dental equipment; certain property acquired after August 8, 1989 and before 1993 for use in a business of selling or providing services such as electronic bar-code scanners, and cash registers used to record multiple sales taxes	100%
13	Property that is leasehold interest (the maximum CCA rate depends on the type of the leasehold and the terms of the lease)	N/A
14	Patents, franchises, concessions, and licences for a limited period—the CCA is limited to the lesser of: • the capital cost of the property spread out over the life of the property; and • the undepreciated capital cost of the property at the end of the taxation year Class 14 also includes patents, and licenses to use patents for a limited period, that are elected not to be included in class 44.	N/A

Approval of the Minister of Environment is required for the following two classes:

24	Water pollution and control equipment.	50%
27	Air pollution control equipment.	50%
29	Manufacturing and processing equipment if acquired before 1988	50%

[†]Revenue Canada, *T2 Corporation Income Tax Guide,* 1994.
[†]CCH Canada Limited, *Preparing Your Corporation Tax Returns,* Don Mills, Ontario, 1994.
Source: Revenue Canada *1994 T2 Corporation Income Tax Guide.* For more information, see CCH Canadian Limited, *Preparing Your Corporation Tax Returns,* Don Mills, Ontario.

Also, non-system software is exempt from the half-year rule. Therefore, it may not be clear at the outset which class of computer software has been purchased.

EXAMPLE 9.5

Half-Year Rule and Declining-Balance Method

Purchase price of equipment = $700 million, CCA = 20 percent. Find depreciation for years 1 to 3 and book value at the end of year 3.

Solution

Year 1 depreciation = $700 M (which is book value or undepreciated
capital cost (UCC)) × 20% CCA rate × 0.5
= $70 M

$$\text{Year 2 depreciation} = (\text{book value or UCC}) \times (20\%/100)$$
$$= (\$700 \text{ M} - \$70 \text{ M}) \times 20\%/100$$
$$= \$126 \text{ M}$$

Note: $(\$350 \text{ M}) \times 0.2 + (\$350 \text{ M} - \$70 \text{ M}) \times 0.2 = \$126 \text{ M}$

$$\text{Year 3 depreciation} = \$700 \text{ M} - \text{total of first and second year depreciation}$$
$$= [\$700 \text{ M} - (\$70 \text{ M} + \$126 \text{ M})] \times (20\%/100)$$
$$= \$101 \text{ M}$$

Book value at the end of year 3 = (undepreciated balance or book value at the beginning of year 3)
$$- \text{year 3 depreciation}$$
$$= \$504 \text{ M} - \$101 \text{ M}$$
$$= \$ 403.00 \text{ M}$$

We can find the UCC without year by year calculations of depreciation and book value.

Another approach:

Undepreciated balance = (purchase price/2)$(1 - \text{CCA rate})^3$
(or book value) at $+ (\text{purchase price}/2)(1 - \text{CCA rate})^2$
the end of year 3 $= (\$700 \text{ M}/2)(1 - 0.2)^3 + (\$700 \text{ M}/2)(1 - 0.2)^2$
$$= \$403.20 \text{ M}$$

9.3.2.5 Capital Cost Allowance Calculations

For the determination of the capital cost allowance, a *Capital Cost Allowance Schedule T2S(8)* must be completed. On this schedule, CCA for each class of property must be calculated separately and then totalled at the end. As noted earlier, land is not a depreciable property.

Column 1: Class number. Each class of property is to be identified and assigned the appropriate class number. Generally all of the depreciable properties within the same class can be grouped together.

Column 2: Undepreciated capital cost at the beginning of the year. Beside each class number, the total undepreciated capital cost is entered. This represents the total value of all the properties within that specific class. This value is the undepreciated capital cost at the end of the previous year.

Column 3: Cost of acquisitions during the year. For each class, the total cost of acquisitions and purchases that were available for use are recorded. The cost of acquisitions includes legal fees, accounting, engineering, and all other fees incurred as a result of the purchase. Note: land is not a depreciable property and therefore not eligible for capital cost allowances.

Column 4: Adjustments. Adjustments that either increase or decrease the total capital cost are made. The usual adjustments may include the following:

- decrease the capital costs by any investment tax credits the business received to reduce taxes payable, or claimed as a refund in the preceding taxation year
- decrease the capital costs by government assistance that the corporation actually received or is entitled to receive in the year
- increase the capital cost of any property for repaid government assistance that was previously used to reduce the capital cost

Column 5: Proceeds of dispositions during the year. Here, record the total proceeds of disposition of property that the business received during the year. If the business disposed of property for more money than its capital cost, enter the capital cost. This results in a capital gain. On the other hand, losses on depreciated property do not result in capital losses.

Column 6: Undepreciated capital costs. The amount in this column is determined by adding the undepreciated capital cost at the beginning of the year, plus the cost of acquisitions paid during the year, plus the adjustments that reduce or increase the capital cost, minus the proceeds of disposition during the year (Column 2 plus 3 plus 4 minus 5).

According to tax regulations, a business cannot claim a capital cost allowance when the undepreciated capital cost is:

- positive but no assets remain in that class at the end of the taxation year. Such a case is treated as a terminal loss and treated like an expense for that particular taxation year.
- negative at the end of the taxation year. This is known as a recapture of depreciation or recaptured capital cost allowance.

A business can claim terminal loss if a business sells the remaining property in a given class for less than its depreciated value. A terminal loss can be used as a deduction from income of the firm.

If the proceeds from the disposition of an asset are higher than the undepreciated capital cost (or book value), the recaptured CCA has to be declared and its tax effect must be added to the income.

Column 7: Half-year rule. In most cases, properties acquired by a business that become available for use during the taxation year are only eligible for 50 percent of the normal maximum capital cost allowance for the year. Therefore, in this column, one-half of the net amount of additions to the class (cost of acquisitions minus the proceeds of disposition) should be entered. While applying the half-year rule, any additions must take into account adjustments that relate to this year's acquisitions.

Column 8: Reduced undepreciated capital cost. This column represents the undepreciated capital cost (Column 6) prior to applying the half-year rule minus the amount of adjustment as a result of the half-year rule (Column 7). The resulting amount is the final undepreciated capital cost value to be used in the calculation of the capital cost allowance.

Column 9: Capital cost allowance rate. Each class of capital cost allowance is defined under the Canadian tax regulations. In this column simply enter the appropriate rate that applies to each class.

Column 10: Capital cost allowance. For claiming the maximum capital cost allowance for each class, multiply the undepreciated capital cost (Column 8) by the capital cost allowance rate (Column 9). Record the result in this column. Any amount up to the maximum allowable capital cost allowance can be claimed by a firm.

Column 11: Undepreciated capital cost at the end of the year. This item is calculated by taking the undepreciated capital cost (Column 6) and subtracting the capital cost allowance (Column 10). The resulting amount will be used for the undepreciated capital cost at the beginning of the next year.

EXAMPLE 9.6

Calculating CCA for Purchase of New Equipment

A small engineering consulting office is planning to purchase a new computer workstation for computer-aided designs. The cost of the work station is $6,800. This equipment is a Class 10 capital cost allowance with a declining balance CCA rate of 30 percent. The company already has $20,000 in Class 10 depreciable property at the beginning of the year. Find the maximum capital cost allowance for this firm's Class 10 depreciable property for this year.

Solution

Undepreciated capital cost at the beginning of the year = $20,000
Cost of acquisition during the year = $6,800

Undepreciated capital cost = $20,000 + $6,800 = $26,800
50% rule adjustment = $ 6,800 × 0.5 = $3,400
Reduced undepreciated capital cost = $26,800 − $3,400 = $23,400
Maximum capital cost allowance = $23,400 × 30% = $7,020

EXAMPLE 9.7

Calculating a Terminal Loss

A manufacturing company is planning to sell its plant and move to a leased location. The company can receive $320,000 for its building. At the end of the year the company will have no more Class 3 depreciable properties. The book value or undepreciated capital cost (UCC) of the property was $370,000 at the time of the sale. Find the tax effect of this asset's disposal.

Solution

Undepreciated capital cost = $370,000
Proceeds for disposition during the year = $320,000
Balance of undepreciated capital cost = $50,000

Since there is an undepreciated capital cost of $50,000 and there is no property in this class remaining, this amount becomes a terminal loss. The loss will reduce income by $50,000 for tax purposes.

EXAMPLE 9.8

Calculating Capital Gains and Recaptured CCA

A well drilling company purchased some specialized drilling equipment last year for $40,000. The equipment currently has an undepreciated capital cost of $36,000. The drilling company has been offered $48,000 for this piece of equipment. The owner of the company wishes to know what the income tax considerations will be for this tax year.

Solution

Sale price of equipment = $48,000
Purchase price of equipment = $40,000

Since the sales price is greater than the purchase price the company will have to claim an $8,000 capital gain.

Depreciated capital cost = (purchase price of $40,000
                                    − UCC of $36,000)
                              = $4,000

Since the sale price is higher than UCC, this is a recaptured depreciation expense.

Therefore this company will have a capital gain of $8,000 and a recapture capital cost allowance of $4,000. This will increase income by $12,000.

9.4 EVALUATION OF DEPRECIATION METHODS

Each depreciation method has unique features that appeal to different management philosophies. A method by which the bulk of the money invested is recovered early in the life of an asset is a popular conservative view. An early write-off guards against sudden changes that could make the equipment less valuable and shift some taxes toward later years. A method in which the annual charge is constant simplifies the accounting procedure. In general, the desirable features of a depreciation method are that it (1) recovers the capital invested in an asset, (2) is easy to apply, and (3) is acceptable to government agencies (i.e., Revenue Canada for Canadian applications). Depreciation based on usage rather than time is appealing because it tends to maintain book values closer to market value.

In Canada, the choice of method for determining book depreciation for financial reporting to shareholders depends upon company practice. As for the calculation of capital cost allowance, since rigid rules of Revenue Canada have to be followed, the question of a choice of depreciation method does not arise.

In Canada, for a given asset, Revenue Canada specifies the *method* to be followed in the determination of the capital cost allowance (CCA). Therefore, a comparison of after-tax effects of depreciation methods is not needed to support engineering economics studies.

9.5 TAX CONCEPTS

Everyone has an opinion about taxes. Some of the more famous ones include:

> The art of taxation consists in so plucking the goose as to obtain the largest possible amount of feathers with the smallest amount of hissing. (*Attributed to Jean Baptiste Colbert, 1665*).

> To tax and to please, no more than to love and be wise, is not given to men. (*Edmund Burke in a speech, "On American Taxation," in 1774*).

> When I catch myself resenting not being immortal, I pull myself up short by asking whether I should really like the prospect of having to make out an annual income tax return for an infinite number of years ahead. (*Arnold J. Toynbee, in* Saturday Review, *1969*).

The federal government has enacted laws that have made tax considerations a major influence in investment analysis and the operation of a

business. Revenue Canada collects taxes and issues regulations that interpret and implement tax laws.

Corporate income taxes are a significant factor in the cash flow of
any investment proposal. All the analyses in previous chapters were
made on a before-tax basis. In many cases before- and after-tax analyses
indicate the same order of preference among competing alternatives
because the alternatives usually have similar characteristics. However,
when some proposals are subject to special tax treatment and others are
not, the order of preference can switch abruptly in an after-tax comparison.
Also, the after-tax analysis reveals the actual cash flow that results from a
proposal.

Tax laws are extremely intricate and subject to frequent changes. Consequently, the intent in this chapter is to present basic tax concepts, not
the details on how to calculate the specific amounts due. Furthermore, the
discussion is mainly limited to federal income taxes; provincial income
taxes are only briefly introduced.

9.5.1 Types of Taxes

Federal, provincial, and sometimes city or county taxes are imposed on
income, property, and/or transactions. The transfer of wealth through the
taxing mechanism is a major concern of governments, and the payment of
those taxes is a major concern of income producers, both corporate and
individual. The principal types and their relevance to engineering economic studies are described below.

1. *Property taxes* are charged by local governments on land, buildings,
   machinery and equipment, inventory, etc. The amount of the tax is a
   function of the appraised value of the assets and the tax rate. Property
   taxes are usually not a significant factor in an engineering economics
   study because of their small magnitude compared to income taxes and
   their minor effect on competing proposals.
2. *Excise taxes*, imposed on the production of certain products such as
   tobacco and alcohol, rarely affect economic comparisons. Other taxes
   that are not normally relevant, but may become so in specific situations, are *sales tax* on retail products, *user's tax, value-added tax,
   unemployment tax,* and *social insurance contributions.*
3. *Income taxes* are levied on personal and corporate income at increasingly higher rates for higher incomes. They are based on net income
   after deductions allowed for permissible "expenses." The tax effects of
   different types of expenses on the cash flow of proposals have significant influence on their acceptability. The rest of this chapter is devoted
   to the examination of income-tax effects.

9.5.2 Changing Taxes

The federal government controls the monetary and fiscal policy of the nation to influence the level of economic activity. Monetary policy influences the availability and cost of credit, and fiscal policy deals with government receipts and expenditures. Taxation is the key instrument in fiscal policy. The principal methods for altering government receipts are (1) changing the tax rate, (2) changing the depreciation requirements, and (3) allowing tax credits.

Tax rates imposed on incomes may be raised to dampen the level of economic activity when rapid expansion threatens inflationary consequences. In theory, the reduction in disposal incomes reduces the purchasing power of individuals and thereby decreases demand for goods and services. An associated reduction in after-tax profits by corporations reduces the funds available for new investments and discourages expansion. The reverse, a tax rate cut, theoretically encourages purchasing and expansion when the fiscal policy attempts to stimulate a depressed economy characterized by high unemployment.

There are changes in tax laws almost every year. Some alter the basic structure, such as changes in depreciation requirements that affect write-offs of depreciable assets. More often the tax rates are changed in response to current fiscal needs.

Engineering economic studies would ideally be based on the tax rates in effect during the lives of the assets being evaluated, but this is an unrealistic expectation, so current or "typical" rates are stated. For the preparation of economic justifications and investment proposals based on after-tax analyses, a knowledge of projected changes to tax regulations (e.g., deductions, exemptions, credits, deferrals, preferences, shelters, etc.) would be desirable since such changes affect returns on investment. The rates utilized in this chapter are representative but not necessarily currently correct.

9.6   CORPORATE INCOME TAXES: CANADA

The tax law requires that income taxes have to be paid by corporations according to Revenue Canada regulations. Taxes become due if revenue exceeds allowable tax deductions. Corporate revenue includes income received from sales of goods and services, interest from loans and securities, rents, royalties, and other gains from ownership of capital or property. A wide range of expenses incurred by businesses are tax deductible, namely, wages, salaries, rents, repairs, interest, taxes, materials, employee benefits, advertising, etc.

Also, according to special provisions of the tax law, other deductions are allowed, such as losses from fire and theft, contributions, capital cost allowance and depletion, bond interest, research and development expenditures, outlays to satisfy legislated objectives such as pollution control, etc. Taxable income is found as the difference between the revenue and deductions.

In general:

$$\text{Taxable income} = \text{gross income} - \text{expenses} - \text{interest on debt} - \text{capital cost allowance}$$

and

$$\text{Corporate income tax} = \text{taxable income} \times \text{effective tax rate}$$

Every corporation has a fiscal year that is used as the taxation year. During its fiscal year, a corporation is required to pay installments of taxes, estimated on the basis of taxes actually owed by the corporation. As a rough estimate, a twelfth of the previous year's taxes can be deposited. A corporation is required to file federal and provincial tax returns within six months of the end of its fiscal year. However, a final tax payment, representing the difference between total income tax payable and the amount paid in monthly installments, has to be made within approximately two months of the end of its fiscal year. The amount of time allowed for paying the final installment varies according to such factors as corporation size and type of industry.

In example problems included in this book, unless otherwise indicated, it is assumed that corporate investments occur at the beginning of each fiscal year, and income taxes will be paid as a lump sum at the end of each fiscal year.

9.6.1 Corporations

Corporations in Canada can be classified as *Canadian controlled private, other private, public,* or *other corporations* for tax purposes. A corporation is classified as a Canadian controlled private corporation if it is incorporated or resident in Canada and not controlled by one or more public corporations and/or nonresident persons. Other private corporations are also resident in Canada but are not public corporations or controlled by a public corporation. Public corporations are resident in Canada and have shares traded on a Canadian stock exchange or are considered by the Minister of National Revenue to be public corporations. Corporations that do not fall into one of the other three categories noted above are regarded as other corporations (e.g., Credit Unions, cooperatives, nonresident-owned investment corporations, and Crown corporations). The reason for classifying corporations is that special tax provisions such as tax rates and deductions apply to each type of business.

Effective income taxes paid by corporations (to federal and provincial governments) reflect the size of the company, the nature of products, and a variety of deductions and special provisions that are applicable during a given tax year. For example, according to the *1994 Annual Report* of the Corel Corporation[†] of Ottawa, the company's effective tax rate for fiscal 1992, 1993, and 1994 amounted to 39.2 percent, 39.8 percent and 31.5 percent, respectively. Corel's 1992 effective tax rate differed from the company's statutory tax rate of 44.3 percent mainly due to the application of the manufacturing and processing deductions and the research and development tax credit. As compared to the 1994 statutory rate of 44.3 percent, a drop in the company's effective tax rate reflects primarily the effect of foreign tax differences associated with a full year of international operations. In fiscal year 1993, international operations amounted to only four months.

In the case of the Bank of Nova Scotia[‡], the 1993 and 1994 statutory tax rate was 42.6 percent. As compared to this level of taxation, the actual effective tax rates for 1993 and 1994 amounted to 40.3 percent and 47.0 percent, respectively. In spite of a lower rate of taxation on income earned by foreign operations on income and by tax-exempt income generated by securities, including load substitutes, a substantial increase in 1994 was primarily caused by the goodwill write-off of Scotia McLeod. Such an expense is not deductible for tax purposes.

9.6.2 Effective Income Taxes: Federal

Tax regulations specify the elements of the corporate tax structure. Businesses are required to submit their tax information on tax return form (T2). The 1994 tax information suggests three rate brackets based on the type of business. These federal corporation tax rates are categorized as (1) general, (2) manufacturing/processing, and (3) small business. The rates are non-progressive, since these do not increase with increased earnings.

At the end of 1994, the basic federal tax rate for a corporation was 38 percent. Using this rate, deductions and surcharges, the federal tax rate amounts to 28.84 percent.

The federal tax abatement (a deduction) is equal to 10 percent of taxable income earned in the year in Canada. Income earned outside Canada is not eligible for the federal tax abatement. The additional surtax is 3 percent, applied to the tax that results following the 10 percent abatement. The manufacturing and processing profit deduction (MPPD) may be claimed by corporations that earn at least 10 percent of their gross income from manufacturing or processing goods in Canada. Income that is eligible for the small business deduction (discussed below) is not eligible for this deduction.

[†]Corel Corporation, *1994 Annual Report,* Ottawa.
[‡]Bank of Nova Scotia, *Scotiabank 1994 Annual Report,* Ottawa.

TABLE 9.4

TABLE 9.4

Federal corporation tax structure for 1994

Type of company	Tax rate (including surtax)
General	28.84%
Manufacturing/processing	21.84%
Small business	12.84%

The application of the manufacturing and processing profit deduction (MPDD) of 7 percent results in a 21.84 percent federal tax rate. Depending upon the size of the Canadian controlled and private corporations, Canadian tax laws permit a corporation to claim a small business deduction (SBD). This deduction is applicable to the first $200,000 of annual taxable income earned in Canada. In terms of effect, it reduces the federal tax rate by 16 percent. With the small business deduction of 16 percent, the federal tax rate amounts to 12.84 percent federal tax rate. These observations are summarized in Table 9.4.

EXAMPLE 9.9

Calculation of the Federal Tax Rate

A company has a net income of $800,000. Calculate the federal tax rate (a) if the manufacturing/processing tax credit and the small business deductions are not applicable, and (b) if the manufacturing/processing deduction in credit is applicable, but the small business deduction is not.

Solution

(*a*) The base tax is 38 percent of $800,000 or $304,000. From this tax amount, 10 percent of net income is deducted or $304,000 − (0.1 × $800,000) = $224,000. A corporate surtax of 3 percent is applied to $224,000 or 3 percent of $224,000 = $6,720. The subtotal of federal tax now becomes $304,000 + $6,720 = $310,720. Next a federal tax abatement of 10 percent of basic income is subtracted from the subtotal or the federal tax payable becomes $310,000 − (10% of $800,000) = $230,720. As a percentage of net income, the tax amounts to 28.84 percent.

(*b*) Now in this case, the MPPD of 7 percent of net income can be deducted from the federal tax. The federal tax becomes $230,720 − 7 percent of $800,000 = $174,720. This amounts to 21.84 percent.

EXAMPLE 9.10

Calculation of the Federal Tax Rate for a Small Business

A small company has a net income of $190,000. Calculate the federal tax rate.

Solution

The base level tax = 38% of $190,000 = $72,200. The 10% deduction results in tax of $72,200 − 10% of $190,000 = $53,200. The corporate surtax = 3% of $53,200 = $1,596. The small business deduction = 16% of $190,000 = $30,400. Therefore the federal tax payable = $72,200 − $19,000 + $1,596 − $30,400 = $24,396 or 12.84% of taxable income.

9.6.3 Effective Income Taxes: Provincial

In addition to federal taxes, provincial corporate taxes have to be paid. The provincial tax rates vary from 5 to 17 percent (and are, of course, subject to change by provincial governments at any time). To continue the example of the corporation with net income of $800,000, suppose that this company was a resident of Ontario in 1994. The provincial corporate tax rate in 1994 was 15.5 percent. (See Table 9.5.) The provincial tax amounts to $800,000 × 0.1550 = $124,000. The combined effective tax rate is 0.2884 + 0.1550 = 0.4434 or 44.34 percent. The combined federal plus provincial tax becomes $800,000(0.2884 + 0.1550) = $354,720.

9.6.4 Income Types, Deductions, Investment Tax Credit, and Incentives

A study of applicable tax rates and adjustments in various parts of the country would suggest considerable variation in average income tax rates

TABLE 9.5

1994 Provincial corporate income tax rates

Province	Standard	Small business
Alberta	15.5%	6.0%
British Columbia	16.0	10.0
Manitoba	17.0	9.5
New Brunswick	17.0	9.0
Newfoundland	16.0	5.0
Nova Scotia	16.0	5.0
Ontario	15.5	9.5
Prince Edward Island	15.0	7.5
Quebec	16.25	5.75
Saskatchewan	17.0	9.0
Northwest Territories	14.0	5.0
Yukon Territory	15.0	6.0

Note: Rates are stated as a percentage of basic taxable income. Surtaxes and rebates for special types of businesses, such as manufacturing, are not included.

due to geographic location and types of business. As noted earlier, many businesses receive the small business deduction on the first $200,000 of earned income. Furthermore, many corporations receive additional tax reductions such as the investment tax credits.

An effective tax rate is to be used for economic analyses. Depending upon the context, the choice of tax rate for economic analysis will depend upon the incremental effect of undertaking the investment on taxable income of the company. That is, the tax rate to be used is the one that applies to the additional taxable income projected in the economic analysis.

Given that the Canadian corporate income tax system is not considered to be progressive, it is easy to find the taxation rate and methodology to be used for a company that is interested in making the investment.

Tax regulations are to be followed for claiming maximum deductions. According to Revenue Canada guidelines, the total deductions cannot exceed revenues. Therefore, the taxable income must be greater than or equal to zero. This means that the deduction may not be fully applicable in a given year. For example, due to insufficient income, it may not be possible to claim all of the CCA in a particular year. In such cases, the unused CCA is claimed in subsequent years.

However, in the examples provided, it will be assumed that for any investment, all available deductions are used at their maximum level in any given year. This may result in a negative taxable income, and taxes become a positive cash flow. The tax savings are used as a credit in the cash flow analysis for an investment under consideration.

Active business income is defined as income derived from exploration, mining, processing, manufacturing, construction, farming, fishing, wholesaling, retailing, transportation, etc. In contrast, passive investment income is generated from such sources as interest or dividends, income from a non-qualifying business, or income from a personal services business. (For more precise information, consult a tax specialist.)

The regular corporate tax rate is normally applicable to interest income received by a corporation. On the other hand, dividend income received by a Canadian public corporation from another Canadian public corporation is excluded from taxable income. The Canadian private corporations are required to pay a special tax on dividend income, but may be refundable back to the corporation under certain conditions. Dividends received from sources outside Canada are taxable at the normal rate.

The interest paid by a corporation on a loan is deducted from its gross income for calculating taxable income. On the other hand, dividends paid to investors are not deductible.

As noted earlier, *manufacturing and processing profits deduction (MPPD)* is allowed for all active Canadian corporations. A *small business deduction (SBD)* is offered to Canadian controlled private corporations. The small business deduction is applied only to the first $200,000 of annual taxable income. The effect of this deduction can be seen for income earned from an active business carried on in Canada in the form of reducing the basic 28.84 percent federal tax rate to 12.84 percent.

The *investment tax credit (ITC)* is a reduction in the year's income taxes equal to a percentage of the cost of any capital assets acquired during the tax year. The investment tax credit (ITC) is intended to stimulate business investment of a certain type in certain areas of the country. The tax regulations are amended to vary the ITC depending on current economic conditions.

In 1994, Canadian controlled private corporations were allowed an ITC rate of 35 percent on the first $2 million of investment in scientific research and development. In the past, the investment tax credit rate has been as high as 60 percent.

The amount of tax credit can be found by multiplying the value of eligible property by the rate of ITC. This amount is subtracted from the value of the property prior to calculating the CCA. In 1994, the investment tax credit was offered to corporations for acquiring qualified property in Newfoundland, Prince Edward Island, New Brunswick, Nova Scotia, Gaspe Peninsula and prescribed offshore areas.

A variety of tax incentives are available from the federal and provincial governments to corporations that can qualify. A number of incentive programs are available. The programs of primary interest to engineers are those for research and development, exports, etc.

9.6.5 Disposal Tax Effects

CCA Tax Shield (Tax Savings/Deductions): Declining-Balance Class

Assumed investment of $1
CCA rate (depreciation) = d
Tax rate = t

Since capital cost allowance = (book value)(depreciation rate), and tax savings due to CAA = (capital cost allowance)(tax rate), we can find these for various years:

> Yr. 1 capital cost allowance = $\$1(d)$
> Yr. 1 tax savings due to CCA = $\$1(d)(t)$
> Yr. 2 capital cost allowance = $(1 - d)(d)$
> Yr. 2 tax savings due to CCA = $(1 - d)(d)(t)$
> Yr. 3 capital cost allowance = $[(1 - d) - (1 - d)(d)]$
> Yr. 3 tax savings = $(1 - d)^2(d)(t)$
>
> .
>
> .
>
> Yr. N tax savings = $(1 - d)^{N - 1}(d)(t)$

Now, sum of tax savings in PW = $(P/F,i,1)(dt) + (P/F,i,2)[(1 - d)(dt)] + (P/F,i,3)[(1 - d)^2(dt)] + \dots + \dots = [(td)/(i + d)]$ This is the CCA tax shield. Note: $(P/F,i,N) = 1/(1 + i)^N$

For full-year rule:

CCA tax shield (in PW) = $[(td)/(i + d)]$

For half-year rule:

$$\text{Tax Shield (in PW)} = 0.5[(td)/(i + d)] + 0.5[(td)/(i + d)][1/(1 + i)]$$
$$= [(td)/(i + d)][(1 + 0.5i)/(1 + i)]$$

From the CCA tax shield, the actual cost to the investor or capital cost tax factor can be found:

Capital cost tax factor (CCTF) = $1 -$ CCA tax shield

If the CCTF is applied to investments, the CCTF based on full-year rule has to be applied to salvage.

CCA Tax Shield (Tax Savings/Deductions): Straight-Line Class

According to Revenue Canada capital cost allowance regulations, a number of assets are classified as straight-line class. The CCA rate is specified as a percentage of the asset's cost (i.e., depreciation cost). In some cases "half-year rule" is applicable, while in other cases this rule does not apply.

Assumed investment of $1.
The CCA rate (depreciation) = $d\%$.
Years required for full depreciation = k
Under half-year rule: $k = [(100\%)/(d\%)] + 1$ (round to lower number)
If half-year rule is not applicable: $k = [(100\%)/(d\%)]$ (round to higher number)

In cases when the half-year rule is not applicable, the depreciation pattern is as follows (sum of d's equals 1):

Years:	1	2	... k
Depreciation:	d	d	... d

PW of CCA tax shields = (PW of Year 1 shield) + (PW of Year 2 shield) + ... + (PW of Year k shield)
$$= td\left[\frac{1}{(1 + i)} + \frac{1}{(1 + i)^2} + \dots + \frac{1}{(1 + i)^k}\right]$$

Tax shield (in PW) = $td(P/A,i,k)$

If half-year rule is applicable, then the depreciation pattern is (Σ of d's =1):

Years: 1   2   ... k
Depreciation: $d/2$ d ... $d/2$

Tax shield (in PW) = $t(0.5)d[1/(1 + i) + 2/(1 + i)^2 + ... + 1/(1 + i)^k]$

EXAMPLE 9.11

Depreciation and Income Tax

A company is considering the purchase of Class 8 equipment in 1995 for $30,000. The revenue is estimated to be $15,000/year for 5 years. Expected salvage value is $2,500. Maintenance cost is $1,400 for the first year and is to increase by $200/year. The effective tax rate is 40 percent and the MARR is 10 percent (after tax). Find the NPW of proposed investment.

Solution

Year	Savings	Maint. cost	Net savings (BTCF)	After-tax cash flow (ATCF)[†]	PW of ATCF[†] @ 10%
1	$15,000	$1,400	$13,600	$8,160	$7,418.00
2	15,000	1,600	13,400	8,040	6,644.70
3	15,000	1,800	13,200	7,920	5,950.45
4	15,000	2,000	13,000	7,800	5,327.55
5	15,000	2,200	12,800	7,680	4,768.66
					30,109.36

[†]Excluding investment, salvage, and disposal tax effects.

PW of salvage = $2,500 $\times$ 0.62092 = $1,552.3

Tax shield (based on half-year rule) = 0.255

Tax shield (full year) = 0.267

NPW = ($-$$30,000) (1 $-$ tax shield based on half-year rule) + (PW of ATCF for years 1 to 5) + (PW of salvage)(1 $-$ tax shield based on full year of use)
    = $8,897.20

Capital Gains

Capital gains may apply to the sale (or exchange) of depreciable assets. If the sale price (i.e., salvage or disposition) is greater than the original purchase, a capital gains tax is applicable at the prescribed rate—e.g., 1/2(tax rate t).

Therefore, (sale price − purchase price) = capital gains and capital gains tax = capital gains × capital gains tax rate. If the sale price equals the purchase price, no capital gain is applicable.

CCA Recapture

Should a depreciable asset be sold after its use for an amount greater than its initial cost, there are two types of gains that are applicable. The first is the capital gain as defined above. The second gain is the depreciation claimed by the firm, equal to the difference between the original purchase and the book value, termed recaptured depreciation or CCA recapture. The CCA recapture is taxable. While the capital gains are taxed at a capital gain tax rate, the recaptured depreciation is taxed at the ordinary income tax rate. The current tax law allows a special lower rate of taxation for capital gains.

Therefore:

Disposal tax effects = capital gains tax + tax on recaptured depreciation
= (salvage value − original purchase price) × capital gains tax rate
+ (original purchase price − book value) × tax rate

Generally, a depreciable asset may be sold below the original purchase price. In such a case, we are interested in finding out whether the salvage income is above, equal to, or below the book value of the asset. The salvage value represents the proceeds from the sale minus any selling expense or removal costs. In order to establish what type of disposal tax effect has to be applied, we have to calculate the book value or undepreciated capital cost at the time of disposition of the asset.

If the sale price is higher than the undepreciated capital cost (UCC) or book value, CCA recapture applies. The recaptured depreciation or recaptured CCA for declining-balance class as well as straight-line class is taxable.

That is:

Tax effect = (Sale price − UCC) × t

where t is tax rate.

It should be noted that here income from disposal of the asset or sale price is less than the original purchase price. Furthermore, if (UCC − sale price or salvage) is 0, both tax shield adjustment and CCA recapture are equal to 0.

Tax Shield Adjustment

Should (UCC − sale price) be greater than 0, the tax shield adjustment could be required. The steps to be followed for finding tax shield adjustment for declining-balance class (if applicable) are given below:

1. Find UCC or book value at the end of service period.
2. Next calculate PW of tax shield adjustment = $(P/F,i,N)$(UCC − sale price or salvage)(tax shield).

For the after-tax cash flow analysis, the NPW after tax = (NPW with salvage & other factors) + (PW of tax shield adjustment).

The PW of tax shield adjustment for straight-line class is $(P/F,i,N)$(UCC − salvage)(tax shield).

EXAMPLE 9.12

Capital Gain and CCA Recapture

The purchase price of a class 8 asset bought 5 years ago was $50,000. The sale price was $60,000 and the effective tax rate was 46 percent. The class 8 CCA rate was 20 percent (declining-balance method class). Find capital gain and CCA recapture, if applicable.

Solution

Capital gain = $60,000 − $50,000 = $10,000

Assumed tax rate for capital gain = 1/2 (effective income tax rate)

Capital gain tax = (1/2)(0.46)($10,000) = $2,300

Undepreciated capital cost (UCC) or book value after 5 years of use (half-year rule):

$$\text{UCC} = \$50,000\ (0.5)\ (1 - \text{CCA rate of } 0.2)^4 + \$50,000(0.5)(1 - \text{CCA rate of } 0.2)^5$$
$$= \$10,240 + \$8,189$$
$$= \$18,429$$

$$\text{CCA recapture} = (\text{purchase price} - \text{UCC}) \times \text{tax rate}$$
$$= (\$50,000 - \$18,429)0.46$$
$$= \$14,522.66$$

$$\text{Total tax} = \$2,300 + \$14,522.66$$
$$= \$16,822.66$$

The asset disposal taxes are affected by the depreciation method used, the timing of asset disposal, and also whether or not the disposal of an asset depletes the asset class. In general, the depletion of an asset class is not a problem due to the asset pool accounting procedure. For problem solving in engineering economics, unless specified otherwise, we assume that the tax implications of the disposal are completely realized in the year of disposal.

Specifically, we assume that the asset disposal occurs just prior to the end of the last year of service. Also, the CCA in the year of asset disposal is determined in the usual manner, and without reference to the disposal. The tax effects arising from asset disposal are therefore over and above the tax savings realized in the year of disposal from CCA.

EXAMPLE 9.13

Disposal Tax Effect on Depreciable Assets

A class 38 power-operated movable piece of equipment was bought by a company for $200,000. According to Table 9.2, it's CCA rate with a declining balance is 30 percent. Find the disposal tax effects under the following assumptions of salvage value after 3 years of service: (a) $200,000, (b) $220,000. The company's tax rate is 40 percent. Assume that the capital gains are taxed at only 3/4 of the company's normal rate (i.e., $0.75 \times 40\% = 30\%$). Find disposal tax effects, and net salvage value.

Solution

The undepreciated capital cost after 3 years of service can be calculated from the given information:

Year	Capital cost allowance CCA = 30%	Book value at the end of year
0		$200,000
1	$30,000[†]	170,000
2	51,000	119,000
3	35,700	83,300

[†]The CCA for year 1 reflects the half-year rule.

The book value at the end of year 3 is $83,300.

(a) The sale price is $200,000, which is the same as the purchase price. Therefore, there is no capital gain. On the other hand, CCA recapture is applicable since the sale price is higher than the book value.

$$\text{CCA recapture} = (\text{salvage} - \text{UCC})(\text{tax rate})$$
$$= (\$200,000 - \$83,300)(0.4) = \$46,680$$

Salvage value after disposal tax = $200,000 − $46,680 = $153,320

(b) Since the sale price of $220,000 is higher than the purchase price of $200,000, the capital gains tax has to be paid. Additionally, the CCA recapture applies.

The capital gains tax = ($220,000 − $200,000)(0.3) = $6,000

The CCA recapture was found in part (a) to be $46,680. Therefore total disposal tax is = $6,000 + $46,680 = $52,680.

Salvage value after disposal tax = $220,000 − $52,680 = $167,320.

EXAMPLE 9.14

Straight-Line Class Depreciation and Income Tax

The capital budget included $45,000 for the purchase of a new machine. The MARR is 12 percent after taxes. Its useful life is 5 years and expected salvage after 5 years is $2,000. During the 5 years, it is estimated to save $23,000 per year in maintenance costs while its annual operating costs are $7,300. The machine is in Class 29 (CCA rate of 50 percent straight-line class). The firm has an effective income tax rate of 42 percent. Should the machine be bought? Apply the half-year rule.

Solution

The half-year rule applies and therefore depreciation rates are: 25 percent, 50 percent, and 25 percent in year 1, year 2, year 3, respectively. In the following table, the year-by-year analysis shows the calculation of CCA, taxable income, and after-tax cash flow.

Year	Before-tax cash flow	CCA rate	CCA	Taxable income	Income tax	After-tax cash flow
0	−$45,000					$−45,000
1	15,700	0.25	$11,250	$4,450	$1,869	13,831
2	15,700	0.50	22,500	−6,800	−2,856	18,556
3	15,700	0.25	11,250	4,450	1,869	13,831
4	15,700			15,700	6,594	9,106
5	15,700			15,700	6,594	9,106
5	2,000 Salvage					2,000
5						Disposal tax −840

At the end of year 3, the asset is fully depreciated. Therefore, at the time of disposal after 5 years of use, the UCC is 0. Since salvage is greater than UCC, CCA recapture applies.

$$\text{Disposal tax effect} = (\text{Salvage} - \text{UCC}) \times t = (\$2,000 - 0)0.42$$
$$= \$840.$$

$$\begin{aligned}
\text{NPW}_{\text{after tax}} &= -\$45{,}000 + (P/F,12\%,1)(13{,}831) + (P/F,12\%,2)(18{,}556) \\
&\quad + (P/F,12\%,3)(13{,}831) + (P/F,12\%,4)(9{,}106) \\
&\quad + (P/F,12\%,5)(9{,}106 + 2{,}000 - 840) \\
&= \$3{,}598.73
\end{aligned}$$

Since the NPW$_{\text{after tax}}$ is positive, the asset should be bought.

9.6.6 Capital Gains and Losses

The capital gains and losses are very complex to calculate since numerous special provisions are applicable. The tax rate specified to capital gains is usually less than that for ordinary income. This preferential rate is allowed in recognition of the risk involved in purchasing and holding capital assets. Given that the regulations are complex, the following discussion is to be regarded only as an introduction to this subject.

Capital gains occur if assets are sold for more than their original purchase price. The sources of capital gain could include sale of non-depreciable assets such as land and/or sale of financial assets such as stocks and bonds. Capital gains of a corporation are not taxed at the normal tax rate. Should a corporation encounter capital losses, these can be used to offset capital gains during the tax year. The net remaining losses, if any, may be carried back or forward.

According to current tax regulations, corporate capital gains are calculated at 75 percent of their actual value. That is, the corporate income tax payable on a capital gain is (3/4) × capital gain × corporate tax rate.

9.6.7 Corporate Loss Carryback and Carryforward

Corporate non-capital losses or operating losses can be carried back to the previous three years and/or forward to the following seven years. These losses can be used to offset taxable income in those years. This category of loss has to be applied first to the earliest year, followed by the next earliest year, etc. Net capital losses can be applied to reduce the amount of taxable capital gains. These can be carried back three previous years and forward in any later years until fully applied against capital gains. For example, a net capital loss in 1994 can be used to reduce taxable income from capital gains realized in 1995, and then any remaining losses can be carried forward.

9.6.8 Deferred Taxes

Businesses have to use the CCA in conjunction with the declining-balance method for tax purposes. But because most firms use straight-line depreciation for reporting their financial information to shareholders and external audience, they show substantial deferred taxes in their annual reports. For engineering economic studies that have to use actual cash flows, such deferred taxes cannot be taken into account. Therefore, the timing effects of tax deferral are considered.

9.7   AFTER-TAX ECONOMIC COMPARISONS

All the economic analyses in the previous chapters were based on before-tax cash flows. In many situations, before-tax analyses provide adequate solutions. When the alternatives being compared are to satisfy required functions and are affected identically by taxes, the before-tax comparison yields the proper preference. Evaluations of public projects rarely include tax effects and are conducted as before-tax analyses.

Tax effects occasionally cause the preference to switch among alternatives between before- and after-tax evaluations. The principal causes are differences in depreciation schedules, deductions for interest payments, and special tax regulations such as applicable investment credits. The net return after taxes, the amount actually available, is often the main concern. This is usable capital, not subject to downward revision when taxes are withdrawn.

A simple adjustment of the rate of return calculated without regard for taxes gives a reasonable approximation to the after-tax rate of return:

$$IRR_{after-tax} = (IRR_{before-tax})(1 - \text{effective income tax rate})$$

Thus, the after-tax rate of return resulting from a before-tax IRR of 15 percent and an effective income tax rate of 35 percent would be

$$IRR_{after-tax} = (0.15)(1 - 0.35) = 0.0975 \text{ or } 9.75 \text{ percent.}$$

This figure is exact only when the assets involved are nondepreciable, financing is by equity capital alone, and no special tax provisions are applicable.

9.7.1   After-Tax Cash Flow

A tabular approach is convenient for modifying the before-tax cash flow to show the effects of taxes. It is normally sufficient to assume that tax payments occur at the end of each period, in the same way that other cash flows are assumed to occur collectively at the year end. The number of entries in the table depends on the number of tax considerations involved. The most common are depreciation and interest deductions. Column headings (and the computations to be performed in the column) based on these tax effects are shown in a tabular form. All the column headings shown might not be required for any specific analysis. For example, if debt financing were not involved with a particular alternative, the debt and interest columns would be eliminated.

It is frequently desirable to expand the table representation when decidedly different types of cash flows occur in a given year or when additional capital investments require alterations in the depreciation structure. For example, a major expansion that needs to be depreciated separately from the original investment could easily be shown on a separate row with additional columns provided for its depreciation schedule. This provides a far clearer picture of the total alternative than pooling all cash flows occurring in that year. The use of CHEER, the computer program ancillary to this text, or spreadsheet software greatly facilitates the computation procedure.

Column heading	Column identification number*	Arithmetic computation in column
Calendar year		
Investment year	(1)	
Before-tax operating cash flow	(2)	
Book value before depreciation	(3)	
CCA rate or MACRS depreciation rate	(4)	
Depreciation charge	(5)	(4) × (3) or (4) × (original basis)
Book value after depreciation	(6)	(3) − (5)
Cash flow for debt	(7)	
Cash flow debt interest	(8)	
Taxable income	(9)	(2) − (5) − (8)
Cash flow for taxes	(10)	Tax rate × (9)
After-tax cash flow	(11)	(2) − (7) − (10)

*The column headings in succeeding examples use these identification numbers.

9.7.2 After-Tax Comparison of Proposals

An after-tax evaluation can be made using any of the comparison methods: EAW, PW, or IRR. All the precautions discussed for before-tax comparisons are applicable to after-tax analyses. Once the tax effects on cash flows have been determined, the computational procedures and interpretations of results are the same.

EXAMPLE 9.15

After-Tax Evaluation of a Depreciable Asset

The budget includes $45,000 for the purchase of a new testing machine requested by the maintenance department. All the major investments in the budget are being checked to see if the required rate of return of 15 percent after taxes can be achieved.

The testing machine is 20 percent CCA declining-balance class. Over 6 years, it is estimated to save $23,000 per year in maintenance costs with annual operating costs being $7,300. It will be depreciated by the declining-balance method and will have no salvage value. The firm has an effective composite income tax rate of 40 percent. Does the proposal to buy the testing machine satisfy the firm's new acceptable rate of return?

Solution

A quick check by the after-tax IRR approximation can be made if the proposal is promising. The cash flow diagram, where savings are considered to be income, is shown in Figure 9.2.

$$PW = -\$45,000 + (\$23,000 - \$7,300)(P/A, i, 6) \stackrel{?}{=} 0$$

Using CHEER, the before-tax IRR is 26.3 percent. Thus,

$$IRR_{after\text{-}tax} = (26.3\%)(1 - 0.40) = 15.8\%$$

which is above the required minimum.

After-tax computations are based on the values in Table 9.6. The depreciation charges result from applying the CCA rate of 20 percent and the half-year rule.

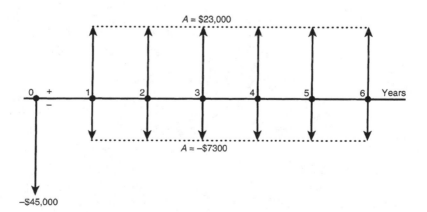

FIGURE 9.2
Cash flow diagram for Example 9.15.

TABLE 9.6

Tabulated after-tax flows for Example 9.15

Investment year (1)	Before-tax cash flow (2)	Depreciation charge (5)	Taxable income (2) − (5) = (9)	Taxes (40%)(9) = (10)	After-tax cash flow (2) − (10) = (11)
0	−$45,000.00				−$45,000.00
1	15,700.00	$4,500.00	$11,200.00	$4,480.00	11,220.00
2	15,700.00	8,100.00	7,600.00	3,040.00	12,660.00
3	15,700.00	6,480.00	9,220.00	3,688.00	12,012.00
4	15,700.00	5,184.00	10,516.00	4,206.40	11,493.60
5	15,700.00	4,147.20	11,552.80	4,621.12	11,078.88
6	15,700.00	3,317.76	12,382.24	4,952.90	10,747.10
6	0 Salvage				0
6	Disposal tax effect				[$13,271.04] × [$(td)/(i + d)$]

Book value or undepreciated capital cost (UCC) at the end of the sixth year = $45,000 − sum of depreciation charges = $45,000 − $31,728.96 = $13,271.04

Since salvage = 0, tax shield adjustment applies.

$$\text{PW of tax shield adjustment} = (P/F, i, 6 \text{ years})[(\text{UCC} - \text{salvage})] \times [(td)/(i + d)]$$

Here, $t = 0.4$ or 40%, $d = 0.2$ or 20%.

Utilizing the after-tax cash flow data in Table 9.6 Column 11 and the tax shield adjustment, we find that the present-worth formula for calculating the rate of return is as shown below.

$$\begin{aligned} \text{PW} = &-\$45,000 + (\$11,220.00)(P/F,i,1) + (\$12,660.00)(P/F,i,2) \\ &+ (\$12,012.00)(P/F,i,3) + (\$11,493.60)(P/F,i,4) \\ &+ (\$11,078.88)(P/F,i,5) + (\$10,747.10)(P/F, i,6) \\ &+ \text{PW of tax shield adjustment} \end{aligned}$$

The present worth of this alternative at the MARR of 15% is $264.81.
At $i = 16\%$, PW is −$979.44.
So, $\text{IRR}_{\text{after-tax}}$ can be found as

$$15\% + 1\%[(\$264.81)/\{(\$264.81 - (-\$979.44)\}] = 15.21\%$$

The proposal apparently meets the after-tax rate-of-return criterion.

Several features of Table 9.6 merit review. The before-tax cash flow in column 2 corresponds to the cash flow diagram displayed in the solution. A comparable after-tax cash flow diagram, represented in column 11, is the one on which the calculations are based. The depreciation charges in column 5 do not represent a cash flow; they are shown only to accommodate the calculation of income taxes.

EXAMPLE 9.16

After-Tax Evaluations Using CHEER

Solve Example 9.15 using the computer program, CHEER.

Solution

The computer program, CHEER, was introduced in Chapter 5 to aid in the solution of BTCF problems. We now demonstrate the program's usage in solving ATCF problems. Details on using the program are given in Appendix B.

The ATCF analysis requires the data specified in the BTCF section. For this example, this corresponds to Figure 9.2 and consists of: (1) project life = 6 years, (2) initial investment = $45,000, (3) annual savings = $23,000, and (4) annual maintenance and operating costs = $7,300. The project life and initial investment are input in the initial screen display (Figure 9.3a). We "click" on Revenue for the gross revenue screen of Figure 9.3b. Similarly, clicking on the Operating/Maintenance Cost on the main screen produces the cost input section (Figure 9.3c). Now that we have entered all the BTCF data, we can click on Calculate on the main screen to obtain a before-tax IRR of 26.3 percent (Figure 9.3d). This was the same value obtained for the before-tax IRR in Example 9.15.

After completing the BTCF data input, we click on the Project option on the main menu. From the resulting menu, shown in Figure 9.3d, we select the After-Tax Cash Flow option. The input screen for ATCF data input is shown in Figure 9.3e. Note that the ATCF option is only activated after the BTCF analysis has been completed.

The two primary inputs for ATCF analysis are depreciation and loan information if debt financing is involved (to be discussed in section 9.7.3). We click on Depreciation Input; the screen shown in Figure 9.3f is displayed. We need to input the following depreciation data: (1) number of assets to be depreciated; and (2) for each depreciable asset, first year in which depreciation starts, depreciable amount; (3) depreciation method, class of asset (discussed earlier); and (4) whether half-year rule is applicable. We click on [1] for the pull-down menu (Figure 9.3g) to specify the method and asset class.

For this example, there is one asset to be depreciated, depreciation starts in year 1, the depreciable amount is the initial cost of $45,000, and the asset is a 20 percent CCA (declining-balance) class. We click on Calculate to obtain the depreciation cash flow and return to the ATCF screen by

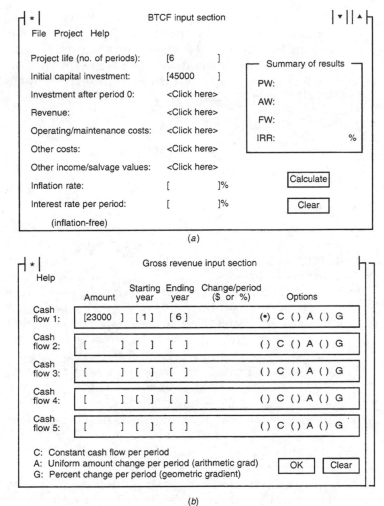

FIGURE 9.3
Computer solution screens for Example 9.16.

selecting File and then Calculate and Exit from the resulting menu. This example does not involve debt financing, so we do not need to enter the loan data.

The other input entered is tax rate = 40 percent and after-tax MARR = 15 percent. We now click on Calculate to obtain the results shown in Figure 9.3e. Finally, we can click on File on the ATCF screen and then click Summary from the resulting menu to view the ATCF results. These include the ATCF table and the tax disposal effects. The program can calculate capital gains tax, CCA recapture, and tax shield adjustment. We can click on Print to get the results that appear on the screen (Figure 9.3h). In the present problem, tax shield adjustment is applicable.

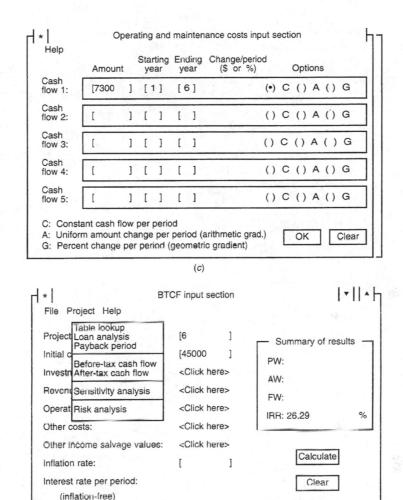

FIGURE 9.3
continued

9.7.3 After-Tax Analysis Including Debt Financing

Corporations frequently pay interest for the use of borrowed funds and occasionally receive interest on investments. Interest earned on invested funds is usually treated as earned income. Interest paid on corporate debt is often a significant expense, affecting taxable income and, consequently, taxes. Both the timing of the receipt of a loan and its repayment schedule affect after-tax cash flows.

Interest paid for money borrowed to carry on a trade or business is deductible from revenue in determining taxable income. It is treated as an expense, being deducted in the year it is paid. The deduction is essentially a federal subsidy for borrowing and thereby reduces the cost of a loan.

```
┌─=│              ATCF input section                    │▼││▲┐
│  File  Project  Help                                          │
│                                                               │
│  Depreciation input:          <Click here>                    │
│                                                               │
│  Non-taxable income salvage                ┌─ Summary of results ─┐
│      value:                   <Click here> │                     │
│                                            │  PW:  264.73        │
│  Loan principal:              [        ]   │  AW:   69.95        │
│                                            │                     │
│  Nominal loan interest rate:  [        ]   │  FW:  612.33        │
│                                            │                     │
│  No. of periods before loan                │  IRR:  15.22        │
│      is repaid:               [        ]   │                     │
│                                            └─────────────────────┘
│  No. of loan payments per
│      period:                  [        ]       ┌──────────┐
│                                                │ Calculate │
│  Tax rate percentage:         [40      ]%      └──────────┘
│                                                ┌──────────┐
│  Capital gains tax rate:      [        ]%      │   Clear  │
│                                                └──────────┘
│  After-tax interest rate:     [15      ]%
│  ┌────────────────────────────────────────────────────────────┐
│  │  Interest rate per period:    [         ]%                   │
│  │      (inflation-free)                                        │
└──└────────────────────────────────────────────────────────────┘
                              (e)
```

```
┌─=│         ATCF: Depreciation input section            │▼││▲┐
│  File  Help                                                   │
│  ┌─DEPRECIATION METHOD:──────────────────────────────────────┐
│  │              PLEASE CHOOSE A DEPRECIATION METHOD            │
│  │  Canadian Tax Depreciation Regulations [  ]  Other Methods [  ]
│  └────────────────────────────────────────────────────────────┘
│
│  Total No. of assets to be     ┌──────────┐ ┌──────┐ ┌───────┐
│  depreciated: (max. = 5)  [ 1 ] │Calculate │ │ View │ │ Clear │
│                                 └──────────┘ └──────┘ └───────┘
│
│            1st yr in
│  Asset   which dep.  Depreciation  ┌ Depreciation CCA Salvage Half-yr. rule
│  no.     to be taken   cost        │  class    rate  Value  applicable?
│  [ 1 ]    [    ]     [        ]    │  [      ] [  ] [  ]   [X=Yes]
│                                    │                        [    ]
│  ┌─────────────────────────────────────────────────────────────┐
│  │ DEPRECIATION CLASS              HALF-YEAR RULE               │
│  │ DB  Declining-balance class     [ X ]  Half-year rule applies│
│  │ SL  Straight-line class         [   ]  Half-year rule exempt │
│  └─────────────────────────────────────────────────────────────┘
│  ┌─────────────────────────────────────────────────────────────┐
│  │  Interest rate per period:      [         ]%                  │
│  │      (inflation-free)                                         │
└──└─────────────────────────────────────────────────────────────┘
                              (f)
```

FIGURE 9.3
continued

Typically, corporations have two methods of borrowing money. The first of these would correspond to a corporate bond where only interest due would be paid during the life of the debt and the total principal would be paid at the termination of the debt. The second method corresponds to a mortgage where both interest and principal are paid with a constant payment. No additional payment would be due at debt termination.

	ATCF: Depreciation input section	|▼||▲|
File Help		

┌─DEPRECIATION METHOD:─────────────────────────────────┐

PLEASE CHOOSE A DEPRECIATION METHOD

Canadian Tax Depreciation Regulations [•]   Other Methods [   ]

Total No. of assets to be
depreciated: (max. = 5)   [1]   [Calculate]   [View]   [Clear]

Asset no. [1]	1st yr in which dep. to be taken [1]	Depreciation cost [45000]	Depreciation class [DB]	CCA rate [20]	Salvage Value [0]	Half-yr. rule applicable? [X=Yes] [X]

DEPRECIATION CLASS   HALF-YEAR RULE

DB   Declining-balance class   [X] Half-year rule applies
SL   Straight-line class   [   ] Half-year rule exempt

Interest rate per period: [   ]%
   (inflation-free)

(g)

AFTER-TAX CASH FLOW

Year	Before-tax cash flow	Dep. expense	Loan data Prin	Int	Taxable income	Tax due is (−)	After-tax
0	45,000.00	0					−45,000.00
1	15,700.00	−4,500.00	0	0	11,200.00	4,480.00	11,220.00
2	15,700.00	−8,100.00	0	0	7,600.00	3,040.00	12,660.00
3	15,700.00	−6,480.00	0	0	9,220.00	3,688.00	12,012.00
4	15,700.00	−5,184.00	0	0	10,516.00	4,206.40	11,493.60
5	15,700.00	−4,147.20	0	0	11,552.80	4,621.12	11,078.88
6	15,700.00	−3,317.76	0	0	12,382.24	4,952.90	13,780.48

UCC @ end of yr. 6 = $13,271.04
Tax shield adjustment applies
Net Present Worth of after-tax cash flow at 15.00% interest = $264.73
Equivalent Uniform Annual Worth is $69.95
After-tax rate of return 15.22%
Inflation rate is 0%

FIGURE 9.3
continued

(h)

EXAMPLE 9.17   **After-Tax Evaluation When Investment Capital Is Borrowed**

A firm with an effective income tax rate of 42 percent is interested in purchasing a new machine for $45,000. In order to pay for this asset, the firm
acquired a $20,000 debt at 10 percent interest, with interest to be paid
annually and principal to be paid at the end. The remaining $25,000 is

from the firm's equity capital. The minimum attractive rate of return is 12 percent (after tax). The useful life of this asset is 5 years, with a zero salvage value after 5 years. Income (estimated to result due to machine) is $23,000/year and annual operating expenses are estimated to be $7,300/year. This results in net income of $23,000 − $7,300 = $15,700. The machine is in Class 8 (20 percent CCA rate, declining-balance class). The investor wishes to find the present worth of after-tax cash flow and therefore to establish the feasibility of the project.

Solution

The first approach used is based on year-by-year analysis. See Table 9.7.

Interest charge/yr. = debt × interest rate = $20,000 × 0.1 = $2,000/yr.

CCA is calculated at 20% rate and by using the half-year rule:

CCA for Yr. 1 = $45,000(0.2/2) = $4,500
CCA for Yr. 2 = [($45,000 − $4,500)]0.2 = $8,100
CCA for Yr. 3 = [($45,000 − (4,500 + 8,100)]0.2 = $6,480
CCA for Yr. 4 = [($45,000 − (Sum of CCA for yrs. 1–3)]0.2 = $5,184
CCA for Yr. 5 = [($45,000 − (Sum of CCA for Yrs. 1 to 4)]0.2
   = $4,147.20

Sum of depreciation or CCA for years 1 to 5 = $28,411.20
   Book value at the end of year 5 = undepreciated capital cost (UCC) = $45,000 − sum (depreciation) = $45,000 − $28,411.20 = $16,588.80

TABLE 9.7

After-tax cash flow for Example 9.17 (tax shield adjustment not shown)

Year (1)	Before-tax cash flow (2)	CCA (5)	Interest charges (8)	Taxable income (9)	Taxes @42% (10)	After-tax cash flow (11)
0	−$45,000.00					−$45,000.00
	20,000.00					20,000.00
1	15,700.00	$4,500.00	$2,000.00	$9,200.00	$3,864.00	9,836.00
2	15,700.00	8,100.00	2,000.00	5,600.00	2,352.00	11,348.00
3	15,700.00	6,480.00	2,000.00	7,220.00	3,032.40	10,667.60
4	15,700.00	5,184.00	2,000.00	8,516.00	3,576.72	10,123.28
5	15,700.00	4,147.20	2,000.00	9,552.80	4,012.18	9,687.82
5						−20,000.00

Net present worth (NPW) @ 12% (after tax) without adjustment for disposal tax effect (i.e., without tax shield adjustment) = $-$45,000 + $20,000 (debt) + $9,836 $(P/F,12\%,1)$ + $11,348$(P/F,12\%,2)$ + $10,667.60$(P/F,12\%,3)$ + $10,123.28$(P/F,12\%,4)$ + $9,687.82$(P/F,12\%,5)$ $-$ $20,000$(P/F,12\%,5)$ = $1,003.77

Present worth of tax shield adjustment = $(P/F,12\%,5\text{yrs})$[(book value) $-$ (salvage)] $\times (td)/(i + d)$

Book value = undepreciated capital cost (UCC) = $16,588.80 (found earlier)

Salvage = $0, $t = 0.42$ (or 42%), $d = 0.2$ (or 20%), $i = 0.12$ (or 12%)

PW of tax shield adjustment = $2,470.91

NPW with the addition of tax shield adjustment = $1,003.77 + $2,470.91 = $3,474.68 (feasible)

The second approach relies upon the use of tax shield for incorporating the CCA allowance.

According to theory, the tax shield based on half-year rule is to be applied to investment and full-year rule is used for salvage. Since in this example, salvage is zero, tax shield based on full-year rule is not calculated.

The capital cost tax factor (CCTF) (half-year rule) = 1 $-$ tax shield based on half-year rule = $1 - [(td)/(i + d)][(1 + 0.5i)/(1 + i)]$

For $t = 0.42$, $d = 0.2$, and $i = 0.12$, the CCTF (half-year rule) = 0.752.

Net present worth (NPW) @ 12% (after tax) = $-$($45,000 of investment)(0.752) + $20,000 debt + $(1 - $ tax rate of 0.42)($23,000 $-$ $2,000 $-$ $7,300)$(P/A, 12\%, 5$ years) $-$ $20,000 of principal repayment $(P/F, 12\%, 5$ years) = $3,454.35 (feasible).

The difference between the answers obtained from the two approaches is due to the approximate nature of the second approach.

9.7.4 After-Tax Replacement Study

Before- and after-tax replacement evaluations are conducted in the same way once the tax effects have been imposed on the cash flow patterns. There are, however, a couple of points that occasionally cause confusion. One is the use of the book value as the worth of the presently owned asset in a replacement study.

The book value is the asset's purchase price less its accumulated depreciation charges. This value is the result of accounting practices and is unlikely to be the same as the asset's value in an open market. The difference between the book value (i.e., the undepreciated capital cost) and the present realizable value is to be estimated. As depicted in Figure 9.4, the actual amount obtainable for a defender in a replacement study is frequently less than its value shown by the accounting records. If the asset is replaced, the sunk cost, following disposal tax adjustments, is a loss for the year. Such a loss is charged against profit. However, part of the loss is

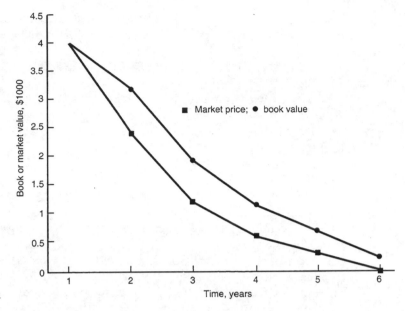

FIGURE 9.4

Sunk cost as a function of book value and actual price (market) of an asset.

absorbed by a reduction in taxes for that year. For instance, let the book value of the asset in Figure 9.4 be $960 and the market value be $300, to produce a sunk cost of $960 − $300 = $660. If the CCA rate is 20 percent, tax rate is 40 percent, and after-tax interest rate is 8 percent, the tax shield adjustment would amount to (UCC − salvage)$[(td)/(i + d)]$ = ($960 − $300)$[(0.4 \times 0.2)/(0.08 + 0.2)]$ = ($660)(0.2857) = $188.56. This amount of money would be added to the after-tax income for the year.

The mental static generated by sunk costs and the refusal to ignore them in decision making is hard to comprehend unless there is personal involvement. A large sunk cost can be detrimental to the current year's profit picture and may cause censure of the current managers, even if they had nothing to do with the original purchase and the depreciation schedule that caused it. There may also be a feeling that "we've got so much invested in it that we can't afford to sell it for what it would bring." The weakness of this argument is that the owners should be looking ahead to determine the course of action that will minimize future costs, not the course that will make past expenditures look good.

The correct way to perform an after-tax replacement study is to determine the defender's current market value and use that figure, adjusted for any disposal tax effects as noted above, as its worth at time zero. Two incorrect ways to conduct replacement studies are to pretend that the book value is always the defender's market value or to add the sunk cost to the challenger's purchase price. Both retard replacement. Operating costs are estimated for the remaining useful life and depreciation charges are based according to tax regulations. Taxes are levied as applicable and the resulting cash flow is compared with the challenger's after-tax cash flow by one of the standard discounting methods: EAC, PW, or IRR.

EXAMPLE 9.18

After-Tax Comparison of A Defender and A Challenger When Revenue Is Unknown

A Class 8 machine with a CCA rate of 20 percent has a book value of $10,000. Because of the technological advances, this existing machine can be sold now for only $8000. This machine can be kept for another 3 years. Its operating costs are $19,000 per year. The function performed by the machine will be needed for 5 more years. It is proposed that a $5000 overhaul be performed which will reduce operating costs to $16,000 per year for the next 6 years of use, at which time it will have no salvage value.

A new Class 8 machine of advanced design can perform the same function as the existing machine for $12,000 per year. This machine is priced at $36,000 and will have a salvage value of $6000 when disposed of at the end of the 6-year use period.

The company has a 40 percent effective composite tax rate. It requires an after-tax rate of return of 8 percent. Which machine will have the lower equivalent annual cost?

Solution

The defender's capital cost for the replacement study is its current market value, $8,000, plus the tax effects associated with disposing of it. The disposal tax effect is ($10,000 − $8,000)[(0.4 × 0.2)/(0.08 + 0.2)] = ($2,000)(0.2857) = $571.40. Therefore, the net "cost" of the defender is −$8000 − $571.40 = $8571.40. This amount is considered to be an outlay at time zero for the comparison displayed in Table 9.8. However, during the next 6 years it will still have yearly deductions of 20 percent of book value for each year. The expected salvage value after 6 years of use is zero. Operating costs, including the $5000 overhaul in year 1, constitute the before-tax cash flows for years 1 through 6. Because no income is attributed to the machine's operation, all before-tax cash flows are negative, except the salvage value of the challenger.

Annual expenses and depreciation are deductible from income and are, effectively, *tax savings*. For the defender in year 1, the sum of operating and overhaul costs ($16,000 + $5,000 = $21,000) provides a tax deduction at the 40 percent rate of ($21,000)(0.40) = $8,400. When depreciation is included with the expenses, $21,000 + $2,000 = $23,000, the tax savings amount to ($23,000)(0.4) = $9,200, which reduces the after-tax cash flow to −$21,000 − (−$9,200) = −$11,800. The remaining charges are recorded in Table 9.8.

The book value for the defender at the end of the sixth year is $2,621.44, whereas the salvage value is zero. The tax shield adjustment is ($2,621.44 − $0 of salvage)[(0.4)(0.2)/(0.08 + 0.2)] = ($2,621.44)(0.2857) = $748.98. In the case of the challenger, the book value is higher than the salvage value. Therefore, in this case the tax shield is applicable as well.

TABLE 9.8

After-tax replacement analysis

Year (1)	Before-tax cash flow (2)	Book value before dep. (3)	CCA charge (5)	Book value after dep. (6)	Taxable income (9)	Tax (10)	After-tax cash flow (11)
Defender							
0	−$8,571.40						−$8,571.40
1	−21,000.00	$10,000.00	$2,000.00	$8,000.00	−$23,000.00	−$9,200.00	−11,800.00
2	−16,000.00	8,000.00	1,600.00	6,400.00	−17,600.00	−7,040.00	−8,960.00
3	−16,000.00	6,400.00	1,280.00	5,120.00	−17,280.00	−6,912.00	−9,088.00
4	−16,000.00	5,120.00	1,024.00	4,096.00	−17,024.00	−6,809.60	−9,190.40
5	−16,000.00	4,096.00	819.20	3,276.80	−16,819.20	−6,727.68	−9,272.32
6	−16,000.00	3,276.80	655.36	2,621.44	−16,655.36	−6,662.14	−9,337.86
6	Tax shield adjustment						+748.98
Challenger							
0	−$36,000.00						−$36,000.00
1	−12,000.00	$36,000.00	$3,600.00	$32,400.00	−$15,600.00	−$6,240.00	−5,760.00
2	−12,000.00	32,400.00	6,480.00	25,920.00	−18,480.00	−7,392.00	−4,608.00
3	−12,000.00	25,920.00	5,184.00	20,736.00	−17,184.00	−6,873.60	−5,126.40
4	−12,000.00	20,736.00	4,147.20	16,588.80	−16,147.20	−6,458.88	−5,541.12
5	−12,000.00	16,588.80	3,317.76	13,271.04	−15,317.76	−6,127.10	−5,872.90
6	−12,000.00	13,271.04	2,654.21	10,616.83	−14,654.21	−5,861.68	−6,138.25
6	Salvage						+6,000.00
6	Tax shield adjustment						+1,319.03

Its value amounts to ($10,616.83 − $6,000.00)(0.2857) = $1,319.03. These values are shown in Table 9.8.

From the after-tax cash flow for each option, their present worth is found. These are:

PW of defender = −$52,871.80

PW of challenger = −$56,679.24

The negative after-tax cash flows represent disbursements that are treated as positive costs in the following equivalent annual cost comparison:

$\text{EAC}_{\text{after-tax}}$ (defender) = −$52,871.80(A/P,8%,6) = −$11,437.23

$\text{EAC}_{\text{after-tax}}$ (challenger) = −$56,679.24(A/P,8%,6) = −$12,260.59

Since the defender exhibits a lower equivalent annual cost, it is preferred over the challenger.

The after-tax replacement study follows the procedures described in Chapter 7. The market value is considered to be the "purchase price" of the asset already possessed, and therefore it represents the best current estimate of ownership cost. A book-value loss, such as the sunk cost in Example 9.18 of $10,000 - $8,000 = $2,000, has no bearing on the current situation, although previously instituted depreciation charges remain in effect. However, any disposal tax effects would have an impact. Note also from the example that overhaul and repair expenses are treated as current expenditures deductible from current income; they are not capital costs of ownership. Overhaul and repair expenses can affect capital cost only by increasing the salvage value as a result of more conscientious care.

The reverse of sunk cost occurs when the amount received for an asset at the end of its useful life is greater than the estimated salvage value. As already observed, the sale of an asset below its book value is treated as an ordinary loss. When the selling price is greater than the book value but less than the original purchase price, the difference is taxed as ordinary income. That portion of the selling price that is above the original capital cost is considered to be a capital gain and is taxed accordingly. The loss or gain is declared in the year in which the transaction takes place.

9.8   PERSONAL INCOME TAXES

The tax law requires individuals to pay taxes on income generated from several sources, including employment and business income, investment income, and profits realized from sale of capital assets. Investment income may consist of dividends received from corporations and interest from bank deposits. Profits resulting from the sale of capital assets such as stocks and bonds are taxable. Income received from business proprietorships and partnerships is taxable.

Calculation of Taxable Income

The starting point is gross income, consisting of earnings as defined by the provisions of the federal income tax laws. Income can be computed as follows:

Gross income = wages and salary + interest income + dividend income + rental/royalty income + capital gains + other income (includes such items as consulting fees).

Tax regulations allow a number of deductions to be made from the gross income. Therefore, the result is:

Net income (before tax) = gross income − [retirement plan contributions (registered pension plans or registered retirement savings plans) + annual union, professional, or like dues, child care expenses + attendant care expenses + business investment loss + moving expenses + alimony or maintenance paid + carrying charges and interest expenses on money borrowed for investment purposes + other deductions].

Also, general other deductions can also be subtracted before calculating the taxable income. These other deductions include: employee home relocation loan, stock option and shares deduction, losses from previous years, capital gains deduction, Northern resident's deduction, and additional deductions.

Following the computation of the taxable income, the federal income tax can be found.

Income Taxes on Ordinary Income

In Canada, three rates for individual taxation can apply. These rates are prescribed to be progressive. That is, as the income rises, a larger percentage is to be paid in taxes. (See Table 9.9.) For every tax year, these rates are announced by Revenue Canada. Although the exact level of these rates may change over the years, the policy of a progressive taxation system is likely to remain unchanged.

Following the determination of the federal income tax, individuals are allowed to subtract nonrefundable tax credits. These credits, consisting of several items, are added and then multiplied by 17 percent. The items constituting nonrefundable tax credits include: basic personal amount, age amount, spousal amount, Canada or Quebec Pension Plan contributions, unemployment insurance premiums, pension income amount, disability amount, disability amount transferred from dependent, tuition fees and education amount transferred from a child, medical expenses less adjustment, charitable donations. (Note: charitable donations over $200 are assigned nonrefundable tax credits at 29 percent rather than 17 percent.)

TABLE 9.9

Individual federal income tax structure for 1994

Taxable income	Tax rate
Less than $29,590	17%
$29,590–$59,180	$5030 on first 29,590 + 26% of taxable income over $29,590
More than $59,180	$12,724 on first $59,180 + 29% of taxable income over $59,180

These steps lead to the amount of the basic federal tax. From this, federal surtax and provincial taxes can be found. It is common practice that Revenue Canada and the provincial governments add individual surtaxes as a means of collecting additional revenue in the short run. However, some surtaxes tend to last for several years.

In 1994, the federal individual surtax was 3 percent of basic federal tax payable and an additional 5 percent on any amounts above $12,500 of federal tax payable.

The provincial tax on personal income has to be paid as well. It is usually specified as a percentage of the basic federal tax payable (which does not include the federal individual surtax). Revenue Canada is the source of information on federal, provincial, territories, and nonresident income tax rates.

The overall tax system is basically progressive in nature. That is, the higher the income, the greater is the percentage of income tax that has to be paid.

Income Taxes on Personal Capital Gains and Losses

Assets owned by individuals such as stocks and bonds are called financial assets. Other assets such as land and buildings are called fixed assets. The term capital assets can be used for everything that an individual owns and uses for personal purposes, pleasure, or investment (e.g., house, car, furniture, and stocks and bonds).

In the event that a capital asset is bought and later on sold for more than the purchase price, a profit is realized that is referred to as a capital gain. On the other hand, if a loss is incurred, it is called a capital loss. Therefore: Capital gain (loss) = selling price − purchase price, where the selling price represents the proceeds from the sale minus any selling expenses, and the purchase price normally includes any improvements and expenses incurred in acquiring the capital asset.

Regulations on capital gains have been changed frequently. For 1990 and following tax years, the taxable part of a capital gain became three-quarters of its monetary value. The tax instrument regarding capital gains has generally been used to encourage capital investment. Prior to February 1994, each person in Canada was entitled to a $100,000 lifetime capital gains exemption. This meant that the first $100,000 of capital gain income was free of taxes. However, since February 1994, this is no longer the case.

Taxation of Dividends from Taxable Canadian Corporations

Dividends received from taxable Canadian corporations are a source of income that are taxed in a slightly different manner in order to encourage investment. Under the Canadian tax law, such dividend income is offered a preferred taxation treatment.

9.9   **REVIEW EXERCISES AND DISCUSSIONS**

EXERCISE 1

A tract of timber was purchased for $500,000. Appraisal data placed a value of $420,000 on 4718 m^3 of standing timber. The land value was appraised at $80,000. What is the depletion allowance for the first year if 1036 m^3 of timber are removed from the parcel? What is the depletion allowance for tax purposes?

SOLUTION 1

The depletion allowance that appears on the income statement of a company's annual report is generally calculated according to the following formula:

$$\text{Depletion allowance} = \frac{\text{Units sold during the year}}{\text{Total number of recoverable units}}$$

Deducting the value of the land from the total investment ($500,000 − $80,000 = $420,000) sets the property cost for the 4718 m^3 of recoverable timber. When 1036 m^3 are removed in one year,

$$\text{Depletion allowance (year 1)} = \frac{\$420,000 \times 1036 \text{ m}^3}{4718 \text{ m}^3} = \$92,226$$

For tax purposes, the depletion method is to apply an allowable depletion percentage to the book value of the property. The percentage is based on the type of exhaustible resource and is applicable to the profits derived from the Canadian resource property. Percentage rates are subject to change, but in general the amount deducted cannot exceed a certain percentage (e.g., 25 percent) of the taxable income derived from the property. Since profits were not given, the depletion allowance for tax purposes cannot be calculated.

EXERCISE 2

A small Ontario food processing firm invested $100,000 in 1996 for new processing equipment. The firm has a taxable income of $180,000. What is its federal income tax liability before tax credits and how much investment tax credit (ITC) can the firm claim if the new equipment qualifies for 10 percent ITC?

SOLUTION 2

The firm qualifies for the small business deductions. If the 1996 rates are the same as those for 1994, shown in Table 9.4, its federal income tax liability is $180,000(12.8 percent) = $23,040. If a 10 percent investment tax credit is applicable, it amounts to $100,000(10 percent) = $10,000. Assuming that the ITC is less than the applicable limit of $15,000, all $10,000 can be used to reduce the 1996 taxes. Thus, the 1996 taxes will be $23,040 − $10,000 = $13,040.

EXERCISE 3

Suppose the machine referred to in Example 9.14 has no salvage value after 5 years of use. (a) Should the machine be bought? Apply the half-year rule.

(b) On the assumption that the half-year rule does not apply, find after-tax present worth.

SOLUTION 3

(a) The half-year rule applies and therefore the tax shields due to straight-line CCA are 25 percent, 50 percent, and 25 percent in year 1, year 2, and year 3, respectively.

The PW of CCA tax shields for $1 invested in Class 29 is: PW of CCA tax shields = (PW of year 1 shield) + (PW of year 2 shield) + (PW of year 3 shield) = $t(0.5)d[1/(1 + i) + 2/(1 + i)^2 + 1/(1 + i)^3] = t(0.5)d(1 + i)(P/A,i,2)^2$

The CCTF then becomes

$$\text{CCTF} = 1 - t(0.5)d(1 + i)(P/A,i,2)^2$$

After-tax PW = $(-\$45,000)(\text{CCTF}) + (1 - 0.42)(\$15,700)(P/A,i,5)$
= $-\$29,886 + \$32,824 = \$2938$

(b) Since the half-year rule does not apply, the present worth of tax shields = (PW of year 1 shield) + (PW of year 2 shield) = $td[1/(1 + i) + 1/(1 + i)^2] = td(P/A,i,2)$

The CCTF then becomes

$$\text{CCTF} = 1 - td(P/A,i,2)$$

The after-tax PW for this example is

$$\text{PW}_{\text{after-tax}} = (-\$45,000)(\text{CCTF}) + \$32,824$$
$$= (-\$45,000)[1 - (0.42)(0.5)(1.6900)] + \$32,824$$
$$= -\$29,029 + \$32,824 = \$3795$$

In this case the stimulative effect of accelerated CCA is higher than in part (a). In part (a) the half-year rule reduces the PW by $3795 − $2938 = $857. The percentage reduction in the incentive is $857/$4158 = 20.6 percent.

EXERCISE 4

A machine has UCC of $10,000 at the beginning of 1996 and 5 years remaining on its originally estimated useful life. Its operating costs are $19,000 per year. The function performed by the machine will be needed for 5 more years, at which time it will have a salvage value of $1000. The market value of this machine is only $8000.

A new machine of advanced design can perform the same function as the existing machine for $12,000 per year. This machine is priced at $24,000 and will have a salvage value of $6000 after 5 years of use.

The company has a 52 percent effective tax rate. It requires an after-tax rate of return of 20 percent. Both machines are in Class 8. Should the old machine be replaced?

SOLUTION 4

The defender's capital cost for the replacement study is its current salvage (market) value, $8000, and this amount is considered to be an outlay at time zero.

The incremental after-tax PW of replacing the old machine is

Incremental PW = (First cost of challenger − Current salvage value of
(after-tax)   defender)(CCTF based on half-year rule)
        + $(1 − t)$(Before-tax operating savings)$(P/A,i,N)$
        + $(P/F,i,N)$(Incremental salvage value)(CCTF based on
        full-year rule)

$$= -(\$24{,}000 - \$8000)\{1 - [td/(i + d)][(1 + (0.5)i)/(1 + i)]\}$$
$$+ (1 - 0.52)(\$19{,}000 - \$12{,}000)(P/A,0.2,5)$$
$$+ (P/F,0.2,5)(\$6000 - \$1000)[1 - td/(i + d)]$$
$$= -(\$16{,}000)\{1 - [(0.52)(0.2)/(0.2 + 0.2)][(1 + 0.1)/(1 + 0.2)]\}$$
$$+ (0.48)(\$7000)(2.9906)$$
$$+ (0.40188)(\$5000)[1 - (0.52)(0.2)/(0.2 + 0.2)]$$
$$= -\$12{,}187 + \$10{,}048 + \$1487$$
$$= -\$652$$

Thus, the correct decision is *not* to replace the machine.

EXERCISE 5
A new system is to be purchased for $110,000. Annual revenues from this operation are expected to be $110,000, while it's annual expenses covering labor, materials, and other expenses are estimated to be $50,000. This system falls in Class 8 with a declining balance CCA rate of 20 percent. A salvage of $48,000 can be expected after 5 years. Find the year-by-year, after-tax cash flow at 40 percent tax rate. Also, find the net present worth at MARR of 15 percent (after tax).

SOLUTION 5
The net income per year = annual revenue − annual expenses = $110,000 − $50,000 = $60,000. This yearly amount is shown as a before-tax cash flow.

Year (1)	Before-tax cash flow (2)	Depreciation CCA (5)	Taxable income (9)	Income tax (10)	After-tax cash flow (11)
0	−$125,000				−$125,000
1	60,000	$12,500	$47,500	$19,000	41,000
2	60,000	22,500	37,500	15,000	45,000
3	60,000	18,000	42,000	16,800	43,200
4	60,000	14,400	45,600	18,240	41,760
5	60,000	11,520	48,480	19,392	40,608
5	+48,000 (Salvage)				48,000
5	Disposal tax effect				−768

The CCA values are calculated at a 20 percent rate, except for year 1. The half-year rule is applied to the year 1 CCA calculation.

The total CCA for years 1–5 is: $12,500 + $22,500 + $18,000 + $14,400 + $11,520 = $78,920.

The book value at the end of year 5 is the purchase cost minus the total CCA, or $125,000 − $78,920 = $46,080.

Since the salvage value of $48,000 is higher than book value of $46,080, CCA recapture is applicable.

The disposal tax effect due to CCA recapture is ($46,080 − $48,000)(0.4) = −$768.00.

In year 5 we show the salvage as a positive value and disposal tax effect as a negative cash item.

$$\text{The NPW at MARR of 15\%} = -\$125,000 + \$41,000(P/F,15\%,1)$$
$$+ \$45,000(P/F,15\%,2) + \$43,200(P/F,15\%,3)$$
$$+ \$41,760(P/F,15\%,4) + (\$40,608 + \$48,000$$
$$- \$768)(P/F,15\%,5) = \$40,632.10$$

EXERCISE 6

For any year, a negative taxable income can result due to low income. In such a case, a negative taxable income from one part of a corporation's activities can be used to reduce the taxable income from other business operations. In the event that the company has no other taxable income in the current tax year, the tax regulations permit that the operating loss can be carried back to each of the preceding 3 years and forward for the following 7 years in order to offset taxable income of those years. Therefore, according to these provisions of the tax regulations, a negative taxable income may result in a tax saving.

As for the use of the tax rate in the evaluation of an investment project, it is frequently assumed that a negative taxable income does not warrant a change in the tax rate since firms have sufficient taxable incomes from other activities.

In Exercise 5 assume that the annual revenues are projected to be $70,000 instead of $110,000. This will change the after-tax cash flow.

SOLUTION 6

Year (1)	Before-tax cash flow (2)	Depreciation CCA (5)	Taxable income (9)	Income tax (10)	After-tax cash flow (11)
0	−$125,000				−$125,000
1	20,000	$12,500	$7,500	$3,000	17,000
2	20,000	22,500	−2,500	−1,000[†]	21,000
3	20,000	18,000	2,000	800	19,200
4	20,000	14,400	5,600	2,240	17,760
5	20,000	11,520	8,480	3,392	16,608
5	48,000 (Salvage)				48,000
5	Disposal tax effect				−768

[†] Tax savings

In the context of this example with reduced annual revenue, the taxable income in year 2 becomes negative. The tax effects and consequently the net cash flow are illustrated above. These computations are based on the assumption that the firm has other positive cash flow so that such incomes can more than offset the negative values for this project and that the company's incremental tax rate still remains at 40 percent.

EXERCISE 7

As noted earlier, corporations frequently borrow money and use such debt capital in conjunction with their equity capital to finance investments in their physical plant and equipment. The debt/equity ratio, represents the percentage of total initial investments made with borrowed funds. Companies with stable income and high tax rates may enhance their return on equity capital through this mechanism given that interest is a tax-deductible expense. It should be noted that the method of loan repayment can also have a significant tax effect.

A firm with an effective income tax rate of 42 percent is considering the purchase of a new machine for $45,000. For the purchase of this new machine, a $20,000 loan will be required at 8 percent interest. The terms of the loan call for equal annual payments for 5 years, covering principal plus interest. The useful life of the machine is 5 years and the minimum attractive rate of return is 8 percent (after tax). Expected salvage is zero. Income estimated to result from machine = $23,000/year and annual operating expenses = $7,300/year. The machine is classified as Class 8 (20 percent CCA rate, declining-balance class). Find the net present worth of this investment.

SOLUTION 7

This problem is in essence the same as Example 9.17 except that the method of debt repayment, interest on debt and the minimum attractive rate of return are different. In the previous example, the principal was paid at the end of the fifth year whereas here both principal and interest are to be paid from years 1 to 5.

In developing this solution, the approach used is based on the use of tax shield (i.e., the capital cost tax factor). Therefore, in the calculation of the after-tax cash flow, tax saving due to CCA allowance is not included. The tax shield is added at the time of calculating the net present worth of the investment.

Loan repayment (in equal annual amounts) = $20,000 (A/P,8%,5) = $5,009.20

Interest payments:

Year 1: $20,000(0.08) = $1,600.00

Year 2: [$20,000 − ($5,009.20 − $1,600)](0.08) = ($16,590.80)(0.08)
= $1,327.26

Year 3: [$16,590.80 − ($5,009.20 − $1,327.26)](0.08) = ($12,908.86)(0.08)
= $1,032.71

Year 4: [$12,908.86 − ($5,009.20 − $1,032.71)](0.08) = ($8,932.37)(0.08)
= $714.59

Year 5: [$8932.37 − ($5,009.20 − $714.59)](0.08) = $371.02

Year (1)	Before-tax cash flow (2)	Loan repayment (7)	Interest (8)	Taxable income (9)	Income tax (10)	ATCF (without CCA) (11)
0	−$45,000					−$45,000.00
	+20,000					20,000.00
1	15,700	$5,009.20	$1,600.00	$14,100.00	$5,922.00	4,768.80
2	15,700	5,009.20	1,327.26	14,372.74	6,036.55	4,654.25
3	15,700	5,009.20	1,032.71	14,667.29	6,160.26	4,530.54
4	15,700	5,009.20	714.59	14,985.41	6,293.87	4,396.93
5	15,700	5,009.20	371.02	15,328.98	6,438.17	4,252.63

Tax savings due to capital cost allowance can be found from the use of:

$$\text{Tax shield (half-year rule)} = \left[\frac{td}{i+d}\right]\left[\left(1 + \frac{1}{2}i\right)\left(\frac{1}{1+i}\right)\right] = 0.2889$$

Capital cost tax factor $= 1 - 0.2889 = 0.7111$

Net present worth of project $= -\$45,000(0.7111) + \$20,000 +$
$\$4,768.80(P/F,8\%,1) + \$4,654.25(P/F,8\%,2) +$
$\$4,530.54(P/F,8\%,3) + \$4,396.93(P/F,8\%,4) +$
$\$4,252.63(P/F,8\%,5)$
$= \$6,129.00$

EXERCISE 8

An investor is interested in acquiring a machine classified as Class 10 (CCA 30 percent, declining-balance class). The capital cost of this asset is $56,000. The estimated useful life of this asset is 7 years and zero salvage value is expected. The expected annual before-tax net income is estimated to be $13,500/year. The tax rate for the business is 45 percent. Assume that cash flows occur at the end of the year. It is of interest to find (a) IRR before tax, (b) approximate IRR after tax, and (c) IRR after tax.

SOLUTION 8

(a) For finding the IRR before tax, we set the NPW = 0.

$$\text{NPW} = -\$56,000 + \$13,500(P/A,i,7 \text{ years}) = 0$$

$$(P/A,i,7) = 4.1481$$

By interpolation we find,

$$\text{IRR} = 15\% + 5\% \, [(4.1604 - 4.1481)/(4.1604 - 3.6045)]$$
$$= 15.1\%$$

(b) Approximate IRR before tax (1 − effective tax rate) = 15.1 (1 − 0.45) = 8.3%.

(c) The after-tax IRR can be found by using the tax shield method (based on half-year rule). Here, $t = 0.45$, $d = 0.3$.

$$\text{Tax shield (half-year rule)} = \left[\frac{td}{i+d}\right]\left[\left(1 + \frac{1}{2}i\right)\left(\frac{1}{1+i}\right)\right] = 0.33186$$

$$\text{NPW} = (-\$56,000)(1 - \text{tax shield}) + (\$13,500)(1 - t)(P/A,i,7 \text{ years})$$

Note: Salvage is zero.
Try $i = 9\%$.

$$\text{NPW} = (-\$56,000)(1 - 0.33186) + \$37,369 = -\$47$$

After further calculations, IRR after tax is found to be 8.97 percent.

EXERCISE 9

A portable electric generator is needed for 3 years. The CCA rate is 20 percent (declining-balance class). The initial purchase price is $460,000. Expected salvage after 3 years (sale price) is $100,000. The before-tax annual net income or (annual revenue − annual costs) is $250,000/year. The after-tax minimum attractive rate of return (MARR) is 15 percent. The effective income tax rate is 54 percent. Find the present worth of after-tax cash flow.

SOLUTION 9

This problem can be solved according to two approaches. The first approach is that of finding the CCA allowance on a year by year basis. The second approach is to use the tax shield. According to the first method, we have to find CCA based on the half-year rule.

$$\text{CCA for year 1} = \text{purchase price} \times 50\% \text{ of CCA rate} = \$460,000(0.2/2) = \$46,000$$

$$\text{CCA for year 2} = \text{Book value} \times \text{CCA rate} = (\$460,000 - \$46,000)(0.2) = \$82,800$$

$$\text{Year 3} = [\$460,000 - (\$46,000 + \$82,800)](0.2) = \$66,240$$

Sum of depreciation for years 1 to 3 = $195,040

$$\text{Book value at the end of year 3} = \text{undepreciated capital cost (UCC)}$$
$$= \$460,000 - \$195,040 = \$264,960$$

Since (book value − salvage or sale price) is greater than 0, tax shield adjustment can be claimed.

$$\text{Tax shield adjustment} = (\text{book value} - \text{salvage})\left(\frac{td}{i+d}\right)$$

where

t = tax rate
d = depreciation rate (CCA)

Tax shield adjustment = ($264,960 - $100,000)$\left(\dfrac{0.54 \times 0.2}{0.15 + 0.2} \right)$

PW of tax shield adjustment = $(P/F,15\%,3 \text{ years}) \times$ (tax shield adjustment)
= $33,469.05

Year (1)	Before-tax cash flow (2)	CCA (5)	Taxable income (9)	Taxes @54% (10)	After-tax cash flow (11)
0	-$460,000.00				-$460,000.00
1	250,000.00	$46,000.00	$204,000.00	$110,160.00	139,840.00
2	250,000.00	82,800.00	167,200.00	90,288.00	159,712.00
3	250,000.00	66,240.00	183,760.00	99,230.40	150,769.60
3	100,000.00 (Salvage)				100,000.00

Note: Taxable income = Before-tax cash flow − CCA

NPW @15% after tax = −$460,000 + ($139,840)$(P/F,15\%,1 \text{ year})$
+ ($159,712)$(P/F,15\%,2 \text{ year})$
+ ($150,769.60)$(P/F,15\%,3 \text{ year})$
+ ($100,000)$(P/F,15\%,3 \text{ year})$
+ PW of tax shield adjustment
= −$19,279.62 (not feasible)

Since the net present worth of this investment is negative, it is not feasible.

In the second approach, instead of applying CCA on a year by year basis, we can apply tax shield (based on half-year-rule) to the investment. Now the amount of proceeds from disposition of the asset (salvage) that the investor will retain can be found from the use of tax shield based on full-year rule.

Here t = 54% or 0.54, d = CCA rate of 20% or 0.2, and i = 15% or 0.15

Tax shield (half-year rule) = $\left(\dfrac{td}{i + d} \right) \left[\left(1 + \dfrac{1}{2}i \right) \left(\dfrac{1}{1 + i} \right) \right]$ = 0.28845

Note: Out of $1 invested, $0.288 is tax shield and therefore 1 − 0.288 = $ 0.712 is the actual cost incurred by the investor.

Tax shield (full year) = $\left(\dfrac{td}{i + d} \right)$ = 0.309

Note: Out of $1 of salvage money, $0.309 is tax and ($1 − $0.309) = $ 0.691 is retained after tax by the investor.

Now NPW @ 15% = −($460,000 of investment)(1 − tax shield based on
half-year-rule) + (1 − tax rate) ($250,000) $(P/A,15\%,3)$ +
$(P/F,15\%,3)$($100,000 salvage)(1 − tax shield)
= −($460,000 of investment)(0.712) + (1 − 0.54) ($250,000)
$(P/A,15\%,3)$ + $(P/F,15\%,3)$($100,000 salvage)(0.691)
= −$19,517.37 (not feasible)

Note that the minor difference between answers obtained from the two approaches
is due to the approximate nature of the tax shield equation.

9.10   PROBLEMS

9.1 A company is considering the purchase of a new piece of Class 8 equipment
for $30,000. The estimated revenue/year is $15,000 for 5 years. Salvage value after
5 years is expected to be $2,500. Maintenance cost is estimated to be $1,400 for first
year and to increase by $200/year. Effective tax rate is 40 percent and MARR is 10
percent (after tax). Find the net present worth of the proposed investment. Assume
that the half-year rule is applicable.

9.2 A machine in Class 8 (CCA rate = 20 percent declining-balance class) was
bought 5 years ago for $50,000. The resale price for this machine is also $50,000.
Effective tax rate is 42 percent. Capital gains are taxable at 1/2(effective tax rate).
Find tax effects of this resale of equipment. Assume that the half-year rule is
applicable.

9.3 An asset cost $400 when purchased 4 years ago. A scrap value of $50 was
expected at the end of its 7-year useful life. The asset is in Class 7. Determine the
depreciation charge during the coming year and the asset's current book value by:
(a) Straight-line depreciation
(b) Declining-balance depreciation

9.4 A production machine with a first cost of $2000 is expected to last 4 years,
when it will be worth $200. Tabulate the book value at the end of each year by the
declining-balance method of depreciation, if the machine is in Class 8.

9.5 An asset has an initial cost of $65,000 and an estimated salvage value of
$5000 after 12 years.
(a) What depreciation rate for the declining-balance method would produce a
book value at the end of year 12 that comes closest to equalling the estimated salvage value?
(b) What is the amount of accumulated depreciation after 5 years if straight-
line depreciation is used?
(c) If the declining-balance depreciation rate is 10 percent, what would the
book value be after 3 years?

9.6 An asset with a life of 7 years was purchased 4 years ago at a cost of $10,000.
It now has a book value of $5,200 based on straight-line depreciation. What is its
expected salvage value?

9.7 Three corporations have the following data for one year of operation:

	Macro, Inc. (Blubber Bay, B.C.)	Meso Ltd. (Whiskey Gap, Alta.)	Micro Co. (Come-By-Chance, Nfld.)
Sales	$20,000,000	$2,000,000	$200,000
Expenses	15,250,000	1,000,000	140,000
Other revenue	750,000	250,000	50,000
CCA	1,000,000	750,000	60,000

What is the effective income-tax rate for each corporation?

9.8 A corporation has an effective tax rate of 54 percent. Gross revenue for the past year was $8 million. Operating expenses and CCA accounted for $6 million. Interest on outstanding debts was $1.2 million. What amount is left for dividends and surplus after taxes?

The following basic data pertain to a proposal that is analyzed according to the conditions and objectives of Problems 9.9 through 9.12.

A proposed investment in Class 10 is expected to produce annual before-tax savings of $13,500. The asset has a first cost of $56,000 and an estimated useful life of 7 years with no salvage value. The effective income tax rate of the organization is 45 percent. Unless otherwise stated, it is assumed all cash flows occur at the end of a year, and any deductions beyond the $13,500 savings can be applied against other income.

9.9 What is the before-tax internal rate of return for the asset described in the basic data? Determine the approximate after-tax IRR from the before-tax figures.

9.10 Compute the after-tax internal rate of return if the asset is purchased now?

9.11 A 10 percent investment tax credit is allowed on the asset's purchase price and is taken on the first year's income. The first cost must be reduced by the ITC. What is the after-tax IRR?

9.12 If the purchase of the asset could be considered an operating expense instead of a depreciable investment, what would be the after-tax internal rate of return? Assume there is sufficient income to charge the entire amount in the first year. The savings from the purchase of the asset will still continue for 7 years.

9.13 A sales representative made an agreement to purchase a building lot by making six annual payments of $9000 each. She was then transferred to a different territory before she could build a home. When she returned 2 years later, she found she could buy an equivalent lot for $30,000 because land values had decreased during her absence. She now feels that she will lose the $18,000 she has already paid if she drops her contract to buy the equivalent lot. Assuming that she will suffer no penalty for reneging on the original contract, discuss the "sunk cost" concept as it applies to the situation. What would you advise her to do? Does the assumption that she can invest her savings at 7 percent have any bearing on the situation?

9.14 Rimrock Construction Co. is purchasing a new piece of equipment in Class 8 for $340,000. The unit is expected to produce annual revenue of $210,000 for each of the next 4 years and will be sold at the end of that time for an expected salvage value of $40,000. Maintenance expenses on the equipment are expected to be $20,000 for the first year and to increase by $5000 per year for each successive year of operation. The company has an effective tax rate of 40 percent and requires an after-tax MARR of 10 percent. What is the present worth of the proposed purchase?

9.15 An aircraft assembly fixture classified as Class 43 (CCA of 30 percent declining balance) has a purchase price of $90,000. Use of this fixture is expected to result in an annual before-tax savings of $30,000 for a period of 6 years, at the end of which time it will be obsolete and virtually worthless. Determine:

    (a) The before-tax present worth of the investment at an interest rate of 20 percent.

    (b) The after-tax present worth of the investment with an effective tax rate of 40 percent and an interest rate of 15 percent.

9.16 Amdex Company purchased three utility vans (declining-balance Class 10 with CCA rate of 30 percent) for $18,000 in the month of March 3 years ago. One van was sold in the month of November last year, but the others will be retained until the month of March 3 years from now. Determine the deductions allowed for each year from the year of purchase to the final year of service.

9.17 Megabit Electronics purchased a new logic test unit for its microprocessor research laboratory 2 years ago. The equipment cost $60,000 and is expected to have an economic life of 8 years. Assume that this asset qualifies for a CCA rate of 30 percent (declining balance). If the tax rate is 40 percent, expected salvage is zero, and the after-tax rate of return is 10 percent, determine the tax effect of this equipment on a yearly basis and in terms of present worth.

9.18 An outmoded paper machine was purchased for $300,000 some 12 years ago. Its annual operating costs are $48,000. It is expected to last 8 more years, at which time it will have zero salvage. A newer model of the paper machine will cost $470,000 and will have an economic life of 15 years. Following a service period of 8 years, assume that the new machine will have a market value equal to its book value. The new machine is expected to have average operating costs of $30,000 per year. The CCA for these machines is 25 percent (declining balance). The required rate of return is 10 percent, and the effective tax rate is 40 percent.

    (a) Assuming that the old machine has a market value equal to its book value, what is its after-tax EAC?

    (b) What is the after-tax EAC of the challenger?

9.19 An investment proposal is expected to have the following characteristics:

	Year 1	Year 2	Year 3
Gross income provided, ($)	17,000	22,000	19,000
Investment needed, ($)	16,000	14,000	0
Operating expenses, ($)	6,000	8,000	11,000
Depreciation charges, ($)	10,000	10,000	10,000

Investments occur during the year and allow the indicated earnings, but both the income and investments are considered to have been made at the end of each year for analysis purposes. In any year in which deductions exceed income, the tax benefits can be considered as additional income because the organization can apply the deductions against income earned from other operations.

    (a)   Determine the rate of return before taxes.

    (b)   If the effective income tax rate is 42 percent, what is the approximate after-tax rate of return?

    (c)   What is the actual after-tax rate of return?

9.20 An asset purchased for $100,000 will have a salvage value of $20,000 at the end of its 6-year economic life. Net earnings attributable to the asset are $32,000 per year. Assuming that it was purchased with equity funds and the corporation has an effective tax rate of 40 percent, determine the after-tax IRR resulting from the use of a declining balance CCA rate of 30 percent.

9.21 A new piece of chemical processing equipment was purchased in 1982 at a cost of $450,000. Its economic life was estimated to be 15 years and depreciation was calculated according to the declining-balance method and a CCA rate of 20 percent. Annual before-tax net operating income from the equipment was $75,000, and it was shut down in 1996. Surprisingly, the equipment was sold for a $60,000 value.

    Using an effective tax rate of 40 percent and a MARR of 15 percent, determine the equivalent after-tax annual worth of the equipment over its service life.

9.22 A consulting engineer in acoustical design has purchased and equipped a mobile sound laboratory at a cost of $50,000. She borrowed $30,000 on a 3-year contract at 10 percent interest compounded annually, with the loan to be repaid in three equal end-of-year installments. Her average annual gross income over the next 6 years is expected to be $100,000, and expenses are expected to be $30,000 annually. The sound laboratory can be depreciated as declining-balance 25 percent CCA rate property. The salvage value at the end of 6 years is expected to be $10,000. Determine the present worth of the engineer's net after-tax income for the 6 years, using a MARR of 15 percent and an effective tax rate of 35 percent.

EXTENSION 9A   DEPRECIATION AND INCOME TAXES IN THE U.S.A.

9A.1 Introduction

The definitions of terms used in the U.S. practice of depreciation and income tax analyses conform to those in the Internal Revenue Service (IRS) Publication 534, *Depreciation*. Over the years, there have been three distinct systems of establishing *depreciation rates* or charges. These systems are somewhat different in concept but have a common link through the *straight-line method* and the *declining-balance method* of computing depreciation charges.

    Depreciation methods used for property placed in service *before 1981* were based on the useful life of an asset. For most assets, these were defined by the IRS through the use of the class life asset depreciation range (CLADR) system. For all assets placed in service from 1981 through 1986, the *accelerated cost recovery system* (ACRS) applied. A *recovery period*, as used in ACRS depreciation accounting, is the increment of years over which the unadjusted basis is recovered according to an asset's assigned property class. The unadjusted basis for recovery is essentially the first cost of the property plus additional investments associated with preparation and installation.

9A.2   Modified Accelerated Cost Recovery System (MACRS): U.S.A.

The Tax Reform Act (TRA) of 1986 combined with the Economic Recovery Act of 1981 produced the most sweeping changes in the U.S. federal tax code since World War II. MACRS is the method prescribed by the TRA of 1986 for the depreciation of all property placed in service after 1986. MACRS is the U.S. equivalent of CCA. It replaced the previous ACRS in 1987. *MACRS recovery property*, as defined for the MACRS, is depreciable tangible property used in trade or business or held for production of income. MACRS provides two subsystems for depreciating property. The main subsystem is called the general depreciation system (GDS), and applies to most property. The second subsystem is called the alternative depreciation system (ADS). In general, ADS rules must be used only for assets used outside the United States, property used in farming, and property used in some tax-exempt manner such as being financed through tax-exempt bonds.

MACRS places assets into classes, each of which has a recovery period of class life, as follows:

- 3-year property includes specially designated tools and devices, and tractor units. It has a CLADR of 4 years or less. This property will be fully depreciated (book value reduced to zero) over a 4-year period.
- 5-year property (with CLADR of more than 4 years but less than 10 years) includes autos, trucks, computers, typewriters, copiers, and other designated equipment. This property will be fully depreciated over a 6-year period.
- 7-year property includes all other items of machinery and equipment, office furniture, and fixtures. The CLADR of this class is at least 10 years but less than 16 years (approximately equivalent to the Canadian CCA Class 8). This property will be fully depreciated over an 8-year period.
- 10-year property with a CLADR of at least 16 years but less than 20 years, includes certain longer lived types of equipment. This property will be fully depreciated over an 11-year period.
- 15-year property includes industrial steam and electric generation equipment, telephone distribution and switching gear, pipeline and conveyor systems, various energy conversion systems, and depreciable improvements made directly to land or added to it, such as roads and bridges. This type of property has a CLADR of at least 20 years but less than 25 years and will be fully depreciated over a 16-year period.

- 20-year property has a CLADR of 25 years or more. Examples include dams, flumes, canals, water treatment and distribution systems, electric power transmission poles and lines, and most farm buildings. This property will be fully depreciated over a 21-year period.

In general, all property in the above classes is treated as though it were purchased in the middle of the year in which it is first placed in use. This is referred to as a *midyear convention*. Therefore, only half of the allowable depreciation charge is permitted for the first year of use. All succeeding years of use are allowed a full year's depreciation charge based on the class of life (N = 3,5,7,10,15, or 20) of the asset. Any book value remaining after the class life has been reached will be recovered by a depreciation charge in the next year (N+1).

The two remaining property classes require the use of a *midmonth convention*. This is similar to the midyear convention except that the month when the asset is placed is the key element. All remaining months of the first year of use receive a full depreciation charge.

- 27.5-year (residential rental) property includes any real property or structure that is rented as a dwelling unit. In order to qualify, 80 percent of the gross rental income must be derived from providing nontransient living accommodations. The recovery period for this property is 27.5 years.
- 31.5-year (nonresidential real) property includes all property of this type such as commercial and industrial buildings. The recovery period for this property is 31.5 years for property placed in service before May 13, 1993, and 39 years for property placed in service after May 13, 1993. The engineer evaluating the acquisition of any manufacturing facility would be concerned with this class.

Each MACRS asset class has a preset table of allowable annual depreciation deductions that are based on a percentage of the asset's first cost. Like the CCA system, MACRS also has a half-year convention for the first year of the asset's useful life. This half-year convention effectively extends the recovery period for an additional year.

Table 9A.1 indicates the MACRS rates for the four most important, non real estate, classes of assets. The yearly depreciation deduction, or recovery allowance, is determined by multiplying the asset's depreciable basis by the applicable recovery percentage, as shown in Table 9A.1. The depreciable basis is not adjusted for salvage value and is approximately equivalent to the depreciable base used in the CCA system, since both are based on generally accepted accounting principles (GAAP).

If a depreciable asset is sold, the sale price (realized salvage value) less any existing undepreciated capital cost (book value) is added to the operating income of the year and taxed at the marginal tax rate.

Notice that the U.S. system, unlike the Canadian one, allows for the entire cost of the asset to be written off during its life.

TABLE 9A.1

Recovery percentages allowed by IRS for property placed in service after 1986 for MACRS 3-,5-,7-,10,15-, and 20-year property classes

Year	Category of property					
	3-Year	**5-Year**	**7-Year**	**10-Year**	**15-year**	**20-year**
1	33.33	20.00	14.29	10.00	5.00	3.750
2	44.45	32.00	24.49	18.00	9.50	7.219
3	14.81	19.20	17.49	14.40	8.55	6.677
4	7.41	11.52	12.49	11.52	7.70	6.177
5		11.52	8.93	9.22	6.93	5.713
6		5.76	8.92	7.37	6.23	5.285
7			8.93	6.55	5.90	4.888
8			4.46	6.55	5.90	4.522
9				6.56	5.91	4.462
10				6.55	5.90	4.461
11				3.28	5.91	4.462
12					5.90	4.461
13					5.91	4.462
14					5.90	4.461
15					5.91	4.462
16					2.95	4.461
17						4.462
18						4.461
19						4.462
20						4.461
21						2.231

As discussed in Extension 9B, the Mexican system, which is important for engineers now that the North American Free Trade Agreement (NAFTA) is in force, also allows for rapid write-offs of the entire cost of depreciable assets.

9A.3 Depreciation Methods: U.S.A.

Under the general depreciation system for MACRS, property in the 3-, 5-, 7-, or 10-year class is depreciated by the 200 percent declining-balance method. Property in the 15- and 20-year classes is depreciated by the 150 percent declining-balance method.

For all these classes of property, the first-year deduction is based on a half-year service period (midyear convention). The annual depreciation amounts are then based on the appropriate declining-balance rate until they are changed to the straight-line method in the first tax year for which the change will yield a larger deduction. The alternative depreciation system of MACRS provides for 150 percent declining-balance depreciation for these same classes of property over a longer recovery period at the election of the taxpayer. In addition, an alternate straight-line depreciation schedule (using GDS or ADS recovery periods) with a midyear convention may also be elected over the entire recovery period. Care must be taken, however, as this election must be applied to all items in a specific property class.

Once the alternate method is selected for a property class, all similarly classified property placed in service during that tax year must be depreciated in the same manner. It is also not possible to switch from the straight-line method to the declining-balance system once the straight-line option has been selected.

All nonresidential real property and all residential rental property are depreciated by a straight-line depreciation schedule. A salvage value of zero is assumed for all property classes under both the GDS and ADS methods. Care must be taken that the book value of an asset is not reduced below a reasonable estimate of its actual salvage value, regardless of the method used for depreciation.

9A.4 Corporate Income Taxes: U.S.A.

Ordinary domestic corporations are subject to the tax rate shown in Table 9A.2. These rates are progressive, since in general the lower rates apply to the lower increments of taxable income, becoming progressively higher with larger incomes. However, these rates are scaled in such a way that once a corporation's taxable income exceeds \$335,000 (and remains less than \$10,000,000), the corporation's total tax rate is 34 percent of its total taxable income.

Most states and some cities also impose a corporate income tax. The federal and state taxes can be merged into a combined marginal income tax rate (also referred to as the effective composite tax rate or simply effective tax rate) that represents the total corporate tax liability for its current level of operations.

Combined marginal tax rate = state marginal tax rate + (1 − state marginal rate)(marginal federal rate)

Currently there are no large, general investment credits allowed for corporations. However, a reinstitution of the credit has been seriously proposed in recent years.

Taxpayers in the U.S.A. were permitted by Section 179 of the 1981 Tax Act to treat the cost of certain qualifying property as an expense rather

TABLE 9A.2

Marginal tax rates (tax on each additional taxable dollar) for corporations

If taxable income is		The corporate tax rate is		
Over	**But not over**	**This amount** +	**This percentage**	**of income over**
$0	$50,000		15%	$0
50,000	75,000	$7,500	25%	50,000
75,000	100,000	13,750	34%	75,000
100,000	335,000	22,250	39%	100,000
335,000	10,000,000	113,900	34%	335,000
10,000,000	15,000,000	3,400,000	35%	10,000,000
15,000,000	18,333,333	5,150,000	38%	15,000,000
18,333,333		35% of all taxable income		

than as a capital expenditure. A modified version of this is continued in the 1986 Tax Reform Act (U.S.A.). For property placed in service after 1986, the maximum cost of trade or business property that may be "expensed" in any year is $17,500. The $17,500 limit is valid until the total investment in property reaches $200,000. From that point, the $17,500 maximum is reduced by $1 for each additional dollar of investment. When total investment in Section 179 property is $217,500 or more, there is no deduction available for that tax year. This limit primarily restricts the usefulness of the provision to small businesses.

The calculation of capital gains and losses is very complex because there are so many special provisions. The tax rate assigned to capital gains usually is less than that for ordinary income. This preferential rate is allowed in recognition of the risk involved in holding capital assets over a prolonged period.

Tax offsets allowed in the current year that exceed the year's income can be applied to previous and future years' incomes. This occurs when a major loss is sustained and/or allowable deductions are unusually large. In general, ordinary income losses can be carried back to the 3 preceding years and carried over to the 15 succeeding years.

9A.5 Personal Income Taxes: U.S.A.

In 1991, it was estimated that 97.8 percent of all businesses in the United States were small (defined as less than 100 employees). A great many of these businesses are sole proprietorships or partnerships. The income of

TABLE 9A.3

Federal tax rate schedule for single taxpayers—Schedule X

If taxable income is		The tax is			
Over	**But not over**	**This amount**	**+**	**This percentage**	**Of the amount over**
$0	$22,100			15%	$0
22,100	53,500	$3,315		28%	22,100
53,500	115,000	12,107		31%	53,500
115,000	250,000	31,172		36%	115,000
250,000		79,772		39.6%	250,000

these businesses is taxed as individual or personal rather than corporate income. Most of the approach to analysis presented in this extension (MACRS depreciation, capital gains and losses, Section 179, etc.) applies equally to individuals and to corporations. However, there is a principal difference in the applicable tax rates that pertain.

Table 9A.3 shows how federal income tax rates climb with rising income levels for a single taxpayer. Taxable income is the taxpayer's adjusted gross income minus standard exemptions and itemized deductions. Due to the diversity of tax laws among different states and municipalities, income taxes other than owed to the federal government are not covered here.

EXTENSION 9B   **DEPRECIATION AND CORPORATE INCOME TAXES IN MEXICO**[†‡§]

9B.1   Depreciation

Tangible fixed assets are depreciated according to the straight-line method. Also, intangible assets are amortized according to the straight-line method. The following are the maximum annual depreciation rates for selected assets for 1994:

[†]J.L. Nolan, A. Woznick, W. LeGro, D.C. Alexander, K.C. Shippey, E.G. Hinkelman, H.I. Vera, and M.F. Pasero, *Mexico Business, The Portable Encyclopedia for Doing Business With Mexico*, World Trade Press, San Rafael, California, U.S.A., 1994.
[‡]Ernst & Young, *Worldwide Corporate Tax Guide*, 1994 Edition.
[§]Coopers & Lybrand, *International Tax Networks, 1995, International Tax Summaries, A Guide for Planning and Decisions*, J. Wiley, Toronto/New York, 1995.

TABLE 9B.1

Assets and depreciation rates (1994) (straight-line method)

Asset	Rate (%)
Buildings	5
Motor vehicles	25
Office equipment	10
Computers	
Mainframe equipment	25
Peripheral equipment	12
Plant and machinery	10
Environmental machinery and equipment	50

The tax law requires that depreciation must be determined according to the annual percentages prescribed by law. The depreciation of new assets has to be calculated on a proportional basis, depending upon the months in which the assets are used. The original cost of fixed assets is the basis of calculating depreciation. The magnitude of depreciation is indexed for inflation as measured by price indices.

For certain assets, businesses may elect the option of taking an immediate deduction for a percentage of the original purchase price rather than claiming depreciation based on the useful lives of assets.

9B.2 Corporate Income Taxes

Corporations resident in Mexico have to pay taxes on their worldwide income earned from all sources. Likewise a nonresident corporation in Mexico is also subject to profits tax on business income earned in Mexico. For corporations to be considered as residents of Mexico, they have to be established under Mexican law. The fiscal year consists of 12 months and always ends on December 31. A three-month time lag is permitted for filing tax returns. The income tax is to be paid in monthly installments, with an adjustment of the installment at the mid-year point.

In Mexico, corporations are taxed only by the federal government. According to Mexico's general system of taxation, a corporation's earnings for a given fiscal year are taxed only once in that fiscal year. Corporate tax rates are shown in Table 9B.2. In 1994, corporate taxable income was subject to federal corporate income tax of 34 percent. The branch tax rate shown in Table 9B.2 is applicable to a Mexican branch plant of a non-Mexican firm.

TABLE 9B.2

Corporate Taxation[††]

Corporate income tax rate (%)	34
Capital gains tax rate (%)	34
Branch tax rate (%)	34
Net operating losses (years)	
Carryback	0
Carryforward	5**

**If the loss is also incurred for accounting purposes, it may be carried forward for an additional 5 years.

Taxable income and profits/loss are calculated according to generally accepted accounting principles. For exceptions, see Nolan et al. 1994[†]. The Mexican tax law permits business losses to be carried forward up to 5 years. Although some limitations apply, the 5-year period may be extended for an additional 5 years if a loss was also incurred for accounting purposes.

The effect of inflation on the following items and transactions is recognized by the income tax law:

- Depreciation of fixed assets
- Cost on sales of fixed assets
- Sale of capital stock (shares)
- Monetary gains and losses
- Tax loss carryforward

A minimum tax on net assets (TNA) of 2 percent is applied to resident corporations and nonresident corporations with a permanent establishment in Mexico. The TNA has to be paid in advance in the form of monthly payments. The nonresident corporations also pay the tax without a permanent establishment in Mexico, provided that they maintain machinery or equipment and inventories for processing in Mexico. The TNA is applied on the average value of a corporation's assets after deducting investments in Mexican companies and loans obtained from resident corporate entities other than financial institutions.

[†]J.L. Nolan, A. Woznick, W. LeGro, D.C. Alexander, K.C. Shippey, E.G. Hinkelman, H.I. Vera, and M.F. Pasero, *Mexico Business, The Portable Encyclopedia for Doing Business With Mexico,* World Trade Press, San Rafael, California, U.S.A., 1994.
[‡]Ernst & Young, *Worldwide Corporate Tax Guide,* 1994 Edition.

If a company pays income tax for the year, the income tax can be credited against the final TNA. The basis for calculating the TNA owed is the average value of a company's assets after deducting investments in shares of Mexican companies and debts payable to resident corporations other than financial institutions. A company may pay TNA as a minimum tax. On the other hand should such a company's income taxes for the next 5 tax years exceed the TNA payable over that period, a refund of TNA may be claimed.

Mexican tax laws regard capital gains as normal income. These are, therefore, taxed at the regular corporate tax rates. The law permits the indexation of the original cost for inflation.

9B.3 Personal Taxation in Mexico

Persons who are residents are taxed on a worldwide income. Nonresidents are taxed only on income earned in Mexico. Taxable employment income items include: salaries, wages, directors' fees, bonuses, gratuities, allowances, certain fringe benefits, benefits in kind, and employee profit-sharing distributions.

A number of items are excluded from taxable income (e.g., retirement benefits and pensions and savings funds).

Income tax rates are applied in a progressive fashion. Maximum rates are shown in Table 9B.3. The income tax rates are adjusted for inflation on a quarterly basis. A fixed tax credit is applied, where the magnitude of the tax credit is based on the amount of the taxpayer's total income. Although no deductions from employment income are allowed, personal allowances and deductions are granted to resident individuals (e.g., medical, dental and hospitalization services, etc.).

9B.4 Income Tax—Self-Employment/Business Income

Persons who earn income from business activities or professional services have to pay taxes. The taxable income is found by deducting from gross

TABLE 9B.3

Personal income taxes, maximum rates

Income tax rates (%)	35
Capital gains tax rate (%)	35
Net worth tax rate(%)	0
Estate and gift tax rate(%)	0**

**This rate is applicable to gifts from relatives. Gifts received from persons other than direct relatives are regarded as taxable income.

revenues the normal expenses such as salaries, fees, rent, depreciation, interest and other general expenses. Directors' fees are taxable. Losses from business activities of self-employed professional persons cannot be carried forward, although losses incurred by a business activity may be carried forward for 5 years against future business income.

CHAPTER 10

EFFECTS OF INFLATION

Inflation means that your money won't buy as much today as it did when you didn't have any.
Anonymous

Inflation causes prices to rise and decreases the purchasing power of a unit of money with the passage of time. Deflation has the opposite effect. Inflation rates are measured by the wholesale price index, producer price index, and consumer price index, the last being the most quoted. One way to consider inflation in economy studies is to treat it superficially. This approach makes sense for before-tax analyses when all cost categories are assumed to be affected identically by the general inflation rate. Then all cash flows are believed to be equally responsive to inflation, and the differences between alternatives remain proportionately the same.

Since not all prices escalate uniformly or at the same rate, explicit rate estimates for certain cash flow components may be necessary. An after-tax evaluation provides a more accurate assessment of the effects of inflation because it accounts for cash flow components that are not responsive to inflation—loan repayments, leases, and depreciation charges. Leasing versus buying is a frequently encountered example of an inflation-sensitive decision. In an inflation-prone economy it becomes even more imperative to conduct inflation-sensitive evaluations in order to detect proposals that promise savings in high-inflation operations.

Up to this point, we have assumed that cash flows are in constant-value dollars where the purchasing power of money remains constant over time. We now present the concepts of inflation and the techniques needed to incorporate this concept into engineering analysis.

L0.1   **CONCEPTS OF INFLATION**

Inflation is a general increase in the price level. Equivalently, inflation results in a decline over time in the purchasing power of a unit of money. An individual perceives inflation as higher prices for food, cars, and other purchased commodities and services. It is worrisome but tends to seem inevitable. For larger purchases made at longer intervals, escalations are more startling and possibly more dismaying. In both cases inflation has eroded the purchasing power of savings and earnings, if interest rates and salary raises have not kept pace with general price trends. The same effects are felt by business and government.

Deflation is the opposite of inflation. The last time prices declined in Canada was in 1953. During the next 30 years prices rose by 314 percent. A dollar worth 100 cents in purchasing power in 1953 shrank to a worth of only 24 cents by 1983. A dollar worth 100 cents in 1986 declined to 75 cents in buying power in 1995. And the decline continues.

10.1.1 Causes of Inflation

Some dictionaries define *inflation* as "an increase in the amount of currency in circulation, resulting in a relatively sharp and sudden fall in its value and a rise in prices; it may be caused by an increase in the volume of paper money issued or of gold mined, or a relative increase in expenditures, as when the supply of goods fails to meet the demand." A more succinct description is "too much money chasing too few goods."

In tune with this explanation, some economists trace the cause of inflation to more money being poured into the economy than the economy is worth. The real wealth of a nation lies in the goods and services it produces. Money is merely a convenient symbol of wealth, the amount of which is controlled by the government, and governments often feel impelled to create more money (or credit) to pay for old debts and new social programs. When money is generated at a faster rate than the growth in goods and services, it is subject to the old economic law that the more there is of something, the cheaper it becomes. In the case of money, cheaper means it loses purchasing power.

Other economists blame inflation on

- Increases in producers' costs that are passed along to customers, sometimes with disproportionate escalations that push prices up, called *cost-push inflation*
- Excessive spending power of consumers, sometimes obtained at the expense of savings, that pulls prices up, called *demand-pull inflation*
- Impact of international forces on prices and markets, most notably the escalation of energy prices

- Unresponsive prices that seldom decline, regardless of market conditions, because wages set by union contracts and prices set by some very large firms almost never fall
- Inflation psychology that leads consumers to "buy ahead," often on easily obtained credit, in the belief that prices will inevitably inflate and loans can be repaid in cheaper dollars

10.1.2 Consequences of Inflation

Everyone is affected to some degree by inflation. The effects may be immediate and conspicuous, such as a hike in rent. Other effects are subtle but pervasive, and they influence decisions both on and off the job. As a consequence of an inflation-prone economy,

- The general standard of living declines as savings and investments are eroded; people on fixed incomes suffer the brunt of the decline, but wage earners are afflicted by tax increases when their inflated incomes push them into higher tax brackets.
- Confidence in the economy declines, with a resulting increase in petty crime, political instability for incumbents, greater unemployment, and spreading discontent.
- Business decisions are distorted by efforts to cope with inflation, partially brought on by lower volume and higher taxes, and the ability of business to compete in foreign markets declines.

The consequences depend on the degree of inflation. When inflation is *mild*—annual price increases of 2 to 4 percent—the economy prospers, but the condition is temporary because employers are tempted to seek larger profits during periods of growth and unions commensurately bargain for higher wages. So *moderate* inflation occurs with price escalations of 5 to 9 percent. Then people start purchasing more because they would rather have goods than money that is declining in value. Increased demand pulls prices still higher.

Severe inflation occurs when the annual rate reaches 10 percent or more. During double-digit inflation, prices rise much faster than wages do. People on fixed incomes are hurt badly. Only debtors benefit by being able to repay debts with dollars less valuable than those that were borrowed. Beyond this dangerous level is *hyperinflation*—rapid, uncontrolled inflation that destroys a nation's economy. Here money becomes essentially valueless, as the government prints it excessively to pay expenses, while citizens go to a *barter economy* in which goods and services are exchanged without using currency.

10.1.3 Control of Inflation

The destructive effects of high inflation are well documented. Less clear are the effective actions to stem rising prices and to lower rates that are already high.

Inflation first became serious in Canada in the 1960s, but few realized how dangerous it was, so strong enough measures to restrain it were not adopted. Among the remedies later attempted were price and wage controls, contraction of the money supply, credit restrictions, reduction in demand by raising taxes, increased demand by reducing taxes, enlarged supply of goods through greater productivity stimulated by investment incentives, and wage-price guidelines backed by political persuasion. Lack of success in applying the remedies has been attributed to inconsistency in applying them, inadequate time allowed for a remedy to become effective, and inattention to other factors while concentrating on only one remedy.

Credit for lowering Canadian double-digit inflation is given to monetary policies such as the *tight-money policy* that reduced the money supply by such actions as raising reserve requirements for banks to limit their lending capacity and increasing banks' discount rates, causing them to raise interest rates on customers' loans. Other methods to control inflation include adjusting *fiscal policy*—spending and taxing programs and imposition of wage and price controls. Each action has its advocates and detractors.

10.1.4 Inflation in Economic Analysis

Causes and corrections for inflation are outside the province of most engineering economists, who should, however, be concerned with the effects of inflation on their economic analyses. As a consequence of inflation, a dollar assumes different values at different times. The uninitiated might overlook the decrease in buying power of future dollars compared with today's dollars, as sometimes happens in reverse when managers nostalgically recall how much less expensive things used to be as they review, and possibly reject, proposals for current expenditures. Yesterday's, today's, and tomorrow's dollars do not have the same value. Treating them the same is like calling 10 meters equal to 10 yards; the numbers of units are the same, but the sizes of the units are different.

Realizing that dollar values are distorted by inflation is a major advance, but the extent of distortion remains difficult to assess. Only foolish forecasters would stake their reputations on multiyear inflation rate predictions. Without reliable forecasts, the accuracy of future cash flow equivalence is suspect. But engineering economists can still show what would happen if inflation became moderate or severe. Such scenarios put competing proposals in perspective.

10.2   MEASURING INFLATION

Inflation is difficult to measure because the prices of different goods and services do not increase or decrease by the same amount, nor do they change at the same time. The calculation of a general inflation rate is further complicated by the geographical differences in prices and changeable buying habits of consumers. Government statisticians attempt to overcome these difficulties by collecting data that profile the types and amounts of expenditures made by a middle-income family. Prices for these goods are obtained monthly and averaged according to demographic distributions. Then the prices are weighted according to the expenditure proportions of the typical family. The result is the *Consumer Price Index* (CPI).

Statistics Canada compiles several indexes to measure inflation. The Consumer Price Index reveals the effect of retail price changes on a selected standard of living. The *Industry Selling Price Index* (ISPI) measures inflation at the wholesale level for both consumer and industrial goods, but not services. The *Implicit Price Index* (IPI) is designed to show the effect of general price-level changes on the Gross National Product (GNP), the total market value of all goods and services produced by a nation's economy. Examples of other price indexes are the *Industrial Product Price Index* (IPPI) and *Raw Material Price Index* (RMPI). Table 10.1 shows a record of recent CPI and IPPI. The CPI is the most-used measure of prices.

Although the indexes measure price changes that have already occurred, they are useful in projecting future price trends. The historical data suggest the general movement of costs. For example, the CPI moved from 130.7 in 1994 to 133.5 in 1995. The rate of increase is (133.5-130.7)/130.7 = 0.021 or 2.1 percent. That is, the inflation rate during 1995

TABLE 10.1

Record of selected Canadian price indexes (1986 = 100)

Year	CPI	IPPI	Year	CPI	IPPI
1986	100.0	100.0	1991	126.2	108.7
1987	104.4	102.8	1992	128.1	109.2
1988	108.6	107.2	1993	130.4	112.7
1989	114.0	109.5	1994	130.7	119.2
1990	119.5	109.8	1995	133.5	128.7*

*Preliminary
CPI   Consumer Price Index
IPPI   Industrial Product Price Index
Statistics Canada Catalogue No. 62-011 Industry Price Indexes

| TABLE 10.2 | | | |

Annual inflation rates based on the CPI (Canada)

Year	Percentage	Year	Percentage
1987	4.4	1991	5.6
1988	4.0	1992	1.5
1989	5.0	1993	1.8
1990	4.8	1994	0.2
		1995	2.1

was 2.1 percent. Table 10.2 presents recent annual inflation rates in Canada.

Since a trend over several periods is usually a better indicator for inflation expectation, an annual compound rate of growth is calculated. For the 1987 to 1995 period, the price trend or inflation rate f can be found as follows:

$$100.0(1 + f)^9 = 133.5$$
$$(1 + f)^9 = 133.5/100.0 = 1.335$$
$$f = 0.0326 \text{ or } 3.26\%$$

10.3   IMPACT OF INFLATION ON ECONOMIC EVALUATIONS

When inflation is modest, 2 to 4 percent per year, it is generally ignored in economic evaluations of proposals. It is argued that all proposals are affected similarly by price changes and that there is too little difference between current and future costs to influence the order of preference. These arguments lose substance when inflation is high and some goods and services escalate much more rapidly than others.

Once analysts recognize that inflation has an impact on most investment opportunities and therefore deserves consideration in their appraisals, they must decide on the most appropriate method in which to include it. There are two basic methods, with a number of refinements available for each.

1. Eliminate inflation effects by converting all cash flows to money units that have constant purchasing power, called *constant,* or *real, dollars.* This approach is most suitable for before-tax analysis, when all cash flow components inflate at uniform rates.
2. Estimate cash flows in the amount of money units actually exchanged at the time of each transaction. These money units are called *future, then-current,* or *actual dollars.* The actual-dollar approach is generally

easier to understand and apply and is more versatile than the real-dollar method.

In an analysis by either method, it is critical that the interest rate used in the analysis corresponds to the assumptions made in determining the cash flows. Two different interest rates are used in economic calculations: market interest rate i_f and inflation-free interest rate i. The market interest rates include the combined effects of the earning value of capital and any expected inflation (or deflation). Market rates are the rates stated by the financial institutions (e.g., loans, bank accounts, bond and stock returns) and used by firms as their minimum acceptable rate of return (MARR) in evaluating their investments. Market interest rates are also referred to as *composite* or *inflation-adjusted* interest rates.

The inflation-free interest rates, also called *real-* or *constant-dollar* interest rates, represent the earning power of capital when inflation effects have been removed. Although referred to as real interest rates, they are abstract, but serve as a useful approach to what market rates might be if there were no inflation.

We have been using the constant or inflation-free interest rate i up until this point because we have ignored inflation. The *market interest rate* i_f is defined as

$$i_f = (1 + i)(1 + f) - 1$$

where f = average inflation rate. If inflation during the next 4 years is expected to be 6 percent and the constant-dollar interest rate is 12 percent, the market interest rate is

$$i_f = (1.12)(1.06) - 1 = 1.1872 - 1$$
$$= 0.1872 \text{ or } 18.72\%$$

Since inflation is measured on an annual basis, it is an effective annual rate, not a nominal rate. Thus, nominal interest rates should be converted to effective interest rates before being combining with the inflation rate. Alternatively, the inflation rate could be converted to an equivalent nominal rate and combined with the nominal interest rate. Consider a loan that can be arranged at a nominal rate of 12 percent compounded monthly. If the inflation rate is expected to be 4 percent, what is the market interest rate? The effective interest rate i corresponding to the 12 percent nominal rate is

$$i_{\text{eff}} = \left(1 + \frac{0.12}{12}\right)^{12} - 1 = 0.127$$

The market interest rate then is

$$i_f = (1 + 0.127)(1 + 0.04) - 1 = 0.172 \text{ or } 17.2 \text{ percent.}$$

Constant dollars in any future year N can be inflated to current dollars by using the expression

Current dollars = (constant dollars)$(1 + f)^N$

or

Current dollars = (constant dollars)$(F/P, f, N)$

Conversely, current dollars can be deflated to constant dollars by using the present-worth factor:

Constant dollars = (current dollars)$(P/F, f, N)$

When the rate of inflation increases, there is a corresponding increase in the market interest rate. If investors anticipate inflation over the terms of their loan, they will increase the interest rate charged to compensate for the declining value of money. Consider the following simplified example, where you borrow $100 from a bank in 1995 to make an attractive investment. You plan to return the loan in 1 year. Inflation is expected to be 100 percent during this period. The bank states that it would like to maintain the purchasing power of money and earn a real return of 5 percent. The accounting of this loan is shown below.

	1995 dollars	1996 dollars
Borrow now	100	200
Repay in 1 year	105	210
Principal payment	100	200
Interest payment	5	10
Real interest rate	5%	5%

In actual dollars, you borrow $100 and repay $210 for a 110 percent interest rate. But most of what is called interest is not interest. The effect of inflation has been to reduce the value of the principal owed by $100. To compensate, the bank charges $110 plus the $100 principal due. However, only $10 is interest, and the rest is principal, adjusted for inflation.

Another way to state this is that the bank uses a market interest rate of 110 percent $[(1 + 0.05)(1 + 1) - 1]$. Anticipation of future inflation affects expectations of returns on invested capital and the degree of risk that is acceptable; this anticipation is built into the market interest rate.

The inflation adjustment to the cost of capital, which manifests itself in the minimum acceptable rate of return, must be consistent with the estimates of future cash flows used in economic evaluations. If the MARR includes an adjustment for 5 percent inflation but estimates of future revenues are based on a higher inflation rate, then a study would be biased toward accepting proposals. Conversely, if cash flow is stated in real dollars and the MARR contains an inflation adjustment, a proposal is penalized by excessive discounting. The bias results because inflating cash flows and discounting them are counteracting procedures.

EXAMPLE 10.1

Use the Same Basis for the Cost of Capital and Cash Flows

A proposal with an initial cost of $2000 is expected to produce net returns of $850 per year for 3 years in real dollars. The minimum acceptable rate of return, based on the market cost of capital which includes inflation of 5 percent, is 15 percent. Should the proposal be accepted?

Solution

If the cash flow were estimated in real dollars of constant purchasing power and the MARR included an inflation adjustment, the proposal would be rejected because its present worth would be negative:

$$PW = -\$2000 + \$850(P/A, 15, 3)$$
$$= -\$2000 + \$850(2.28323) = -\$59$$

This evaluation unfairly penalizes the proposal because the MARR is based on the assumption that the cash flow will state the actual amount received each year. Real dollars can be converted to actual dollars by inflating them to an amount that is equivalent in purchasing power to their value today. For 5 percent annual inflation, the future cash flow equivalent to constant purchasing power of $850 a year is as follows:

End of year	Real dollars (no inflation)	×	5% Inflation	=	Actual dollars (inflated cash flow)
0	−2000				
1	850	×	1.05	=	893
2	850	×	$(1.05)^2$	=	937
3	850	×	$(1.05)^3$	=	984

The inflated cash flow indicates that 3 years from now it would take $984 to acquire goods that could be purchased today for $850. When the inflated receipts are discounted at the inflation-adjusted MARR, the proposal has an acceptable present worth:

$$PW = -\$2000 + \$893(P/F, 15, 1) + \$937(P/F, 15, 2) + \$984(P/F, 15, 3)$$
$$= -\$2000 + \$893(0.86957) + \$937(0.75614) + \$984(0.65752)$$
$$= \$132$$

The proposal merits approval.

10.4   ## BEFORE-TAX CONSTANT-VALUE COMPARISONS

Actual-dollar flow indexed to a base year is frequently used to compare economic performance in different years. For instance, 1994 could be the base year for measuring the productivity of a firm. If the consumer price index were used to convert actual-dollar flow in future years to real-dollar amounts in the base year, the output and input figures in 1995 would be deflated to their 1994 worth by using CPI *deflator:*

$$\text{CPI deflator (1995 − 1994)} = 1 + \frac{\text{CPI}(1995) - \text{CPI}(1994)}{\text{CPI}(1994)}$$

$$= 1 + \frac{133.5 - 130.7}{130.7}$$

$$= 1.021$$

The result is, of course, the same as the annual inflation rate given in Table 10.2. Then an output of, say, $408,952 in 1995 actual dollars would be deflated to $408,952/1.021 = $400,540.65 to compare it on an equivalent basis with an output of, say, $390,000 in 1994. The output has thus increased by $10,540.65, for the year in constant terms.

It is generally easier to estimate future costs in constant dollars because the estimator is familiar with today's values. It is a simple matter to convert estimates in real-dollar flow to actual-dollar flow when inflation is assumed to be a constant rate. Consider the two proposals shown below for which the estimates have been made in real dollars.

	Cost, $	Cash flow, real dollars				PW at 12%, $
	Year 0	Year 1	Year 2	Year 3	Year 4	
Proposal *A*	−10,000	4,000	4,000	4,000	4,000	
Proposal *B*	−14,000	5,500	5,500	5,500	5,500	
Net difference	−4,000	1,500	1,500	1,500	1,500	556

The net difference might also have been estimated in actual dollars to show what receipts would have to be in years ahead to equal today's purchasing power. If inflation during the next 4 years is expected to be 6 percent per year, then using the compound-amount factor $(F/P, f, N)$ would result in the net difference shown in the table at the top of page 450.

The same present worth is obtained by using the market or inflation-adjusted interest rate that represents both the minimum required rate of

	Cost, $	Cash flow, actual dollars			
	Year 0	Year 1	Year 2	Year 3	Year 4
Proposal A	−10,000	4,240	4,495	4,764	5,050
Proposal B	−14,000	5,830	6,180	6,551	6,944
Net difference	−4,000	1,590	1,685	1,787	1,894

return and the inflation rate. For $i = 12$ percent and $f = 6$ percent, the combined interest-inflation rate $i_f = 1.12(1.06) − 1 = 0.1872$ or 18.72 percent. Applying this rate to the given net difference expressed in actual dollars produces the same present worth as previously calculated and confirmed in Table 10.3. Rather than interpolating for the 18.72 percent value, the reader is advised to use the CHEER program to determine the $(P/F, 18.72, N)$ values. Also, CHEER will do the overall present-worth analysis automatically.

TABLE 10.3

Inflation-adjusted interest rate applied to actual-dollar cash flow to obtain before-tax present worth

Year N	Cash flow in actual dollars	(P/F, 18.72, N)	Present worth, $
0	−4000	1.00000	−4,000
1	1590	0.84237	1,339
2	1685	0.70964	1,195
3	1787	0.59786	1,068
4	1894	0.50372	954
			556

EXAMPLE 10.2

Equivalence of Real-Dollar and Actual Cash Flow in a Before-Tax Analysis

A productive asset can be purchased for $120,000. It will have no salvage at the end of its 6-year useful life. Operating costs will be $12,000 per year while it provides a revenue of $40,000 annually. Estimates are based on current economic conditions without consideration of price or cost escalations. Evaluate the proposed purchase according to the real-dollar data and actual-dollar cash flow when the inflation rate is 8 percent. The MARR is 15 percent without an adjustment for inflation, and taxes are not included in the analysis.

Solution

The real dollar cash flow is composed of an immediate $120,000 outlay followed by net receipts of $40,000 − $12,000 = $28,000 at the end of each of the next 6 years. This flow, discounted at 15 percent, yields

$$PW = -\$120,000 + \$28,000(P/A,15,6)$$
$$= -\$120,000 + \$28,000(3.7844) = -\$14,037$$

Real dollars are converted to actual dollars by applying the *inflation factor* $(1+f)^N$ to each of the annual receipts, where N equals the year in which the receipt occurs. The resulting actual-dollar cash flow is discounted by the combined interest inflation rate i, to obtain the present worth of the "then-current" dollars; $i_f = (1.15)(1.08) - 1 = 0.242$. The calculations are shown in Table 10.4.

TABLE 10.4

Present worth of actual-dollar cash flow when discounted by the combined Interest-inflation factor to determine its real-dollar equivalence

End of year N	Real-dollar cash flow	Inflation factor, f = 8% $(F/P,8,N)$	Actual-dollar cash flow	Combined Interest-inflation factor $(P/F,i_f,N)$	Present worth of cash flow
0	−$120,000		−$120,000		−$120,000
1	28,000	1.0800	30,240	0.80516	24,348
2	28,000	1.1664	32,659	0.64827	21,172
3	28,000	1.2597	35,272	0.52196	18,410
4	28,000	1.3604	38,091	0.42025	16,007
5	28,000	1.4693	41,141	0.33838	13,921
6	28,000	1.5868	44,430	0.27244	12,105
					$14,037

The present worths from Table 10.4 and the PW formula agree, of course, because $(P/F,24.2,N) = (P/F,8,N)(P/F,15,N)$. The combined interest-inflation rate thus represents an inflation adjusted MARR applied to inflation-adjusted cash flow.

10.5   AFTER-TAX ACTUAL CASH FLOW COMPARISONS

Two weaknesses limit the usefulness of the constant-dollar approach: Tax effects are ignored, and no provision is made for differences in escalation rates among price and cost components.

Tax effects are significant because deductions allowed for depreciation and loan interest are *not responsive* to inflation. That is, depreciation is based strictly on the purchase price of an asset, not on its inflation-elevated replacement price, and interest payments on loans are set by contract in actual dollars that are not subject to correction for inflation.

Inflation is differential rather than uniform. Prices for goods and services do not change proportionately over time. For example, differences in escalation rates apply for such items as medical care, college tuition, appliances and electronic equipment, etc. When differential inflation is significant for factors in an economic study, it can affect the preference among alternatives. For instance, two alternatives with identical real-dollar cash flows would be equally promising, but if the revenue for one resulted from energy savings that inflated 20 percent annually, while revenue for the other came from labor savings that escalated 10 percent per year, then the energy-saving proposal would be preferred.

10.5.1 Nonresponsive Charges in After-Tax Analysis

Several financial charges are made in real dollars that are not responsive to inflation, primarily loans, leases, and depreciation. Loans and leases that specify actual-dollar cash flows benefit borrowers and lessees when inflation rises faster than anticipated in the agreements. The reverse is true during deflation, when interest rates and costs drop below those agreed to in contracts. The significance of nonresponsive cash flows is demonstrated in Example 10.3.

EXAMPLE 10.3

Difference in After-Tax Present Worth Caused by Nonresponsive Cash Flows during Inflationary Periods

The proposal described in Example 10.2 is to be subjected to an after-tax analysis. Both earnings and expenses are responsive to the general inflation rate of 8 percent. The asset is in Class 8. The tax rate is 40 percent.

Solution

An after-tax evaluation performed does not reveal the effect of nonresponsive cash flow components.

The calculations below correct for inflation-induced loss of purchasing power through the use of actual-dollar cash flows. A modified real dollar approach is developed in a later section to reaffirm the equivalence of real- and actual-dollar analyses.

Actual-dollar before-tax cash flow (BTCF) based on 8 percent inflation is shown in column 2 of Table 10.5. CCA charges in column 3 are subtracted from column 2 to get the taxable income for the year in column 4. Taxes are calculated in column 5 and deducted from the BTCF to reveal the actual-dollar, after-tax cash flow (ATCF) in column 6. It is then neces-

TABLE 10.5

PW calculation procedure for an after-tax analysis, which includes components that are not responsive to inflation

End of year N (1)	BTCF, actual dollars (2)	(CCA) (3)	Taxable income (2) − (3) = (4)	Taxes at 40% (5)	ATCF, actual dollars (2) − (5) = (6)	Inflation factor, (P/F,15,N) (7)
0	−$120,000				−$120,000	
1	30,240	$12,000	$18,240	$7,296	22,944	0.92593
2	32,240	21,600	10,640	4,256	27,984	0.85734
3	35,272	17,280	17,992	7,197	28,075	0.79383
4	38,091	13,824	24,267	9,707	28,384	0.73503
5	41,141	11,059	30,082	12,033	29,108	0.68059
6	44,430	8,847	35,583	14,233	30,197	0.63017

End of year N (1)	ATCF, real dollars (6) × (7) = (8)	Discount factor, (P/F,15,N) (9)	Present worth (8) × (9) = (10)
0	−$120,000		−$120,000
1	21,245	0.86957	18,474
2	23,992	0.75614	18,141
3	22,287	0.65752	14,654
4	20,863	0.57175	11,928
5	19,811	0.49718	9,849
6	19,029	0.43233	8,227
		CCA Tax Shield Adjustment	1,068
			−$37,658

sary to convert the actual dollars back to real dollars, as shown in columns 7 and 8. Finally, the real-dollar ATCF is discounted at the inflation-free 15 percent rate to yield the present worth, column 10. *The present worth includes the CCA tax shield adjustment calculated at the combined interest-inflation rate of 24.2 percent because the CCA tax shields for years 7 through infinity are in actual dollars.*

The same PW solution would have resulted from discounting column 6 by the combined interest-inflation factor, 24.2 percent. However, columns 7 to 9 descriptively display how the actual dollar ATCF is converted to real dollars to allow discounting at the unadjusted MARR, 15 percent. It should be apparent that inflation has not increased the real value of the net revenue; column 2 shows the number of actual dollars required in each year to equal the buying power of $28,000 per year in real dollars. Therefore, actual-dollar cash flow must be discounted by an inflation-adjusted MARR.

The present worth of the proposal is lower when inflation is accounted for because the CCA charges do not escalate in tandem with revenue. The result is higher annual taxes. Consequently, a more realistic evaluation is obtained from actual-dollar, after-tax data when inflation is significant.

The tedious mechanics of manually including inflation and tax effects in an analysis can be avoided by using CHEER, the computer program available with this text. The use of CHEER was discussed in Chap. 5. The initial screen display is shown in Fig. 5.1. An option available on the initial screen is specification of inflation rate. Since we ignored inflation in Chap. 5, we did not specify a value for inflation. However, if an economic analysis involves inflation, we specify a value for the inflation rate. The computer program converts cash flows to actual dollars. It should be emphasized that with inflation specified, CHEER works with actual dollars and it is the user's responsibility to specify cash flows in actual dollars. The MARR specified is the inflation-free rate. The market interest rate (i_f) is automatically computed by the program.

10.5.2 Multiple Inflation Rates in an After-Tax Analysis

Often one or more components in a cash flow stream have escalation rates prominently different from the general inflation rate. The flow patterns for such components may be stated as specific estimates of actual-dollar transactions or in terms of specific inflation rates that vary from the general rate. Specific enumeration of annual flows permits year-by-year variations in the rate of escalation, whereas assigning a stable inflation rate commits the cash flow to a continuous growth pattern. Both options are accommodated by the procedure demonstrated in Example 10.4.

EXAMPLE 10.4

Evaluation of a Proposal in which Cash Flow Components Escalate at Different Rates

The conditions for the proposal described in Example 10.3 remain the same, except for the inflation rate of revenue. It is now believed that revenue will escalate at a 20 percent rate while expenses will continue to increase at the general inflation rate of 8 percent. Determine the present worth under the new assumption.

Solution

Recall from Example 10.2 that the net receipts of $28,000 per year resulted from annual revenue of $40,000 and annual expense of $12,000; then actual dollar revenue in Table 10.6 (column 2) is obtained by applying an

TABLE 10.6

PW calculations for a proposal when revenue inflates at 20 percent and expenses at the general inflation rate of 8 percent. After-tax actual dollars are deflated at the combined interest-inflation rate, i_f = 24.2 percent.

	BTCF IN ACTUAL DOLLARS		
End of year N (1)	Revenue @ f = 20% $40,000(F/P,20,N)$ (2)	Expenses @f = 8% at 40% $12,000(F/P,8,N)$ (3)	Net revenue (2) − (3) = (4)
0		$120,000	−$120,000
1	$ 48,000	12,960	35,040
2	57,600	13,997	43,603
3	69,120	15,116	54,004
4	82,944	16,325	66,619
5	99,532	17,632	81,900
6	119,436	19,042	100,394

End of year N (1)	CCA (5)	Taxable income (4) − (5) = (6)	Taxes at 40% (7)
0			
1	$ 12,000	$ 23,040	$ 9,216
2	21,600	22,003	8,801
3	17,280	36,724	14,690
4	13,824	52,759	21,118
5	11,059	70,841	28,336
6	8,847	91,547	36,619

End of Year N (1)	ATCF actual dollars (4) − (7) = (8)	Discount factor, i_f $(P/F,24.2,N)$ (9)	Present worth (8) × (9) = (10)
0	−$120,000		−$120,000
1	25,824	0.80516	20,792
2	34,802	0.64827	22,561
3	39,314	0.52196	20,521
4	45,501	0.42025	19,122
5	53,564	0.33838	18,125
6	63,775	0.27244	17,375
		CCA Tax Shield Adjustment	1,068
			−$ 436

inflation factor of $(F/P,20,N)$ for each N year, and actual expense (column 3) in year N is $12,000(F/P,20,N)$. Taxable income is the difference between revenue and the sum of expenses plus CCA (column 6). After-tax actual dollars are discounted at the combined interest-inflation rate of 24.2 percent (column 9) to determine the present worth of the revised proposal (column 10).

It is no surprise that the proposal's PW increases notably, compared to Example 10.3, from the disproportionately rapid rise in revenue. The rationale for using the general inflation rate to discount actual dollars to their real-dollar equivalency is that the overall inflation rate is the weighted average of all price escalations and is therefore a reasonable standard for uniformly deflating all cash flow components.

The general inflation rate may not be the most appropriate discount factor to use in certain studies. A unique inflation-factor index—a composite inflation rate for a given firm or area—could be calculated for any organization from the weighted average of price changes that the organization expects for its operations. Because escalations vary with geography and product mix, a customized inflation factor would more accurately represent future cash flow expectations. The composite rate is calculated from forecasted inflation rates for critical cash flow components weighted according to the proportion of utilization of each component. An example of the computation and use of a custom-built composite inflation index is given in Review Exercise 2.

10.5.3   After-Tax Modified Cash Flow Comparison

It is also possible to utilize real dollars for an after-tax evaluation under the conditions stipulated for the proposal in Example 10.4. To do so, it is necessary to modify all components that inflate or deflate at a rate different from the general inflation rate. In Example 10.4, revenue escalates faster than the general inflation rate, and depreciation charges are constant (which means they deflate with respect to the general inflation rate). Therefore, these revenue and depreciation components must be modified to make their value correspond to the real-dollar value of expense, which is the only component expected to escalate at the general inflation rate.

Real-dollar equivalence can be calculated with the geometric series factor introduced in Chap. 2. When using method 2 from Chap. 2, an explicit growth rate g higher than the general inflation rate f conforms to case 1:

$$i^* = \frac{1+g}{1+f} - 1$$

When g is less than f, case 2 applies:

$$i^* = \frac{1+f}{1+g} - 1$$

The special interest rate i^* is then used in the expression $(1 + i^*)^N$ to inflate or deflate applicable cash flow components. The resulting after-tax cash flow is discounted at a MARR that has *not* been adjusted for inflation.

Table 10.7 on page 458 shows a real-dollar analysis that corresponds to the actual-dollar analysis given in Table 10.6. Both methods produce the same present worth for identical data. Either approach can be utilized, but the actual-dollar procedure is more descriptive, is easier to comprehend, facilitates irregular cash flows, and is generally more convenient to apply.

10.6   **LEASE OR BUY?—AN INFLATION-SENSITIVE DECISION**

The concepts of leasing were introduced in Chap. 7 when we covered replacement analysis. *Leasing* refers to a method of financing an asset through payments over an agreed period rather than actually purchasing the asset. Virtually any asset can be leased. In particular, if an asset has a high investment cost and low utilization rate, it is a good candidate for the lease-or-buy consideration. For example, many building contractors may find it more economical to rent large construction equipment such as bulldozers, cement mixers, rock drills, and transportation equipment than to purchase them.

The leasing of capital equipment has grown enormously in the past decade. There are many reasons why leasing may be more attractive than purchasing. These include

- Use of an asset's services if a firm lacks cash or the borrowing capacity to purchase the asset
- Less effect on future borrowing capacity than debt financing
- Imposition of fewer financial restrictions than accompany a loan for purchase of a comparable asset
- Possible reductions in the risk of obsolescence and escalation in ownership costs due to inflation
- Tax advantages under certain conditions

The most frequently cited reasons for leasing are income tax advantages and the ability to free working capital by enabling the acquisition of needed equipment without going into debt. However, the decision to lease or buy an asset involves financial, accounting, and tax considerations; a thorough economic comparison should be made before the decision is readied.

From a tax perspective, a lease is treated as an annual expense directly deductible from income; a purchase is an investment subject to a multiyear

TABLE 10.7

Modified real-dollar analysis of the proposal described in Example 10.4. The special interest rate for revenue is $(1.20/1.08) - 1 = 0.1111$ (where $g = 20$ percent and $f = 8$ percent) and i^* for depreciation charges is $(1.08/1.00) - 1 = 0.08$ (where $g = 0$ and $f = 8$ percent). Revenue is inflated at 11.11 percent annually (column 2), and depreciation charges are deflated at 8 percent per year (column 5). After-tax cash flow (column 8) is discounted at MARR = 15 percent to obtain the present worth (column 9).

BTCF IN MODIFIED REAL DOLLARS

End of year N (1)	Revenue $i^* = 0.1111$, $\$40{,}000(1 + i^*)^N$ (2)	Expenses (3)	Net revenue (4)
0			−$120,000
1	$ 44,444	12,000	32,444
2	49,382	12,000	37,382
3	54,869	12,000	42,869
4	60,965	12,000	48,965
5	67,738	12,000	55,738
6	75,264	12,000	63,264

End of year N (1)	Modified CCA $i^* = 0.08$ $CCA = (1 + i^*)^{-N}$ (5)	Taxable income $(4) - (5) = (6)$	Taxes at 40% (7)
0			
1	$ 11,111	$21,333	$ 8,533
2	18,519	18,863	7,545
3	13,717	29,152	11,661
4	10,161	38,804	15,522
5	7,527	48,211	19,284
6	5,575	57,689	23,076

End of year N (1)	ATCF in modified real dollars $(4) - (7) = (8)$	Present worth MARR = 15% (8) $(P/F,15,N)$
0	−$120,000	−$120,000
1	23,911	20,792
2	29,837	22,561
3	31,208	20,521
4	33,443	19,122
5	36,454	18,125
6	40,188	17,375
	CCA Tax Shield Adjustment	1,068
		−$ 436

depreciation schedule. Many tax factors, such as investment credits and carryovers, make investing more or less attractive in comparison with leasing. Tax implications of inflation also affect the lease-or-buy question. Like a fixed-rate loan and depreciation charges, a lease contract that specifies fixed payments is insensitive to price escalations.

10.6.1 Types of Leases

A lease is a contract between the owner of an asset, called a *lessor,* and a *lessee,* who makes periodic payments for the right to use the asset. When there is also a lender involved who furnishes capital to the lessor to purchase the asset, the lease is said to be *leveraged.*

An *operating lease* can be canceled by either the lessee or lessor at any time after due notice has been given. A commitment by both parties to specified charges for the use of an asset for a definite period is a *financial lease.* Typically, payments under a financial lease are spread over a period of time equal to the major portion of the useful life of an asset. Temporary use of vehicles, computers, and furniture typifies operating leases. More expensive assets are usually subject to financial leases: real estate, railroad cars, airplanes, and construction equipment.

It is common practice for a firm that needs certain equipment to get a price agreement from the manufacturer or distributor and then find a lessor who will purchase the equipment. A commitment is made to pay to the lessor a specified rental that will ensure the lessee use of the equipment for the period needed and will provide an adequate return on the lessor's investment. It is also possible for a firm to sell an asset it already owns and lease it back from the buyer. This *sale-and-leaseback* arrangement allows a firm to obtain cash and still have the use of its asset.

10.6.2 Lease or Buy?

The comparison methods presented in previous chapters are applicable to the lease-or-buy question. The two alternatives can be evaluated according to their PW, EAW, or incremental IRR. An after-tax analysis is usually more revealing. The *buy* alternative should include the loan cost if the asset is purchased with all or partly borrowed funds. The *lease* alternative typically includes the following elements:

Cash flow (lease) = revenues − operating expenses − lease costs
                    − (tax rate)(revenues − expenses − lease costs)

Particulars for the calculations depend on the specific lease arrangement, such as who pays maintenance costs and which tax provisions apply.

An operating lease is normally considered to be an expense that is deductible from taxable income in the year it occurs. However, leases are subject to several criteria that determine their eligibility as deductions. For instance, a rental agreement cannot qualify as an operating lease if it transfers ownership to the lessee at the end of the lease term, if it has a bargain purchase option, or if the lease term is equal to 75 percent of the estimated life of the new leased asset. As is the case for most tax questions, expert advice is needed when a situation does not fit standard prescriptions.

The degree of protection from obsolescence and inflation that a lessee achieves by leasing an asset depends on the contract. The lessor is also aware of the risks. A lease appears as a "bargain" to a lessee who views the future differently from the lessor and perceives an advantage. Which way the risk shifts as a result of the lease, if it shifts at all, is a function of forecasting ability.

EXAMPLE 10.5

Leasing versus Buying

Two options are available to a U.S. branch of a Canadian construction company for acquiring a piece of heavy construction equipment required to work on a long-term project in the U.S.A. It can be bought outright or it can be leased. The initial cost is $100,000, and it will have no salvage value at the end of its 8-year useful life. The equipment is classified according to U.S. tax regulations as 7-year MACRS property for depreciation purposes. (See Extension 9A for details.) The company expects that funds committed to new investments should earn at least a 10 percent rate of return after taxes.

The lease would have an annual rental charge of $20,000 with an option to buy the equipment at the end of the eighth year for $5000. Assuming that the option is exercised, the company must elect to expense the purchase in year 8.

Compare the alternatives. The construction company has an effective tax rate of 40 percent. It is assumed that rental expense for the leased asset is deductible from income.

Solution

Tax savings (column 2) in Table 10.8 for the cash purchase result from multiplying the annual depreciation charge (column 1) by the 40 percent tax rate; the total discounted cash flow (column 3) is the sum of the present worth of total tax savings and the purchase price.

Tax savings (column 5) for the lease-or-buy plan result from the 40 percent tax rate multiplied by the annual lease cost and the expensed purchase. The present worth of the cash flow (column 6) is the net summation (column 4 + column 5) discounted at 10 percent. The $5000 cost at the end of year 8 to exercise the buy option is treated as an expense in that year. The 8-year lease has the higher tax savings that are spread over the length

TABLE 10.8

Calculation of present worth of alternative financing plans

End of Year V	Annual depreciation charge, $ (1)	Cash purchase, $			Lease-or-buy alternative, $		
		Tax savings (2)	PW of cash flow (3)	Annual rental charge (4)	Tax savings (5)	PW of cash flow (6)
0			−100,000			
1	14,290	5,716	5,196	−20,000	8,000	−10,909
2	24,500	9,800	8,099	−20,000	8,000	−9,917
3	17,490	6,996	5,256	20,000	8,000	−9,016
4	12,500	5,000	3,415	−20,000	8,000	−8,196
5	8,920	3,568	2,215	−20,000	8,000	−7,451
6	8,920	3,568	2,104	−20,000	8,000	−6,774
7	8,920	3,568	1,831	−20,000	8,000	−6,158
8	4,460	1,784	688	−20,000	8,000	−5,598
8				−5,000	2,000	−1,400
			−71,286			−65,419

of the lease to reflect the lease payments as operating costs instead of being concentrated in the early years, as in an accelerated depreciation schedule.

10.7   DECIDING WHEN AND HOW TO CONSIDER INFLATION

Including the effect of inflation is a second-order refinement for economic evaluations; the first-order refinement was the inclusion of the effect of taxes on basic cash flow. Many proposals do not deserve the additional inflation refinement, because their cash flows are too small, are immune from inflation, escalate in concert with competing proposals, or are so uncertain that fine-tuning of cash flow is not justified. Other proposals, especially those subject to a wide range of price escalations among cash flow components, are obvious candidates for inflation-sensitive analyses. Estimating future cash flows and inflation rates is difficult, particularly when prices spurt ahead spasmodically as a result of shortages, political events, and other causes of economic turbulence. An indication of the sensitivity of a decision to the effects of inflation can be obtained by using the *sensitivity analysis* techniques presented in Chap. 11.

It is critical that inflated cash flows be discounted according to an appropriate inflation adjustment to the minimum acceptable rate of return. If we perform an economic analysis using constant dollars (cash flows that have constant purchasing power, as if there were no inflation), the MARR used in the calculations should be the real inflation-free interest rate. On the other hand, if actual dollars that we experience in our everyday life are used, then the market interest rate should be used that includes both the real rate and the inflation rate. The interest rates should be adjusted for taxes for an after-tax evaluation. The table below summarizes the different scenarios. Note that whether the dollars are constant or actual depends on the absence or presence of inflation.

Inflation	Cash flow dollars	Taxes	MARR
No	Constant	No	Before-tax real interest rate i
No	Constant	Yes	After-tax real interest rate $i_t = i\,(1 - \text{tax rate})$
Yes	Actual	No	Before-tax market interest rate $i_f = (1 + i)\,(1 + f) - 1$
Yes	Actual	Yes	After-tax market interest rate $(1 + i_t)\,(1 + f) - 1$

Actual-dollar analysis is recommended for most applications, owing to its practicality, and all after-tax analysis is recommended because it reveals the effect of cash flow components that are not responsive to inflation.

10.8   REVIEW EXERCISES AND DISCUSSIONS

EXERCISE 1
The rise in the Canadian consumer price index from 1993 to 1995 is shown in Table 10.1. What return on investment would be required to have a real rate of return of 7 percent during the period from 1993 through 1995?

SOLUTION 1
The compound rise in the CPI for 3 years starting in 1993 was

$$126.2(1 + f)^3 = 133.5$$
$$(1 + f)^3 = 133.5/126.2 = 1.058$$
$$f = 1.019 - 1 = 0.019 \text{ or } 1.9\%$$

Combining the real interest rate and the inflation rate yields an inflation-adjusted rate of $(1.07)(1.019) - 1 = 0.090$ or 9.0 percent.

EXERCISE 2
A company has developed its own inflation-factor index to allow a closer evaluation of future cash flows. The index was prepared by categorizing costs of production, determining the proportion spent in each category according to local conditions. Then the inflation factor index was calculated as the weighted average of all the inflation factors. The result is shown below.

Cost factors	Budget proportion	Inflation rate, %	Weighted rates
Labor (for the company work force)	0.25	8	2.0
Material 1 (raw materials)	0.10	5	0.5
Material 2 (subassemblies)	0.10	15	1.5
Energy (electricity, fuel, etc.)	0.25	20	5.0
General services (general inflation rate)	0.30	10	3.0
		Inflation-factor index	12.0%

A proposal is being evaluated to reduce labor costs and material waste by the purchase of automated equipment. The equipment is expected to be in service for 3 years with no salvage value. To simplify this example, straight-line depreciation is used and the tax rate for the company is 50 percent. Data from the proposal are summarized below.

Annual revenue	
Net savings in labor	$60,000
Net savings in material	$140,000
First cost	$150,000
Annual costs	
Additional energy required	$70,000
Added maintenance expense	$30,000

Evaluate the proposal.

SOLUTION 2
After-tax calculations that include the effects of the unique individual inflation rates are shown in Table 10.9. Each revenue and cost component is projected from real dollars to actual dollars by its exclusive inflation rate. (Maintenance falls within the general-service category, where the inflation rate is 10 percent.) Note that the BTCF in actual dollars is lower than in real dollars because expenses increase at a faster rate than savings. Actual dollars are converted back to real dollars in the ATCF by applying the inflation-factor index, 12 percent.

The BTCF in actual dollars for annual net revenue in years 1,2, and 3 is determined from the following formula by employing a different inflation rate for each cash-flow component:

$$\text{BTCF (actual dollars)} = \$60,000(F/P,8,N) + \$140,000(F/P,5,N)$$
$$- \$70,000(F/P,20,N) - \$30,000(F/P,10,N)$$

The proposal is evaluated by the rate-of-return method. A preliminary before-tax rate of return without considering inflation shows a promising value of

$$(A/P,i,3) = \$100,000/\$150,000 = 0.66667$$

TABLE 10.9

After-tax cash flow using exclusive inflation factors and an inflation-factor index

Year, N	BTCF, real dollars	BTCF actual dollars	Depre- ciation	Taxable income	Taxes at 50%	ATCF, actual dollars	ATCF, real dollars at f = 12%
0	−$150,000	−$150,000				−$150,000	−$150,000
1	100,000	94,800	$50,000	$44,800	$22,400	72,400	64,646
2	100,000	87,234	50,000	37,234	18,617	68,617	54,701
3	100,000	77,624	50,000	27,624	13,812	63,812	45,421

for which i is about 45 percent. A more realistic assessment, *still not considering inflation*, is obtained from an after-tax rate of return calculated as shown below.

$$(A/P,i,3) = [\$100,000 - \$50,000(0.5)]/\$150,000 = 0.5 \text{ and IRR} = 23.4\%$$

The *rate of return* calculated *when inflation effects are included* drops still lower:

$$PW = -\$150,000 + \$64,646(P/F,i,1) + \$54,701(P/F,i,2) + \$45,421(P/F,i,3) = 0 \text{ at IRR}$$

At $i = 5$ percent,

$$PW = \$150,000 - \$61,568 + \$49,615 + \$39,236 = \$419$$

At $i = 6$ percent

$$PW = \$150,000 + \$60,987 + \$48,684 + \$38,136 = \$2193$$
$$IRR = 5.2\%$$

The reason for the drop is twofold: Depreciation charges are not responsive to inflation and the costs (energy and services) in the proposal increase at a higher inflation rate than the savings (labor and material).

EXERCISE 3
An asset can be purchased for $80,000 and will have a 10-year useful life. A suggested lease arrangement is to pay $28,000 for the first 4 years and then make annual payments of $1500 for the remaining 6 years. Evaluate the suggestion.

SOLUTION 3
A closer look at the lease is needed. It is probable that Revenue Canada would consider the described "lease" as a disguised purchase aimed at reducing the total tax paid by the two parties. Conditions of the "lease" suggest that the lessee is actually

assuming an ownership position for the asset as a consequence of the large initial payments and minimal subsequent payments. The payment schedule would produce a fine return to the lessor, and the lessee's expenses would provide larger and earlier deductions from income than allowed for CCA of a comparable purchased asset. The lease plan is feasible only if it could be proved that the asset did indeed lose almost its entire value in 4 years.

10.9　PROBLEMS

10.1　Use the consumer price index data in Table 10.1 to determine the annual rate of inflation for the following periods.
- (*a*)　1986 through 1989
- (*b*)　1990 through 1995

10.2　Calculate the decline in purchasing power of the dollar over the following periods.
- (*a*)　1986 through 1989
- (*b*)　1990 through 1995

10.3　Electric energy costs within a specific geographic area are expected to increase at an annual rate of 5 percent over the next 5 years. Use an inflation-free discount rate of 10 percent to determine the present worth of this actual-dollar series of cash flows.

10.4　Over the next 5 years the inflation rate is forecast to be 6 percent compounded annually. A potential investment will pay a market interest rate of 10 percent for the first 3 years and 12 percent for the last 2 years. What is the average inflation-free rate of return?

10.5　A $10,000 investment would return a series of $3000 year-end payments over the next 5 years if no inflation were present. However, an average inflation rate of 6 percent is expected to increase the payments accordingly. If the annual market rate of interest remains at 13 percent, determine the present equivalent worth of the investment.

10.6　The investor in Prob. 10.5 has an opportunity to accept a revised proposal in which a single $27,000 lump-sum repayment will be made at the end of the 5-year period. Which plan is preferable?

10.7　Net cash flow from purchase of an asset for $1000 is expected to be responsive to inflation. The inflation rate is forecast to be 5 percent for the next 3 years. Based on this forecast, the expected cash flow in actual dollars is shown below.

Year	0	1	2	3
Cash flow, $	−1000	400	600	500

- (*a*)　What is the inflation-adjusted interest rate if the organization expects a real return on investments of 10 percent?
- (*b*)　Using this interest rate, calculate the present worth.
- (*c*)　What cash flow estimates in real dollars would produce the same present worth when discounted at 10 percent?

(d) Do you feel it is better practice to estimate future cash flow in then-current actual dollars or in now-current real dollars? Why?

10.8   The general inflation rate is 8 percent, and a company requires a real rate of return of 10 percent. A machine purchased for $10,000 will have no salvage value at the end of its 7-year useful life. It is expected to produce a revenue of $2000 the first year, with annual increases of 20 percent in subsequent years. Operating costs are $1000 in year 1 and will rise in proportion to the general inflation rate.

(a) Calculate the actual-dollar cash flow, convert it to real dollars, and determine the present worth.

(b) Show that the solution for part a can also be obtained by discounting the actual-dollar cash flow at i_f.

(c) Use the special interest rate i^* for a geometric series to calculate a modified revenue, and show that the resulting PW at $i = 10$ percent is the same as that determined in part a.

10.9   On completion of a doctorate degree in industrial engineering, a student has been offered two jobs. A faculty position in a university pays a starting salary of $45,000 with expected raises of 8 percent over the next 5 years. A research position in the R&D group of an aerospace company has a starting salary of $52,000 with annual raises of 5 percent over the next 5 years. If inflation is expected to be 5 percent per year and the market interest rate is 15 percent, find the present equivalence that represents the difference between these two offers, using (a) constant-dollar analysis and (b) actual-dollar analysis.

10.10   A city engineer is considering two alternatives for development of a riverfront park. Alternative A will cost $500,000 and is estimated to have a useful life of 20 years. Alternative B will cost $650,000 with a useful life of 30 years. If the market interest rate is 15 percent and inflation is expected to average 5 percent per year, which is the preferred alternative?

10.11   A couple is planning to save for their 9-year-old child's college expenses in advance. Assuming that the child enters college 10 years from now, it is going to require $10,000 per year in today's dollars to support college expenses for 4 years. Inflation over this time span is expected to average 5 percent per year. The couple can invest their savings in a fund that yields a market interest rate of 10 percent. Determine the equal amount the couple should save each year for 10 years to support their child's future college expenses. Assume that college payments are made at the start of the year.

10.12   A company can purchase a piece of equipment for $20,000 and sell it for $4000 (in today's dollars) at the end of its 8-year service life or can lease the unit for the same period by make beginning-of-the-year payments of $3000. Compare the two alternatives, using an inflation-adjusted interest rate of 15 percent. Assume that the salvage value increases at the general inflation rate of 5 percent per year.

10.13   A proposal has been submitted in real dollars that will produce a revenue of $110,000 annually for the next 10 years. It will require an initial investment of $150,000 in depreciable equipment that will be fully written off in 10 years by straight-line depreciation; no investment credit is applicable. Operating costs will be $52,000 per year. In addition, facilities will be leased for $6000 per year for 5 years; then the lease will be renegotiated for 5 more years at a constant annual charge of $6000(1 + f)^5$. The general inflation rate over the study period is expected to be 6 percent. The firm is subject to a tax rate of 46 percent and requires an after-tax, inflation-free rate of return of 4 percent. What is the present worth of the proposal?

10.14   Assume that a firm has an inflation-adjusted rate of return of 24 percent. The general inflation rate is 10 percent. Explain why the firm's real required rate of return is not 14 percent. What is it?

10.15   A $10,000 investment can be made today that will produce savings of $2000 annually for the next 7 years. There is no salvage value involved. Calculate the present worth of the investment at a real MARR of 10 percent. Show that the same PW results when the real-dollar savings inflate at 8 percent annually. Apply the inflation-adjusted interest rate to discount the actual-dollar cash flow.

10.16   Sales of a new product are expected to grow at a 12 percent compound rate for the next 3 years. Current sales are $1.2 million. The price of the product should increase at the national inflation rate of 6 percent per year. Production cost categories and associated expected inflation rates are shown below.

Production cost category	Current total cost, $/year	Inflation rate, %
Materials	200,000	9
Energy	150,000	12
Labor	150,000	8
All other	100,000	6

Depreciation charges for assets associated with production of the product amount to $200,000 per year. The company's effective tax rate is 45 percent.
   (a)   Assuming that marketing, overhead, and other nonproduction costs associated with the product amount to 50 percent of the production costs, determine the after-tax cash flow without considering inflation (the initial investment is the sum of the depreciation charges). Assume that sales revenue and total costs both grow annually at 12 percent.
   (b)   What is the before-tax rate of return when inflation is ignored?
   (c)   What is the after-tax rate of return when inflation is ignored?
   (d)   Determine the after-tax cash flow when it is assumed that price and production costs will inflate at the given unique rates while other costs will rise at the inflation factor index rate based on production costs only.
   (e)   What is the after-tax inflation-adjusted rate of return for the cash flow pattern in part d?

10.17   Consider the asset described in Table 10.10. Its cost is $6194, and it is expected to produce receipts of $1000 (column 1) in present buying power for 10 years. There is no salvage value. Depreciation and interest charges are based on 30 percent financing at 5 percent interest and straight-line depreciation (column 2). These charges remain the same regardless of the effect of inflation upon receipts. With an inflation rate of 3 percent, the real-dollar receipts in column 1 would grow to the values in column 3 in N years.
   (a)   Calculate the after-tax rate of return for the asset's purchase based on the real-dollar cash flow (columns 1 and 2). The effective income-tax rate is 50 percent.

TABLE 10.10

Cash flow of an asset purchased for $6194 and partly financed by an $1843 loan at 5%. Actual dollars responsive to 3% inflation result from real dollars multiplied by $(1.03)^N$

End of year N	Net receipts in real dollars (1)	Depreciation and interest charges, $ (2)	Net receipts in actual dollars (3)
0	−4351	0	−4351
1	1000	711	1030
2	1000	702	1061
3	1000	693	1093
4	1000	684	1126
5	1000	675	1159
6	1000	665	1194
7	1000	656	1230
8	1000	647	1267
9	1000	638	1305
10	1000	629	1344

(b) Calculate the after-tax rate of return based on actual-dollar cash flow when the tax rate is 50 percent.

10.18 A third option for purchasing a piece of construction equipment becomes available to the construction company described in Example 10.5. The equipment can be purchased by using a 8-year financing plan. This plan will use a bank loan of 8 years at an interest rate of 9 percent. The loan requires a 10 percent down payment. Compare this option with the two options evaluated in Example 10.5.

10.19 According to Sullivan and Bontadelli,[†]

At a time when the most productive use of capital is so important, it would be foolish to ignore the anticipated effects of inflation and take the risk of losing competitive position because of indifference (or ignorance) in this regard. Omitting inflation from engineering economy studies is the same as assuming that the monetary unit is a constant-valued measure of worth. This is clearly out of tune with the present and expected future conditions in the business environment.

Do you agree? Why?

10.20 During periods of severe inflation, consumers tend to spend money as soon as it is received and to use credit for large purchases instead of saving money to buy them later. Businesses also have common reactions to severe inflation.
   (a) Lending rates are higher. Why?
   (b) Investments that increase rapidly in value are prized. What types of investments are most popular to counter double-digit inflation?

[†] W. G. Sullivan and J. A. Bontadelli, "How an IE Can Account for Inflation in Decision Making," *Industrial Engineering*, vol. 12, no. 3, pp. 24–33, 1980.

SENSITIVITY
ANALYSIS

There are two times in a man's life when he should not speculate:
when he can't afford it, and when he can.

Mark Twain (Samuel Clemens),
Following the Equator, 1899

Sensitivity analysis provides a second look at an economic evaluation. It questions whether the original estimates adequately represent the future conditions that could affect a proposal if it were implemented. Its purpose is to assist decision makers. In almost any economic environment, some of the elements are based on the best guess of experienced personnel or very cursory analysis of minimal data. It is, therefore, extremely important to determine the degree of sensitivity of results to the values used. If the preference is reversed, either from acceptance to rejection or between competing alternatives, with slight variations in some of the elements, this may provide the motivation and the justification of expenditure of additional time and money to obtain more accurate estimates. On the other hand, if the results do not change over wide fluctuations in the values of the elements, no further effort is needed or justified, and the results will help reassure the decision maker of the thoroughness of the study and the validity of the results.

A sensitivity analysis can be performed with PW, EAW, or IRR calculations by using before-tax or after-tax cash flows, but should be on an after-tax basis if taxes are involved and are expected to influence the decision. The sensitivity of any of the elements used in the calculations can be checked. Analyses can be displayed on sensitivity graphs that show the effects of percentage variations for key parameters. The graphs are useful because they consolidate analytical data in a single, easily understood display.

469

Several formats are suitable for sensitivity studies. Cash flow factors can be investigated individually or in pairs, as in an isoquant. More favorable or less favorable estimates can be used to obtain a range of values for a proposal's worth. All the approaches are geared to the question, What if?

11.1   WHAT IF?

Lurking behind every meaningful decision are "what if" doubts: What if sales differ from forecasts? What if cash flow does not follow the planned pattern? What if a new, far better challenger becomes available? What if inflation is higher than expected? What if shortages disrupt operations? For major decisions the list of what-if's resulting from inadequate information or lack of predictability of the economic environment is discouragingly long, but decisions still have to be made. To escape inertia caused by doubts, first decision makers must accept the fact that they will seldom, if ever, know all conditions with absolute certainty. Then they can focus on one or more critical factors and investigate what would happen to a proposal as a result of variations in those factors. That is the purpose of sensitivity analysis.

Sensitivity analysis involves repeated computations with different cash flow elements and analysis factors to compare results obtained from these substitutions with results from the original data. If a small change in an element leads to a proportionately greater change in the results, the situation is said to be *sensitive* to that assumption or variable. In an economic study, the critical point is the level at which an analysis factor causes an economic proposal to change from acceptable to not acceptable or reverses a preference between alternatives.

Sensitivity studies are the first step in investigating risk. *Risk* refers to lack of predictability about the economic environment and about the outcomes and choices that are available in the decision situation. Sensitivity analysis results in identification of elements that cause substantial changes in a performance measure. The second step, referred to as *risk analysis,* consists of estimating such elements in greater depth and evaluating their effect on the performance measures. Risk analysis is the subject of Chap. 13.

An informal sensitivity assessment is natural for most decisions. Variability in cash flow estimates and the effects of different values of i, N, P, and S were considered in several chapters. In this chapter, formal procedures for evaluating deviations from basic data are discussed, with emphasis on the value of graphical representations.

Consideration of the sensitivity of assumptions begins at the preproposal stage, where it is decided whether ideas for improvements are worthy of further development, and continues to the proposal presentation stage, where a case is made for the final acceptance or rejection decision. Graphs, charts, and tables are often prepared to explain the sensitivity of proposals to key decision makers. The data for the visual aids are generated by substituting different values for the critical variables into formulas used during proposal analysis. The purpose of pictorial presentations is to clarify the considerations pertinent to a proposal's acceptance and to present results in a compact but readily understood format. The role of sensitivity analysis in proposal planning and evaluation is explored in the following examples.

EXAMPLE 11.1

What If an Investment Is Made that Increases Fixed Costs?

An engineer has suggested an improvement in a production line that requires a substantial investment. This alteration will increase the fixed cost of production. While it can be shown that the alteration improves quality and reduces variable costs, the question remains of whether future sales revenue will provide sufficient additional income to make the investment worthwhile.

Figure 11.1 displays the considerations involved, in the form of a break-even chart (break-even analysis and break-even charts are presented in Chap. 12). The annual cost of the proposed improvement is represented by an increase in the fixed cost of production. This increase raises the total production cost, which is the sum of variable costs and fixed costs. The total cost increases as a function of annual output volume, as does sales revenue when the output is sold. Potential variations in costs and revenues are shown by shaded areas. If it is reasonable to expect sales revenue to increase enough to offset the added fixed costs, or if the proposal will decrease variable costs enough to pay for itself, or if a combination of greater sales revenue and lower variable costs will produce a large enough positive cash flow, then the proposal merits further development.

FIGURE 11.1

Possible results of an investment that increases fixed cost to improve quality and reduce variable costs. The critical factor is whether the output volume will be sufficient to support the investment.

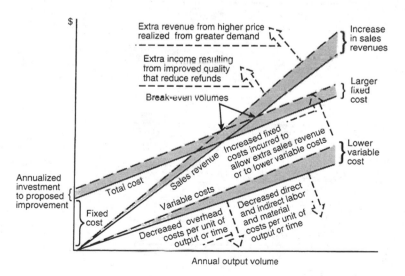

It is doubtful that a chart would be drawn to enunciate the prospective operation variables in the example. The sensitivity analysis would more likely be a mental evaluation or preliminary calculation to confirm that receipts or savings could plausibly be expected to cover the investment. Then the idea would emerge from the preproposal to the proposal stage.

EXAMPLE 11.2

What If Demand for Services and Labor Costs Change?

In most service industries, demand fluctuates in response to local or national trends. Inflation, unemployment, size of harvests, and other conditions that cannot be confidently forecasted affect the cash flow of a proposal. In deciding whether to introduce a new labor-intensive service, a company is concerned about the demand for the new service and possible increases in labor costs.

The nature of the service to be offered suggests that demand might exceed the basic estimate by 10 percent or might fall short of expectation by 10 percent. Labor costs could increase by 5 or 10 percent over original estimates. The effect of these variations is analyzed by calculating the present worth of the project at each level of anticipated demand and labor costs. Results of the calculations are shown in Table 11.1.

From the table it appears that PW is not very sensitive to labor costs; it is unlikely that a labor-cost estimating error will lead to a "wrong" decision because the proposal's PW does not rise disproportionately to labor costs. However, a 10 percent increase or decrease in demand causes a pronounced change in the present worth, a variation of 17 to 43 percent from the basic data. This sensitivity indicates that more study may be justified to ensure that the demand level used in the original data is supportable.

TABLE 11.1

Present worth, $, of proposal as it is affected by changes in demand and increases in labor costs

| Labor costs | Demand level | | |
	Decrease of 10%	Original data	Increase of 10%
Basic data	250,000	300,000	420,000
Increase of 5%	255,000	310,000	440,000
Increase of 10%	265,000	325,000	465,000

11.2   SENSITIVITY OF A SINGLE PROPOSAL

Assume that a decision is to be made about a business opportunity based on the following estimates and tentative before-tax analysis:

Economic factors	PW for a 10-year study period at $i = 13\%$, $
First cost ($170,000)	−170,000
Annual receipts ($35,000)	+189,917
Annual disbursements ($3000)	−16,279
Salvage value ($20,000)	+5,892
Net PW	+9,530

The first cost is the most reliably known value in the problem, owing to its immediacy. The other factors could vary considerably over the 10-year period, owing to unforeseeable deviations from anticipated conditions. Even the study period may be inappropriate if the asset's useful life is shorter than 10 years (or longer than 10 years), or if the function the asset serves does not continue to yield the stated receipts for the full study period. And the 13 percent rate of return might be questioned. Should it be higher to compensate for inflation and the risk of losing invested capital? Or should it be lower?

11.2.1   Single-Parameter Sensitivity

Assume that the estimate for annual receipts is questionable; the estimate varies over the range of $30,000 to $40,000. The resulting values for present worth are obtained by substituting annual-receipts values in the PW formula

$$PW = -\text{first cost} + (\text{salvage value})\,(P/F,\, i,\, N)$$
$$+ (\text{receipts} - \text{disbursements})\,(P/A,\, i,\, N)$$

while holding the values of all other factors constant. This new information is shown graphically in Fig. 11.2. This is referred to as a *sensitivity graph*.

The two alternatives available to the decision maker are either to accept the proposal or to reject the proposal and invest the funds elsewhere. The intersection of the curve with the horizontal x axis in Fig. 11.2 represents the point where a change from one alternative to the other is indicated. This point is also referred to as the *break-even point*. That is, the break-even point is that value of the parameter (in this case, annual

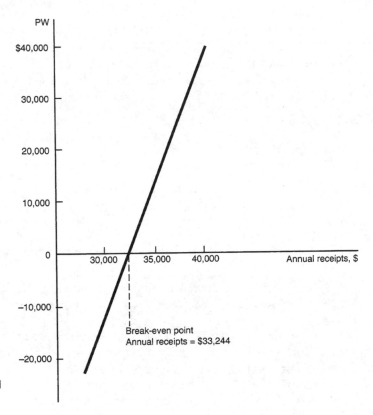

FIGURE 11.2
Sensitivity graph showing the effect of changes in annual receipts on net PW.

receipts) that results in a zero net present value. This value may be determined either algebraically, by setting PW to zero and solving for annual receipts, or graphically.

In this example, the proposal outcome is sensitive to changes in annual receipts in that the break-even point (annual receipts = $33,244) lies within the expected range of values for annual receipts ($30,000 to $40,000) and may result in a decision reversal. The decision maker may choose to forgo the investment opportunity even though the PW associated with the initial estimate was positive. An alternative strategy would be to invest additional resources in an effort to resolve the uncertainty surrounding the initial estimates.

An alternative approach is to examine net PW as a function of deviation percentage from the estimated value. For the example,

$$PW = -\$170{,}000 + \$35{,}000(1 + x)(P/A, 13, 10) - \$3000(P/A, 13, 10) \\ + \$20{,}000(P/F, 13, 10)$$

where x is the deviation in the estimate of annual receipts. The curve in Fig. 11.3 is generated by substituting various values of x into this formula.

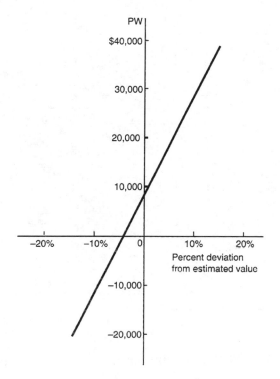

FIGURE 11.3
Sensitivity graph
showing net PW as
a function of devia-
tions from estimated
values in annual
receipts.

The x axis of the graph is the percentage of deviation from original values. The point where the curve crosses the x axis represents the break-even point. As shown, the break-even point is −5 percent, which is consistent with the previous result:

$$\frac{\$33,244 - \$35,000}{\$35,000} = -0.05$$

The dimensionless scale on the x axis resulting from using the deviation in parameter estimates puts all the factors in the same perspective to allow direct comparison of curve shapes, as shown in Fig. 11.4. A more steeply rising or falling curve indicates greater sensitivity of the proposal's worth to that factor.

Errors of ±50 percent are not uncommon when one is forecasting the rate of inflation. The sensitivity graph reveals that deviations of up to 50 percent of the original estimates for salvage value and annual disbursements will not affect the acceptance of the proposal. The other factors—minimum acceptable rate of return (MARR), number of years the proposal will stay in effect, and amount of annual receipts—could change the decision to the do-nothing alternative if they deviate by only 10 percent from the original estimates. This condition suggests that extra care be given to

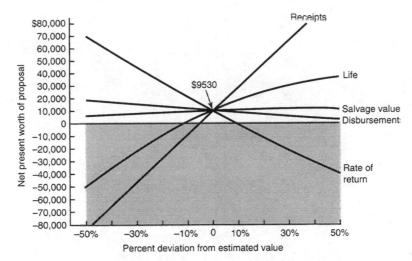

FIGURE 11.4
Sensitivity graph of the effect on a proposal's net PW when factors deviate from their original estimates.

forecasts of future business conditions that could affect income flow or the continued demand for the asset purchased.

11.2.2 Two-Parameter Sensitivity

The analyst may wish to test for the sensitivity of the outcome of two parameters, say, life of an asset and size of receipts, both considered simultaneously. This situation is not uncommon in cash flow analysis, as variation in one factor may affect the values of other factors. A common example is a decrease in salvage value with the life of an asset. What is required is a technique that considers variations in both factors simultaneously.

Family-of-curves approach. In this approach, one variable is held constant at a specific value, say, $N = 10$ years, and the present worth is plotted as a function of the other variable. The process is then repeated for other values of N. The values selected for N are usually those of greatest interest to the decision maker.

Assume that in the previous example, the values of interest for N range from 7 to 13 years and for annual receipts from $30,000 to $40,000. The resulting family of curves is shown in Fig. 11.5. The shaded area in Fig. 11.5 represents all possible combinations of annual receipts and proposal life. The proposal yields negative present worth over the range of annual receipts for $N = 7$ years and positive present worth over the range of annual receipts for $N = 13$ years. Breakeven points can be readily determined from this graph.

Isoquants. Another approach to study variations in two factors simultaneously utilizes isoquants. An isoquant represents an *indifference line*, which indicates the combinations of proposal duration and size of receipts

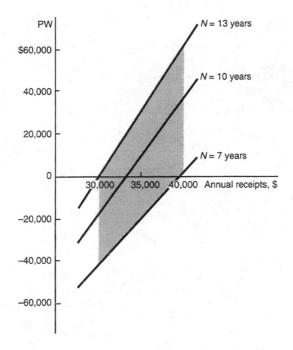

IGURE 11.5
amily of curves
howing variation in
present worth as a
unction of annual
eceipts for different
alues of a pro-
osal's life.

that make the present worth of the proposal neither positive nor negative (indifference condition), when the other factors are unchanged. Figure 11.6 shows combinations of proposal life and annual receipts at which the present worth is zero. Thus, a reduction in the life of the asset from 10 to 8 years must be accompanied by an increase in annual receipts for 8 years of at least $36,859 - $35,000 = $1859 for the proposal to be minimally acceptable at $i = 13$ percent:

$$\text{PW} = -\$170,000 + \$20,000(P/F, 13, 8) + (\$36,859 - \$3000)(P/A, 13, 8)$$

$$0 = -\$170,000 + \$20,000(0.37616) + \$33,859(4.7987)$$

An indifference line divides a chart into acceptance and rejection zones. Any combination that falls above the indifference line in Fig. 11.6 indicates that the proposal is acceptable when other factors remain constant. Indifference lines are usually nonlinear when project life or interest rates are variables.

Still another approach is to use graphs of percentage of deviation for two factors in the isoquant format. A formula is written to determine the present or annual worth of the proposal in which one parameter is associated with the x axis and the other with the y axis. The intent of the formulation is to develop an expression relating values of parameter x and parameter y that generate zero present worth or annual worth. The resulting expression is represented by a line on the sensitivity graph. Percentage

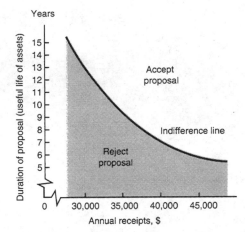

FIGURE 11.6
Isoquant showing combinations of proposal life and annual receipts at which present worth is zero.

changes from the original data that occur on one side of the line maintain a positive worth for the proposal, while changes that fall on the other side cause a negative worth. This approach is illustrated in Example 11.3.

EXAMPLE 11.3

Two-Parameter Sensitivity Study

The proposal pictured in Figs. 11.4, 11.5, and 11.6 is to be tested for sensitivity to annual receipts and disbursements. The intent is to determine how large a joint percentage change in these critical parameters can be sustained without rejecting the proposal; it will be rejected if the equivalent annual worth is negative. Develop a sensitivity graph that identifies the acceptance and rejection zones.

Solution

Letting x represent a percentage change in receipts and y a percentage change in disbursements, we find that the equivalent annual worth (EAW) for the proposal is

$$
\begin{aligned}
\text{EAW} = &-\$170{,}000(A/P, 13, 10) + \$35{,}000(1 + x) - \$3000(1 + y) \\
&+ \$20{,}000(A/F, 13, 10) \\
= &-\$170{,}000(0.18429) + \$35{,}000 + \$35{,}000x - \$3000 - \$3000y \\
&+ \$20{,}000(0.05429) \\
= &\$1757 + \$35{,}000x - \$3000y
\end{aligned}
$$

where x and y represent changes from the original data.

The proposal will be profitable, and therefore acceptable, as long as EAW > 0, or

$$
x > \frac{3000}{35{,}000}\, y - \frac{1757}{35{,}000}
$$

so

$$x > 0.0857y - 0.0502$$

When this inequality is plotted on a graph with the x and y axes scaled in percent (Fig. 11.7), the indifference line separates the chart into acceptance and rejection zones. The acceptance zone is on the side of the line where EAW > 0, and the rejection zone is on the other side. The nearly vertical slope of the line indicates that the proposal is highly sensitive to changes in the x factor (receipts) and quite insensitive to the y factor, as is obvious from a comparison of the magnitude of annual receipts relative to annual disbursements.

The center of the sensitivity graph ($x = 0$, $y = 0$) in Fig. 11.7 represents the original conditions for the proposal, where EAW = $1757. At $x = -5$ percent and $y = 0$,

$$\text{EAW} = \$1757 + \$35,000(-0.05) - \$3000(0.0) = \$7$$

At $y = -5$ percent and $x = 0$,

$$\text{EAW} = \$1757 + \$35,000(0.0) - \$3000(-0.05) = \$1907$$

Thus the sensitivity study clearly emphasizes the criticality of an accurate forecast of future receipts.

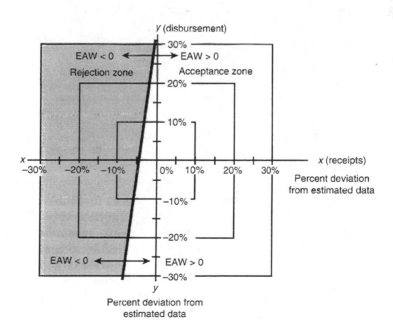

FIGURE 11.7
Sensitivity graph of percentage changes for two factors (receipts and disbursements) that define acceptance and rejection zones for a proposal when all other factors are held constant.

11.2.3 More than Two Parameters

Using the previous example, we now assume that, in addition to uncertainty about annual savings and proposal life, there is uncertainty about the discount rate and salvage value. Two approaches are available for analyzing simultaneous variation in more than two parameters.

The first involves reducing the problem to a series of two-dimensional graphs. For this example, the first graph may show present worth as a function of annual receipts, given $i = 13$ percent and $S = \$20,000$ and a family of curves for $N = 7$, 10, and 13 years; the second graph could plot present worth as a function of annual receipts for $i = 10$ percent and $S = \$20,000$ and a family of curves for $N = 7$, 10, and 13 years; and so on. This approach suffers from two disadvantages. First, although a series of smaller problems is solved, the simultaneous variation in multiple factors is not tested. Second, the number of graphs required grows exponentially as the number of uncertain factors increases.

The second approach is called *scenario generation*. An intensive assessment of a proposal's cash flow is provided by a scenario approach that asks, What if the future is more favorable or less favorable than originally estimated? By bracketing the most likely cash flow condition with optimistic and pessimistic scenarios, the analyst reveals the shortcomings and strengths of the proposal. Each element of the proposal is questioned with respect to conditions envisioned for the bleak and promising scenarios. Most elements will probably vary from initial estimates, but some elements may be stable. The sensitivity of the proposal to each scenario is revealed by comparing the PW, EAW, or IRR values of the three sets of data.

Range of estimates.   The range is developed from

1. *An objective estimate*—the most likely cash flow and the one that would be used if only a single estimate were made
2. *A more favorable estimate*—an optimistic appraisal based on an advantageous interpretation of future events
3. *A less favorable estimate*—a pessimistic assessment of the future that adversely affects the cash flow

Neither the more favorable nor the less favorable estimate is based on an extreme—the best or worst that could conceivably happen. They assess the outcomes of border conditions that are reasonably likely to occur. The three-estimate approach is also applicable to uncertainties besides price; analyses based on ranges of possible levels of activity, such as utilization rates and output quantities, or on levels of performance may be more useful than single-estimate evaluations.

Suppose that the following range of values is possible for the previous example:

Uncertain factors	Less favorable estimate	Objective estimate	More favorable estimate
Annual receipts, $	30,000	35,000	40,000
Salvage value, $	0	20,000	40,000
N, years	7	10	13
i, %	15	13	10

The present worth for the less favorable estimate is −$57,669, for the objective estimate $9530, and for the more favorable estimate $104,411.

If the present worths for the optimistic and pessimistic estimates were negative, the proposal should be rejected. Conversely, if both present-worth values had been positive, a decision to accept would have been indicated. Unfortunately, as in this example, the extreme conditions rarely yield a clear result. Nevertheless, such analyses are recommended. The computations involved are relatively easy, and the results do provide reassurance to the decision maker or justification for additional effort.

Item-by-item estimates are more credible than collective estimates. Additional work is required to develop estimates for smaller cash flow categories; but the resulting summations are more likely to be accurate than are block estimates, and the effort expended makes the analyst better informed about the situation. The cost of extra calculations and estimating is usually insignificant compared with the value of even a small improvement in the decision process. Therefore, when price instability casts doubt on future cash flows, or when operating levels cannot be anticipated with any assurance, an evaluation encompassing a range of itemized estimates is a sound practice.

EXAMPLE 11.4

Range of Estimates that Reflect Uncertain Future Prices for a Training Proposal

A proposal has been made to introduce a training program to improve a production process that relies primarily on manual operations. New motions and fixtures for individual operators are expected to lower manufacturing costs from their present level by about $50,000 per year. It is difficult to predict the benefits of the training proposal because the size of the savings depends on the scale of operations and on prices, which are functions of the marketplace and general economic conditions.

The table below shows a range of estimates for possible future conditions. Should the training program be adopted?

Items estimated	Less favorable estimate	Objective estimate	More favorable estimate
Additional units produced annually	60,000	75,000	100,000
Price per unit, $	2	3	3.50
Annual income, $	120,000	225,000	350,000
Duration of income, years	5	6	7
Training cost per year, $	45,000	35,000	30,000
Required period of intensive training, years	2	2	1
Operating expenses of new processes, $	90,000	160,000	275,000
Investment in consumable supplies, $	30,000	30,000	30,000

Solution

A before-tax analysis using a 15 percent required rate of return is conducted by calculating the present worth of the cash flows for the three possible conditions: *less favorable (LF), objective estimate (OE),* and *more favorable (MF).*

$$PW(LF) = (\$120{,}000 - \$90{,}000)(P/A, 15, 5) - \$45{,}000(P/A, 15, 2)$$
$$- \$30{,}000$$
$$= \$30{,}000(3.35216) - \$45{,}000(1.62571) - \$30{,}000$$
$$= \$100{,}565 - \$73{,}157 - \$30{,}000$$
$$= -\$2592$$

$$PW(OE) = (\$225{,}000 - \$160{,}000)(P/A, 15, 6) - \$35{,}000(P/A, 15, 2)$$
$$- \$30{,}000$$
$$= \$65{,}000(3.78448) - \$35{,}000(1.62571) - \$30{,}000$$
$$= \$245{,}991 - \$56{,}900 - \$30{,}000$$
$$= \$159{,}091$$

$$PW(MF) = (\$350{,}000 - \$275{,}000)(P/A, 15, 7) - \$30{,}000(P/A, 15, 1)$$
$$- \$30{,}000$$
$$= \$75{,}000(4.16042) - \$30{,}000(0.86957) - \$30{,}000$$
$$= \$312{,}032 - \$26{,}087 - \$30{,}000$$
$$= \$255{,}945$$

Although there is a chance that the training program will result in a small loss if the less favorable scenario occurs, the opportunity for a very large gain under more favorable conditions makes the proposal very attractive. The three-phase analysis admits the chance of low returns and shows how good returns can be if things turn out favorably.

11.3   **SENSITIVITY OF ALTERNATIVES**

An alternative A_2 has been developed to accomplish the same mission as the proposal A_1 described by the sensitivity relationships in Fig. 11.4. Both alternatives are expected to have the same revenue, but proposal A_2 has a lower first cost. However, the annual disbursements for A_2 will increase significantly each year, as shown by the following cash flow estimates:

Factor	Alternative A_1	Alternative A_2
First cost, $	170,000	116,400
Annual receipts, $	35,000	35,000
Salvage value (year 10), $	20,000	0
Annual disbursements, $	3,000	2500 the first year and increasing by 2500 each year

On the basis of the given estimates and a study period of 10 years with $i = 13$ percent, proposal A_2 results in higher net PW:

$\text{PW}(A_1) = \$9530$ from the data given in Sec. 11.2.

$$\begin{aligned}
\text{PW}(A_2) &= -\$116{,}400 + [\$35{,}000 - \$2500 \\
&\quad -\$2500(A/G,13,10)](P/A,13,10) \\
&= -\$116{,}400 + [\$32{,}500 - \$2500(3.51619)](5.42624) \\
&= \$12{,}254
\end{aligned}$$

11.3.1   Single-Parameter Sensitivity

Let's assume that the most questionable feature is the study period. A sensitivity graph for the alternatives' possible useful lives is given in Fig. 11.8.

The break-even point may be determined either graphically or algebraically. The algebraic solution is found by equating the present-worth relations for the two alternatives. The graph in Fig. 11.8 indicates that A_2 is preferred to A_1 when the likelihood is that the period of need will be less than 11 years. At $N = 7$, neither proposal is profitable. Proposal A_1 offers much larger gains should the period of need be 11 years or more.

The most critical cash flow elements that distinguish one alternative from another are usually quite evident. If one alternative has an exceptionally large salvage value, estimates for N and i should be scrutinized. An after-tax evaluation of proposals where one alternative has a particularly favorable loan arrangement suggests close inspection of interest rates. Any of the elements so picked for further examination can be graphed.

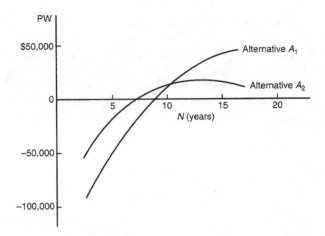

FIGURE 11.8
Sensitivity of two proposals to deviations from their estimated lives.

Often a graph will assist in a decision by narrowing the judgments that must be made. For instance, growth rate is frequently a debatable parameter. Growth may be a function of inflation because it affects certain cash flow elements or a function of the rate of service expansion, as in higher production rates needed to satisfy increasing demand for a product. Growth rate is shown on the x axis of Fig. 11.9, where the present worths of three alternatives are graphed.

Intersections of the plotted lines indicate the range of growth over which each alternative is preferred. Where proposals are presented in this fashion, it is not necessary to substantiate the selection of a certain growth rate for the study; the managers who are responsible for the final selection can use their personal judgment about which alternative best serves their

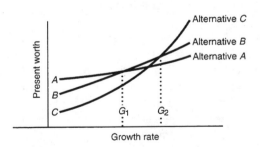

FIGURE 11.9
Sensitivity comparisons of present worth of three alternatives that have different growth rates. Alternative A is preferred if the anticipated growth rate is less than G_1, and alternative C is the choice when growth is expected to exceed G_2. Between G_1 and G_2, alternative B has the highest present worth.

vision of future conditions. Also, the decision makers do not have to fret over a specific growth rate; they need only pick a range in which they expect it to fall.

Decision reversal. Another way to assess the degree of sensitivity of results to variation in factors is to compute the percentage change in a factor that will cause a reversal in preference for alternatives, assuming that all other factors are held at the most likely estimates. For the two alternatives in Fig. 11.8, the net PW for A_2 is higher than that for A_1 for the most likely estimates. For A_1 to be preferred, either initial costs or operating costs have to decrease; or annual receipts, salvage value, or study period has to increase. The percentage change in each variable can be computed by equating the PW relation for A_1 to the net PW of A_2, while holding all but one variable at the most likely values. Thus, for the initial cost x,

$$\$12,254 = -x + (\$35,000 - \$3000)(P/A, 13, 10) + \$20,000(P/F, 13, 10)$$

from which $x = \$167,276$. Thus a $2724 ($170,000 - $167,276) decrease in initial cost would make A_1 more desirable than A_2. Similar estimates associated with salvage value and estimated life of A_1 are as follows:

Factor	Most likely estimate	Estimate to make A_1 preferable	Change in estimated value	Percentage change
Initial cost	$170,000	$167,276	$2724	1.6
Salvage value	$20,000	$29,246	$9246	46.2
Estimated life	10 years	10.35 years	0.35 year	3.5

Small changes in either the initial cost or the estimated life will cause a reversal in preference. On the other hand, errors in estimation of salvage value will not affect the decision.

11.3.2 Multiple-Parameter Sensitivity

Quite frequently, estimates of more than one factor are in question. The scenario generation approach involving a range of estimates for the sensitive factors can be effectively used for multiple alternatives.

Range of estimates. Assume that the estimates for annual receipts and salvage value are in question for the two proposals. The possible ranges of values for these two parameters are as follows:

	Annual receipts, $	Salvage value, $
Alternative A_1:		
Less favorable	30,000	0
Most likely	35,000	20,000
More favorable	40,000	40,000
Alternative A_2:		
Less favorable	28,400	0
Most likely	35,000	0
More favorable	42,600	20,000

The net PWs in dollars for alternatives A_1 and A_2 for the three scenarios are as follows:

	Less favorable	Most likely	More favorable
PW_{A_1}	−23,491	9,530	42,555
PW_{A_2}	−23,560	12,254	59,385
$PW_{A_2-A_1}$	−69	2,724	16,830

The net PW for A_2 is higher than that for A_1 for the most likely and the optimistic scenarios; the performances of the two alternatives are equivalent for the pessimistic case. Thus A_2 is the better alternative for the system under study.

The differences in net PW for the two alternatives make sense if variations in likely scenarios for the alternatives are *perfectly correlated*. That is, if the pessimistic scenario prevails for A_1, it also prevails for A_2. Similarly, both alternatives experience optimistic conditions at the same time. What this means is that the two alternatives are similar in terms of the technology used; thus variations in economic conditions cause variations in cash flows in the same direction, although the magnitudes of variation may be different.

In addition to the amount of variation, the direction of variation may vary among alternatives. Advancements in technology are most evident in manufacturing and process industries. Engineering economists must evaluate the merit of replacing machines with updated versions or with models that perform the same function in an entirely different way, perhaps requiring a whole new support system. Cash flow patterns for alternatives in such situations are very different from each other.

Isoquants. Isoquants can be used to test the sensitivity of decision reversal to simultaneous variations in two factors. The alternatives in Fig. 11.8 have to be tested for sensitivity to annual receipts and disbursements.

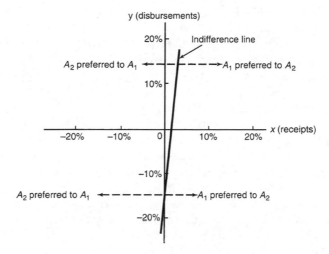

FIGURE 11.10
Sensitivity graph of the percentage change for two factors (receipts and disbursements) that define preference zones for two alternatives.

Let x and y represent the percentage changes in receipts and disbursements for alternative A_1. Then alternative A_1 is better than A_2 if

$$-\$170{,}000 + [\$35{,}000(1 + x) - \$3000(1 + y)](P/A, \, 13, \, 10)$$
$$+ \$20{,}000(P/F, \, 13, \, 10) > \$12{,}254$$

or

$$x > 0.0857y + 0.01434$$

This inequality is plotted in Fig. 11.10. Any point on the indifference line indicates the two alternatives to be equally desirable. Alternative A_1 is preferred to A_2 to the right of the indifference line. The reverse is true to the left of the line. Similarly, indifference lines may be based on variation in receipts and disbursements for alternative A_2.

11.4   DATA CONSIDERATIONS IN ECONOMIC ANALYSIS

In the previous chapters we saw how different data are factored into cash flows. The engineering economist then uses economic models to develop data to assist the decision maker in arriving at a logical and informed decision. The purpose of this section is to discuss some issues related to sources of cash flow data. Most cash flow data can be secured from familiar sources: competitive bids, price quotes, accounting records, standard times and costs, cost indices, etc. The final decision to fund or reject a proposed investment depends upon the quality of input data.

Economic analyses are built from data as a house is built of bricks, but an accumulation of data is no more an analysis than a pile of bricks is a house. There are piles of data everywhere. They fill the shelves of libraries and accumulate limitlessly from the unending parade of statistics and information issued by all kinds of agencies, public and private. Yet, when a particular fact is crucial to an analysis, it may be elusive or impossible to procure. Data difficulties range from an overabundance, when the problem is to digest information into a usable form, to a scarcity that may force guesses to substitute for facts.

Information is both the raw material and the finished product of an engineering economic evaluation. The evaluation process is similar to familiar production processes. Bits of data, the raw materials, are received from many sources and are inspected for accuracy before being accepted. They are fed into the engineering economics "machinery," where they are translated and transformed into the desired product: an economic comparison. As in any product process, it is necessary to know the raw materials needed, the best sources, and the ways to determine whether these are adequate.

A new project may be identical in design and mission to one just completed, but the cash flows for the two will probably differ considerably. This variation from one study to the next is characteristic of economic analyses. Unlike physical laws that consistently follow an orderly cause-and-effect relation, economic laws depend on the behavior of people, and people are erratic. However, past behavior is still a respectable clue to future behavior.

Engineers are well prepared to judge the future performance of materials and machines. Past performance can be extrapolated, and modified if necessary, to predict performance on the next project. The monetary values for the future conditions are less reliably predicted. Strikes, shortages, competition, inflation, and other factors that affect unit costs cannot always be anticipated. Therefore, estimating starts with the calculation of design amounts based on known physical relations and concludes with the assignment of comparatively less known monetary measures for the design conditions.

11.4.1 Sources of Cost Data

Figure 11.11 shows the traditional cost and price structure for a manufactured product. Most of the categories are also appropriate for service functions. The principal variation occurs in the relative sizes of the cost categories; manufacturing usually has a higher material/labor ratio than does service. Public services would be represented by the model in Fig. 11.11 by eliminating the top two tiers.

The quantities and types of materials required can be determined quite accurately from past records and engineering design documents (e.g., the bill of materials and parts list that accompany blueprints). Current prices are also readily assessable. Difficulties creep in as the price quotes are pushed farther into the future. Experts from the purchasing department in

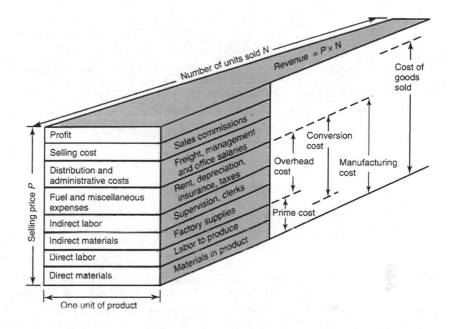

FIGURE 11.11
Composition of costs traditionally used in accounting for the price of a manufactured product.

a large firm can assist with predictions through their experience with commodity futures and knowledge of the firm's policies toward *speculating* (buying in large quantities to take advantage of price fluctuations, or buying contracts for future deliveries at prices set now, called *hedging*). A vital part of any estimating process is to be aware of the organization's economic policies and practices.

When purchasing experts are not available, many types of *cost indices* can furnish information. As discussed in Chap. 10, a cost index is a dimensionless number that indicates how cost or price for a class of items changes with time. It provides a comparison of cost or price changes from year to year for a fixed quantity of goods or services at particular locations. For building construction alone, there are a dozen major U.S. indices compiled for different parts of the country and different types of construction. The Bureau of Labor Statistics is the primary source of national data.

Labor costs are a function of skill level, labor supply, and time required. The saying *time is money* is especially true in estimating the cost of work. Standards for the amount of output per labor-hour have been developed for many classes of work. Time standards are based on a "normal" pace for an activity, with allowances included for personal relief and unusually severe working conditions. Standard times combined with expected wage rates provide a reasonable estimate of labor costs for repetitive jobs. Labor costs for specialized work can be predicted from bid estimates or quotes by professionals and agencies offering the service. A project involving a new type of work will likely have higher labor costs at first, while experience is being gained.

Remember that the cost of labor includes more than direct wages. Fringe benefits may amount to more than half the base wage in accounting for accident, health, and unemployment insurance; vacation and retirement pay; and special agreements such as guaranteed annual wages or sabbatical leaves. Extra costs due to relocation allowances, accidents, and sickness should also be considered.

Maintenance costs are the ordinary costs required for the upkeep of property and the restoration required when assets are damaged but not replaced. Items under maintenance include the costs of inspecting and locating trouble areas, replacement of minor parts, power, labor, materials, and minor changes in or rearrangements of existing facilities for more efficient use. Maintenance costs tend to increase with the age of an asset because more upkeep is required later in life and the trend of wages and material prices is upward.

Property taxes and insurance are usually expressed as a percentage of first cost in economic comparisons. Although the value of property decreases with age, taxes and insurance seldom show a corresponding decrease. Therefore, a constant annual charge is a realistic appraisal of future expense.

The *first cost* of acquiring a major asset may rise well above expectation, especially if the asset originates from a new design or untried process. Cost overruns are legendary in government projects, and they haunt the private sector, too. After a design is set, direct acquisition costs are readily determined from manufacturers' quotes or competitive bidding. When errors occur, they are typically on the low side, as a result of using incomplete listings of desired features and neglecting less obvious costs such as the following:

- Materials (freight, sales tax, storage costs, damage)
- Installation (extra costs for special arrangements and unconventional designs)
- Interest, taxes, salaries, and insurance during a design or construction phase
- Change orders during construction (installation costs for additions to or deletions from the original plans)
- Investigation, exploratory, and legal fees
- Promotional costs
- Engineering and associated fees
- Debugging and start-up costs

Most construction projects include a *contingency cost* category to account for undefined costs that will assuredly crop up. Although such expenses are difficult to tally, they can drain capital as thoroughly as can design changes for physical assets.

Current levels of costs used in estimating investments may not be applicable to future conditions. Generally this is not a serious problem, but two situations bear watching. One occurs when an old alternative is resurrected for reconsideration. Old cost estimates may be outdated by new methods or different price levels. The other situation arises when current levels reflect abnormal or temporary prices. If prices are adjusted for first costs, similar adjustments should be investigated for other costs.

First costs can immediately eliminate some alternatives. Insufficient capital is a genuine reason to turn down an investment proposal, even though it has a handsome rate of return. An investment that would be wise for a firm with adequate capital could be a futile or even disastrous course of action for a firm with limited finances and big ambitions.

Overhead cost is, by definition, that portion of the cost that cannot be clearly associated with particular operations or products and that must be prorated among all the cost units on some arbitrary basis. The reason for this catch-all category is the prohibitive expense of assigning and charging to each product a specific proportion of such costs as wages of supervisors, factory heat and light, janitorial services, secretarial help, and incidental supplies. *Fixed cost* and *indirect cost,* as will be explained in Chap. 12, are generally taken to be synonymous with *overhead cost.*

Several methods are used to allocate the composite overhead expense to a product or operation. Traditional cost accounting systems allocate overhead costs to products by using direct labor cost or direct labor hours as the base. The primary criticism against this allocation scheme is that, for many systems, the direct labor costs are not the most important cost component; over 50 percent of product cost may be overhead compared with less than 15 percent attributable to direct labor.[†] Activity-based costing is based on the concept that activities (or operations) affect costs. It thus focuses on allocating costs to activities and then allocating the activities and costs to products. Procedures for allocating overhead expense differ among companies because of differences in the nature of production; it is not uncommon to find different overhead rates used within one firm.

An important condition to recognize in economic comparisons is that *overhead costs are associated with a certain level of output.* This can be a critical factor in a comparison such as the purchase of either a $200,000 numerically controlled milling machine or a standard $20,000 general purpose milling machine. If the labor rate of operators of both machines is $9 per hour and the burden rate is based on a direct labor ratio of 300 percent, then the machine-hour costs of both machines are $27 per hour. This figure has to be an incorrect machine-hour costing because the investment in the numerically controlled machine is 10 times that in the standard model. Fortunately, overhead costs often have an identical effect on several alternatives. That is, the same value for overhead costs would apply for different alternatives being compared, making their inclusion redundant in the comparison.

[†]W. M. Baker, "Understanding Activity-Based Costing," *Industrial Management,* vol. 36, no. 2, pp. 28–30, 1994.

11.4.2 Sources of Income Data

In an industrial setting, *revenue* is the money received from customers for the services or products sold to them. There are many patterns of revenue flow. A retail store has an essentially continuous influx of revenue during working hours. Plumbers are often paid after each service call. Utility services are paid by the month. Farmers usually get their money after a crop is harvested. A home builder has to wait until a house is sold before receiving revenue. The timing of the revenues associated with an alternative may have a significant bearing on its acceptability. One of the main reasons that new businesses often fail is the time lag between incurred first costs and the establishment of an expected level of revenue.

Revenue is somewhat harder to estimate than costs for many industrial projects. If a new investment is to serve the same purpose as an existing asset, historical data provide a reliable estimate of future revenue. When the investment is destined to satisfy a new function, revenue estimates are less certain. What looks like a sure bet on the drawing board may end as a miserable flop in the market, where it is exposed to the buying whims of the public.

Revenue often takes the form of a value-increasing benefit to people served by an investment, particularly in public sector projects. Occasionally, a precise measure of revenue contribution is impossible. Sums spent on customer *goodwill* and improved employer-employee relations are at best extremely difficult to measure in terms of revenue increments. This situation often results in setting aside a certain sum for public relations or investment in intangible returns. Then the sum is divided among projects rated according to their perceived worth in satisfying certain intangible values.

Funds for government or public activities come from various types of taxes, charges for specific services, and borrowing. Everyone is familiar with income taxes and charges for services such as mail delivery. Both are revenue sources secured from the public for benefits expected from governing agencies. Because of their mandatory nature and long history, they can be estimated quite accurately. And as a supplement, when the perceived demand for public expenditures exceeds public revenue, governments at all levels tend to engage in deficit financing. The money so borrowed is a pledge that future members of society will pay for projects undertaken by the present society. (The economics of public projects was examined in Chap. 8.) Although the base for public revenues is broad and solid, the portion justified for a specific public project is as difficult to determine as it is with industrial projects.

Privately owned public utility companies occupy a position midway between government and industry. This position results from the great amount of invested capital required to provide public services such as electricity, water, telephone communications, and railroad transportation. Only by developing a high use factor can an acceptable return on invested capital be obtained from low service rates. To ensure both reasonable returns and reasonable rates, an exclusive geographical franchise is allotted to a utility company. Coupled with the grant of a monopolistic position are regulations controlling rates and standards of service. A regulatory body seeks to set a quality of service that satisfies the customers while permitting rates that allow the utility to earn an acceptable rate of return. Because of this control, revenue can be quite accurately forecast.

Once the needed data have been determined, a comparison of investment alternatives follows the general procedures previously introduced. Specific procedures vary among industrial organizations. Some firms use only the payback criterion for relatively small investments. Larger investments are usually subjected to a discounted cash flow analysis including sensitivity studies.

11.4.3   Life-Cycle Costing

A study that gives special attention to both direct and indirect cash flows over the *complete* life of a project is called *life-cycle costing (LCC)*. The intent of LCC is to direct attention to factors that might be overlooked—especially inputs that occur during the inception stage, to get a project underway, and activities associated with the termination phase.

LCC has been a strength of engineering economics for over 50 years, but it was singled out for special recognition in the 1960s when the concept was adopted by U.S. government agencies as a means of enhancing the cost-effectiveness of equipment procurement. The use of LCC has since spread to the commercial sector, for product development studies and project evaluations.

LCC is expected to reduce the total cost by selecting the correct designs and components to minimize the *total* cost of service, not only the first cost. For instance, additional expenditures for the preliminary design might lower operating costs and thereby reduce total costs.

Expenditures during the life of most projects roughly follow the pattern shown in Fig. 11.12. The first stage—design—accounts for research, engineering design, administration, and financing costs. The development stage takes the basic plan and converts it to hardware or services through charges for fabrication, installation, delivery, training, trial runs, and material purchases. After the process is established, operating costs required to keep it going include personnel, consumable supplies, overhead, maintenance, and services.

Design to cost is a variation of LCC that sets a limit on the total lifetime cost and forces designers to work backward from the disposal phase to the operating expenses through production costs and finally to initial design charges. For example, a government request for proposals for training services might specify a limit on the funds available. Submitted proposals that start from this upper limit would be expected to designate costs for course development, setup arrangements for the instruction, educa-

FIGURE 11.12
Cost/time distributions represent typical stages in life-cycle costs for a product or project. Each stage has its own pattern. Both stage and aggregate effects are considered in life-cycle analysis.

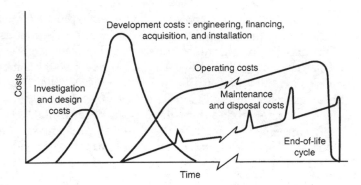

tional services and supplies per student, follow-up training, and evaluation procedures for determining the value of training provided. Proposals so structured provide costs by phases, which makes monitoring easier.

Projects, products, and systems of a similar nature tend to share common life-cycle patterns. Once identified, the distributions of cash flow as a function of time that are exhibited by one undertaking may be used to estimate costs for a similar undertaking in the future. The cost/time distributions may also be helpful during the planning phase when tradeoffs are evaluated, such as the balance between higher construction costs that allow lower operating and maintenance costs over the life of an investment. Studies of military hardware systems show that approximately two-thirds of life-cycle costs are firmly established during the design stage. The LCC profile that results from aggregating individual cost/time distributions is subjected to standard discounted cash flow analysis to determine its economic attractiveness.

11.4.4 Postaudits

Following the progress of a design from the drawing board through construction to on-the-job performance is a natural progression to engineers. This process generally involves modifications to improve performance, with designers realizing they will be able to make future designs better by knowing what was previously successful and what failed. Follow-up activities on capital investments tend to be neither as extensive nor as rigorous. Engineering economists would be well served by the same monitoring instinct displayed in other engineering pursuits.

The purpose of auditing investments is not to punish those who approved the proposals, any more than quality control inspections are intended to penalize a production process. The aim is to improve future analyses. How else can analysts learn whether their estimated cash flows are realistic? Many factors influence estimated receipts and disbursements; some are easily overlooked unless they are brought to someone's attention by postaudits.

A major advantage of a systematized postaudit program is the availability of the most recent cost data for categories not itemized in cost accounting records. Maintenance costs for various types of machines, operating efficiency during training periods, labor costs for specific activities such as installation or setup activities, and other data utilized in preparing requests for expenditure would be available from postaudits.

11.5   REVIEW EXERCISES AND DISCUSSIONS

EXERCISE 1

Data for a youth corps training program are shown below. The expected duration of the program is 6 years. Both benefits and costs are uncertain. Analyze the desirability of the program from the given data.

| | Benefit B | | | Cost C | | | | Present worth | | | | | |
| | | | | | | | | Minimum | | Expected | | Maximum | |
Year N	Min.	Exp.	Max.	Min.	Exp.	Max.	(P/F, 10, N)	B	C	B	C	B	C
1	0	0	5	10	15	25	0.90909	0	9.1	0	13.6	4.5	22.7
2	5	10	15	10	10	15	0.82645	4.1	8.3	8.3	8.3	12.4	12.4
3	15	20	25	5	5	10	0.75132	11.3	3.8	15.0	3.8	18.8	7.5
4	20	30	30	4	5	8	0.68302	13.7	2.7	20.5	3.4	20.5	5.5
5	10	20	25	3	5	6	0.62092	6.2	1.9	12.4	3.1	15.5	3.7
6	5	15	20	2	5	5	0.56448	2.8	1.1	8.5	2.8	11.3	2.8
							Totals	38.1	26.9	64.7	35.0	83.0	54.6

SOLUTION 1

The benefit/cost ratio based on the most likely values is

$$\frac{B}{C} = \frac{64.7}{35.0} = 1.85 \quad \text{and} \quad B - C = 29.7$$

which makes the program acceptable. As is apparent in the table, the B/C ratios under all three conditions are greater than 1.0. However, if maximum cost occurred while the benefit was at a minimum, then

$$\frac{B}{C} = \frac{38.1}{54.6} = 0.70$$

and

$$B - C = -16.5$$

The worst combination might be excused from consideration if supporting evidence could be collected to show that the chance is very remote that the highest cost would accompany the lowest benefit.

EXERCISE 2

The proposal summarized below is being considered to reduce labor costs and material waste by the purchase of automated equipment. The cost elements are subject to individually unique inflation rates. Since forecasting future inflation rates is always an uncertain proposition, a sensitivity analysis is appropriate. The critical cost factors are labor, material, and energy. Develop a sensitivity graph for deviations from initial inflation estimates.

Proposal to purchase automated equipment designed to reduce labor costs and material waste

---

Automated equipment:
  P = $150,000
  S = 0
  N = 3 years
Annual revenue:
  Net savings in labor = $60,000; f = 8%
  Net savings in material = $140,000; f = 5%
Annual costs:
  Additional energy required = $70,000; f = 20%
  Added maintenance expense = $30,000; f = 10%
Effective tax rate = 50%; MACRS depreciation

SOLUTION 2

The effects of deviations from the expected inflation rates are determined by calculating an IRR for each percentage change in the inflation rate of one factor while all other conditions are held constant. For the values shown in the table above, the after-tax IRR is 17.83 percent. The curves shown in Fig. 11.13 summarize the results of all the computations.

The intersection of the curves is at the IRR calculated for the most likely inflation rates. The most sensitive cost element is material because it has a proportionately much larger dollar value than do the other factors in the proposal; an increase in the inflation rate from 5 to 9 percent increases the rate of return by 30 percent (savings from decreased use of material are worth more as the price of the material goes up). Energy is the next most sensitive factor, owing to its much higher starting inflation rate, even though it is applied to a factor only one-half as large as material.

EXERCISE 3

The concept of cyclic replacement was introduced in Chap. 7. It is applicable when an asset continues to be replaced by another asset of the same type. Since the most economic life for the asset is the period of service that minimizes its equivalent annual cost (EAC), the replacement period is calculated from

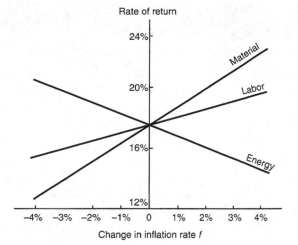

FIGURE 11.13
Sensitivity graph of
effects of different
inflation rates on
IRR of automated
equipment proposal.

EAC = capital recovery + equivalent annual operating cost

when taxes and inflation are ignored.

It is revealing to observe how sensitive the replacement period is to certain factors used in its calculation. An asset with the characteristics given below is examined. The asset has a purchase price of $15,000 and a potential physical life of 12 years.

Year N	Salvage value at end of year N, $	Annual operating cost, $
0	15,000	
1	11,000	3,000
2	8,000	3,500
3	6,000	4,100
4	5,000	4,800
5	4,000	5,600
6	3,000	6,500
7	2,500	7,500
8	2,000	8,600
9	1,500	9,800
10	1,000	11,100
11	700	12,500
12	500	14,000

SOLUTION 3
A tabular format for calculating the minimum-cost cycle is shown in Table 11.2; it indicates replacement at the end of the fifth year when the MARR is 10 percent and when taxes and inflation are not included in the analysis.

TABLE 11.2

Before-tax equivalent annual cost of an asset subject to cyclic replacement at MARR = 10%. The minimum-cost replacement cycle is 5 years

				End of year N			
	0	**1**	**2**	**3**	**4**	**5**	**6**
(1) Salvage value	15,000	11,000	8,000	6,000	5,000	4,000	3,000
(2) Operating costs		3,000	3,500	4,100	4,800	5,600	6,500
(3) Decrease in salvage value		4,000	3,000	2,000	1,000	1,000	1,000
(4) Interest on (1), $i = 10\%$		1,500	1,100	800	600	500	400
(5) Capital recovery, (3) + (4)		5,500	4,100	2,800	1,600	1,500	1,400
(6) Total cost, (2) + (5)		8,500	7,600	6,900	6,400	7,100	7,900
(7) Present worth, (6) × $(P/F, 10, N)$		7,727	6,281	5,184	4,372	4,408	4,460
(8) ΣPW (cumulative)		7,727	14,008	19,192	23,564	27,972	32,432
(9) EAC, (8) × $(A/P, 10, N)$		8,500	8,071	7,718	7,434	7,379	7,447

By substituting different minimum acceptable rates of return in the tabular format, the sensitivity of the replacement cycle to the MARR is revealed. Higher MARRs cause the capital cost to increase but reduce the effect of rising operating costs. The results of repeated calculations with different rates of return provide the data for the sensitivity graph shown in Fig. 11.14. The replacement cycle increases

FIGURE 11.14
Sensitivity of the cycle for like replacements to changes in the required rate of return. Increasing the MARR increases the replacement cycle. Equivalent annual costs are before-tax amounts.

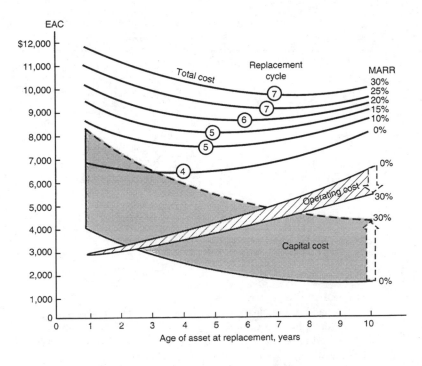

from 4 to 7 years as the MARR is raised from 0 to 30 percent, primarily from the effect of higher interest charges on the capital cost of ownership.

When essentially the same procedure is followed to check the sensitivity of other influential factors, the following observations become evident:

- Inflating both capital and operating costs at the same rate does not affect the replacement period in a before-tax analysis; it simply escalates the EAC.
- The replacement period is always longer in an after-tax analysis; for instance, for a tax rate of 50 percent the minimum-cost cycle changes from 5 to 8 years with the data used in Table 11.2 (at MARR = 10 percent).
- There is no change in the replacement interval when different methods of depreciation are used in an after-tax analysis.
- Higher tax rates increase annual costs and tend to lengthen the replacement period only slightly.
- Using borrowed capital for funding lowers the after-tax EAC, depending on the interest paid on the loan, but has little effect on the replacement period.
- A general inflation rate of 10 percent applied to both capital and operating costs in an after-tax analysis at a MARR of 10 percent reduces the replacement period to 7 years (as opposed to 8 years without inflation), but further increase in the inflation rate to 40 percent does not change the 7-year period.
- When operating costs inflate at a 15 percent rate while salvage values escalate at a 10 percent rate and MARR is 10 percent, the replacement period drops to 6 years. Higher inflation rates for operating costs of 20, 25, and 30 percent decrease respective replacement cycles to 5, 4, and 4 years.
- Raising the percentage of borrowed funds makes a purchase more sensitive to inflation rates in after-tax analyses. The respective replacement periods for operating-cost inflation rates of 10, 15, 20, 25, 30, and 40 percent are 7, 6, 5, 4, 4, and 3 years, respectively, when one-half the purchase price is borrowed at $i = 15$ percent and MARR = 10 percent.

EXERCISE 4

A U.S. branch of a Canadian company is planning to purchase a new pick-and-place robot for $35,000. The unit is expected to produce annual revenues (in cost savings) of $20,000 for each of the next 6 years and will be sold at the end of that time for an expected salvage value of $5000. Maintenance expenses on the robot are expected to be $2000 for the first year and to increase by $500 per year for each successive year of operation.

The company is purchasing the equipment by paying $15,000 down and financing the balance at an effective interest rate of 10 percent to be repaid in three equal end-of-year payments. The company will be using MACRS depreciation with a 5-year life for computing income taxes. The company has an effective tax rate of 40 percent and requires an after-tax MARR of 10 percent.

Because uncertainty surrounds the savings, maintenance costs, salvage value, and MARR estimates, it is desired to evaluate the sensitivity of the proposed investment to ±50 percent changes in the estimate of these parameters.

SOLUTION 4

We use the computer program CHEER to solve this problem. CHEER has an explicit feature for performing sensitivity analysis on a before-tax or an after-tax basis. The procedure for data input for ATCF analysis was explained in Example 9.16. The steps involved in this analysis are summarized below.

- Use the BTCF section to input (1) project life = 6 years, (2) initial investment = $35,000, (3) annual revenue = $20,000, (4) annual maintenance expenses = $2000 for the first year and increase by $500 for each successive year (arithmetic gradient), and (5) salvage value in year 6 = $5000.
- Use the ATCF section to input (1) depreciation information = 5-year MACRS; (2) loan information that consists of loan amount = $20,000, loan interest rate = 10 percent, years before loan is repaid = 3, and number of payments per year = 1; (3) tax rate = 40 percent; and (4) after-tax interest rate = 10 percent.
- We now obtain the results from the ATCF analysis (Fig. 11.15a). The results show that the purchase of the robot will result in a net present worth of $23,059, if the most likely estimates given in the problem are used.

To perform sensitivity analysis, we click on the Project option in the ATCF analysis screen (Fig. 11.15b). From the resulting menu, shown in Fig. 11.15b, we select the Sensitivity analysis option. At this stage, we are asked if we want to save the results from sensitivity analysis (Fig. 11.15c) and, if so, to input a file name for saving the results. In either case, the system returns with Fig. 11.15d, which shows the numerical results of sensitivity analysis. Figure 11.15d shows the net present worth if each of the four parameters—revenues, costs, salvage value, and interest rate—is varied ±50 percent from the most likely value, one at a time, while all other parameters are held at the expected value. Note that 0 percent deviation in Fig. 11.15d refers to the most likely condition.

Five options are available at this stage: (1) Exit, to exit the sensitivity analysis section of the system; (2) View, which shows the results of sensitivity analysis graphically (Fig. 11.15e) (to print the graph, use the PrintScreen function on the keyboard); (3) Print, to print the numerical results (Fig. 11.15d); (4) Chart, for changing the color, title, font, or line pattern for the graphical display; and (5) Help, which provides information on the functions available in the sensitivity analysis section of CHEER.

AFTER-TAX CASH FLOW

Period	Before-tax cash flow	Deprec expense	Loan data Prin	Loan data Int	Taxable income	Tax due is (−)	After-tax cash flow
0	−35000	0	20000	0	0	0	−15000
1	18000	−7000	−6042	−2000	9000	−3600	6357
2	17500	−11200	−6646	−1395	4904	−1961	7496
3	17000	−6720	−7311	-731	9548	−3819	5138
4	16500	−4032	0	0	12468	−4987	11512
5	16000	−4032	0	0	11968	−4787	11212
6	20500	−2016	0	0	18484	−7393	13106

Net present worth of after-tax cash flow at 10.0% interest is 23059.04.
Equivalent uniform annual worth is 5294.53.
After-tax rate of return is 46.34%.

Inflation rate is 0.00%.

Cash flow includes a loan of 2000.00 for 3 years at 10.00% interest rate.

Remaining depreciation of 0 was recaptured at end of project life.

FIGURE 11.15
CHEER analysis of
Review Exercise 4.

(a)

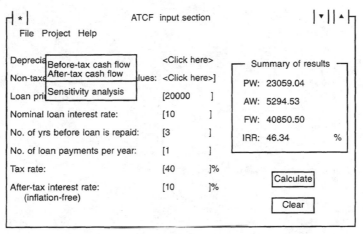

(b)

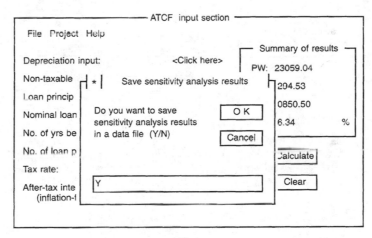

(c)

Sensitivity of proposal's NPW to input parameters

Deviation from estimated value	Revenue	Cost	Salvage value	Interest rate
−50%	−3072.53	27124.82	22212.33	30329.92
−40%	2153.78	26311.66	22381.67	28720.92
−30%	7380.10	25498.51	22551.01	27194.33
−20%	12606.41	24685.35	22720.35	25744.97
−10%	17832.72	23872.19	22889.70	24368.02
0	23059.04	23059.04	23059.04	23059.04
10%	28285.35	22245.88	23228.38	21813.87
20%	33511.66	21432.73	23397.72	20628.68
30%	38737.98	20619.57	23567.06	19499.88
40%	43964.29	19806.41	23736.41	18424.16
50%	49190.60	18993.26	23905.75	17398.40

FIGURE 11.15
continued   (d)

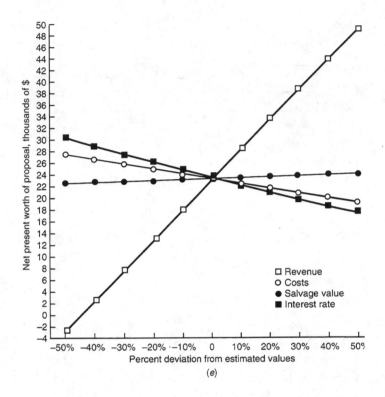

FIGURE 11.15
continued

As shown in Fig. 11.15*d*, the proposal is sensitive to estimates of revenues resulting from cost savings. These should be carefully evaluated. The other three factors—maintenance costs, salvage value, and interest rate—have little effect on the desirability of the project.

11.6   PROBLEMS

11.1 Why should sensitivity analysis be considered in engineering economic analysis?

11.2 Discuss the costs associated with undertaking sensitivity analysis.

11.3 A manufacturer is considering a semiautomated machine to replace a certain manual operation. The machine is available for $7000 with an expected life of 5 years. Savings resulting from the use of the machine are estimated to be $3000 per year. Should the machine be purchased if the cost of capital is 15 percent? The machine is expected to have negligible salvage value.

11.4 Would the machine in Prob. 11.3 be purchased if the minimum acceptable rate of return were 20 percent?

11.5 Suppose that the service life of the machine in Prob. 11.3 is uncertain. Evaluate the sensitivity of the PW to ±40 percent change in useful life.

11.6 A completely automated machine is available as an alternative to the machine described in Prob. 11.3. The following estimates are available for this new machine:

First cost	$16,000
Life	5 years
Annual savings	$5000
Salvage value	$2000

Compare this new machine with the semiautomated machine in Prob. 11.3.

11.7 Consider the following two alternatives:

	Alternative 1	Alternative 2
First cost	$20,000	$16,000
Annual expense	$5000	$3000
Annual income	$11,500	$11,500
Salvage value	$4000	$0
Economic life	8 years	4 years

Suppose that the salvage value of alternative 2 is known with certainty. By how much would the estimate of salvage value for alternative 1 have to vary so that the initial decision based on the data above would be reversed? The minimum acceptable rate of return is 15 percent.

11.8 Develop an isoquant to test the sensitivity of decision reversal to variations in expenses and income for the alternatives in Prob. 11.7.

11.9 A proposal is described by the following estimates: $P = \$20,000$, $S = 0$, $N = 5$, and net annual receipts = $7000. A rate of return of 20 percent is desired on such proposals. Construct a sensitivity graph of the life, annual receipts, and rate of return for deviations over a range of ±20 percent. To which element is the decision most sensitive?

11.10 A university is planning to purchase a new mainframe computer for research and administrative use. The university's industrial engineering department has developed the following most likely estimates:

Investment	$150,000
Annual savings	$30,000
Annual costs	$5000
Useful life	10 years
Salvage value	$25,000

Because considerable uncertainty surrounds these estimates, it is desired to evaluate the sensitivity of the PW of the proposed investment to ±50 percent changes in the most likely estimates of (a) annual savings, (b) annual costs, (c) useful life, and (d) salvage value. Assuming a MARR of 10 percent, graph the results and determine the factor to which the decision is most sensitive.

11.11 The purchase of rental property is being considered in a neighborhood where real estate prices are increasing rapidly. The following estimates have been developed for a preliminary before-tax analysis:

First cost	$140,000
Annual income from rent	$9600
Annual maintenance	$1000
Investment period	6 years
Resale value	$196,000
Cost of capital	10%

(a) Given that the first cost of the property and the investment period are fixed, construct a sensitivity chart showing the effect of changes in all the other elements on the NPW.

(b) Construct a sensitivity chart for joint variation within a ±30 percent range of annual income and cost of capital; indicate the acceptance and rejection zones.

11.12 Three designs to perform the same function have the cost patterns indicated:

Design 1   Initial cost is $12,000, and annual expenses are uniform at $4000 per year.

Design 2   A low initial cost of $5000 is possible because refinements will be made while the facility is in operation. The first year's operating and refinement cost will be $7500, and it will decrease by $500 each year.

Design 3   Initial cost is $15,000, with annual disbursements that start at $2000 and increase by $1000 each year.

The principal uncertainty in the evaluation is how long the function will be needed for which the designs were developed. All the designs could perform the function for 12 years, if the function lasts that long; and none of the designs would have any salvage value at any time. Determine the range of life over which different designs would be preferred if the minimum attractive rate of return were 11 percent.

11.13 An aluminum company must decide whether to install a new type of air float conveyor for extra-thin aluminum sheets or to retain its conventional conveyors. A pilot test reveals that the float conveyor moves the sheets faster and reduces damage, but maintenance costs to keep it operating properly may be high. The amount of savings expected from the new design depends on the quantity of aluminum sheeting produced in the future and the reliability of the new equipment. The engineering department has provided the following estimates:

First cost	$180,000
Economic life	4 years
Annual maintenance expense	$40,000
Annual savings	$100,000

There is no realizable salvage value because the cost of removing the equipment would about equal the scrap value. The company uses a minimum attractive rate of return of 12 percent.

(a) Because there is still some doubt about the effectiveness of the air float conveyor design, some of the analysts feel that a higher rate of return should be required for the project. Make an isoquant of the maximum first cost that could be incurred to earn rates of return between 5 and 25 percent.

(b) Assuming the life, maintenance cost, and savings may vary as much as 50 percent on both sides of the given estimate, develop a graph of the effects of individual variations on the net present worth of the project. Do you recommend that the new conveyor system be installed? Why?

11.14 Current mail-sorting operations on one line at a mail distribution center cost about $1 million per year. A newly developed and essentially unproved but promising system for sorting mail by automatic address readers is being considered. Although the devices have been tested and approved in laboratories, there is still doubt about how they will perform in regular service. Questionnaires describing less than favorable and more than favorable operating conditions were sent to people familiar with the devices and with the mail distribution process. Consensus data from the two scenarios and the most likely estimates are shown below.

Factors estimated	Pessimistic estimate	Most likely estimate	Optimistic estimate
First cost, including installation, $	2,112,000	985,000	915,000
Life in years of full utilization	2	2	6
Annual maintenance and minor repair, $	221,000	81,000	75,000
Annual operating cost and standbys, $	929,000	714,000	588,000

Calculate the range of EACs and discuss the results. MARR = 10 percent.

11.15 There is considerable doubt about the need for and performance to be obtained from a new process developed by the R&D department. A decision about launching a small-scale pilot project is being evaluated. Three estimates of possible outcomes of the pilot project are given below.

	Objective estimate	Less favorable estimate	More favorable estimate
Income per year, $	200,000	150,000	250,000
Expenses per year, $	80,000	90,000	80,000
Start-up cost, $	300,000	350,000	300,000
Life of project, years	3	1	4
Salvage value, $	100,000	50,000	100,000

(a) What is the present worth of each possible future outcome when the minimum attractive rate of return is 15 percent?

(b) What other considerations could affect the decision to launch the pilot project? Should the money already invested in research and development be a consideration? Why?

(c) Compare the range-of-estimates method of evaluation with sensitivity analysis.

11.16 Three revenue-producing projects are being considered. Estimates of future returns are uncertain because the projects involve new products. The initial investment is expected to provide adequate production capability for any reasonable project life, and the lives of all projects are considered to be equal. Regardless of useful life, there will be no salvage value.

Project I Has a first cost of $200,000 and uniform annual net revenue of $65,000

Project O Has a low initial cost of $100,000 and will return $50,000 the first year, but net revenue will decline each year by an amount $0.5G$, where G is a uniform gradient

Project U Has a high initial cost of $250,000 and returns $50,000 the first year, with the expectation that new revenue will increase by an annual uniform amount G

Compare the three projects by constructing sensitivity graphs according to the following assumptions, and discuss the results.

(a) Let the project life be 6 years and $G = \$7500$ to test project preference for sensitivity to minimum rates of return up to 25 percent.

(b) Let the project life be 6 years and MARR = 12 percent to test project preference for sensitivity to values of G from 0 to $15,000.

(c) Let MARR = 12 percent and $G = \$7500$ to test project preference for sensitivity to project life.

11.17 An electronics circuit-board manufacturer belonging to a Canadian company is considering the purchase of a new robot for component insertion. The robot will cost $50,000 and is expected to be technologically obsolete in 6 years, at which time the manufacturer plans to donate it to the local university for $5000. It is estimated to save $24,000 per year in labor costs with annual operating costs being $7500. The robot is a 5-year MACRS recovery asset. The manufacturer has an effective income tax rate of 42 percent and an after-tax MARR of 12 percent. Investigate the proposal's sensitivity to (a) annual savings, (b) operating costs, and (c) salvage value on an after-tax basis. Ignore inflation.

11.18 A project will have a life of 10 years and is to be evaluated at a discount rate of 9 percent. It has an initial cost of $1 million, and expected annual costs are $100,000. However, it is possible that these annual costs could consistently increase by $10,000 each year or could decrease by $5000 per year. The most likely annual benefits are $350,000, but there is a chance that benefits will decrease by $25,000 per year.

(a) What is the worst possible B/C ratio that could occur with the given scenario?

(b) What maximum first cost could be incurred for an acceptable project in which annual cash flows follow the expected (most likely) estimates?

BREAK-EVEN ANALYSIS

No matter of fact can be mathematically demonstrated, though it may be proved in such a manner as to leave no doubt on the mind.

Richard Whately, *Logic IV,* 1826

In sensitivity analysis, if a decision is reversed, either from acceptance to rejection or between competing alternatives, then as a certain parameter is varied over a range of possible values, the decision is sensitive to that parameter; otherwise it is insensitive. Break even analysis expresses a similar concept. Here the value of the parameter at decision reversal is determined. Break-even analysis is a limited form of sensitivity analysis. We are interested in determining a set of values for which an investment alternative is justified economically.

Many economic comparisons are a form of break-even analysis. The lease-or-buy question from Chap. 10 could be rephrased to ask about what level of service or time leasing becomes more expensive than buying. The point where the two alternatives are equal is the *break-even point.* Most sensitivity studies involve an indifference level for a given cash flow element at which two alternatives are equivalent—the break-even point for the given element. The choice between the two then rests on a judgment about which side of the break-even point the element will likely register.

In this chapter, break-even analysis is directed to the point at which operations merely break even, neither making nor losing money; changes in operations are evaluated according to their effect on this point. Break-even analysis, known also as *cost-volume-profit analysis,* is widely used for financial studies because it is simple and extracts useful insights from a modest amount of data. The studies necessarily include an examination of production costs and operating policies.

507

Break-even analyses focus on cost-volume-profit relations that hold only over a short run. Over the long run, the relationships are altered by internal factors (new products, production facilities, etc.) and external impacts (competition, state of the general economy, etc.). Many of the internal activities that affect long-run changes are initiated from analyses of current cost-volume-profit conditions. Thus, a break-even analysis is like a medical checkup: The physical examination reveals the current state of health and provides clues about what should be done to become or stay healthy.

12.1   BASIC CONCEPTS

In break-even analysis, costs and revenues are expressed as a function of production rates. The cost-revenue-profit relations are exposed by breaking down a unit of output into its component dollar values. The rectangular block in Fig. 12.1a represents a unit of output. This output can be a product, such as an automobile, or it can be a service, such as collecting garbage from a subscriber. The unit is divided into three segments that classify the producer's interests. The overall height or price for which it can be sold is a function of the consumer's regard for the item.

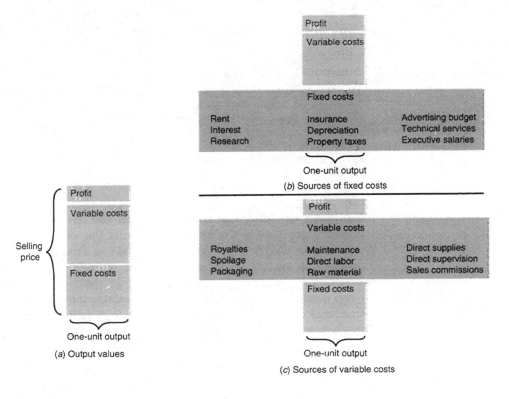

FIGURE 12.1
Unit costs.

(a) Output values

(b) Sources of fixed costs

(c) Sources of variable costs

Costs can be classified into two major categories: fixed and variable. Costs that remain relatively constant regardless of the level of activity are known as *fixed,* or *indirect, costs.* This description implies that the fixed level is maintained whether output is zero or at 100 percent capacity. In some cases this assumption is not valid; fixed costs may tend to increase as output increases, and they can vary with time. However, the change is usually not significant for short-run studies.

Some of an organization's expenditures that can be considered as fixed are shown in Fig. 12.1b. These costs may be thought of as "preparation" expenses. They arise from measures taken to provide the means to produce a product or service. Before painters can paint a house, they must have paintbrushes. Whether they paint one house or a dozen with the brushes, the expense has already been incurred and shows as a fixed cost. The painter's insurance and advertisements for work would also be indirect costs.

Costs that are generally proportional to output are called *variable,* or *direct, costs.* Such costs are relatively easy to determine because they are directly associated with a specific product or service. When there is no output, variable costs are zero. The input material and the time required to make a unit give rise to variable costs. For example, the specific type and quantity of paint used by house painters is a variable cost. The more houses they paint, the more paint they use; the quantity used is a function of their output. In a similar manner, the time they spend painting is a direct cost. Some sources for variable costs are shown in Fig. 12.1c.

Revenue results from sales of output. Profits represent the difference between revenue and total costs. The dimension of quantity must be included to examine the competitive aspects of profit. A single unit of output is relatively immune to competition. In isolated instances, a fair-sized output distributed in a local area to satisfy a particular need is also shielded from competition. However, as output quantity expands, competition is an increasingly apparent factor. Profit is the cause and effect of competitiveness.

A profit (or loss) figure attracts a great amount of attention. It is a handy yardstick of success. Like a thermometer, it measures only the level achieved; it does not control the source it measures. Unlike a thermometer, however, its continued low readings may convince the financial temperature takers to eliminate the source.

There are basically three ways to increase profit: increase the selling price, increase the value to increase sales, and decrease the selling price to increase sales. The profit expansion descriptions are oriented to consumers' interests. The issues become more complicated when we look at them from the producer's viewpoint. Figure 12.2 shows some of the consequences of selling-price manipulations.

The original price-cost-quantity conditions are shown in Fig. 12.2a. The *total revenue* is the product of n units sold at selling price P. The *total cost* is the sum of variable and fixed costs incurred in producing n units.

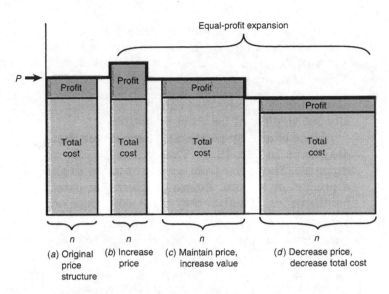

Equal-profit expansion

$P \rightarrow$

Profit	Profit	Profit	
Total cost	Total cost	Total cost	Profit
			Total cost

n — (a) Original price structure

n — (b) Increase price

n — (c) Maintain price, increase value

n — (d) Decrease price, decrease total cost

P = selling price, n = quantity

FIGURE 12.2
Methods for expanding profit.

Profit is the difference between revenue and total cost (when revenue exceeds costs).

Figure 12.2*b* through *d* shows increased profit. Conditions of free enterprise are assumed—similar products or services are available from a number of vendors. The shaded profit areas of Fig. 12.2*b, c,* and *d* are equal to or larger than the profit in *a*. The dangers and limitations of profit expansion methods are as follows:

Increased selling price. Competing products or services set an upper limit to price increases. This limit is ultimately controlled by the consumers. Their willingness to pay is a function of the value they expect to receive and their loyalty to a product. Prices higher than those of competing products of equivalent value will reduce the number of units sold. The shrinking share of the market eventually causes a decline in total profit.

Unchanged selling price. One way to increase profit without changing the selling price is to sell more units by increasing the value. The greater value perceived by the consumer can result from better quality, more quantity, or more effective advertising. All these measures increase the total cost of the producer. Higher total cost leads to a lower margin of profit per unit sold. If the market is unstable, a very low profit margin can seriously limit recuperative powers during market fluctuations.

A straightforward means to increase profit while holding prices constant is to reduce total cost. Such a task is the continuous aim of engineers and managers. The problem is that it becomes increasingly difficult to make more and more savings in an established operation. At first it is easy. When a product or service is new, it meets a high current demand that compensates for operational inefficiencies. As competition forces the price down, the "fat" is removed from operations. Further effort to reduce costs meets diminishing returns. It is like trying to make a horse run faster. A small whip may help at first, but using ever-larger whips fails to force proportional returns in ever-greater speeds.

Reduced selling price. New areas of cost reduction are exposed by changing the level of operations, or capacity. A greater output often allows new methods to be incorporated. Some of the savings resulting from the new methods are passed on to consumers in the form of a lower selling price. In theory, the decreased price should lead to the sale of more units, which in turn satisfies the conditions for incorporating the new methods.

Limitations are inherent throughout the cost reduction–lower price–increased sales cycle. Cost reductions are limited by minimum levels of quality, maximum levels of expenditure for new equipment, and basic labor or material costs that resist lowering. Reduced prices may be an insufficient incentive to attract enough new sales. However, with reasonable care the cycle rewards the producer and leads to a better standard of living for the consumer.

12.2   LINEAR BREAK-EVEN ANALYSIS

In linear break-even analysis, revenue and variable costs are directly proportional to output. There are three primary conditions for linear break-even analysis:

1. Income is only from operations under consideration.
2. Fixed costs, per-unit variable costs, and per-unit sales prices remain constant over time and over output.
3. All units produced are sold.

12.2.1   Break-Even Charts

The break-even chart presents two curves: a total-cost curve and a curve showing income from sales. The name *break-even chart* is derived from the concept it depicts—the volume or level at which the revenue and the total cost of operations exactly break even. At this point, one additional unit made and sold would produce a profit. Until the break-even point is attained, the producer operates at a loss for the period.

Properties of a typical break-even chart are displayed in Fig. 12.3. The vertical scale shows the revenue and costs in monetary units. The horizontal scale indicates the volume of activity n during the period pictured. The

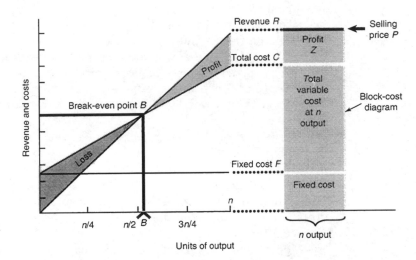

FIGURE 12.3
Standard format for break-even charts.

units of volume can be in sales dollars, number of units produced and sold, or output quantity expressed as a percentage of total capacity.

The horizontal line above the x axis shows the fixed costs F, which are constant throughout the range of volume. The sloping line originating at the intersection of the fixed-cost line and the vertical axis represents variable costs V plus the fixed costs. For linear relations, variable costs are directly proportional to volume; each additional unit produced adds an identical increment of cost. The sum of variable and fixed costs is the total cost C. The sloping line from the origin of the graph is the revenue line. Revenue R is also assumed to be directly proportional to the number of units produced and sold at price P.

The break-even point B occurs at the intersection of the total-cost and revenue lines. It thus specifies the dollar volume of sales and the unit volume of output at which an operation neither makes nor loses money. The vertical distance between the revenue line and the total-cost line indicates a profit Z to the right of B and a loss to the left.

A block-cost diagram used in the discussion of profit expansion is shown alongside the break-even chart in Fig. 12.3. For a specific output level n, the costs, revenue, and profit are the same in both formats. The break-even chart further indicates the profit or loss expectation at levels of output other than the specific quantity n. This feature helps explain such statements as "A very low profit margin can seriously limit recuperative powers during market fluctuations." *A very low profit margin* means that the output is barely on the profit side of the breakeven point. An unstable market could easily cause sales to fall below point B and show a loss for the period.

A break-even analysis often tends to oversimplify the decision environment. This is an attribute for presentation purposes and for gross evaluations. It can also be a shortcoming for problems in which detailed measures are needed. A decision to lower the break-even point for an operation can result from a study of total revenue and costs, but the study alone seldom reveals the in-plant operations that engineers and managers must conduct to implement the decision. The inability to identify tactical procedures is not a defect of a break-even analysis; it merely indicates that decision makers should be aware of the limitations of the approach in order to apply it appropriately. The validity of a break-even chart is directly proportional to the accuracy of the data incorporated in the chart. When several products are lumped together and represented by one line on a chart, there is a distinct possibility that poor performance by one product may go undetected. A firm should have a good cost accounting system, but data from past performances are not always indicative of future performance. However, examining graphs of previous break-even conditions calls attention to developing trends in revenues and costs.

Break-even relationships suggest where engineering efforts can be of most use to an organization. Field or factory-floor engineers can observe the present state of financial affairs and use such observations to guide their cost control activities. As an engineer's managerial responsibilities increase, the interplay of price, cost, and quantity becomes a greater concern. Then the combined effect of the system's operations and the underlying economic principles steer strategic decisions.

12.2.2 Algebraic Relationships

The graph format is convenient for clarifying or presenting economic relationships. It is possible to obtain quantities for particular conditions by scaling values from the chart. However, the same conditions can be easily quantified by formulas. Calculations generally provide greater accuracy. Using the symbols already defined, we have

$$\frac{\text{Revenue}}{\text{Period}} = R = nP$$

$$\frac{\text{Total cost}}{\text{Period}} = C = nV + F$$

$$\frac{\text{Gross profit}}{\text{Period}} = Z = R - C = n(P - V) - F$$

$$\frac{\text{Net profit}}{\text{Period}} = Z' = Z(1 - t)$$

where n can also be a fraction of total capacity when P and V represent total dollar volume at 100 percent capacity, and t is the tax rate.

At the break-even point, profit equals zero. To determine the output to simply break even, we have, at B,

$$Z = 0 = R - C = n(P - V) - F$$

and letting $n = B$, we have

$$B = \frac{F}{P - V}$$

The term $P - V$ is called the *contribution*. It indicates the portion of the selling price that contributes to paying off the fixed cost. At $n = B$ the sum of contributions from B units equals the total fixed cost. The contribution of each unit sold beyond $n = B$ is an increment of profit.

EXAMPLE 12.1

Break-Even Analysis by the Numbers

An airline is evaluating its feeder routes. These routes connect smaller cities to major terminals. The routes are seldom very profitable themselves, but they feed passengers into the major flights which yield better returns. One feeder route has a maximum capacity of 1000 passengers per month. The contribution from the fare of each passenger is 75 percent of the $120 ticket price. Fixed costs per month are $63,000. Determine the break-even point and net profit when the effective income tax rate is 40 percent.

Solution

To find the average percentage of seats that must be sold on each flight to break even, the cost and revenue data could be converted to the graphical break-even format shown in Fig. 12.4. The same information displayed in the break-even chart is supplied by the following calculations:

Total maximum revenue per month is

$$nP = 1000 \text{ passengers} \times \$120/\text{passenger} = \$120,000$$

Total contribution = $0.75 \times \$120,000 = \$90,000$

$$B(\% \text{ of capacity}) = \frac{F \times 100\%}{\text{contribution}}$$

$$= \frac{\$63,000}{\$90,000}(100\%) = 70\%$$

or

$$B(\text{passengers}) = \frac{F}{P - V} = \frac{\$63,000/\text{month}}{0.75 \times \$120/\text{passenger}}$$

$$= 700 \text{ passengers per month}$$

With a tax rate t of 40 percent, the net profit at full capacity is

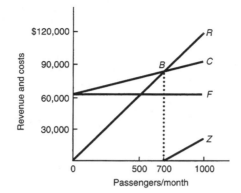

FIGURE 12.4
Break-even chart for
an airline operation.

$$
\begin{aligned}
\text{Net profit} &= Z(1 - t) \\
&= (R - C)(1 - t) \\
&= [n(P - V) - F](1 - t) \\
&= [1000 \text{ passengers}(0.75 \times \$120/\text{passenger}) - \$63{,}000](0.60) \\
&= \$27{,}000 \times 0.60 = \$16{,}200
\end{aligned}
$$

A gross-profit line is shown in the lower right corner of the chart, starting at $B = 700$. Net profit is a fraction of Z, which depends on the tax rate for the total earnings of the organization.

12.2.3 Break-Even Point Alternatives

Any change in costs or selling price affects the break-even point. We observed the gross effects of profit expansion as a function of selling price. Now we can consider the interaction of revenue, variable costs, and fixed costs in terms of output.

A lower break-even point is a highly desirable objective. It means that the organization can meet fixed costs at a lower level of output or utilization. A sales level well above the break-even output is a sign of healthiness. Three methods of lowering the break-even point are shown in Fig. 12.5. The original operating conditions are shown as light lines and are based on the following data:

$$V = \$7 \text{ per unit}$$

$$P = \$12 \text{ per unit}$$

$$R(\text{at } n = 100 \text{ units}) = \$1200$$

$$C(\text{at } n = 100 \text{ units}) = \$1100$$

$$F = \$400$$

$$B = 80 \text{ units}$$

$$B = \frac{\$600,000}{\$12,000/\text{unit}} = 50 \text{ units}$$

There are, of course, many factors to consider in such a decision. If the market is stable, the margin of profit is less important. Some alternatives are easier to implement than others. Some outcomes are more certain than others.

12.2.4 Dumping

Dumping occurs when a manufacturer sells a portion of the output n at one sales price P and the remaining output n' at a lower sales price P'. This can be accomplished by selling to foreign markets at a lower price or by selling the same product at different prices under different names. There are many dangers in this practice; but if it works, profit will increase because of increased plant utilization.

Firms engaged in dumping might encounter some problems. Customers might find out who is making the less expensive version and then refuse to buy the primary product because it costs more. Retaliation to dumping often takes the form of duties or taxes in foreign markets.

Algebraically, gross profit Z is

$$Z = n(P - V) + n'(P' - V) - F$$

The dumping alternative for the firm described in Example 12.2 is illustrated in Fig. 12.7. Dumping is applied to the original data on waste disposal-unit sales: 48 units are sold at the regular price ($P = \$35,000$) to account for 60 percent utilization. If 100 percent utilization could be

FIGURE 12.7
Effects of dumping on price, cutting profit, and utilization.

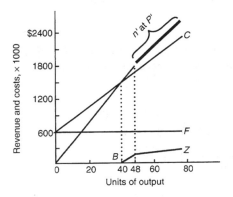

achieved by dumping the remaining capacity (32 units) at a sales price P' of \$25,000 per unit, the gross profit would increase to

$$Z = [48 \text{ units}(\$35,000/\text{unit} - \$20,000/\text{unit})$$
$$+ 32 \text{ units } (25,000/\text{unit} - \$20,000/\text{unit})] - \$600,000$$
$$= \$280,000$$

12.2.5 Multiproduct Alternatives

More than one product can be shown on a break-even chart. Including a whole product line allows the decision maker to evaluate the combined effect of the product mix on plant utilization, revenue, and costs. A slightly different format for the break-even chart accentuates the effect of multiple products. This type of graph, displayed in Fig. 12.8, is called a *multiproduct profit,* or *contribution, chart.*

The chart is constructed by plotting fixed costs as a loss on the vertical axis. The horizontal axis denotes sales revenue. At zero sales the only costs associated with a product are the negative preparation, or fixed, costs. As production and sales develop, each unit sold makes a contribution toward paying off the fixed costs. When enough units have been sold to pay off these costs, the break-even point is reached and the contribution from further sales is profit.

Three products A, B, and C are represented in Fig. 12.8. The plotted values are based on the following data for the period shown in the chart:

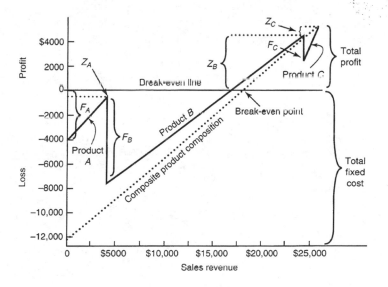

FIGURE 12.8
Multiproduct profit chart.

	Product		
	A	B	C
Selling price per unit	$8	$5	$4
Contribution per unit	$6	$3	$3
Fixed cost	$4000	$7000	$1000
Number of units sold	600	4000	400

Product A is entered in the chart by making its fixed costs ($4000) on the negative side of the break-even line at zero sales revenue. The total contribution of A is 600 units times $6 per unit, or $3600. Subtracting the fixed costs from the total contribution leaves a loss of $400 ($Z_A$ in Fig. 12.8) from total sales of $4800.

The remaining products are dealt with in a similar manner. Each fixed cost is entered as a vertical line attached to the highest point on the contribution line for the preceding product. The results are cumulative. The total contribution of B is $12,000 resulting from 4000 units times $3 per unit. Adding this to the prior cumulative value of −$7400 (loss of $400 from A plus $7000 fixed cost of B) results in a profit Z_B of $4600. Similarly, reducing this amount by the fixed cost of C and increasing it by contribution of C result in cumulative profit of $4800.

The distance that the last contribution segment extends above the break-even line is the total plant profit. The dotted line extending diagonally across the chart is the composite contribution line. The point at which this line crosses the break-even line establishes the sales volume at which fixed costs are exactly covered.

A *composite contribution rate,* shown by the sloping dotted line in Fig. 12.8, is the sum of each product's contribution, weighted according to its percentage of total sales. That is,

$$\text{Weighted contribution} = \text{product contribution} \times \frac{\text{product sales}}{\text{total sales}}$$

Then the composite contribution rate is the sum of the weighted contributions, and the total contribution is the composite contribution rate times total sales, which makes the gross profit equal the total contribution less the fixed cost. This concept is further explored in Review Exercise 3.

The value of multiproduct break-even charts lies in their use for product comparisons. The portion of fixed costs borne by each product is easily observed. A product is preferred when its contribution line is steeper than the composite contribution line. Such considerations are important in decisions to add new products or drop old ones.

12.2.6 Multiple Alternatives

In the previous sections, break-even analysis has been applied where the choices confronting the decision maker are related to a single alternative. Break-even analysis can easily be extended to multiple alternatives.

A frequently encountered situation is the *make-or-buy decision*. It occurs when an item can be made in-house at a lower total cost than the purchase price of the item from a vendor. The point at which the alternatives are equal depends on the first cost required to begin the in-house production.

A similar problem arises in a decision to lease or buy an asset. The costs of ownership (purchase price, installation cost, etc.) must be added to the operating costs in comparing an owned item to one that is leased. Any fixed-cost investment to lower variable costs with respect to a strictly direct-cost alternative depends on the time period required to pay off the investment from variable-cost savings. One advantage of diagramming a break-even comparison, as shown in Fig. 12.9, has to do with the attention focused on the break-even point B, which designates the level of activity and implies the time period separating the preference for alternatives.

Automation of manufacturing facilities is perceived by many manufacturers to meet today's market needs. Higher productivity and better quality and flexibility are a few of the advantages that can be achieved by implementing computer-controlled manufacturing systems. However, automated technologies and their implementation schedules can only be evaluated in the context of product demand growth and the impact of alternatives in terms of current and future capital expenditures, production costs, and market responsiveness.

A break-even chart for comparing two alternatives for discrete parts manufacturing is shown in Fig. 12.10. The automation alternative may represent a flexible manufacturing system designed as autonomous production cells, whereas the conventional system may be a typical job shop production environment. Automation and flexible manufacturing require higher capital outlay than the job shop system, but result in lower per-unit

FIGURE 12.9
Lease-or-buy comparison.

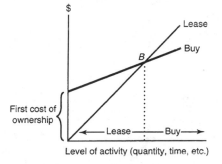

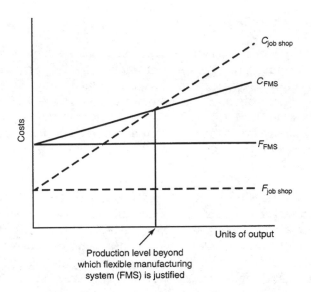

FIGURE 12.10
Break-even chart for comparing manufacturing alternatives.

production costs. The total cost at low production volumes is high for the flexible system due to underutilization of equipment. The break-even point represents the production volume required to justify the investment in the flexible manufacturing system.

12.3   NONLINEAR BREAK-EVEN ANALYSIS

Cost and revenue functions do not always follow convenient linear patterns. Often realistic cost relationships develop a nonlinear pattern, as typified by Table 12.1. The first four columns in the table relate output n to total fixed cost F, total variable cost, denoted by TV, and total cost C. The right side of the table shows average and marginal costs derived from the figures tabulated on the left.

Characteristic patterns of average and marginal costs based on Table 12.1 are pictured in Fig. 12.11.

Average fixed cost. Since fixed costs are independent of output, their per-unit amount declines as output increases. This feature is recognized when business people speak of "higher sales spreading the overhead":

$$\text{Average fixed cost} = \frac{F}{n}$$

Average variable cost. The typical saucer-shaped average-cost curve declines at first, reaches a minimum, and then increases thereafter. It reflects the law of diminishing returns. Initially, combining variable resources TV with fixed resources F produces increasing returns, but a point is reached where more and more variable resources must be applied

TABLE 12.1

Cost in dollars for nonlinear break-even analysis

Total product n	Total fixed cost F	Total variable cost TV	Total cost C	Average fixed cost F/n	Average total variable cost TV/n	Average total cost C/n	Marginal cost $\Delta C/\Delta n$
0	3,000	0	3,000	—	—	—	
1	3,000	700	3,700	3,000	700	3,700	700
2	3,000	1,300	4,300	1,500	650	2,150	600
3	3,000	1,800	4,800	1,000	600	1,600	500
4	3,000	2,400	5,400	750	600	1,350	600
5	3,000	3,100	6,100	600	620	1,220	700
6	3,000	3,900	6,900	500	650	1,150	800
7	3,000	4,900	7,900	429	700	1,129	1,000
8	3,000	6,200	9,200	375	775	1,150	1,300
9	3,000	7,800	10,800	333	867	1,200	1,600

to obtain each additional unit of output. Stated another way, a fixed plant is underemployed when its output is below the minimum average-cost point. As output expands, more complete utilization of the plant's capital equipment will make production more efficient. But continually increasing variable costs will eventually create a condition in which overcrowding and overutilization of equipment impair efficiency:

$$\text{Average total variable cost} = \frac{TV}{n}$$

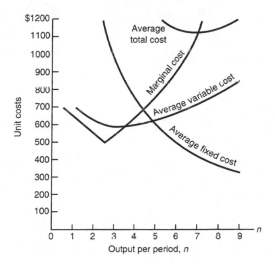

FIGURE 12.11
Relationship of average and marginal costs. Minimum points on the average- and total-cost curves occur where they cross the marginal-cost curve.

Average total cost. Because the average total cost is simply the sum of average fixed and average variable costs, it shows the combined effects of spreading out fixed charges and diminishing returns from variable resources:

$$\text{Average total cost} = \frac{C}{n}$$

Marginal cost. The key to the cost pattern in Fig. 12.11 is contained in marginal-cost concepts. Marginal cost is calculated from either C or TV as the *extra increment of cost required to produce an additional unit of output*. If the last increment of cost is smaller than the average of all previous costs, it pulls the average down. Thus, *average total cost declines until it equals marginal cost. Equivalently, the rising marginal-cost curve also intersects the average total variable cost curve at its minimum point*:

$$\text{Marginal cost} = \frac{\Delta C}{\Delta n}$$

12.3.1 Marginal Revenue and Profit

Both nonlinear revenue and cost schedules may be expressed as formulas. When such equations are available, their analysis is not much more difficult than that of linear models. Since an assumption of linearity makes all monetary increments constant over an extended range of output, nonlinear models call more attention to marginal relationships.

Marginal revenue is the additional money received from selling one more unit at a specified level of output. For linear revenue functions, the marginal revenue is a constant value P. That is, for each additional unit sold, the total revenue is increased by P dollars. Consequently, a greater output automatically increases the total profit:

$$\text{Marginal revenue} = \frac{\Delta R}{\Delta n}$$

When the linear relationship is replaced by an expression such as

$$\text{Selling price } P = 21,000n^{-1/2} \qquad \text{dollars per unit}$$

the price of each unit is not so obvious. Such expressions are examined with differential calculus. For the price function above, the rate of change of revenue with output is

$$\text{Marginal revenue} = \frac{dR}{dn} = \frac{d(nP)}{dn} = \frac{d(21,000n^{1/2})}{dn}$$
$$= 10,500n^{-1/2}$$

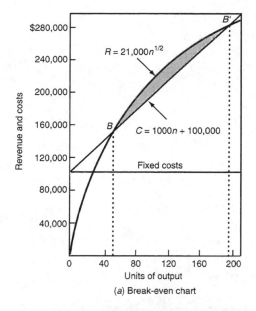

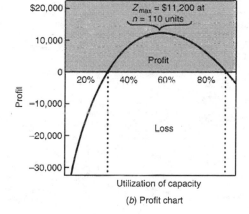

FIGURE 12.12
Nonlinear break-even
charts for decreas-
ing marginal revenue
and linear costs.

Figure 12.12a shows a decelerating revenue rate and linear costs. Decreasing marginal revenue is more realistic because it takes into account the likely condition that could result from a policy of lowering prices in order to achieve a higher plant utilization. The effect is that of increasing revenue, but at a decreasing rate.

The nonlinear revenue curve fixes two break-even points. Between these two points the firm operates at a profit. Outside the break-even points a loss is incurred, as shown in the profit chart, Fig. 12.12b.

The graphs are based on the following data:

$n - 1$ unit produced and sold per period

$V = \$1000$ per unit

$F = \$100,000$ per period

$P = \$21,000n^{-1/2}$ per unit

Using the formula for total revenue and the selling-price function $R = nP = 21,000n^{1/2}$ leads to a gross-profit equation of

$$Z = R - C = R - (nV + F)$$
$$= 21,000n^{1/2} - 1000n - 100,000$$

Knowing that $Z = 0$ at a break-even point allows the value or values for B to be determined by rearranging the terms for Z:

$$Z = 0 = -10^3 n - 10^5 + 21(10^3 n^{1/2})$$

or

$$10^3 n + 10^5 = 21 \times 10^3 n^{1/2}$$

Squaring each side of the equation and dividing by 10^6 result in

$$n^2 + 200n + 10^4 = 441n$$

and by collecting terms, we get

$$n^2 - 241n + 10^4 = 0$$

Solving for the break-even points by using the quadratic formula[†] gives

$$n = \frac{241 \pm \sqrt{(241)^2 - 4 \times 10^4}}{2} = \frac{241 \pm 134}{2}$$

or

$$B = 54 \text{ and } 188 \text{ units}$$

The point of maximum profit is especially important when two break-even points are present. As indicated in Fig. 12.12b, the rate of profit is

---

[†]This expression is a quadratic equation of the form

$$ax^2 + bx + c = 0$$

the roots of which can be obtained from

$$x = \frac{-b \pm \sqrt{b^2 - 4ac}}{2a}$$

increasing to the left of the point of maximum profit and is decreasing to the right. The rate of change of profit with respect to output is the *marginal profit*. At the point of maximum profit, the rate of change (and the marginal profit or slope of the profit line) is zero. Therefore, to find this point, differentiate the profit equation, set the derivative equal to zero, and solve for n:

$$\frac{dZ}{dn} = \frac{d(21,000n^{1/2} - 1000n - 100,000)}{dn} = 0$$
$$= 10,500n^{-1/2} - 1000 = 0$$

and

$$n = \left(\frac{10,500}{1000}\right)^2 = 110 \text{ units}$$

12.3.2 Marginal Cost and Average Unit Cost

As production increases, the total cost per unit may also increase, owing to greater maintenance needs, overtime payments to workers, and general inefficiency caused by congestion during stepped-up operation. Under these conditions there is an increasing *marginal cost* (rate of change of total cost with output).

One possible pattern of marginal costs and linear revenue is shown in Fig. 12.13. There could be many patterns: two break-even points (as in Fig. 12.12), decreasing marginal costs owing to savings realized from quantity purchases or near-capacity mechanized production, nonlinear functions for both revenue and costs, etc.

The feature points of a break-even analysis are determined in the manner described previously. To find B, set the profit equation equal to zero and solve for n. Differentiate the profit equation with respect to n, and set the derivative equal to zero to solve for the output that produces maximum gross profit. In doing so, note that

$$\frac{dZ}{dn} = \frac{d(nP - nV - F)}{dn} = 0$$
$$= \frac{d(nP)}{dn} - \frac{d(nV + F)}{dn} = 0$$

or

$$\frac{d(nP)}{dn} = \frac{d(nV + F)}{dn}$$

Marginal revenue = marginal cost

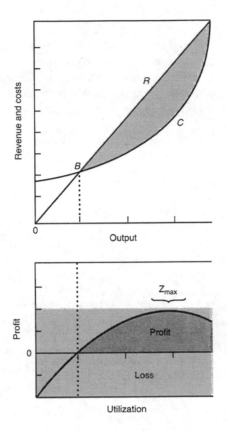

FIGURE 12.13
Break-even and
maximum-profit
points for increasing
marginal cost and
linear revenue.

at the operating level that produces maximum profit, which means that
when the change in revenue from one additional sale equals the change in
cost of producing one more unit, the point of maximum profit is attained.
Graphically, this point is located at the output at which the vertical distance between the total-cost curve and the revenue curve is greatest. If
marginal revenue and marginal cost were plotted, the output for maximum
profit would be at the intersection of the two curves.

For linear functions, the average unit cost is

$$\frac{nV + F}{n} = V + \frac{F}{n}$$

where n = a specific output. In this case the average unit cost continually
decreases with increasing output. For nonlinear costs this condition is not
necessarily true. If the average cost goes through a minimum point and
then increases, the slope of the curve will be zero at the output for the lowest average unit cost:

$$\frac{d(V + Fn^{-1})}{dn} = 0$$

$$\frac{dV}{dn} - \frac{F}{n^2} = 0$$

$$\frac{dV}{dn} = \frac{F}{n^2}$$

From this equation and the maximum-profit equation it is clear that for nonlinear relations, the point of minimum average unit cost does not necessarily coincide with the maximum-profit point (see Review Exercise 5).

12.4   EFFECTS OF INFLATION ON BREAK-EVEN ANALYSIS

Moderate inflation rates do not affect break-even volumes as severely as they affect returns from individual proposals, but they are still influential. One reason why break-even volumes are less affected is that fixed cost is not responsive to inflation. Since fixed cost is largely composed of depreciation, taxes, and contracts that are typically renegotiated annually (janitorial services, administrative salaries, maintenance agreements, etc.), there is no continuous impact of inflation. In contrast, variable costs and prices are consistently influenced by inflation and tend to rise accordingly.

Effects of escalations on the cost-volume-price relationship can be accounted for by linear or continuously compounded growth. A linear inflation model is conveniently used when inflation rates are moderate and the time taken to reach break-even volume is short. This model is examined because it is simple yet conceptually complete.

To the symbols already defined for break-even analyses (P = price per unit, V = variable cost per unit, F = fixed cost per period, n = number of units produced, and B = break-even volume), the following are added:

$M = P - V$ = contribution margin at beginning of analysis period

N = output or production rate per period (normally 100% utilization)

a = inflation rate per period for variable cost V

b = inflation rate per period for price P

T = time ($T = 0$ at start of period, and $T = 1$ at end of period)

Then $n = NT$ and $B = NT^*$, where T^* is the time when the break-even point occurs.

Knowing that revenue equals total cost at B, we include the effect of inflation on price (PbT) and variable cost (VaT) at time T in the break-even relationship as

$$\int_{T=0}^{T^*} (P + PbT)N \, dT = F + \int_{T=0}^{T^*} (V + VaT)N \, dT$$

By integrating with respect to T and rearranging terms, we get

$$\frac{(PbN - VaN)T^{*2}}{2} + (PN - VN)T^* - F = 0$$

Note that if there is no inflation, then $a = b = 0$, and the first term in the equation above is eliminated to give

$$(PN - VN)T^* = F$$

and since $T^* = B/N$,

$$\frac{B}{N} (P - V)N = F$$

or

$$B = \frac{F}{P - V} = \frac{F}{M}$$

Substituting the value of T^* in the quadratic equation yields

$$\frac{(PbN - VaN)B^2}{2N^2} + \frac{(PN - VN)B}{N} - F = 0$$

$$\frac{(Pb - Va)B^2}{2N} + (P - V)B - F = 0$$

or

$$\frac{(Pb - Va)B^2}{2} + MNB - NF = 0$$

Solving for B in the quadratic equation yields

$$B = \frac{-MN \pm \sqrt{M^2N^2 + 2(Pb - Va)NF}}{Pb - Va}$$

As an illustration of the linear inflation model, let $a = 0.5$ percent per month and $b = 1$ percent per month for the feeder airline situation described in Fig. 12.4. Given $P = \$120$ per unit, $V = \$30$ per unit, $F = \$63,000$ per month, and $N = 1000$ units (seats available) per month, without inflation

$$B = \frac{F}{M} = \frac{\$63{,}000/\text{month}}{(\$120 - \$30)/\text{unit}} = 700 \text{ units per month}$$

When the price of a ticket is going up faster than the variable cost ($b > a$), the break-even point goes down, as shown by

$$B = \frac{-90(1000) \pm \sqrt{90^2(1000^2) + 2[120(0.01) - 30(0.005)](1000)(63{,}000)}}{120(0.01) - 30(0.005)}$$

$$= \frac{-90{,}000) \pm \sqrt{8100 \times 10^6 + 2(1.20 - 0.15)(63 \times 10^6)}}{1.05)}$$

$$= \frac{-90{,}000 \pm 90{,}732}{1.05} = \frac{732}{1.05} = 697 \text{ units per month}$$

When the percentages are reversed ($a = 1$ percent and $b = 0.5$ percent), prices are still climbing faster than costs in terms of dollar amounts, and

$$B = \frac{-90{,}000 + 90{,}209.75}{0.30} = 699 \text{ units per month}$$

For the given data, the change in the break-even point is slight, mainly because the contribution margin per unit is so large. The effect of inflation is more pronounced when the contribution margin is small and the production rate is high.

12.5   REVIEW EXERCISES AND DISCUSSIONS

EXERCISE 1

An engineering consulting firm won a contract to design and supervise construction of a sewage treatment plant at a remote location. The installation phase will last at most 2 years, and two engineers from the firm will supervise on site operations. They will need both living accommodations and an office. Three alternatives are available, with the costs shown below.

1. Rent a building with furnished living accommodations and an office: $3000 per month including upkeep and utilities.
2. Buy two furnished trailers to live in and rent an office: The purchase price of a house trailer is $24,000 per trailer (the seller will buy back a used trailer for 40 percent of its purchase price anytime within 2 years); trailer upkeep, site rental, and utilities are $200 per trailer per month; and office rental is $800 per month.
3. Buy three trailers—two house trailers as in alternative 2 and a smaller one to serve as an office, purchased for $16,000 from the same seller.

If all the alternatives provide adequate facilities, which do you recommend?

SOLUTION 1

Total costs C for the three alternatives are calculated as

$$C_1 = \$3000N \qquad N = \text{no. of months needed}$$

$$\begin{aligned}
C_2 &= (2 \times \$24{,}000)(0.6) + [(2 \times \$200) + \$800]N \\
&= \$28{,}800 + \$1200N
\end{aligned}$$

$$\begin{aligned}
C_3 &= [(2 \times \$24{,}000) + \$16{,}000](0.6) + (3 \times \$200)N \\
&= \$38{,}400 + \$600N
\end{aligned}$$

As is apparent in Fig. 12.14, $C_1 = C_2$ at $N = 16$ months, $C_1 = C_3$ at $N = 16$ months, and $C_2 = C_3$ at $N = 16$ months. The decision thus narrows to a choice between alternatives 1 and 3, which, in turn, depends on the engineers' estimate of how long the project will take. If it takes longer than 16 months, alternative 3 is preferred. Otherwise, alternative 1 is less expensive. The convenience offered by the rented building (alternative 1 has upkeep and utilities paid, no trade-in hassles, etc.) would likely sway the decision.

EXERCISE 2

A would-be engineer spent so much time seeing movies while she was enrolled in engineering school that she never passed the differential equations course. After she dropped out, she inherited $100,000 on her twenty-first birthday (perhaps that is why she did not bother to study much). She greeted this inheritance as a chance to satisfy her passion for movies by leasing a soon-to-be vacant supermarket and converting it to a CinemaCenter consisting of four small theaters in one building. Based upon what she remembered from the engineering economics course she took before leaving school, she prepared the following cost estimates:

Renovation cost	$95,000
Contingency fund	$15,000
Estimated life of renovations	9 years

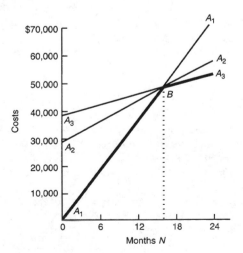

FIGURE 12.14
Break-even comparison for three alternatives. Alternative A_2 is dominated by the other two, making the choice between A_1 and A_3.

Salvage value	$0
Annual operating cost (365 days = 1 year)	$70,000
Annual lease expense	$50,000
Other annualized expenses	$16,000

The CinemaCenter will have 280 deluxe seats in the four projection areas and an elaborate lobby. Income per movie goer should average $7, including net profit from refreshments purchased. There will be 2 shows per day for each movie.

The most questionable estimate involved in this economic evaluation is the number of people who will attend the shows. What percentage of capacity is necessary to break even (assuming that receipts accumulate to year-end totals and the local cost of capital is 12 percent)? What influencing factors should be considered in forecasting utilization rates?

SOLUTION 2

The percentage of seats occupied by paying customers X needed to break even is found from

$$0 = \$7(2)(280)(365)(X) - (\$95,000 + \$15,000)(A/P, 12, 9) - \$70,000 - \$50,000$$
$$- \$16,000$$
$$= \$1,430,800X - \$110,000(0.18768) - \$136,000$$

and

$$X = \frac{\$20,645 + \$136,000}{\$1,430,800} = 0.1095 \text{ or } 10.95\%$$

Factors to consider in forecasting the utilization rate include the number and success of competitors, demographic data on the number of people in age groups most likely to attend the type of movies to be shown, and the average wage and spending habits of the local population.

EXERCISE 3

A fertilizer plant is operating at capacity with production of four mixes that have a total sales volume of $2 million. The sales and production-cost figures for mixes W, X, Y, and Z are as shown:

	Mix W	Mix X	Mix Y	Mix Z	Totals
Percentage of total sales	10%	20%	30%	40%	100%
Contribution (percentage of P)	45%	40%	45%	35%	
Fixed cost charged	$70,000	$180,000	$210,000	$220,000	$680,000
Profit	$20,000	−$20,000	$60,000	$60,000	$120,000

Recognizing the loss incurred with product X, the company is considering dropping the product or replacing it with another mix. If the product is dropped without a replacement, the new sales and cost figures are estimated to develop as follows:

	Mix W	Mix Y	Mix Z	Totals
Percentage of total sales	15%	35%	50%	100% (for R of $1,800,000)
Contribution (percentage of P)	45%	45%	35%	
Fixed cost charged	$100,000	$250,000	$290,000	$640,000

Construct a multiproduct profit chart to compare the two alternatives.

SOLUTION 3

The anticipated and original conditions are displayed in Fig. 12.15 in a slightly different form of multiproduct break-even chart. In this version, the first entry is made at zero revenue and the point of maximum fixed cost. Then the contributions of each product are plotted progressively to the right. All other interpretations are the same for the two forms of multiproduct charts.

To explain the values in Fig. 12.15, consider mix W. The contribution of W (value on the y axis) is given by $n_W (P_W - V_W)$. Since profit associated with W is 10 percent of $2 million with mix X included, $n_W V_W$ in the contribution expression can be computed from

$$Z_W = n_W P_W - (n_W V_W + F_W)$$

or

$$\$20,000 = \$200,000 - n_W V_W - \$70,000$$

$$n_W V_W = \$110,000$$

Note that the sales revenue from $W = n_W P_W = 10\%$ of $2 million total sales = $200,000. The contribution of W is $200,000 – $110,000 = $90,000. This corresponds to the cumulative value of –$680,000 + $90,000 = –$590,000 that is plotted corresponding to the sales revenue of W. Similarly, contributions of X, Y, and Z are $160,000, $270,000, and $280,000, respectively, for the original product mix. The total profit is then given by $90,000 + $160,000 + $270,000 + $280,000 – $680,000 = $120,000.

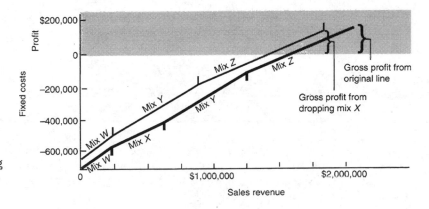

FIGURE 12.15
Multiproduct contribution chart showing reduced profit from the revised mix.

The new product line without mix X would be less profitable than the former line:

	Mix W	Mix Y	Mix Z	Total
Profit	$21,500	$33,500	$25,000	$80,000

The main reason gross profit falls from $120,000 to $80,000 is that most of the fixed costs carried by mix X did not disappear with its elimination from the product line; depreciation, taxes, engineering services, and other indirect costs are still required to run the batch plant, and their magnitude is not reduced appreciably by dropping mix X. The situation is further aggravated by having the largest sales increase occur for mix Z, which has a lower contribution rate than does the product eliminated.

EXERCISE 4
A manufacturing company produces several different products that are manufactured on the same equipment but are marketed individually. An audit of one product reveals the data shown in Table 12.2; all figures are corrected to a base year to avoid distortion by inflation or the general economy. The portion of manufacturing overhead allocated to the product as its fixed cost is $400,000. Analyze the product's life cycle costs and revenues.

SOLUTION 4
The fixed cost chargeable to the product totals $400,000 and is included in the analysis, as shown in the second column of Table 12.3. Variable costs were high during the start-up period, dropped as production became more efficient, and climbed during the third and fourth years as a result of "relearning" when production runs were not continuous, owing to declining sales. Although the average fixed cost drops consistently with additional output, the average variable cost and total-cost figures show the effect of increasing production costs.

TABLE 12.2

Cumulative output, cost, and revenue

Product life, age	Output, units	Variable cost, $	Revenue earned, $
Year 1	1000	80,000	200,000
	2000	112,000	400,000
	3000	134,000	600,000
Year 2	4000	160,000	780,000
	5000	190,000	930,000
Year 3	6000	252,000	1,050,000
	7000	352,000	1,160,000
Year 4	8000	480,000	1,270,000

The machine costs $40,000 and has a 25 percent salvage value at the end of 5 years. It is to be depreciated by MACRS depreciation, 5-year property class. The company currently has an effective tax rate of 40 percent and expects a return on investment of 12 percent after taxes.

(a) Conduct an after-tax analysis to determine how much could be paid annually for a constant-value lease that would produce the same present value as the loan purchase plan.

(b) Calculate the annual lease payment that would make the lease and loan plans equivalent if the loan were repaid in four equal installments (the interest rate is still 8 percent).

12.19 A company is being organized to produce a new type of one-piece fishing rod and reel to be called the *Fish Machine*. One million dollars has been budgeted for fixed costs over a 3-year period, including the advertising budget. Sales in the first year are expected to be 20,000 units, and the units will be priced to recover one-half the fixed cost. Second-year sales are expected to be double first-year sales. After all fixed costs have been recovered, the selling price of the Fish Machine may have to be reduced to encourage more sales. In the third year, production will be increased to 50,000 units, and variable costs are expected to rise sharply because production facilities will be operating over their design capacity. The expected total variable cost (TV) pattern is given below.

n	TV, $	n	TV, $
10,000	320,000	70,000	1,540,000
20,000	520,000	80,000	1,840,000
30,000	700,000	90,000	2,160,000
40,000	880,000	100,000	2,500,000
50,000	1,050,000	110,000	2,860,000
60,000	1,260,000		

(a) Prepare a graph of marginal cost, average variable cost, and average total cost.

(b) How much total profit would result if the price could be held at the original level for 3 years?

(c) Assume that the selling price holds at the original level for 2 years but then it must come down to meet competition from larger manufacturers that have entered the market. During the third year, prices must be dropped by 10 percent to sell each additional increment of 10,000 Fish Machines. What is the total profit for 3 years? Show that the maximum profit would be obtained if production were terminated at the output where marginal revenue equals marginal cost.

12.20 A company manufactures industrial clips for assembly work. The marginal revenue has been determined to be

Marginal revenue = $100 - 0.02n$

where n is the number of clips produced. Variable costs plus fixed costs are calculated by the formula

$$\text{Total cost} = 2n^2 \times 10^{-4} + 10{,}000$$

Compute the production in clips per year for the following:
- (a)   Minimum unit cost of sales
- (b)   Production for maximum profit
- (c)   Break-even volume

12.21   Assume that a company can sell all the units it produces, but costs are subject to diminishing returns. Its revenue and cost functions (in thousands of dollars) are

$$R - \frac{3n}{4} \quad \text{and} \quad C - \frac{n^3 - 8n^2 + 25n + 30}{25}$$

- (a)   Construct a graph of the cost and revenue curves with the break-even points indicated.
- (b)   At what output n will profit Z be maximum?

12.22   For a rough analysis of different bridge designs, it is assumed that costs are proportional to the span length X between piers. As the span length increases, a greater amount of steel is required to support the superstructure. However, fewer piers are required when span lengths are longer. The cost of each span for a certain bridge design is

$$C_s = 50X^2 + 5000X - 100{,}000$$

and the cost of a pier or an abutment is given by

$$C_p = 200{,}000 + 1000X$$

- (a)   Use the tabular approach to find the minimum cost for a bridge crossing a 300-meter bay.
- (b)   Use the formula approach to find the number of spans that minimizes the cost for bridging a 300-meter bay.

RISK ANALYSIS

Take calculated risks. That is quite different from being rash.
George S. Patton, *Letter to His Son,* 1944

The outcome of any economic decision is usually subject to an environment of uncontrollable influence. The longer the planning horizon, the greater the exposure to chance events. Inputs and outputs for short-term investment alternatives are usually subject to less variability than are long-term investment proposals. Risk is the chance of loss. As applied to engineering economics, risk is the chance that cash flow will fall short of, or exceed, expectation. In previous evaluations we have assumed that cash flow is known with certainty, although sensitivity analysis questioned the effect of cash flow deviations and the cost of capital when risk is considered. In this chapter, risk is a specified dimension for investment decisions. It is quantified as the probabilities of occurrence of different cash flows.

Risk analysis is appropriate when significant outcome variations are likely for different future states and meaningful probabilities can be assigned to those states. The time to consider risk is before one makes a commitment to a course of action. Perhaps a portion of the potential profit should be traded for partial immunity to risk. Mathematical models of the riskiness of operations assist decision makers by suggesting the impact of chance events on economic outcomes.

Under *complete uncertainty,* the probability distributions associated with future events are unknown or without meaning. Probabilities may not be estimated because data and past experience are lacking or because the environment is unstable and continuously changing. Analyzing such situations is referred to as *decision making under uncertainty.*

Decisions under risk and uncertainty are initially treated in the same way. Possible future states are identified, and outcomes are estimated for each alternative by assuming that each state will indeed occur. The difference between risk and uncertainty depends on the capability of estimating the likelihood of future states. When state probabilities can legitimately be prescribed, it is a decision under risk and the expected-value criterion is appropriate. When probabilities are unattainable, other criteria must be applied to select the preferred alternative. Decision-making under uncertainty is briefly examined in Sec. 13.7.

13.1   RECOGNIZING RISK

Economic analyses in previous chapters were based on the assumptions that complete information was available and that any uncertainty connected with a comparison could be tolerated. Thus, a salvage value assigned today is expected to be valid, say, 15 years hence. A positive cash flow of $1000 per year in a comparison model presupposes that exactly $1000 will become available each period on schedule. Unfortunately, real-world conditions do not always follow the models developed to represent them.

Variability is a recognized factor in most engineering and management activities. People are expected to possess individual skills and temperaments and to behave impetuously when exposed to some situations. The properties of materials vary over time. Seemingly identical machines exhibit diverse operating characteristics. Environmental factors are never constant, and economic conditions change irregularly. But recognizing variability is much easier than is including its consequences in economic comparisons.

We can respond by ignoring the variability associated with future events, assuming that they will happen as planned and adapting to changes if they do not; or we can try to anticipate contingencies through selection of the most promising course of action. Which response we follow depends largely on the consequences, although there are gamblers who habitually dare the future and risk avoiders who worry incessantly over trivialities and do nothing. A realistic response to economic risk is to admit that cash flows are subject to change, to question the potential effects of change with respect to consequences, and to use insights from the analysis to guide decisions.

Informal responses to risk take the form of arbitrary increases in the discount rate and contraction of payback periods. The vexing problem with these responses is the size of the adjustment. Considerations of inflation, sensitivity analysis, and comparisons based on a range of estimates were modifications of assumed uncertainty to deal with unpredictable future events.

Risk analysis contributes to a more complete economic evaluation when there are *significant* risks involved that can be represented by the

guesses is a gullible act, and basing them on the valid-experience judgments is a venturesome one. The use of subjective assessments in decision analysis is further explored in Chap. 15.

In practice, prior knowledge of probabilities may not be applicable to present or future conditions. Usually it is necessary to look at past records of events and use this empirical knowledge as a basis for current probabilities. However, vigilance is required to determine the relation of historical records to the present action; seemingly unrelated events could influence each other. Moreover, the records of one machine can sometimes be used to predict the performance of a similar machine. Experimental and other measurements that provide after-the-fact—*a posteriori*—probabilities are necessarily approximate, but they can still be the basis for practical applications.

13.3.1 Probability Concepts

This discussion of probabilities is not meant to be exhaustive. Rather, it introduces some basic probability concepts so that you can understand and apply risk analysis. A more exhaustive treatment can be found in textbooks on probability.

Betting in poker is a decision under risk. By keeping track of the cards played and relating them to the known distribution of card values in a complete deck, a betting policy can be developed to theoretically maximize returns. However, it takes considerable discipline to abide by the policy consistently and to do it long enough for the laws of probability to have effect. Somewhat the same problems affect economic decisions under risk. Each uncertain parameter or variable has multiple outcomes each with a probability of occurrence associated with it. The *probability* of something is the number of ways it can occur divided by the total number of ways things can turn out. It can be discouraging when an undesirable outcome occurs that had odds against it of 99 to 1; but in the long run, probability theory promises that if the odds are accurate, the temporary disappointment will be replaced by satisfaction when the same situation is replicated a number of times.

Consider a business investment that requires an initial cost of $25,000 and is expected to produce annual revenues of $8000 for 5 years. Based on an anticipated interest rate of 10 percent over 5 years, the present worth of the investment is

$$-\$25,000 + \$8000(P/A, 10, 5) = \$5326$$

Values of interest rate and future revenues represent estimates generally obtained from experienced personnel or by extrapolating past trends. Realistically, however, these variables may vary over the project life depending upon factors such as the economic environment, competition, technical innovation, and the like. We have already looked at the range-of-estimates or scenario generation approach in Chap. 11. Risk analysis is an extension of that approach in that it requires estimation of the range of possible future values and probabilities of occurrence associated with each of the value estimates.

Let the interest rate i be represented by three values: a worst-scenario value of 12 percent, a most likely value of 10 percent, and a best-scenario value of 7 percent. In this case, i has a number of possible numeric values. The value of i at any given time is not known until the actual occurrence of the event, although the probability of a value's occurring can be assigned in advance. Let the 12, 10, and 7 percent values for i have respective probabilities of occurrence of .10, .70, and .20. The interest rate is a *random variable,* a discrete random variable to be precise, since it takes on discrete values. If i could take on any value over the continuum from 7 to 12 percent, it would be a continuous random variable.

The range of possibilities for each feasible outcome of a variable and the probability of each outcome's occurring together make up the probability distribution. The probability distribution could be discrete or continuous, depending on the nature of outcomes: discrete or continuous over a range.

Variables can be statistically either independent or dependent. Statistical *dependence* means that the probability of an outcome of a variable is dependent on or influenced by the occurrence of some other variable, whereas an *independent* variable is not affected by the occurrence of any other variable. Interest rates and cash flow from sales may be independent variables. On the other hand, salvage value and life of an asset are dependent variables; in general, salvage value decreases over time. Dependent events are discussed in Chap. 14 when we consider sequential decision making by using decision trees.

Let the *interest rate* and *annual revenues* be two independent random variables defined by the following discrete probability distributions:

Interest rate		Annual revenues	
i, %	$P(I = i)$	x, \$	$P(X = x)$
12	.10	5,000	.05
10	.70	8,000	.85
7	.20	10,000	.10

In functional notation, the probability of $i = 12$ percent is represented as $P(I = 12 \text{ percent}) = .10$, where P is the probability, capital letters (I and X) represent random variables, and the small letters (i and x) represent specific values of the random variables. Collectively, the probabilities of mutually exclusive outcomes add up to 1.0:

$$P(I) = P(I = 12\%) + P(I = 10\%) + P(I = 7\%)$$
$$= .10 + .70 + .20 = 1.0$$

A probability distribution function provides information about the probability that a random variable will take on any one value within its range. A cumulative distribution function gives the probability of a random value's being less than or equal to a specified value. Cumulative distribution functions are obtained from the probability distribution function. Using the probability distribution function for i, we get the following:

i, %	$P(I = i)$	$F(I = i)$
12	.10	.10
10	.70	.80
7	.20	1.00

where F represents the cumulative probability.

EXAMPLE 13.1

Additive Probabilities

The output of a machine has been classified into three grades: superior (A), passing (B), and failing (C). The items in each class from an output of 1000 items are 214 in A, 692 in B, and 94 in C. If the run from which this sample was taken is considered typical, the probability that the machine will turn out each grade of product is

$$P(A) = \frac{214}{1000} = .214$$

$$P(B) = \frac{692}{1000} = .692$$

$$P(C) = \frac{94}{1000} = .094$$

What is the probability of making at least a passable product?

Solution

The probability of producing a passable product includes the set of superior and passing grades:

$$P(A + B) = P(A) + P(B) = .214 + .692 = .906$$

or

$$P(A + B) = 1 - P(C)$$
$$= 1 - .094 = .906$$

The probability that two or more independent variables will occur together is the product of all the individual probabilities. In terms of interest rates and revenues, the probability of $i = 10$ percent and $x = \$8000$ is

$$P(I = 10\% \text{ and } X = \$8000) = P(I = 10\%)P(X = \$8000)$$
$$= .70(.85) = .595$$

A probability tree provides a pictorial representation of sequential events or values of independent variables occurring simultaneously. In the probability tree of Fig. 13.2, the joint probabilities are the product of individual probabilities. The sum of independent probabilities in each column of circles is 1.0 and represents all possible outcomes.

EXAMPLE 13.2   **Multiplication of Probabilities**

A two-step manufacturing process involves two sequential operations with inspections after each operation. Manufacturing defects may be introduced in a part at either of two operations. Past data indicate that the first

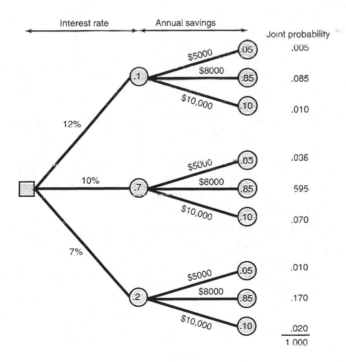

FIGURE 13.2
Probability tree for two independent variables.

inspection station can identify a defective part 92 percent of the time. The success rate of identifying defects at the second inspection station is 95 percent. What is the probability that a defective part will go undetected through the system?

Solution

Assuming that the two inspections are independent, the probability of not identifying a defective part at the two inspection stations is

P(no detection at inspection 1)P(no detection at inspection 2)
= $(1 - .92)(1 - .95)$
= $.004$

13.3.2 Expected Value

Expected value is a standard measure for economic comparisons involving risk. It incorporates the effect of risk on potential outcomes by means of a weighted average. Outcomes are weighted according to their probability of occurrence, and the sum of the products of all outcomes multiplied by their respective probabilities is the expected value. For the random variable X, the *expected value*, denoted by EV, is

$$\text{EV}(X) = \sum_{i=1}^{n} P(X = x_i)x_i$$

where n is the number of possible outcomes for variable X, $P(X = x_i)$ is the probability that $X = x_i$, and

$$\sum_{i=1}^{n} P(X = x_i) = 1.0$$

The EV for interest rate is (12 percent)(.10) + (10 percent)(.70) + (7 percent)(.20) = 9.6 percent. Similarly, the EV for annual revenues is $5000(.05) + $8000(.85) + $10,000(.10) = $8050.

As a common example of the expected-value approach, consider the coin-flipping game: A coin is flipped; if it comes up a *head*, you win the coin; but when a *tail* shows, you lose. Let the coin be a "fair" dime; then the probability of a head or a tail is, of course, .5, and the expected value of winnings from the game is

EV(flipping dimes) = P(H)($0.10) + P(T)(–$0.10)
= .5($0.10) + .5(–$0.10)
= 0

The given probabilities of future states are collectively exhaustive (both heads and tails are accounted for, and $\Sigma P = .5 + .5 = 1.0$); an outcome is associated with each future state (the gain or loss of a dime); and the expected value is the long-term expectation from repeated performances under the same conditions.

A profit-seeking individual or organization prefers a positive expected value, when gains are plus and losses are minus. In comparing alternatives, we find that the one with the highest EV is preferred, other things being equal. For instance, a variant of the coin-flipping game might be to pay $1 for the chance to flip two coins. The payoff could be to win $2 for two heads, $1 for two tails, and nothing when the coins split head and tail. The expected-value calculation

$$\begin{aligned} \text{EV} &= P(\text{HH})(\$2 - \$1) + P(\text{HT})(-\$1) + P(\text{TH})(-\$1) + P(\text{TT})(\$1 - \$1) \\ &= .25(\$1) + .25(-\$1) + .25(-\$1) + .25(0) \\ &= -\$0.25 \end{aligned}$$

shows that this is not a very good game to get into because the *average* loss per play is $0.25. But the *actual* outcome for any given gamble is a gain of $1, a loss of $1, or no change.

The appropriateness of the expected-value model for a once-in-a-lifetime decision is questionable. Other decision criteria such as those presented in Sec. 13.7 would enter the verdict. However, truly unique decisions do not occur often in actual practice; alternatives vary individually with respect to amounts, possible futures, and probabilities, but their evaluation is based on a consistent long-term objective of profit maximization or cost minimization. Since most industries and governments are long-lived and new investment projects are being continually initiated, expected value is a rational measure for most comparisons that recognize risk.

13.3.3 Measures of Variation

Useful quantitative measures of variability for a random variable are its variance and standard deviation. The variance, denoted by Var (X) or σ_x^2, is a measure of the dispersion or spread about the expected value. Mathematically, for discrete random variables

$$\text{Var}(X) = \sum_{i=1}^{n} [x_i - \text{EV}(X)]^2 \, P(X = x_i)$$

This formula reduces to

$$\text{Var}(X) = \sum_{i=1}^{n} P(X = x_i) x_i^2 - [\text{EV}(X)]^2$$

or

$$\text{Var}(X) = \text{EV}(X^2) - [\text{EV}(X)]^2$$

The *standard deviation* σ_x is equal to the positive square root of the variance of X:

$$\sigma_x = \sqrt{\text{Var}(X)}$$

The EV of the annual revenues considered previously is $8050. The variance associated with the estimate of revenues is equal to $.05(5000)^2 + .85(8000)^2 + .10(10,000)^2 - (8050)^2 = 847,500$, and the standard deviation is $921. Note that the standard deviation has the same units as X.

Consider the outcomes from two investment proposals depicted below. Both have the same expected value, but the range of estimated outcomes indicates that the forecaster is more confident that proposal A will return close to $1000. Histograms for proposals A and B would both show a central bar at $1000 on the horizontal axis with a height indicating a probability of occurrence of .6 on the vertical axis, but the equal-height ($P = .2$) bars representing the other two outcomes for proposal A would be much closer together than the corresponding bars for proposal B.

| | **Demand, $** | | | |
	P(low) = .2	*P*(average) = .6	*P*(high) = .2	**Expected value, $**
Proposal *A*	900	1000	1100	1000
Proposal *B*	400	1000	1600	1000

The variance of proposal A is equal to

$$\text{Var}(A) = .2(900)^2 + .6(1000)^2 + .2(1100)^2 - (1000)^2$$
$$= 4000$$

and the standard deviation is $63.25.

The visually obvious greater variability of proposal B is confirmed as

$$\text{Var}(B) = .2(400)^2 + .6(1000)^2 + .2(1600)^2 - (1000)^2$$
$$= 144,000$$

and the standard deviation is $379.47.

If the three states of demand in the above table were visually expanded to include all possible demand levels represented by their respective variances, the result would be a continuous distribution for each proposal. Figure 13.3 illustrates the two proposals with their respective variances in continuous form.

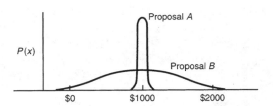

FIGURE 13.3

Variability of two proposals that have the same expected values.

The distribution forms shown in Fig. 13.3 are those of the *normal distribution,* a commonly used theoretical distribution in risk analysis. The mathematical representation of a random variable distributed normally depends on the two parameters μ and σ, its mean and standard deviation, respectively. Probability in a continuous distribution is given by the area under the distribution curve, and the expected value can be computed by integration. For the normal distribution, a table of probability values catalogued by standard deviations from the mean is provided in App. F. Here, observations from any normal random variable X are transformed to a new set of observations of a normal random variable Z with mean 0 and standard deviation 1. This is accomplished by the transformation

$$Z = \frac{X - \mu}{\sigma}$$

where Z is commonly called the standard normal deviate. Whenever X assumes a value x, the corresponding value of Z is given by $(x - \mu)/\sigma$. The mean of the symmetric distribution is the expected value of the random variable, transformed to the Z scale, represented by the horizontal axis.

Other distribution forms commonly used in describing random variables in risk analysis, particularly in the presence of minimal data, are the *uniform* and the *triangular* distributions. A uniform distribution implies that there is an equal likelihood for all possible outcomes of a random variable within a specified range to occur. At times under uncertainty we cannot reasonably estimate outcome probabilities. Therefore, a simple but obvious alternative is to treat each outcome probability as the same.

A uniform distribution is specified by two parameters, the lower limit a and the upper limit b for values of the random variable X. Then the expected value of X is

$$\text{EV}(X) = \frac{b + a}{2}$$

and its variance is

$$\text{Var}(X) = \frac{(b - a)^2}{12}$$

A triangular distribution is based on three estimates: a minimum anticipated value l, mode m, and a maximum anticipated value h. It is an easy distribution to use since it requires only a mode (as an estimate of the most likely outcome) and an estimate of the range of possible outcomes. The expected value and variance of a triangular distribution are given by the following expressions:

$$\text{EV}(X) = \frac{l + m + h}{3}$$

and

$$\text{Var}(X) = \frac{l^2 + m^2 + h^2 - lh - mh - ml}{18}$$

Once a well-behaved theoretical distribution is assumed to adequately represent outcome probabilities, an estimate of the standard deviation is necessary. It can be estimated directly or derived from an assessment of the risk associated with a certain outcome. For instance, assuming that the normal distribution is appropriate and has a mean of $1000, we can estimate the standard deviation forthrightly, say, $100. An assessment of the probability that the outcome will be less than $875 is obtained from the relationship

$$P(O < x) = P\left(Z < \frac{x - \mu}{\sigma}\right)$$

where O is a normally distributed outcome, x is a selected outcome value with a subjective estimate of the probability of its occurrence, and Z is the standard normal deviate. The desired probability is

$$\begin{aligned} P(O < \$875) &= P\left(Z < \frac{\$875 - \$1000}{\$100}\right) \\ &= P(Z < -1.25) \\ &= .1056 \end{aligned}$$

The .1056 probability is obtained by entering the table in App. F at $Z = 1.25$. At this point the area under the curve as measured outward from the mean is 0.3944. Since Z is negative in the formula, the left tail of the curve is indicated. Its area, which is the probability that $Z < 1.25$, is $0.5 - 0.3944 = 0.1056$.

By similar computations, a standard deviation can be obtained from such an assessment as "there is a 20 percent chance that the outcome will exceed the expected value of $1000 by $200 or more." The mathematical counterpart of this statement is

$$P(O \geq \$1200) = .2 = P\left(Z \geq \frac{\$1200 - \$1000}{\sigma}\right) = P\left(Z \geq \frac{200}{\sigma}\right)$$

which leads to an estimate that

$$.84 = \frac{\$200}{\sigma}$$

or $\sigma = \$238$. We found $Z = .84$ by scanning the normal table for the Z value that gives a probability of $(.5 - .2) = .3$.

The appropriateness of how well a distribution describes observed data can be checked by using goodness-of-fit tests such as the chi-squared and Kolmogorov-Smirnov tests. In some situations, a theoretical distribution may not accurately represent the probability estimates of a random variable. Instead, one can estimate directly the probability distribution of the random variable by using the pessimistic, most likely, and optimistic estimates. A number of distribution forms can be used to describe a given data set. What is sought is a distribution form that best describes one's beliefs about the outcome of the random variable. The final distribution obtained is generally quite insensitive to minor deviations in the shape of the distribution. A discussion of the different distribution forms and goodness-of-fit tests can be found in any standard probability and statistics text.

13.3.4 Coefficient of Variation

The standard deviation can be a misleading indicator of risk when alternatives differ in size. Let a third proposal C be added to the alternatives given in Fig. 13.3. For the same future states, proposal C has expected outcomes of \$980,000, \$1,000,000, and \$1,020,000, with respective probabilities of .2, .6, and .2. The expected value is obviously \$1 million, and the standard deviation is

$$\begin{aligned} \sigma_C &= \sqrt{.2(980,000 - 1,000,000)^2 + .6(0)^2 + .2(1,020,000 - 1,000,000)^2} \\ &= \sqrt{160,000,000} = \$12,649 \end{aligned}$$

A direct comparison of σ_C with $\sigma_A = \$63$ and $\sigma_B = \$379$ might be taken as an indication that proposal C is riskier because the standard deviation is much larger. The erroneous impression is erased by calculating the *coefficient of variation*.

The customary way to handle this situation of scale is to divide the standard deviation by the mean expected value to obtain

$$\text{Coefficient of variation} = \frac{\sigma_x}{\text{EV}(X)}$$

For proposal C,

$$\text{Coefficient of variation} = \frac{\$12,649}{\$1,000,000} = 0.0126$$

Comparing this value with the coefficient of variation for proposal A ($63/$1000 = 0.063) and proposal B ($379/$1000 = 0.379) makes it apparent that proposal C is subject to less outcome variability.

13.4 APPLICATION OF PROBABILITY CONCEPTS

The *expected-value* measure of preference is a standard measure for economic comparisons involving risks. The use of an expected value is based on the premise that the decision maker desires to maximize returns, when gains are plus and losses are minus. *Investment risk profiles* and *acceptable-investment diagrams* are graphic aids that assist in the evaluation of expected values. The *expected value of perfect information* can be calculated to suggest the maximum amount that can be spent to obtain more accurate forecasts of future states. Other criteria such as the *variance, most probable future,* and *aspiration level* may influence the final selection of the preferred alternative.

13.4.1 Payoff Tables

A format for organizing and displaying outcomes of alternative courses of action is called a *payoff table* or a *decision matrix*. Each row in the table represents an alternative, with its outcomes arranged in columns according to respective future states. In the payoff table below, the present worths of two new products A and B are shown for three states of sales success during a 3-year marketing period.

Alternative	State of market acceptance, $		
	Rejection	**Average**	**Domination**
Product A	−50,000	200,000	500,000
Product B	−200,000	100,000	1,000,000

The initial cost of developing product A is $50,000; this amount would be lost if the product were rejected by consumers. If product A received average acceptance, the expected net gain would be $200,000; and if it dominated the market, the payoff would be $500,000. Product B would cost 4 times as much as product A to put into production; but if it became a bestseller, it would double A's profit. Because production costs for B are higher, an average demand would result in only one-half the payoff expected from A.

Some conclusions might be drawn from only the payoffs included in the table. For instance, a loss of $200,000 could be considered disastrous to the company, while a loss of $50,000 would at least be tolerable. With such a severe penalty for failure, alternative B would practically be eliminated regardless of the potentially large payoff. However, even more meaningful observations can be made by including the relative likelihood for each outcome. The payoff table below has been modified to incorporate probability factors:

	State of market acceptance: Outcome and risk, $		
Alternative	Rejection $P(R) = .1$	Average $P(A) = .6$	Domination $P(D) = .3$
Product A	−50,000	200,000	500,000
Product B	−200,000	100,000	1,000,000

It might have been necessary to assign probabilities to each outcome of each alternative, but it is assumed that products A and B are similar enough to possess the same consumption pattern. In the example both products have a probability of .1 of rejection, .6 of normal demand, and .3 of booming acceptance. The requirement that probabilities of future states add to 1.0 means that outcomes must be assigned to all possible future states.

After we conclude that the future states are indeed representative, the probability assignments are realistic, and outcomes are estimated as accurately as possible, calculation of the expected values is easy; and preference among alternatives is clearly distinguished. For the comparison between product A and product B,

$$\text{EV}(A) = .1(-\$50,000) + .6(\$200,000) + .3(\$500,000)$$
$$= \$265,000$$

$$\text{EV}(B) = .1(-\$200,000) + .6(\$100,000) + .3(\$1,000,000)$$
$$= \$340,000$$

Product B is clearly preferred, assuming that all other factors affecting the decision are equal.

EXAMPLE 13.3

Expected Value of Risky Alternatives

A process line that will continue to be needed for 3 years has annual costs of $310,000, which are expected to remain constant. A novel redesign for the line has been suggested. The new approach will cost $150,000 to install and has a 50 percent chance of cutting annual operating costs to $210,000. However, there is a probability of .25 each that annual costs for the redesigned line will increase from $210,000 for the first year by either $20,000 or $75,000 in each of the next 2 years. If a 12 percent rate of return is required, should the new design be installed?

Solution

Equivalent annual costs for each future state of the redesigned process line are as follows:

$$\text{EAC(at } P = .5) = \$150,000(A/P, 12, 3) + \$210,000$$
$$= \$150,000(0.41635) + \$210,000$$
$$= \$272,453$$

$$\text{EAC(at } P = .25) = \$150,000(A/P, 12, 3) + \$210,000 + \$20,000(A/G, 12, 3)$$
$$= \$272,453 + \$20,000(0.92461)$$
$$= \$290,945$$

$$\text{EAC(at } P = .25) = \$150,000(A/P, 12, 3) + \$210,000 + \$75,000(A/G, 12, 3)$$
$$= \$272,453 + \$75,000(0.92461)$$
$$= \$341,799$$

These costs are inserted in a payoff table, as shown below, where the calculated expected values indicate that the redesign should be attempted even when there is one chance in four of increasing the process-line costs.

Alternative	$P(.5)$, $	$P(.25)$, $	$P(.25)$, $	Expected value, $
No change	310,000	310,000	310,000	310,000
Redesign	272,453	290,945	341,799	294,413

13.4.2   Expected Value of Perfect Information

A decision is at risk whenever the occurrence of the events involved in it is in doubt. The likelihood of outcomes may be known, such as when probabilities are available for future states, but which state will actually exist when an alternative is exercised is still unknown. Knowledge of when each state will occur would allow a decision maker to utilize the most profitable alternative on each occasion. This condition of prescience provides *perfect information* for decision making. The probabilities of future states happening are not changed by the acquisition of perfect information. The future states occur in the same proportion in any case; but perfect information reveals the maximum expected loss due to imperfect information.

In a decision situation represented by a payoff table, the expected result from possessing perfect information is determined by multiplying the best outcome in each column by its probability and then summing the products. For the outcomes in the payoff table of Example 13.3, the redesign alternative has the lower cost for two future states ($272,453 when $P = .5$ and $290,945$ when $P = .25$) and the no-change alternative has a lower cost in the other future state ($310,000 at $P = .25$). These are the outcomes that the decision maker would choose to have for each future state by exercising the appropriate alternative, if it were known which state would occur. Therefore, the *expected result given perfect information*, denoted by EV|PI, is

$$\text{EV}|\text{PI} = \$272,453(.5) + \$290,945(.25) + \$310,000(.25)$$
$$= \$286,463$$

The difference between the expectation with perfect information and the expected value without prior knowledge is called the *expected value of perfect information*. From Example 13.3, where the expected value of the redesign alternative was computed to be $294,413,

$$\text{Expected value of perfect information} = \text{EV}|\text{PI} - \text{EV}$$
$$= \$286,463 - \$294,413$$
$$- -\$7950$$

which is a negative cost that corresponds to a saving of almost $8000. This calculation suggests the maximum investigation costs that could be justified to find out which state will exist each time the decision is due.

EXAMPLE 13.4   **Value of Perfect Information**

An ambitious entrepreneur has signed a regionally well-known rock band to give a concert on the first of July. The concert can be staged in a conveniently located pasture or in a school auditorium. If the weather is sunny, a concert in the pasture could be very profitable, but rain would ruin attendance and cause a loss due to the high fixed costs of preparing the site. Attendance at the auditorium would be largely unaffected by weather, but the maximum capacity is far less than that of the pasture. Weather records indicate that odds against rain on July 1 are 9 to 1. Using the probabilities given and the estimated returns shown for concerts held at the two locations, calculate the expected value and the amount of money that could be paid for perfect information about the weather, if it could be obtained.

	Net return, $, if there is	
Alternative	**Rain**	**No rain**
Auditorium	24,000	30,000
Pasture	−27,000	90,000

Solution

The payoff table below indicates that holding the concert in the pasture has the greater expected value.

	Rain, $ (P = .1)	No rain, $ (P = .9)	Expected value, $
Auditorium	24,000	30,000	29,400
Pasture	−27,000	90,000	78,300

If the entrepreneur knew that it was going to rain on the first of July, the concert would surely be scheduled in the auditorium to reap a $24,000 profit instead of a loss. Equivalently, assurance of dry weather would lead to a profit of $90,000 from the concert held in the pasture. Since it is dry 9 out of 10 times on the first of July, the expected result given perfect information is

$$\$24,000(.10) + \$90,000(.9) = \$83,400$$

and the amount that could be paid for it is $83,400 − $78,300 = $5100, the difference between the returns from a commitment to hold the concert in the pasture and the option to schedule it at the site better suited to the weather. This is the expected value of perfect information.

13.4.3 Investment Risk Profiles

The range-of-estimates approach discussed in Chap. 11 can be modified to reflect risk. Probabilities of occurrence are assigned to each future state in the range. Then all possible combinations of outcomes are collected, and their dollar amounts and joint probabilities are calculated. The result is an *investment risk profile* that reveals the likelihood for an investment to realize various net present-worth (NPW) returns.

Assume that an investment proposal for income expansion requires an initial outlay of $200,000. The most likely outcome is for after-tax returns to amount to $100,000 per year for 4 years. There is no salvage value, and the minimum attractive rate of return (MARR) is 9 percent. Under the assumption of certainty,

$$PW = -\$200,000 + \$100,000(P/A, 9, 4)$$
$$= -\$200,000 + \$100,000(3.23972) = \$123,972$$

A risk analysis of the same proposal recognizes that the most likely cash flow has a probability of only .5. A pessimistic appraisal of the future concedes returns might amount to only $50,000 per year. Under the most optimistic assessment, returns could total $125,000 per year. The probabilities of pessimistic and optimistic returns materializing are .3 and .2, respectively. The duration of returns is also questionable; probabilities for 2, 3, 4, and 5 years are, respectively, .2, .2, .5, and .1. These data are summarized on the decision probability tree shown in Fig. 13.4.

The joint probability for each outcome is the product of the independent probabilities representing each factor involved in the outcome. These probabilities are entered in the nodes of the probability decision tree, and the factors are labeled on the lines connecting the nodes. For example, the joint probability of returns of $50,000 per year for 2 years (top of the column in Fig. 13.4) is .06. It results from multiplying the probability of the definite investment (1.0) by the probabilities of $50,000 returns (.3) and a 2-year period (.2).

The present worths of the outcomes are calculated by the usual procedures. The value listed at the top of the PW of Outcome column, based on a required rate of return of 9 percent, is computed as

FIGURE 13.4
Decision tree format for an investment risk profile analysis. Node entries indicate probabilities for the economic factors noted on lines leading to the nodes. Each burst represents one economic condition subject to risk.

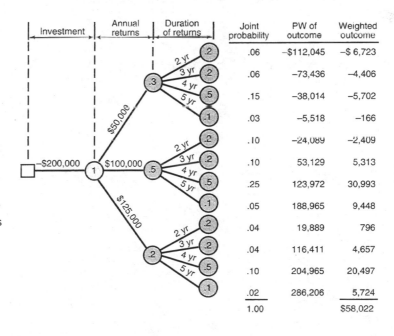

	Joint probability	PW of outcome	Weighted outcome
2 yr .2	.06	–$112,045	–$ 6,723
3 yr .2	.06	–73,436	–4,406
4 yr .5	.15	–38,014	–5,702
5 yr .1	.03	–5,518	–166
2 yr .2	.10	–24,089	–2,409
3 yr .2	.10	53,129	5,313
4 yr .5	.25	123,972	30,993
5 yr .1	.05	188,965	9,448
2 yr .2	.04	19,889	796
3 yr .2	.04	116,411	4,657
4 yr .5	.10	204,965	20,497
5 yr .1	.02	286,206	5,724
	1.00		$58,022

$$\begin{aligned}
\text{PW}(P = .06) &= -\$200{,}000 + \$50{,}000(P/A,\ 9,\ 2) \\
&= -\$200{,}000 + \$50{,}000(1.75911) \\
&= -\$112{,}045
\end{aligned}$$

The weighted value of this present worth is the top entry of the rightmost column in Fig. 13.4 and is the product

$$\begin{aligned}
\text{Joint probability}(i) \times \text{PW}(\text{outcome } i) &= .06(-\$112{,}045) \\
&= -\$6723
\end{aligned}$$

The remaining outcomes are computed similarly. The sum of these values is the expected value of the proposal EV = \$58,022. For the given probabilities of occurrence, the expected value is much less than the present worth based on the most likely outcomes. Although the probability estimates are quite likely subject to some error, the exercise of calculating an investment profile contributes to a more complete analysis and a better appreciation of the factors involved in the proposal.

An investment risk profile highlights more than the expected value. When the outcomes and related probabilities are graphed, a proposal's prospects are clearly displayed for capital-budgeting discussions. The data of Fig. 13.4 are graphed in Fig. 13.5. Lines connect the outcome-risk points to better define the cumulative probability distribution of net present values. The connected points make it quite evident that the proposal has a probability greater than .4 of showing a loss.

13.4.4   Acceptable-Investment Diagrams

Another graphic display to assist in the evaluation of alternatives subject to risk is called an *acceptable-investment diagram (AID)*. Its format is a horizontal axis representing rates of return and a vertical axis scaled to show the probability that an investment will surpass a given rate of return. Criteria for an acceptable investment are blocked off in the chart by setting limits for

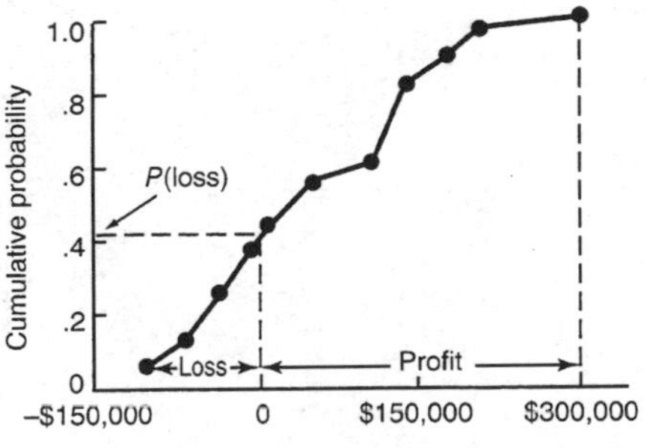

FIGURE 13.5
Tabulated data and graph of an investment risk profile.

Investment risk present worth	Cumulative probability
−\$112,045	.06
−73,436	.12
−38,014	.27
−24,089	.37
−5,518	.40
19,889	.44
53,129	.54
116,411	.58
123,972	.83
188,965	.88
204,965	.98
286,206	1.00

1. The required probability that an investment's rate of return exceeds a minimum percentage (loss coefficient)
2. The desired probability that an investment's rate of return will exceed an attractive level (payoff coefficient)
3. A line connecting the two coefficients, called an *aspiration level*

Any investment risk profile that does not intrude on the rejection area defined by the listed limits is considered an acceptable investment; its risk-return potential is greater than the minimum risk-return requirements.

EXAMPLE 13.5   **Application of an AID**

An investment of $1000 for 1 year has the possible after-tax returns shown in the table below. The probability of each outcome is estimated, and the rate of return is apparent, as shown in the table in the last column.

The investors seek proposals that provide a probability of .95 that they will not lose more than 5 percent and a .30 likelihood that their rates of return will be greater than 15 percent. Use an AID to determine the acceptability of the $1000 investment proposal.

Net return (outcome), $	Rate of return, %	Probability of outcome	Probability that investment's RR will exceed rate of return
−900	−10	.05	.95
1050	5	.15	.80
1150	15	.40	.40
1300	30	.30	.10
1500	50	.10	.00

Solution

The rejection area for the acceptable-investment diagram in Fig. 13.6 results from lines connecting the loss coefficient horizontally to the ordinate, the loss coefficient diagonally to the payoff coefficient, and the payoff coefficient to the abscissa. The sloping line is the implied aspiration level relating desired returns to allowable risk. The investment's risk-return potential is represented by lines connecting the rates of return associated with their probabilities of occurrence.

Because part of the risk-return curve crosses the rejection area, the investment is not acceptable according to the given criteria. Investments passing these criteria can be further evaluated on other merits such as timing of returns, capital availability, and the decision criteria discussed next.

FIGURE 13.6
Acceptable-invest-
ment diagram (AID)
for evaluating the
risk-return potential
of a proposal
according to the
investor's risk-return
requirements. The
investment proposal
shown is unaccept-
able because it
enters the rejection
region.

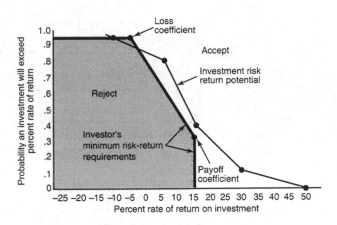

13.4.5 Auxiliary Decision Criteria

Once an investment risk profile is developed, there are several ways to appraise its desirability. The basic criterion, as already observed, is *maximization of expected returns,* which is determined by expected-value calculations. Other criteria include the *expectation variance, most probable future,* and *aspiration level.* These criteria are illustrated by reference to Table 13.1.

The expectation variance principle focuses attention on the variance associated with each alternative. It is desirable to minimize variance. Thus, if two or more alternatives have the same expected cost or return, the one with the smallest variance of cost or return should be selected (see Fig. 13.3). Conversely, if two (or more) alternatives have the same variance, the one with the smaller expected cost or larger return should be selected (Fig. 13.7). If, as is usually the case, both the expected returns and variances are unequal for the alternatives, then the alternative with both the higher returns and lower variance is preferable. This situation is shown in Fig. 13.8 for two alternatives, where alternative *A* is clearly

TABLE 13.1

Probability of returns from three equal-size, equal-life investments

Alternative	Possible net present worths of proposals, $					
	-1000	**0**	**1000**	**2000**	**3000**	**4000**
A	0	.11	.26	.22	.02	.39
B	.29	.18	.07	0	0	.46
C	.14	.10	.11	.37	.28	0

FIGURE 13.7
Comparison of alter-
natives with the
same variance but
different expected
values.

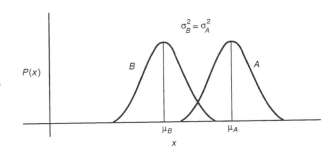

FIGURE 13.8
Comparison of alter-
natives with differ-
ent means and vari-
ances, and one
alternative domi-
nates the other.

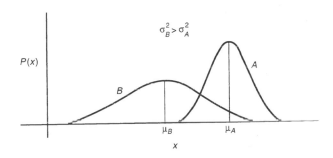

FIGURE 13.9
Comparison of alter-
natives with differ-
ent means and vari-
ances and no
domination.

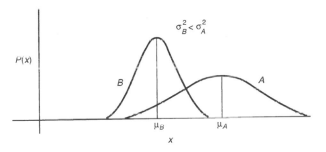

preferable to B. If the comparison indicates no clear dominance of one alternative over the other, as in Fig. 13.9, then the decision maker must trade the maximization of expected returns off the minimization of variance or risk. Other principles discussed below can also be used as secondary criteria.

These are the expected returns and standard deviations (square root of variance) for the three alternatives shown in Table 13.1:

Alternative	Expected return, $	Standard deviation, $
A	2320	1476
B	1620	2257
C	1550	1359

most situations: probable life pattern, alternative courses of preventive action, and outcome costs for the alternatives. The objective is to find the interval at which preventive action is most suitable and then to compare this with the alternative of remedial action to decide which is more economical.

To illustrate a maintenance policy, we will assume that a factory has 30 similar machines that exhibit the probability distribution of failures shown in the table below. The cost of remedial action after a breakdown averages $100, and the cost of providing preventive maintenance is $30 per machine.

Months after maintenance	Probability of failure
1	.2
2	.1
3	.1
4	.2
5	.4

The total cost of a preventive maintenance program is the sum of servicing expenses for all the machines each maintenance period (30 machines $\times$ $30 per machine = $900) and the cost of breakdowns occurring between services. For a monthly preventive maintenance policy PM_1, the cost is $900 plus $100 for each breakdown expected in the first month after servicing. This amounts to

$$PM_1 = \$900 + \$100(30)(.20) = \$1500 \text{ per month}$$

A *bimonthly* policy must again include the $900 basic group-servicing cost and the cost of individual breakdowns. In the first month of the period, $30 \times .20 = 6$ machines are expected to break down. During the second month, $30 \times .10 = 3$ machines serviced at the regular period are likely to break down, and 20 percent of the individual breakdowns treated during the first month will fail *again*. These calculations are depicted in Table 13.2, where a modified expected-value table is utilized.

The first alternative in the table represents a monthly preventive maintenance policy. The expected value of this alternative is 6 machines treated each month, which agrees with previous calculations. The second line of outcomes depicts the failures of the second month. The total number of expected breakdowns in 2 months is the cumulative value for both months: $6 + 4.2 = 10.2$ machines. The cost of a bimonthly policy PM_2 is

$$PM_2 = \$900 + (\$100 \times 10.2) = \$1920$$

which makes the cost per month equal to $1920/2 = $960.

TABLE 13.2

Expected failures for two PM periods

PM periods	Individual failures during month		Expected value	
	PM$_1$ (.2)	PM$_2$ (.1)	Individual	Cumulative
1	30	0	6	6
2	6	30	4.2	10.2

A policy of servicing all the machines every 3 months would lead to the expected failure record shown in Table 13.3. Now a pattern can be observed. Some of the original group of 30 machines continue to break down each month, and some of those repaired fail again individually. The repairs made each month start a new cycle which must follow the failure distribution. Thus, the expected number of breakdowns from 1 month is always the first outcome (.20 probability of failure) for the next month. Similarly, the expected value 2 months ago is the second outcome for the current month, and the cumulative value is the total number of expected breakdowns for a cycle of so many months. A 3-month cycle would have a total cost of

$$PM_3 = \$900 + (\$100 \times 14.64) = \$2364$$

or a monthly cost of \$2364/3 = \$788.

TABLE 13.3

Expected failures for three PM periods

PM periods	Individual failures during month			Expected value	
	PM$_1$ (.2)	PM$_2$ (.1)	PM$_3$ (.1)	Individual	Cumulative
1	30	0	0	6	6
2	6	30	0	4.2	10.2
3	4.2	6	30	4.44	14.64

TABLE 13.4

Expected cost of preventive maintenance alternatives, $

PM periods	Individual failure costs during month					Expected value		PM cost	Total cost	Monthly cost
	PM_1 (.2)	PM_2 (.1)	PM_3 (.1)	PM_4 (.2)	PM_5 (.4)	Individual	Cumulative			
1	3000	0	0	0	0	600.00	600.00	900	1500	1500
2	600	3000	0	0	0	420.00	1020.00	900	1920	960
3	420	600	3000	0	0	444.00	1464.00	900	2364	788
4	444	420	600	3000	0	791.00	2255.00	900	3155	789
5	791	444	420	600	3000	1564.60	3819.60	900	4719	944

Table 13.3 can be converted to costs and expanded to include all the necessary calculations for the cost of every preventive maintenance alternative. The outcomes are converted from units of machines to dollar values by multiplying the number of machines by the individual remedial cost ($100). Columns are added to account for the cyclic group PM costs, the sum of individual and group costs, and the prorated monthly costs. The completed table in Table 13.4 displays the same recurring pattern of outcomes described previously.

The last step is to determine the costs associated with a policy of performing no preventive maintenance; machines are serviced whenever they break down. The expected period between breakdowns is calculated from the original failure distribution. The expected period is

$$1 \text{ month} \times .2 + 2 \text{ months} \times .1 + 3 \text{ months} \times .1 + 4 \text{ months} \times .2$$
$$+ 5 \text{ months} \times .4 = 3.5 \text{ months between breakdowns}$$

Then with the cost of servicing individual breakdowns at $100 per breakdown, a remedial action policy costs

$$\frac{30 \text{ machines} \times \$100 \text{ per machine service}}{3.5 \text{ months per service}} = \$857 \text{ per month}$$

A comparison of the $857 monthly cost for the remedial action alternative with the minimum monthly cost of a preventive maintenance policy from Table 13.4 ($788) indicates that the latter alternative is preferable. Both the 3- and 4-month preventive maintenance periods show a lower expected cost than that for dealing with machines only after they fail.

This approach can be applied to a variety of situations. The items being evaluated could fail completely, such as electric lightbulbs or electronic tubes. Failures may represent personnel who are no longer available owing to transfers or retirement, and replacement could be the recruiting or training policy. There are also numerous modifications that fit special maintenance and repair situations.

L3.5 SIMULATION IN ECONOMIC ANALYSIS

To simulate is to imitate. In engineering economics, simulation is used to model a real system in order to observe and learn from the behavior of the replica. It derives statistical estimates of performance measures for the system under study through repeated experimentation.

Computer simulation is an effective way to deal with complex economic relations without suffering the penalties of direct trial-and-error experiences. It is usually easier, less disruptive, far less expensive, and possibly more illuminating to confine one's attention to characteristics of particular interest. Some problems do not yield conveniently to ready-made solution methods and models, such as problems with many variables and complex dependency relationships. In such cases, when no simple analytical models are available, problems can be "simulated" to see the numerical effect of different alternatives.

The disadvantages associated with simulation generally refer to the precision and accuracy of the results and to the cost of creating the model. Because simulation uses sampling procedures to estimate system parameters, its outputs are only statistical estimates. If the inputs used in simulation are realistic representations of the actual system parameters, the estimations of performance measures can come close to their true values; otherwise, the estimates are inaccurate. In most cases, the cost of using simulation will be greater than that of using any analytical solution, if such can be found, because simulation models are usually more complex. The increased complexity is due to the increased number of interactions and interdependencies that are represented in a simulation model.

13.5.1 Monte Carlo Simulation

Monte Carlo is a simulation technique in which random numbers are generated to select events from a probability distribution of occurrences. The name is derived from possible random number generators: a flipped coin, a tossed die, a cut of a deck of cards, or even a roulette wheel. However, the most used generator is a random number table, as displayed in Fig. 13.13. The groups of numbers follow no pattern or special order; they are randomly distributed. The main concern a user should have is to avoid imposing a pattern by repeatedly using the same set in a consistent order. The figures can be read in any manner desired—by rows or columns, diagonally, up or down, etc.

From this distribution an inventory policy can be developed that establishes a minimum-cost balance between holding and opportunity costs. A more direct tactic would be to set a tolerable limit for stockouts per year and hold a safety stock which conforms to this limit.

It is logical that the greater the number of trials, the more closely the simulation will correspond to the actual inventory pattern. Computers are almost always used for simulation because actual distributions usually cover a far greater range than those used in the example, and a relatively large number of trials are required to give reliable information.

13.5.2 Cash Flow Simulation

The computational effort required to analyze risk is apparent from the section on cash flow aggregation. For more extensive applications, computerized simulation is a sensible alternative. Sufficient trial outcomes can be obtained at a reasonable cost to reveal the approximate distribution of the returns. Since most of the distributions for cash flow components are subjective forecasts, the approximation by simulation forfeits negligible reality. Therefore, a decision to use cash flow simulation rests on the cost and time of direct analysis versus the availability and expense of computer simulation; the alternative of manual simulation is seldom feasible because of the exhausting tediousness of cumbersome iterations.

The general procedure for the simulation of an investment's return is shown in Fig. 13.15. Inputs may be any of the cash flow factors for which distributions are obtainable. Random numbers are generated to establish quantitative values for all the variable inputs in each trial run. The number of digits selected for a random number depends on the precision of the probability distribution. Normally, 2-or 3-digit random numbers are sufficient for most simulation studies. These simulated inputs are then combined with other known factors according to relationships written into the computer program. Each trial then produces one outcome for the characteristics of interest (PW, IRR, AW, or a factor such as asset life N). When enough outcomes have been accumulated, a pattern emerges that suggests the distribution and expected value.

A graphic representation of the sources of data for the statistical trials is given in Fig. 13.16. The discrete distribution in Fig. 13.16a is an asset's life; $P(N = 1) = .2$, $P(N = 2) = .3$, $P(N = 3) = .4$, and $P(N = 4) = .1$. A comparable chart for normally distributed random variables is shown in Fig. 13.16b; the mean of the distribution is zero, and deviations from the mean are expressed in standard deviations. A manual simulation application using these distributions is presented in Example 13.9.

It is important to validate any simulation model. Both the basic model and its internal logic, including program debugging, should be verified. Verification starts with a check of model assumptions against the purpose of the study and extends to checking the output against reality. Checking

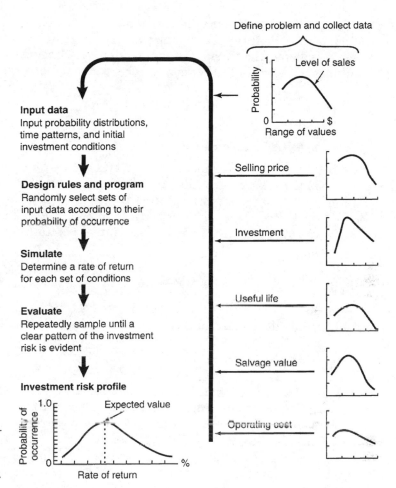

FIGURE 13.15

Flowchart for simulation procedures to evaluate an investment subject to risk.

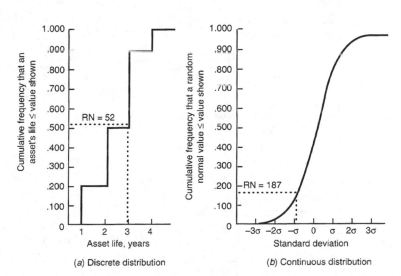

FIGURE 13.16

Sample cumulative distributions for manual simulations for data described in Example 13.9.

includes the sufficiency of the number of trials. An easy way to determine the stability of a solution is to plot the average outcome (vertical axis) against the number of trials; when the line connecting average outcomes is essentially horizontal, the range of error for the solution is narrow.

EXAMPLE 13.9

Manual Monte Carlo Simulation

Construction at an exploration site has a mean cost of $2 million and a standard deviation of $500,000. Costs are assumed to be normally distributed. The project may last from 1 to 4 years with the distribution shown in Fig. 13.16a. If the before-tax rate of return is 20 percent and no salvage value is expected, what is the annual capital recovery charge for the project?

Solution

Assuming that the construction costs and life of the project are statistically independent, we can calculate the equivalent annual cost (EAC) as

$$EAC = FC(A/P, 20, N)$$

where *first cost FC* and life N are simulated in each trial. The first cost is estimated by associating a random number with a normal deviate from Fig. 13.16b. For instance, a three-digit random number would correspond to each number between .000 and .999 on the vertical axis: A random number of 500 is associated with zero deviation and produces FC = $2,000,000; a random number of 834 matches 1σ, which means that FC = $2,000,000 + $500,000 = $2,500,000. By an equivalent procedure, random numbers of 500 and 834 lead, respectively, to lives of 2 and 3 years in Fig. 13.16a. The values so generated are substituted in the equation above to determine the EAC for one trial.

Ten trials are shown in Table 13.7. Random numbers for FC are taken from the first three digits of numbers in the right-hand column of Fig. 13.13. The last two digits in each random number in the same column are used to determine N. The top number in the column (18752) provides 187 as the entry shown in Fig. 13.16b, which leads to a standard deviation of −0.89. (A more exact reading can be taken from App. F, where 187 corresponds to the Z value for a proportion of 0.500 − 0.187 = 0.313.) The last digits in the same random number are 52 and indicate a life of 3 years, as shown in Fig. 13.16a. The equivalent annual cost for the first trial is

$$EAC(\text{trial } 1) = [\$2,000,000 - 0.89(\$500,000)](A/P, 20, 3)$$
$$= \$1,555,000(0.47473) = \$738,205$$

TABLE 13.7

Ten simulations of FC and life to determine EAC of project

First cost simulation			Project life simulation			
Random number	Normal deviate ND	FC = $2,000,000 + ND($500,000), $	Random number	Life N, years	(A/P, 20, N)	Equivalent annual cost = FC(A/P, 20, N), $
187	−0.89	1,555,000	52	3	0.47473	738,205
616	0.30	2,150,000	91	4	0.38629	830,524
491	−0.02	1,990,000	97	4	0.38629	768,717
194	−0.86	1,570,000	36	2	0.65455	1,027,644
648	0.38	2,190,000	93	4	0.38629	845,975
642	0.37	2,185,000	22	2	0.65455	1,430,192
523	0.06	2,030,000	60	3	0.47473	963,702
686	0.49	2,245,000	23	2	0.65455	1,469,465
301	−0.52	1,740,000	22	2	0.65455	1,138,917
321	−0.47	1,765,000	31	2	0.65455	1,155,281
						10,368,622

The estimate of EAC based on the very limited 10-trial sample is the average value of the outcomes

$$\frac{\$10,368,622}{10} = \$1,036,862$$

As mentioned before, computers are used for simulation due to the large number of trials required to obtain reliable estimates. The computer program provided with the text can be used for cash flow simulations; its use is illustrated in Example 13.10.

EXAMPLE 13.10   **Using a Computer for Cash Flow Risk Simulation**

An electronics company is considering the purchase of a new *surface-mount technology (SMT)* machine to support increased demand. The initial cost of the machine is $100,000. The sales forecast calls for an annual production rate of 50,000 units, although fluctuations in output may occur as a result of changes in market demand. These fluctuations can be approximated as being normally distributed with a standard deviation of 5000 units. Variations in equipment availability and raw material costs may affect unit production costs. In the absence of prior data, management feels that a triangular distribution can be used to model the worst, modal (estimator of most likely), and best scenarios: These estimates on a per-unit basis are $0.50, $0.70, and $1.10, respectively.

Management would like to maintain a constant sales price of $1.35 per unit. The salvage value at the end of the equipment's useful life of 10 years is estimated to be uniformly distributed between $10,000 and $20,000. Assuming a desired rate of return of 15 percent, use simulation to compute the net present worth of the investment and the probability of a positive present worth.

Solution

The steps involved in data input and getting the results using CHEER are summarized in Fig. 13.17 and briefly explained below. Results from 100 simulation trials give a present worth estimate of $44,989 with a standard deviation of $32,570.

CHEER has an explicit feature for performing risk simulation. To access this feature, we click on the Project option in the initial BTCF screen. From the resulting menu we select the Risk Analysis option. The initial screen display is shown in Fig. 13.17a. The user should access locations for data input by using a mouse. For each of the stochastic (or random) variables, clicking on the arrow next to Distribution produces a distribution choice menu (Fig. 13.17b). Selection of a distribution produces a screen specific to the distribution; these screens require users to input data for the parameters of the distribution. Data input for normal distribution for production rate, constant values for initial cost and sales price, triangular distribution for unit production costs, and uniform distribution for salvage value are shown in Fig. 13.17c through g. The three deterministic parameters (interest rate, study period, and number of simulation runs) are specified in the initial screen (Fig. 13.17h). The box at the bottom of the screen displays parameters of the *active* variable (i.e., the variable being worked on).

There are two options for specifying revenues and expenses as shown in Fig. 13.17a: $/unit and $. If production rate is specified, the $/unit option is activated and Revenues and Expenses are calculated as production rate × $/unit. Alternatively, revenues and expenses can be directly specified in dollars. Production rate is not used with this option.

After the data are input, we click on the Simulation option in the initial screen. The menu in Fig. 13.17h is displayed; click on Start simulation. The Probability calculation option is available for computing the probability of PW less than a specified value. When the simulation is complete, the message *Simulation Complete* is displayed on the screen.

The random number seed option can be used to specify a different string of random numbers for each distribution used in the simulation study. Selecting different seeds (an integer number) provides a much larger range of random numbers which is important in large-scale simulation studies.

The results can be displayed on the screen or sent to a printer by selecting the View results or Print option from the menu obtained by clicking on the File option in the initial screen. The results show the value of initial cost, annual revenue, annual expenses, salvage value, and resulting net present worth (NPW) for each trial; the mean and standard deviation of PW from the 100 trials; and the probability of NPW < 0 (Fig. 13.17*i*). We can click on the Graph option in the initial screen and then click on Chart and View on subsequent menus to obtain the distribution of NPW in Fig. 13.17*j*. The graph can be printed by using the PrintScreen function on the keyboard.

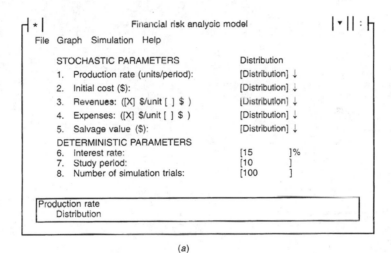

(a)

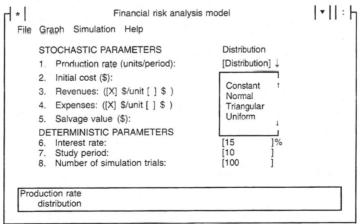

(b)

FIGURE 13.17
Using CHEER for cash flow simulation.

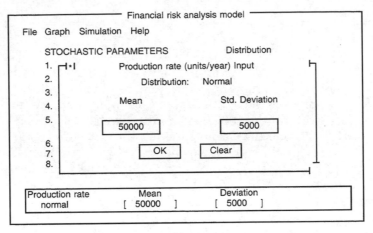

(c)

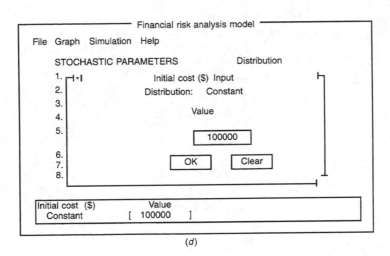

(d)

FIGURE 13.17
continued

(e)

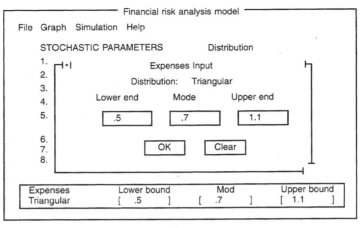

(f)

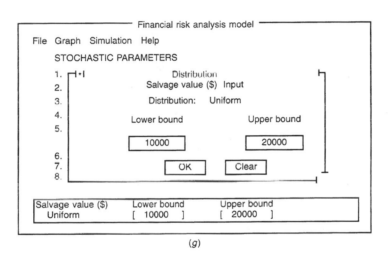

(g)

File Graph Simulation Help

STOCHASTIC PARA	Start simulation		Distribution
1. Production rate	Probability calculations		[Normal] ↓
2. Initial cost ($):		Define random number seeds	[Constant] ↓
3. Revenues: ([X] $/unit [ ] $)			[Constant] ↓
4. Expenses: ([X] $/unit [ ] $)			[Triangular] ↓
5. Salvage value ($):			[Uniform] ↓

DETERMINISTIC PARAMETERS
6. Interest rate:	[15	]%
7. Study period:	[10	]
8. Number of simulation trials:	[100	]

Salvage value ($)	Lower bound	Upper bound
Uniform	[10000]	[20000]

(h)

FIGURE 13.17

continued

If proposal 2 were accepted, the standard deviation would be

$$\sigma_{\text{total cash flow}} = \sqrt{.2(240 - 190)^2 + .6(190 - 190)^2 + .2(140 - 190)^2}$$
$$= \$31.62$$

By adding the outcome from proposal 1 to the firm's other cash flow, the range of variation from boom to bust conditions is reduced from $200 − $120 = $80 to $220 − $160 = $60. Proposal 1 is plainly preferable.

13.7   DECISIONS UNDER UNCERTAINTY

The term *decisions under uncertainty* refers to situations where probabilities associated with future states are unknown or cannot be estimated. Several future states are possible, but evidence is not available on which to base statements of their probabilities. The expected value and variance principles cannot be applied. The most difficult aspect of problems under uncertainty is to decide what type of criteria to use for making a decision. In essence, we must determine the criteria for the criterion. The choice should be consistent with management philosophy. Is the current management outlook optimistic or pessimistic, conservative or adventurous? Certain criteria are compatible only with certain management views. Thus, it is necessary to understand both management policy and the principles of choice before a decision is made.

13.7.1   Equal-Likelihood Criterion

When it is possible to assign probabilities to future states, we use the expected-value criterion to select a preferred alternative. An extension of this approach is the basis of the *equal-likelihood criterion*. Under uncertainty we admit that we cannot reasonably estimate outcome probabilities. Therefore, since we have no excuse to believe otherwise, why not treat each outcome as the same? The rationale behind this theory is that there is insufficient reason to believe one future state more probable than another, so each should be assigned an equal probability of occurrence.

The equal-likelihood criterion is certainly the simplest to apply. Under the assumption that each future state is equally likely to occur, the expected value of an alternative becomes its average outcome.

13.7.2   Minimum-Maximum Criterion

A conservative approach to a decision is to look at the worst possible outcome for each alternative and to select the course of action that ensures the best results for the worst conditions. This pessimistic philosophy dictates that attention be focused on only the most damaging outcomes, in order to limit the damage as much as possible.

The words *minimax* and *maximin* are derived from the measures taken to identify the limiting loss or the guaranteed gain. A *minimax decision* minimizes the maximum loss. The *maximin principle* is associated with positive payoffs, where it maximizes the minimum gain or profit. For either criterion the smallest payoff (or greatest loss) for each alternative is noted. Then the alternative having the most favorable of the collected worst payoffs is selected.

13.7.3 Maximax Criterion

A *maximax* philosophy is one of optimism and adventure. The principle of choice is to identify the maximum gain possible for each alternative and then choose the course of action with the greatest maximum gain.

13.7.4 Hurwicz' Criterion

A moderate outlook between the extremes of optimism and pessimism is allowed by the Hurwicz criterion. The degree of optimism is established by a coefficient α (alpha), which may take any value between 0 and 1.0, with the following interpretation:

Coefficient of optimism α: .0   1.0

Decision maker's philosophy: Pessimistic $\longrightarrow$ Optimistic

After the value of α is chosen that measures the decision maker's degree of optimism, maximum and minimum gains are identified for each alternative. The maximum payoffs are multiplied by α and the minimum payoffs by $1 - \alpha$. The two products for each alternative are added, and the alternative with the larger sum is chosen.

The minimax-maximin and maximax criteria are special cases of the Hurwicz criterion. When $\alpha = 1$, only the maximum payoffs are included in the final alternative selection, because the minimum payoffs have been eliminated by multiplication by zero. The opposite is true for $\alpha = 0$, a completely pessimistic outlook. Any value of α other than 1 or 0 is a compromise opinion.

13.7.5 Minimax Regret Criterion

Opportunity costs have been used in previous chapters to express the loss incurred by not selecting the best alternative. The minimax regret criterion is based on similar costs. The opportunity costs are determined for each future state by subtracting the largest for a state from all other payoffs for that state. The absolute value of each subtraction is the amount of *regret* that results from not selecting the best alternative for the occurrence of a given state.

A rational decision maker attempts to minimize regret. By applying the minimax principle, we select the alternative that minimizes the maximum regret. In general, the minimax criterion tends toward a conservative viewpoint.

13.7.6 Evaluation of Decision Criteria

Several different criteria for making decisions under uncertainty have been offered because no one criterion is unanimously preferred. Each has certain weaknesses. Often one criterion is more intuitively appealing than the others. This appeal seems to vary among individuals and with time or circumstances. Inasmuch as there is no universal preference, a sound recourse is to investigate the criteria limitations in order to select the principle that accommodates a given decision environment.

None of the criteria is perfect. None can take the place of an accurate forecast. The criteria should be considered guidelines that will help in the interpretation and consideration of possible choices. Note that most of the reservations about the criteria are intuitive rather than deductive. Perhaps the adoption of a certain criterion must also rely to some degree upon intuition, because such insight is often a function of knowledge not yet formalized into distinct views. Nevertheless, the decision maker must understand the characteristics of each principle to be able to select the one that corresponds most closely to the uncertainties of a situation.

EXAMPLE 13.12   **Application of Criteria for Decisions under Uncertainty**

The owners of an import shop in a medium-size city have been successful enough to be in a position to expand their operations. Three courses of action are deemed most desirable: *Expand* their present operations by opening a store in a nearby city, denoted by *E;* start a *catalog* business from their present location, denoted by *C;* or invest their extra money in *real estate and rentals,* denoted by *R.* Each alternative will utilize about the same amount of capital and will require equivalent management. The owners recognize that the returns from each of these investments depend on the national economy (prosperity versus recession) and on the local economy (growth versus stagnation). However, the owners have no consensus of the probabilities of future conditions.

Outcomes of each alternative have been developed for four possible levels of business activity: *very high (VH), high (H), medium (M),* and *low (L).* The payoffs shown in the table are the estimated percentage returns on invested capital for the three alternatives:

	Future business activity			
Alternatives	**VH**	**H**	**M**	**L**
E	20	12	8	4
C	26	10	4	−4
R	10	8	7	5

For the data shown, which alternative should be selected under each of the described decision criteria?

Solution

The procedures followed for each criterion reduce the original matrix to a single column of outcomes from which the desired value is selected. The results and preferences indicated by applying all the criteria are as shown:

Alternative	**Equal likelihood**	**Maximin (pessimist)**	**Maximax (optimist)**	**Hurwicz ($\alpha = .50$)**	**Minimax regret**
E	11*	4	20	12*	6*
C	9	−4	26*	11	9
R	7.5	5*	10	7.5	16

To obtain the values for the Minimax regret criterion, we use a *Regret* matrix. The maximum payoff is selected for each future state. The values in each column of the Regret matrix are the absolute difference between the maximum payoff and all other payoffs—i.e., regret for not selecting the best outcome. Since we minimize the maximum regret, we select the maximum regret for each alternative; the minimum of the resulting values corresponds to the preferred alternative:

Alternative	**VH**	**H**	**M**	**L**	**Maximum (row)**
E	6	0	0	1	6
C	0	2	4	9	9
R	16	4	1	0	16

It should not be too surprising that each criterion indicates a different preferred alternative (indicated by * in the table). Each criterion has a slightly distinct underlying principle. The key is to decide which criterion best fits the decision environment for each specific application.

13.8   **REVIEW EXERCISES AND DISCUSSIONS**

EXERCISE 1

A construction company has determined that it costs $8700 to prepare a bid for a major construction project. It even costs $500 to decide not to submit a bid. The annual profit earned from winning a bid for a major construction project is $400,000. For such projects the competition is severe, and the chance of submitting the lowest bid is small. How often must the company's bids win to make the bidding worthwhile?

SOLUTION 1

Outcomes from the alternatives of bidding and not bidding are shown below for the future states of winning and losing:

	Win bid $P(W)$, $	Lose bid $P(L)$, $
No bid	−500	−500
Bid	400,000	−8700

How often the company must win a bid to break even on its bidding can be determined from a graph, as shown in Fig. 13.19. A *win* occurs when $P(W) = 1$, and a loss occurs when $P(W) = 0$. As indicated by the no-bid line, the outcome is constant because there is no chance of winning when no bid is submitted. The point where lines representing the bid and no-bid options cross is the indifference, or breakeven, point.

By letting $P(W)$ and $P(L) = 1 - P(W)$ be the probabilities for the two future states (win and lose), we can calculate the indifference probability from

$$\text{EV(no bid)} = \text{EV(bid)}$$

$$P(W)(-\$500) + [1 - P(W)](-\$500) = P(W)(\$400,000) + [1 - P(W)](-\$8700)$$

FIGURE 13.19
Graph of two alternatives based on their probability of occurrence. At the indifferent point, expected values for alternatives are the same.

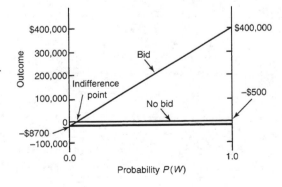

to yield

$$P(W) = \frac{\$8700 - \$500}{\$400,000 + \$8700} = .02$$

which means that the construction company must win over 2 percent of the times it submits bids for new projects. From a slightly different viewpoint, it means that a project is worth bidding on when there is at least a 2 percent chance that the submitted bid will be chosen.

EXERCISE 2

Owing to the lack of other suitable land, a mill is forced to construct its new settling ponds for waste disposal along the bank of a river. The stream has no dams to control its flow. Flood-level records for the past 70 years reveal that the river rose above the minimum required height of the settling pond walls 42 times. Therefore, the economic analysis must include not only construction costs but also the risk of flood damage. Building the walls higher increases the initial investment but lowers the threat of flooding. Engineering calculations for the cost of higher retaining walls in 1.5 meter increments and the expected damage from floods of different crests are shown in the following table.

River levels above minimum wall height in range, meter	Years the river crests in given range above wall height F		Probability of river cresting in range above height F	Flood damage when river crests above walls, $	Cost to construct walls to height F, $
0–1.5	at $F = 0$:	14	.20	70,000	135,000
1.5–3	at $F = 1.5$:	14	.20	105,000	200,000
3–4.5	at $F = 3$:	8	.11	150,000	280,000
4.5–6.0	at $F = 4.5$:	6	.09	200,000	370,000
Over 6.0 meter	at $F = 6.0$:	0	.0	0	450,000

The settling ponds are expected to be needed for 10 years before the process can be improved sufficiently to eliminate the need for special waste treatment. A rate of return of 10 percent is used by the mill to evaluate federally mandated investments. To what height should the retaining walls be built to minimize annual costs?

SOLUTION 2

The initial cost of the settling ponds is translated to an equivalent annual cost by the capital recovery factor. For the minimum wall height $F = 0$, the equivalent annual investment cost is

$$\begin{aligned} \text{EAC(investment at } F = 0) &= \$135,000(A/P, 10, 10) \\ &= \$135,000(0.16275) \\ &= \$21,971 \end{aligned}$$

Equivalent annual investment costs for successively higher retaining walls are calculated similarly.

Data arranged for the calculation of expected values of flood damage for alternative wall heights are shown in Table 13.8. The outcomes in the payoff table indicate damages expected from floods exceeding a given wall height by amounts F. Thus, for the minimum wall height, flood waters will cause damage 3 years in every 5 years, on average, to produce an expected value of

$$EV(F = 0) = \$70,000(.20) + \$105,000(.20) + \$150,000(.11) + \$200,000(.09)$$
$$= \$14,000 + \$21,000 + \$16,500 + \$18,000$$
$$= \$69,500$$

which, when added to the equivalent annual investment cost, makes a total expected cost for the minimum-height settling pond walls of $21,971 + $69,500 = $91,471. Expected values for other wall heights are calculated in the same manner, as indicated in the shaded area of Table 13.8. Note that the probabilities do not add to 1.0 because river levels below $F = 0$ (probability = .40) have no bearing on the flood damage expectations.

The settling pond retaining-wall height that minimizes total annual cost is 3 meters above the minimum level.

EXERCISE 3
The most likely cash flow for a cost reduction proposal is for an investment of $4000 to produce after-tax present-worth savings of $1200 per year for 5 years. The net present worth is

$$PW(\text{most likely}) = -\$4000 + \$1200(5) = \$2000$$

TABLE 13.8

Payoff table (shaded) for five alternative wall heights for settling ponds. Total expected annual costs are the sums of expected flood damages and equivalent annual investment costs

| Wall height above minimum, meter | Probability of river cresting above wall height in range, meter | | | | Expected value, $ | Equivalent annual investment, $ | Total expected annual cost, $ |
	0–1.5 $P = .20$	1.5–3.0 $P = .20$	3.0–4.5 $P = .11$	4.5–6.0 $P = .09$			
0	$70,000	$105,000	$150,000	$200,000	69,500	21,971	91,471
1.5	0	70,000	105,000	150,000	39,050	32,550	71,600
3.0	0	0	70,000	105,000	17,150	45,570	62,720
4.5	0	0	0	70,000	6,300	60,218	66,518
6.0	0	0	0	0	0	73,238	73,238

Flood damage from incremental river levels above alternative settling pond wall heights F

Upon further investigation it appears that the initial investment has probabilities of .4 of being as high as $5000 and .6 of being $3000. The after-tax present worth of annual savings could amount to $2000, $1200, or $800, with respective probabilities of .2, .3, and .5. Determine the investment risk profile and the expected value of the proposal.

SOLUTION 3
If I and S represent investment and savings levels, respectively, then the pattern of possible future outcomes is shown in the following table. There is a 20 percent chance the proposal will lose money, but the expected value is $2000.

Possible futures	Net after-tax present worth, $	Joint probability	Weighted outcome, $
$S(P = .2)I(P = .6)$	$2000(5) - 3000 = 7000$	$(.2)(.6) = .12$	840
$S(P = .3)I(P = .6)$	$1200(5) - 3000 = 3000$	$(.3)(.6) = .18$	540
$S(P = .5)I(P = .6)$	$800(5) - 3000 = 1000$	$(.5)(.6) = .30$	300
$S(P = .2)I(P = .4)$	$2000(5) - 5000 = 5000$	$(.2)(.4) = .08$	400
$S(P = .3)I(P = .4)$	$1200(5) - 5000 = 1000$	$(.3)(.4) = .12$	120
$S(P = .5)I(P = .4)$	$800(5) - 5000 = -1000$	$(.5)(.4) = .20$	$\underline{-200}$
			2000

EXERCISE 4
Given the anticipated outcome distributions for proposals M and W, analyze the risk:

	Probability of outcomes				
	$O_1 = -11$	$O_2 = -3$	$O_3 = 5$	$O_4 = 13$	$O_5 = 21$
Proposal M	.2	.2	.2	.2	.2
Proposal W	.0	4	.3	.2	.1

SOLUTION 4

$$EV(M) = .2(-11) + .2(-3) + .2(5) + .2(13) + .2(21)$$
$$= 5$$

$$EV(W) = .4(-3) + .3(5) + .2(13) + .1(21)$$
$$= 5$$

$$\sigma_M = \sqrt{.2(-11 - 5)^2 + .2(-3 - 5)^2 + .2(5 - 5)^2 + .2(13 - 5)^2 + .2(21 - 5)^2}$$
$$= 11.31$$

$$\sigma_W = \sqrt{.4(-3 - 5)^2 + .3(5 - 5)^2 + .2(13 - 5)^2 + .1(21 - 5)^2}$$
$$= 8$$

Both proposals have the some expected value, but proposal W is preferred because it has lower risk, owing to less variability of outcomes.

EXERCISE 5

A proposed investment of $9000 will produce annual revenue of $4000. The investment risk is how long the revenue stream will continue. The given estimate of probabilities for the investment's duration appears reasonable.

Year N	3	4	5	6
Probability $P(N)$	.1	.4	.3	.2

Regardless of N, there will be no salvage value, and a before-tax rate of return of 15 percent is required.

(a) What are the expected present worth of the investment and its variance?

(b) Determine the probability of a positive present worth.

SOLUTION 5

(a) The expected value of the investment is the sum of the four possible cash flow outcomes, weighted according to their probabilities of occurrence:

$$PW(N = 3) = -\$9000 + \$4000(P/A, 15, 3) = -\$133$$

$$PW(N = 4) = -\$9000 + \$4000(P/A, 15, 4) = \$2420$$

$$PW(N = 5) = -\$9000 + \$4000(P/A, 15, 5) = \$4408$$

$$PW(N = 6) = -\$9000 + \$4000(P/A, 15, 6) = \$6138$$

$$EV(PW) = -\$133(.1) + \$2420(.4) + \$4408(.3) + \$6138(.2)$$
$$= \$3505$$

The variance is calculated from the relationship

$$Var(PW) = EV(PW^2) - [EV(PW)]^2$$

for which $EV(PW)$ has already been determined. Then

$$EV(PW)^2 = (-\$133)^2(.1) + (\$2420)^2(.4) + (\$4408)^2(.3) + (\$6138)^2(.2)$$
$$= 15{,}708{,}477$$

and

$$Var(PW) = 15{,}708{,}477 - (3505)^2 = 3{,}423{,}452$$

and the standard deviation is $1850.

(b) The probability of a positive present worth, based on the discrete distribution of project duration, is the sum of the probabilities of outcomes that have a positive value. From part a, where PWs were calculated for each N,

$$P(PW > 0) = P(N = 4) + P(N = 5) + P(N = 6)$$
$$= .4 + .3 + .2 = .9$$

EXERCISE 6

Analyze the proposals below, and select the most promising one based on coefficients of variation and correlation.

Proposal	Coefficient of variation	Correlation with other cash flows
P_1	.8	.4
P_2	.4	.2
P_3	.3	−.2
P_4	.3	.0
P_5	.5	.2

SOLUTION 6

Proposal P_1 is the riskiest proposal because it has the highest correlation with the firm's other cash flows and the highest coefficient of variation. Proposal P_3 offers the least risk because of its negative correlation and low variation. The order of preference from least to greatest risk is P_3, P_4, P_2, P_5, and P_1.

EXERCISE 7

A new cost reduction proposal is expected to have annual expenses of $20,000 with a standard deviation of $3000, and it will likely save $24,000 per year with a standard deviation of $4000. The proposed operation will be in effect for 3 years, and a rate of return of 20 percent before taxes is required. Determine the probability that implementation of the proposal will actually result in an overall loss and the probability that the PW of net savings will exceed $10,000.

SOLUTION 7

The expected value of the present worth of savings and costs is

$$EV(PW) = (\$24,000 - \$20,000)(P/A, 20, 3)$$
$$= \$4000(2.10648)$$
$$= \$8426$$

The variance is calculated from the relation

$$\sigma^2_{savings - costs} = \sigma^2_{savings} + \sigma^2_{costs}$$

to obtain

$$Var(PW) = (\$3000)^2(P/F, 20, 2) + (\$3000)^2(P/F, 20, 4)$$
$$+ (\$3000)^2(P/F, 20, 6) + (\$4000)^2(P/F, 20, 2)$$
$$+ (\$4000)^2(P/F, 20, 4) + (\$4000)^2(P/F, 20, 6)$$
$$= 37,790,000$$

from which

$$\sigma_{PW} = \sqrt{\text{Var(PW)}} = \$6147$$

Assuming that the PW is normally distributed, we find that

$$P(\text{loss}) = P\left(Z < \frac{0 - \$8426}{\$6147}\right) = P(Z < -1.37)$$
$$= .0853$$

and

$$P(\text{PW} > \$10,000) = P\left(Z > \frac{\$10,000 - \$8426}{\$6147}\right) = P(Z > 0.256)$$
$$= .40$$

These probabilities are represented graphically by the shaded areas under the normal distribution curve shown in Fig. 13.20.

EXERCISE 8
A new product is expected to be marketable for 5 years. The first cost of necessary production equipment is estimated at $40,000 with a standard deviation of $2000; it will have no salvage value when the product is discontinued. The contribution per unit produced, exclusive of capital recovery costs, has a predicted mean of $3 and standard deviation of $1.50. The before-tax MARR is 15 percent.

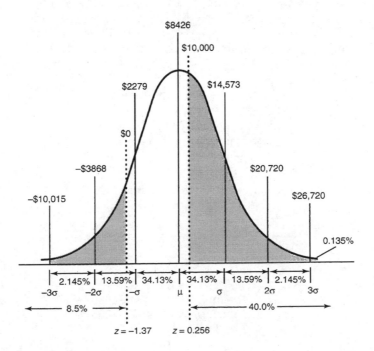

FIGURE 13.20
Normal distribution of present worth with mean of $8426 and standard deviation of $6147.

(a) What is the annual break-even volume?

(b) Determine the mean and standard deviation of the present worth at a production level of 10,000 units per year.

SOLUTION 8

(a) The expected values of first cost FC and contribution C are used to determine the break-even point B as

$$B = \frac{FC}{PW_C} = \frac{\$40,000}{\$3/\text{unit} \, (P/A, 15, 5)} = \frac{\$40,000}{\$3/\text{unit} \, (3.35216)} = 3978 \text{ units}$$

(b) $EV(PW) = -\$40,000 + \$3(10,000)(P/A, 15, 5) = \$60,563$

The previously applied formula in Sec. 13.4.8 for calculating the variance

$$\text{Var(PW)} = \sigma_0^2 + \sigma_n^2 \sum_{n=1}^{N} (1 + i)^{-2n}$$

is made computationally easier when cash flow is uniform by utilizing the relation

$$\sum_{n=1}^{N} (i + i)^{-2n} = \frac{(P/A, i, 2N)}{2 + i}$$

to obtain

$$\text{Var(PW)} = 2000^2 + \frac{(1.50 \times 10,000)^2 (P/A, 15, 10)}{2 + 0.15}$$

$$= 4 \times 10^6 + \frac{(225 \times 10^6)(5.01877)}{2.15}$$

$$= 529.22 \times 10^6$$

and

$$\sigma_{PW} = \sqrt{529.22 \times 10^6} = \$23,007$$

EXERCISE 9

A large number of replaceable purifier units are required in a production process. The units cost $8 apiece and have the following failure pattern:

Week	1	2	3	4	5	6	7
Proportion of units that fail during week	0.30	0.05	0.05	0.10	0.20	0.25	0.05

Total charges for replacing a single unit that fails during operation are $50 for maintenance and downtime. The cost of replacing one unit during a blanket replacement over a weekend is $10 for labor plus the cost of the unit.

(a) Determine the expected cost per week of a replace-upon-failure policy.

(b) The current policy is to replace all units on a 4-week cycle, with individual replacements made as needed. Consideration is being given to a new 5-week blanket replacement cycle. Is this a better policy?

SOLUTION 9

(a) The expected replacement time for individual units is

$$0.30(1) + 0.05(2) + 0.05(3) + 0.10(4) + 0.20(5) + 0.25(6) + 0.05(7) = 3.8 \text{ weeks}$$

This expectation yields

$$\text{Individual replacement cost} = \frac{\$50/\text{unit} + \$8/\text{unit}}{3.8 \text{ weeks}} = \$15.26 \text{ per unit per week}$$

(b) The pattern of individual replacements during blanket replacement cycles, for a reference base of 100 units, is as follows:

Cycle	Replacements during week per 100 units	
Week 1	100(0.30)	= 30
Week 2	100(0.05) + 30(0.30)	= 14
Week 3	100(0.05) + 30(0.05) + 14(0.30)	= 10.7
Week 4	100(0.10) + 30(0.05) + 14(0.05) + 10.7(0.30)	= 15.4
Week 5	100(0.20) + 30(0.10) + 14(0.05) + 10.7(0.05) + 15.4(0.30)	= 28.86

During a 4-week cycle, individual replacements per 100 units will be 30 + 14 + 10.7 + 15.4 = 70.10 units. Including the group replacement cost per 100 units of 100($18) = $1800, we have

$$\text{Total cost per unit (4-week cycle)} = \frac{70.10(\$58) + \$1800}{100\text{-unit cycle}} \times \frac{\text{cycle}}{4 \text{ weeks}}$$
$$= \$14.66 \text{ per unit per week}$$

By a similar process,

$$\text{Total cost per unit (5-week cycle)} = \frac{(70.10 + 28.86)(\$58) + \$1800}{100\text{-unit cycle}} \times \frac{\text{cycle}}{5 \text{ weeks}}$$
$$= \$15.08 \text{ per unit per week}$$

The present 4-week blanket replacement policy is therefore preferable.

13.9   PROBLEMS

13.1 A new product introduced by a company has been so successful that the company is now considering ways to expand production. It can do so by adding facilities or by increasing the utilization of present facilities. The choice depends on forecasts of future market trends for the new product.

The best available probability estimates for future demand are .1 to decline slightly from current sales, .3 to remain constant, and .6 to increase rapidly. If a major expansion of facilities is undertaken now, the company should be able to capture most of the new demand before competitors can gear up for production. However, the company would suffer considerable loss from unused capacity if the demand failed to increase or declined. The conservative alternative is to increase utilization of existing facilities from the present 85 percent rate to 100 percent, but there is no way to meet higher levels of potential demand with existing production capacity.

The equivalent annual worth in dollars expected to result from each alternative according to each level of future demand is shown in the payoff table below:

	Decline $P(D) = .1$	**Constant** $P(C) = .3$	**Increase** $P(I) = .6$
Add new facilities	−1,800,000	−50,000	900,000
Increase utilization	−100,000	100,000	400,000

(a) Calculate the expected values.
(b) Determine what other factors might affect the decision.

13.2 A logging company must decide the most advantageous duration for a paving project. The beginning date of the project has been definitely set. A critical path analysis has shown that three project durations are feasible. If the paving is completed in 4 months, the basic project cost will be $80,000. A 5-month duration will allow construction savings of $20,000, and it will cost an extra $40,000 over the basic cost to reduce the project to 3 months. However, transportation expenses can be cut by $10,000 over the 4-month schedule if the paving is done in 3 months, and an extra transportation expense of $15,000 will be incurred for an extension of the paving time to 5 months.

Since the project must be completed during a period of expected foul weather, the extra expense due to possible weather conditions should be considered. Weather records indicate that the probabilities for mild rain, heavy rain, and wind and rain are, respectively, .3, .5, and .2. The costs in dollars that must be included for these conditions are given in the following table:

Weather conditions	**3 Months**	**4 Months**	**5 Months**
Mild rain	10,000	15,000	5,000
Heavy rain	10,000	40,000	60,000
Wind and rain	15,000	55,000	65,000

Which duration has the lowest expected total cost?

13.3 There are several methods available to discover defective welds. A company has investigated two methods. Method 1 costs $0.50 per inspection and detects defects 80 percent of the time. Method 2 costs $2.00 per test but always detects a defective weld. When a defective weld goes undetected, the estimated cost to the company is $30 for replacement and other incidental costs. The probability of a defective weld is .05. Using the expected-value criterion, determine whether method 1 or 2 should be used or whether the company is better off with no inspection procedure.

13.4 A payoff table (in thousands of dollars) is given below for three investments of equal size and duration:

Alternative	Boom $(P = .3)$	So-so $(P = .5)$	Bust $(P = .2)$
A	1000	200	−500
B	300	400	0
C	400	600	−300

Which alternative would you select? Why?

13.5 An investment is being considered that requires $1 million and commits the money for 10 years. During that period it is equally likely that the annual returns from the investment will be $100,000, $150,000, and $200,000. The probability is .75 that the salvage value will be $300,000, but there is 1 chance in 4 that it will be zero. A minimum rate of return of 10 percent is expected.

    (a) Construct an investment risk profile for the proposal on a chart in which the horizontal axis registers the net PW and the vertical axis is a probability scale ranging from 0 to 1. Draw the curve to show the probability of returns equal to or less than the scaled PWs.

    (b) How could the investment risk profile contribute to the economic evaluation of the million-dollar investment?

13.6 Three mutually exclusive alternatives that show the probabilities of earning rates of return are described by the data below:

Alternative	Rate of return, % −5	0	10	20
A	.3	.1	.2	.4
B	0	.3	.5	.2
C	.15	.15	.4	.3

    (a) Which alternative would be selected by using the most probable future criterion? Why?

    (b) Which alternative would be selected by using the expected-value criterion? What is the EV?

(c) Which alternative would be selected if the decision maker had an aspiration level of 10 percent? Why?

(d) Construct an acceptable-investment diagram with a loss coefficient of –5 percent at $P = .7$ and a payoff coefficient of 10 percent at $P = .3$. Which alternative would be eliminated by the AID?

13.7 A cost-saving modification to an existing process is being evaluated. The savings will affect products 1 and 2. The rate of return earned by the investment in the modification depends on how much the process is utilized, which depends on the market conditions for future sales of the two products. Three future states have been identified: good, with IRR = 20 percent; average, with IRR = 10 percent; and bad, with IRR = –5 percent. Since there are two products involved, the maximum possible rate of return is additive; i.e., under good conditions it is 20 percent + 20 percent = 40 percent. The probability of each future for both products is given below.

| | **Future** | | |
Product	**Good**	**Average**	**Bad**
1	.20	.70	.10
2	.40	.30	.30

(a) What is the expected value of the cost-saving modification?

(b) Draw an investment profile for the proposal on an acceptable-investment diagram. The ordinate is the probability that the investment will exceed the percentage return, and the horizontal axis is the rate of return. The investment criteria are to limit losses to 5 chances in 100 of –10 percent return and to be 90 percent sure that the rate of return is at least 20 percent. Should the proposal be accepted? Why?

13.8 An asset has a first cost of $50,000 and a salvage value that is dependent upon how long the asset remains in service. For service periods of 4, 5, 6, and 7 years, the respective estimated salvage values are $20,000, $15,000, $12,000, and $10,000. Given that all the service periods are equally likely, determine the mean and standard deviation of the asset's present worth, using an interest rate of 15 percent.

13.9 An asset is expected to produce a net annual operating profit of $18,000, $24,000, or $30,000 per year during the 5 years it remains in service. Assuming that the profit amounts are independent from year to year and that each value has an equally likely probability of occurrence, determine the mean and standard deviation of the net present worth, using an interest rate of 15 percent.

13.10 Determine the expected value and the standard deviation of the PW for the situation described in Prob. 13.9 if the annual profits are uniformly distributed in a continuous distribution between $18,000 and $30,000.

13.11 The six proposals described in the table below are under consideration for funding:

Investment proposal	Expected value, $	Standard deviation, $	Correlation with the firm's other cash flows
A	700,000	400,000	.4
B	200,000	0	.0
C	1,000,000	400,000	.6
D	600,000	100,000	−.3
E	400,000	100,000	.1
F	500,000	250,000	−.2

(a) Compute the coefficients of variation and rank the proposals accordingly.
(b) Rank the investments according to their correlation with other cash flows within the firm.
(c) Comparing the lists developed in parts a and b, indicate how you would rank the proposals in terms of risk. Where there is no clear choice, indicate the reasoning that you would use to make your selection.

13.12 Given the following estimates of a project's cash flows, in which the flows are assumed to be independent of each other, determine the probability that the present worth will be positive and hence desirable at an interest rate of 20 percent:

End of year	Expected value of cash flow, $	Standard deviation, $
0	−20,000	0
1	8,000	1,500
2	8,000	2,000
3	8,000	2,500
4	8,000	3,000

13.13 An investment proposal requires an immediate payment of $50,000 and is expected to provide an annual return of $18,000 for each of the next 6 years. However, the positive cash flow which is independent from year to year has a standard deviation of $3000.

(a) Determine the expected value and the standard deviation of the PW for this investment, using an interest rate of 20 percent.
(b) Determine the probability that the investment will result in a rate of return below a MARR of 20 percent if the annual cash flows are expected to be normally distributed.

13.14 Given the cash flows shown in the table below, determine the probability that the investment will provide a positive net present worth if interest is charged at 15 percent:

End of year	Expected value, $	Standard deviation, $
0	−30,000	0
1	10,000	1,000
2	9,000	1,200
3	8,000	1,400
4	7,000	1,600
5	6,000	1,800

13.15 An equipment supplier states that there is a 90 percent probability that annual maintenance costs on a new machine will be between $4800 and $9600 over a 5-year service life. Using a before-tax interest rate of 20 percent, determine the expected value and the standard deviation of the present worth of these costs.

(a) Assume that the costs are uniformly distributed.
(b) Assume that the costs are normally distributed.

13.16 Estimates for the construction of a new dock and breakwater indicate a need for 100,000 cubic meters of fill material. The average total cost for placing the material has been estimated at $2.50 per cubic meter with a standard deviation of $0.20. Given that the estimators are 90 percent confident that the amount of fill material required will be between 85,000 and 115,000 cubic meters, determine the mean and standard deviation of the total cost of the filling operation.

13.17 A project is estimated to require an investment of $25,000 and have an annual net cash flow of $16,000 with zero salvage value. The life is estimated to be 1 year, 5 years, and 10 years with respective probabilities of .1, .5, and .4. If the minimum acceptable rate of return is 15 percent, what are the expected value and variance of the net annual worth?

13.18 A project is estimated to require an investment of $25,000 and to have no salvage value. Expected revenue outcomes in dollars at the end of each potential duration are shown below. The MARR is 15 percent.

Life	Probability	Probability		
		.3	.5	.2
3 years	.25	30,000	35,000	40,000
5 years	.40	50,000	50,000	50,000
8 years	.35	75,000	85,000	100,000

(a) Plot a histogram showing the probabilities of different present worths.
(b) Calculate EV(PW).
(c) Calculate Var(PW).
(d) What is the probability that the present worth will be positive?

13.19 A proposed acquisition of material-handling equipment will likely have annual operating and capital recovery costs of $12,000 with a standard deviation of $2000. Estimated gross savings from the use of this equipment are $15,000 per year with a standard deviation of $4000. Assuming that the figures are given in discounted constant dollars, determine the probability that in actuality a loss will result from installation of the equipment.

13.20 An initial investment of $120 in a productive asset results in annual receipts of $50 until production is terminated. The before-tax required rate of return is 20 percent.

- (a) If the salvage value is zero at all times and the probabilities of receipts continuing for 3, 4, and 5 years are, respectively, .5, .4, and .1, what is the expected present worth?
- (b) What is the probability of a loss for the conditions given in part a?
- (c) If the salvage value has an equal chance of being −30 percent or +30 percent of the first cost in any year and if the distribution of asset life is unchanged from that in part a, what is the expected present worth?
- (d) What is the probability of a negative present worth for the conditions in part c?
- (e) If the life of the asset is certain to be 4 years but the annual receipts have a normal distribution with a standard deviation of $20, what is the expected present worth when the salvage value is still zero?
- (f) What is the probability of a loss for the conditions in part e?
- (g) If the initial investment may vary with a standard deviation of $40, what is the probability of a loss when $N = 4$, $A = \$50$, and $S = 0$ are known with certainty?

13.21 Annual sales of a new product are expected to average 10,000 units with a standard deviation of 1500 units. The sales price of the product has been set by market conditions at $29.95, and total variable manufacturing costs have been estimated at $23.00 with a standard deviation of $1.10. Fixed manufacturing costs are expected to average $20,000 with a standard deviation of $2000.

- (a) Determine the mean and variance of the net annual profit for this item.
- (b) Research and development costs for the product totaled $80,000. Assuming that it will remain on the market for 5 years, determine the mean and standard deviation of the net present worth, using a before-tax interest rate of 30 percent.

13.22 The local school board is considering the installation of a large trash-compacting system to reduce the number of trips necessary to pick up refuse at the high school. The compactor will be purchased on a bid basis, but it is expected to have a first cost of $65,000 with a possible standard deviation of $3000. The equipment is expected to last 6 years, and no significant salvage value is projected. Operating expenses have been estimated at $12,000 per year with a 90 percent probability that they will be between $10,000 and $14,000. The gross savings should average $35,000 annually, but this estimate is thought to have a standard deviation of approximately $5000.

- (a) Determine the mean and variance of the net present worth of this proposal, using an interest rate of 20 percent.
- (b) Determine the probability that a net loss results from installation of the compactor.

13.23 It has been suggested to a data processing firm that it adopt a policy of periodically replacing all the components in certain pieces of equipment. A given type of component is known to have the mortality distribution shown in the table below. There are approximately 1000 components of this type in all the combined equipment. The cost of replacing the components on an individual basis is estimated to be $1.00 per component, and the cost of a group replacement policy averages $0.30 per component. Compare the costs of preventive versus remedial replacement.

Component failure during week	Probability of failure
1	.3
2	.1
3	.1
4	.2
5	.3

13.24 A vending machine operator has machines in 40 locations. There is an equal probability each day during a 10-day period that the machines in one location will be emptied. After 10 days all the machines will be empty. The cost to individually replenish the machines at one location (travel and working time) is $18. The loss in profit from idle machines in one location is $10 per day. Replenishments may be made individually as requested when the machines in one location are empty, or they may be made all at one time with a total cost to service the 40 locations of $250. What is the lower-cost replenishment policy?

13.25 An assembly line has 30 identical machines. The pattern of breakdowns is shown in the accompanying table. Breakdowns can usually be fixed in a short time, but the disruption of the production line creates considerable expense. One way to eliminate this disruption is to provide standby machines. The daily cost of keeping a standby machine is estimated to be $12. The cost of an out-of-order machine is $150 per day. How many standby machines should be provided?

Number of machines out of order at one time	Probability
0	.5
1	.2
2	.1
3	.1
4	.1

13.26 Operators working in a clean-room environment use magnifying equipment that has a breakdown pattern that follows an arithmetic progression: In 50 percent of the shifts there are no equipment failures, in 25 percent of the shifts one unit fails, in 12.5 percent two fail, in 6.25 percent three fail, etc. The 30 operators now have 5 standby machines. The cost of each standby is $40 per shift; the cost of production and servicing for a down machine averages $300 per shift. There is also a lost-time cost of $30 to get the replacement machine in position when breakdown occurs. Determine whether the present number of standby machines is the optimum number.

13.27 A chemical company uses a large number of sacrificial catalysts to protect specialized production equipment. The units cost only $10.00 each but are subject to sudden failure, and emergency replacement costs amount to $50.00 in labor and lost production. Analysis of production records has revealed the information shown below concerning failure patterns:

Week	Proportion of units failing during week
1	.25
2	.05
3	.05
4	.15
5	.20
6	.25
7	.05

(a) Determine the expected weekly cost per unit of a replace-as-they-fail policy.

(b) The company currently uses a blanket replacement policy on the weekend following a 4-week cycle. The labor cost involved in replacing one unit during weekend shutdown is $9.00. Management feels that this cycle should be extended to 5 weeks. What do you recommend?

(c) A suggestion has been made to place all units on a test bench for 1 week to minimize the initial high failure rate. The surviving units would then be placed in the production line. The test cost is $2.00 per unit for the equipment and personnel involved, and the company will use a replace-as-they-fail policy. Compare the cost of this plan to that obtained in part a.

13.28 A machinery supply and service company advertises that orders received by 8:00 a.m. will be delivered that day or else the customer will have to pay only one-half the price for the order. The amount of an average order is $372. The number of orders received before the deadline varies according to the following pattern:

Orders per day	16	17	18	19	20	21	22	23
Probability	.05	.10	.10	.20	.25	.15	.10	.05

Each order is delivered by van. The fixed cost of a van is $30 for a normal 8-hour working day. Van variable costs depend on the time required to deliver an order. The daily average order time distribution and the associated variable costs are as shown:

Average hours per order during 1 day	Variable cost per order, $	Probability
0.50	3.50	.40
1	7.00	.30
1.50	10.50	.20
2	14.00	.10

Use simulation to determine an average profit associated with the policy of operating four vans.

13.29 A new type of automatic assembly equipment costs $100,000 and may be in use for 4, 6, or 8 years, depending upon the development of new markets for the product line being serviced and technological changes in the industry. The salvage value of the equipment will be $40,000, $20,000, or $10,000, depending on how long the unit is retained in service. Maintenance costs are expected to be $25,000 for the first year, and they will continue to increase at a rate of $5000 per year for each year of use. Annual cost reductions resulting from installation of the equipment are unknown at this time but are expected to be closely approximated by a normally distributed random variable with a mean of $35,000 and a standard deviation of $10,000. If the probabilities with the three potential service periods are equal, determine by simulation the distribution of the present worth resulting from installation of this equipment. Use a before-tax rate of return of 20 percent.

13.30 The estimated first cost of a piece of equipment is $100,000. However, there is some doubt about this figure, because several bids are being received. The estimated standard deviation of the bids is $10,000, and their dispersion is assumed to be normally distributed.

Annual expenses associated with the equipment are also normally distributed as follows:

Maintenance	$\mu_M = \$5000$	$\sigma_M = \$700$
Number of breakdowns per year	$\mu_B = 10$	$\sigma_B = 2$
Cost per breakdown	$\mu_C = \$900$	$\sigma_C = \$200$

In addition, direct labor expenses are expected to be uniformly distributed between $4000 and $7000 per year.

If $N = 5$ and MARR = 10 percent (disregarding taxes), determine by simulation the approximate annual income required to make this a feasible purchase.

13.31 Sales of a new product are expected to follow a normal distribution with a mean of 10,000 units and a standard deviation of 1500 units. The sales price of the product has been set at $30 per unit. The unit manufacturing costs are estimated to be $24, distributed normally, with a standard deviation of $1.50. Fixed manufacturing costs are expected to follow a uniform distribution over the range of $15,000 to $25,000. The product's life is expected to be 5 years. Use simulation to determine the mean and standard deviation of the net present worth for this project. Assume MARR = 20 percent.

13.32 A project requires investment in a machine that costs $25,000. Other data pertinent to this operation are as follows:

Savings: Normal distribution, μ_s = $15,000, σ_s = $2000
Expenses: Normal distribution, μ_e = $2500, σ_e = $250
Salvage value: triangular distribution, minimum = $1000, mode = $1200, maximum = $1800

The machine will be in use for 5 years. If the minimum acceptable rate of return is 15 percent, use simulation to determine the expected value and the standard deviation of the net present worth.

13.33 Fancyfree Products has received a low-rate industrial loan to enable it to build a manufacturing plant in an economically depressed area. Effects of future economic and political conditions influence the site selection. As a preliminary study of the situation, ratings have been assigned as outcomes for operating the plant at each site under each of the more likely future conditions:

	Possible conditions			
Site	1	2	3	4
NW	0	2	8	20
NE	4	14	12	10
SW	16	6	6	8
SE	4	4	18	6
C	4	14	10	9

(a) Which site is dominated? (Dominance refers to the condition where one alternative produces greater payoff than another alternative for every future condition.)
(b) Which site is preferred according to the maximin criterion?
(c) Which site is preferred according to the maximax criterion?
(d) Which site gets a preference when the equal-likelihood principle is applied?
(e) When $\alpha = 0.75$, which site has the highest rating by the Hurwicz principle?
(f) Which site is preferred according to the regret principle?

13.34 Venture Capitalists, Inc., has $500,000 to invest in any one of the mutually exclusive projects shown below. Each of the projects has a life of 4 years, and the outcomes shown are annual returns in thousands of dollars of after-cash flow. Since each of the proposals depends upon public acceptance of an untested new product, there is considerable doubt about the state of each return. Apply the six principles of choice listed in Prob. 13.33, and comment on the diversification of preference.

	Potential market conditions			
Project	**W**	**X**	**Y**	**Z**
A	200	200	200	200
B	50	150	500	0
C	100	300	200	100
D	400	350	200	50
E	300	200	100	0

13.35 Based on the payoffs in the matrix below, answer the following:

	Future state		
Alternative	S_1	S_2	S_3
A_1	20	10	0
A_2	40	0	−20
A_3	5	25	−5

(a) If S_1, S_2, and S_3 have respective probabilities of occurrence of .3, .4, and .3, which alternative is preferred according to the expected-value principle?
(b) What is the value of perfect information?
(c) If the probabilities of S_1, S_2, and S_3 are unknown, at what values of α in the Hurwicz criterion will different alternatives be preferred?
(d) For unknown future states, what would be the preferred alternative by using the regret principle?

13.36 The expected rates of return for investment in securities and investment in expanded plant facilities are estimated for two levels of future business activity:

	Recession	**Inflation**
Securities	5	7
Expansion	1	15

The company is undecided about the likelihood of the future conditions. It has been suggested that each future should be considered equally likely. Then the probability of each future at which the two alternatives are equivalent can be calculated. These are *indifference probabilities*. The decision rule is to select the alternative that has the highest return for the future state that has the greatest difference between the equal-likelihood probability and the indifference probability. Apply this decision rule and comment on the results.

CHAPTER 14

MULTISTAGE SEQUENTIAL ANALYSIS

Uncertainty and expectations are the joys of life.
W. Congreve, *Love for Love*, 1695

ituations that require multistage sequential decisions over time are common in business and industry. Capital-budgeting decisions for allocating resources to new ventures, production scheduling and inventory replacement policies in the face of fluctuating demand requirements, and long-range strategies for replacing depreciating assets are examples of situations that require multiple decisions spread over time. The decisions made at different times are not independent of each other. The outcomes from previous decisions provide input to subsequent decisions. In other words, the decision made at any given time is made in view of its pyramiding effect on the remaining decisions.

Managing today's organizations requires continuous decision making. The increasing pace of technological change confronts managers with tough investment choices. New electronic and computer-based technologies are revolutionizing design, manufacturing, and service functions. The market dictates what companies will develop and produce. Managers are continuously faced with the design and production of increasingly sophisticated products with shorter and shorter market lives. Additional uncertainty is introduced by variation in economic factors such as inflation rates and interest rates. Managers must make decisions today that affect the organization's future. The results from these decisions must be regularly monitored. Original decisions may have to be revised and new alternatives considered, as companies confront growing national and international competition that emphasizes productivity, new-product introduction, and quality and reliability.

Risk analysis in Chap. 13 examined economic decisions in uncertain environments. Problems with multistage sequential decisions introduce an additional level of complexity. The sequence of decisions and uncertain events link the initial decisions to the final outcomes. Direct choice among the initial alternatives is very difficult. A sequential analysis procedure that starts at the end and "roll backs" toward the initial decision is used to analyze multistage sequential problems. The computations begin with expected values calculated for the most distant decision and roll back to the present by accepting the preferred alternative at each distant decision as the outcome for the next-closer decision. A completed backward pass discloses the present worth of each immediate course of action.

Decision trees display the effect of successive decisions over a time horizon where outcomes of the alternatives are uncertain. The graphic quality of decision trees contributes to comprehensive analysis and cogent communications. Nonrepetitive decisions involving substantial outcomes exposed to risk are well served by the systematic evaluation methodology promoted by decision trees.

14.1   BASIC CONCEPTS

To illustrate the basic concepts in the application of decision trees to problems requiring multiple sequential decisions, consider the following facility expansion problem when uncertainty is ignored. Plans are being developed for expansion of a production facility. The study period is 10 years. One alternative is to expand now. If the company decides not to expand, then the decision can be reevaluated in 5 years when the company will have additional information on whether its growth will support the expansion. The situation is shown graphically in Fig. 14.1.

There are two decision points: the at-present and 5 years from today. The choices at each decision point are to expand or not to expand. If the decision today is to expand, then no more future decisions have to be made. However, if the do-not-expand path is taken, then the decision is reevaluated in 5 years. If, on one hand, after 5 years the prediction is still for a relatively stable growth pattern, then the decision will be to continue at the current production level. If, on the other hand, growth is expected in the

FIGURE 14.1
Deterministic decision tree for a facility expansion decision.

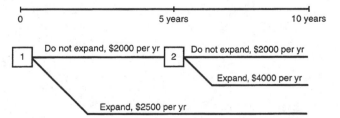

demand for services provided by the company, then the production facilities can be expanded. The *net* cash flows for each action are shown in Fig. 14.1.

The optimal sequence of decisions is found by starting at the leaves of the tree (farthest point in time) and "rolling backward" until the starting decision node is reached. This procedure takes into account the expected decisions of the future.

For the expansion problem, the evaluation process begins at decision node 2. Assuming an interest rate of 15 percent, we can calculate the present worths of the two outcomes at this decision point as follows:

$$PW_{t=5}(\text{do not expand}) = \$2000(P/A, 15, 5)$$
$$= \$2000(3.35216) = \$6704$$

$$PW_{t=5}(\text{expand}) = \$4000(P/A, 15, 5)$$
$$= \$4000(3.35216) = \$13,409$$

The best choice at decision node 2 is to expand the facility.

Decision node 1 also has two alternatives. The preferred choice at decision node 2 is now part of the top branch of the decision tree. The present worth of this branch is

$$PW_{t=0}(\text{no expansion for 5 years, then expansion})$$
$$= \$2000(P/A, 15, 5) + \$13,409(P/F, 15, 5)$$
$$= \$2000(3.35216) + \$13,409(0.49718)$$
$$= \$13,371$$

The bottom branch at decision node 1 is to expand now. The present worth is calculated as

$$PW_{t=0}(\text{expand for 10 years}) = \$2500(P/A, 15, 10)$$
$$= \$2500(5.01877)$$
$$= \$12,547$$

The optimal result then is not to expand now, but to expand in 5 years.

The decision tree in Fig. 14.1 is deterministic; it shows only decisions separated by time. Branches from a decision point represent alternatives that can be chosen at that point. A *discounted* decision tree also shows *chance events* that represent factors that may affect the choice of decision alternatives. Examples of such events include market demand, available technology, and interest and inflation rates. Typically, multiple outcomes are associated with each chance event. For example, different levels of demand represent future market conditions. Each outcome of an event is described in terms of a probability or likelihood of occurrence of that outcome. The occurrence of a specific outcome of a chance event may, in turn, trigger a new decision point. Thus, a succession of decisions and events may extend into the future. Furthermore, every combination of a decision

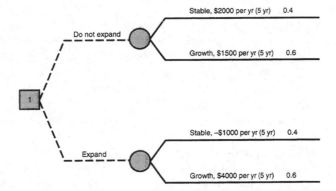

FIGURE 14.2
Discounted decision tree for initial decision for facility expansion problem.

and an outcome has a cost (or value) associated with it. The economic measure generally used in a discounted decision tree analysis is the expected present value.

Consider a single decision associated with the facility expansion problem at present. Let us say that the uncertain event is the future market condition. Assume, further, that the market condition is described as *stable* or *growth*. The decision tree resulting from this scenario is shown in Fig. 14.2.

A decision tree has three components:

1. Decision alternatives with associated future events
2. Outcomes for each alternative, given the occurrence of each future event
3. The probability of occurrence of each event

The nodes of the tree are either *decision* nodes or *event* nodes. The branches from a decision node represent alternatives, and those from the event nodes represent outcomes associated with events. The occurrence of chance events is random; the decision maker has no control over their outcome, although the probability of occurrence of different states can be predicted.

In a convenient set of symbols to graphically portray the decision situation, decision points are squares and outcomes are circles. Dotted lines between squares and circles symbolize different courses of action, and solid lines from the circles represent the possible consequences of the actions. The decision criterion is the expected value of alternatives at each decision point.

The structure of the decision tree in Fig. 14.2 shows that the initial decision is to expand or not to expand. However, unlike the deterministic tree in Fig. 14.1, the returns from these actions depend on future market conditions. There are different returns associated with each combination of an alternative and an event outcome. If the company decides not to expand and if the market remains stable, the company will meet its customer base with current resource levels. If, however, the company does not expand but the demand for its services increases, then the company will lose a share of the market due to inadequate resources to meet the increased demand. The company would be well prepared to meet this growth if it did decide to expand. However, if the company were to expand and the market did not grow, the company would incur cost because of nonutilized resources. As is apparent from this example, there are costs and benefits associated with each decision alternative; their realization depends on the outcome of uncertain events.

How useful a decision tree is in making an accurate decision for a problem depends to a large degree on the determination of costs and revenues and on the prediction of outcomes of each uncertain event and the associated probabilities. These probabilities, along with the net cash flows for each alternative course of action, are shown on the branches emanating from the event nodes in Fig. 14.2.

Analysis of the decision tree in Fig. 14.2 uses expected values according to the procedures outlined in Chap. 13. We will assume that the study period is 5 years and that the interest rate is 15 percent. The expected value at the event node following the do-not-expand decision is

$$[\$2000(P/A, 15, 5)](0.4) + [\$1500(P/A, 15, 5)](0.6) = \$5699$$

and at the event node following the expand decision is

$$[-\$1000(P/A, 15, 5)](0.4) + [\$4000(P/A, 15, 5)](0.6) = \$6704$$

Comparing the two values, we see that the preferred decision is to expand.

Analysis of more complex discounted decision trees requires the use of *conditional probabilities*. Additional information about a decision is used in *bayesian analysis* to revise the probability of a future event. We will briefly review the concepts of conditional probabilities and bayesian analysis prior to further analysis of discounted decision trees.

14.2   PROBABILITY CONCEPTS FOR DECISION TREES

Independent events and their probability relationships were examined in Chap. 13. These relations were applied to evaluate risk-affected situations according to the expected-value criterion. Independent outcomes that could logically be expected for each alternative course of action were displayed in a payoff table or in a decision tree format (Fig. 13.2). In this chapter the same general approach to economic risk is followed, but possible rewards from obtaining additional information are incorporated in the decision tree. In the process, some events become dependent on the occurrence of other events.

An event is termed *statistically dependent* when its occurrence is affected by the occurrence of one or more other events. For instance, your probability of becoming a millionaire 10 years from now might be .9 if you were given $500,000 next year. The event of becoming a millionaire would thus be dependent on the receipt of $500,000. If the probability of receiving $500,000 is .01, then your likelihood of being a millionaire in 10 years according to this specific situation is

P(become a millionaire *and* receive $500,000)
 = P(making 1 million *given* $500,000) × P(receiving $500,000)
 = .90 × .01 = .009

The millionaire status obviously depends on the likelihood of the occurrence of the $500,000 acquisition.

Dependent relationships are illustrated by the classic "balls in a box" example depicted in Fig. 14.3. Two boxes, labeled *X* and *Y*, contain black balls and white balls. Box *X* contains three white and two black balls; box *Y* holds one white and four black balls. The probability of drawing a ball of a given color clearly depends on which box is chosen for the draw.

The *marginal probability* of drawing a white ball in this situation is .4. Even though two events may be related, a marginal probability refers to only one of the dependent events. From the probability tree in Fig. 14.3, it is clear that the probability of drawing a white ball is affected by the box from which it is drawn. Therefore, the two events (drawing from one of the boxes and drawing a white ball) are related, but the marginal probability

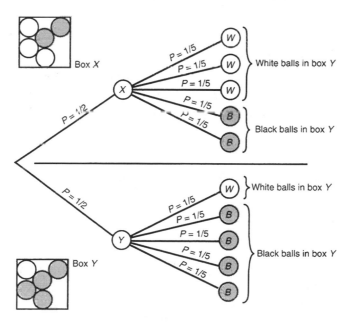

FIGURE 14.3

Population of black and white balls in boxes *X* and *Y*. Each burst of probability-labeled lines represents additional available information.

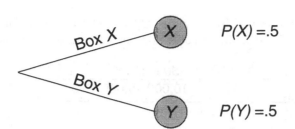

FIGURE 14.4
First event in the
bayesian analysis
illustration box
selection.

of each box is known but that the identity of the boxes is unknown. This
situation is equivalent to knowing the outcome of two possible futures
without being certain which future will occur.

In this case we want to identify which box is X and which is Y. Since
the two boxes are indistinguishable, there is an equal opportunity that
either could be nominated as X or Y. The first event is a random selection
of one of the boxes. The prior probability of this event is represented by the
probability tree of Fig. 14.4.

Next a ball is drawn from whichever box was picked in event 1. We will
assume that it is a black ball. Since we know the proportion of black to
white balls in each box, we can calculate the probability of drawing a black
or a white ball, given that it came from a designated box. In box X three of
the five balls are white, so the conditional probability for the top branch of
an expanded probability tree in Fig. 14.5 is .6. The likelihood of drawing a
ball of a given color from a given box is shown by the joint probability for
each branch of the tree. The complete tabulation of joint probabilities (collectively exhaustive) adds to 1.0, but we are interested primarily in the
probabilities relating to black balls, because our first draw was black. The
sum of the probabilities pertaining to black balls is the marginal probability of drawing a black ball and is shown in to the right in Fig. 14.5.

The posterior probability of identifying the boxes, based on the additional information derived from the draw, is calculated by Bayes' basic for-

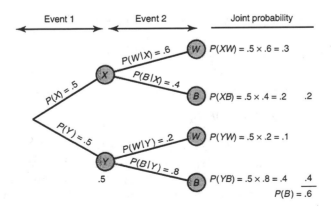

FIGURE 14.5
Box selection and
first draw.

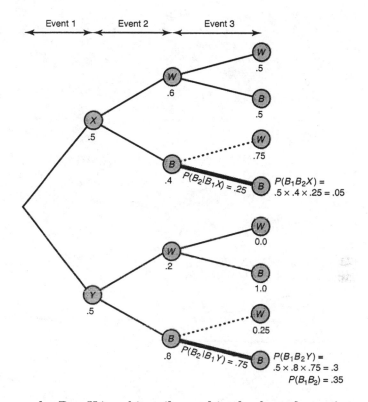

FIGURE 14.6
Box selection and
two draws.

mula. Box Y is arbitrarily used in the formula to give

$$P(Y \mid B) = \frac{P(YB)}{P(B)} = \frac{.4}{.6} = .67$$

Thus the added data have allowed us to revise our probability estimate from .5 to .67 that the selected box is indeed box Y. The process of acquiring additional information in this fashion is called *sampling*.

Now assume that another ball is drawn from the same box and is black. Conditional probabilities for this draw are calculated on the basis of the four balls remaining in the box after the first draw. Then the joint probabilities are determined for two successive black draws from either box. These procedures are depicted in the probability tree in Fig. 14.6.

A further revision of the likelihood that the chosen box is box Y now becomes

$$P(Y \mid B_1 B_2) = \frac{P(B_1 B_2 Y)}{P(B_1 B_2)} = \frac{.3}{.35} = .857$$

Suppose that the second draw had revealed a white rather than a black ball. This possibility is represented by the dotted lines in the probability tree. A format for revising the probability that the draws (B_1 and W_2) were from box Y is given in the following table:

Event 1	Event 2 = B_1	Event 3 = W_2	$P(E_1 E_2 E_3)$
$P(X) = .5$	$P(B_1|X) = .4$	$P(W_2|B_1 X) = 0.75$	$(.5)(.4)(.75) = .15$
$P(Y) = .5$	$P(B_1|Y) = .8$	$P(W_2|B_1 Y) = 0.25$	$(.5)(.8)(.25) = \underline{.10}$
			.25

$$P(Y \mid B_1 W_2) = \frac{.10}{.25} = .40$$

We would intuitively suspect that a reversed order of the draws (W_1 and B_2) would not alter the revised probability. This suspicion is confirmed by the following values:

Event 1	Event 2 = W_1	Event 3 = B_2	$P(E_1 E_2 E_3)$
$P(X) = .5$	$P(W_1|X) = .6$	$P(B_2|W_1 X) = .5$	$(.5)(.6)(.5) = .15$
$P(Y) = .5$	$P(W_1|Y) = .2$	$P(B_2|W_1 Y) = 1.0$	$(.5)(.2)(1.0) = \underline{.10}$
			.25

$$P(Y \mid W_1 B_2) = \frac{.10}{.25} = .40$$

As a final possibility, again assume that the first two balls drawn were black and now a third black ball is picked from the same box. We have obviously been drawing from box Y, because box X originally contained only two black balls. Although formal calculations are unnecessary in this case, the conclusion is verified easily by recognizing that

$$P(3 \text{ black draws} \mid \text{box } X) = .4(.25)(0.0) = 0$$

and

$$P(3 \text{ black draws} \mid \text{box } Y) = .8(.75)(.67) = .4$$

which makes the marginal probability of three successive black draws .0 + .4 = .4, so

$$P(\text{box } Y \mid 3 \text{ black draws}) = \frac{P(B_1 B_2 B_3 Y)}{P(B_1 B_2 B_3)} = \frac{.4 \times .5}{.4 \times .5} = 1.0$$

14.3 DISCOUNTED DECISION TREE ANALYSIS

A discounted decision tree shows decisions separated by time intervals and susceptible to external influencing factors. Branches from an initial deci-

FIGURE 14.7

Decision trees for a gamble to select box X or Y when the ante is –$100 and the payoff for correctly selecting the named box is $180.

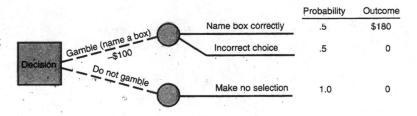

	Probability	Outcome
Name box correctly	.5	$180
Incorrect choice	.5	0
Make no selection	1.0	0

sion point indicate the primary alternatives. Each main branch is divided to show foreseeable outcomes associated with possible future events. The events are then rated with respect to their probable occurrence. When gains can be maximized by introducing new alternatives at a future date, a second decision point is established. A succession of decision points can extend to the limit of forecasting ability. The time value of monetary outcomes is affected by discounting the outcomes to a common point in time.

Suppose that it costs $100 to play the game of picking which box is X and which is Y when the contents of the boxes are known, but outwardly the boxes are identical. Success in naming a box correctly is rewarded by winnings of $180 (net gain of $80 since it costs $100 to play the game). Because the boxes are indistinguishable to the gambler, there is a 50-50 chance of guessing correctly. The expected value from repeatedly playing the game is

$$-\$100 + .5(\$180) = -\$10 \text{ per play}$$

A decision tree representation of the gamble is shown in Fig. 14.7.

Now assume that another option has been added to make the game more interesting. A gambler can select one ball from either box for a sampling fee of $25. After the charge is paid and a ball is drawn, the original conditions of the game then apply. The advantage of the sampling draw for the gambler is to gain additional information before making a selection between boxes. The question is whether the additional information provided by the draw can change the expected value of the game to the gambler's favor. The sequential alternatives are displayed in Fig. 14.8.

Probabilities for the sampling option are based on the known distribution of black balls and white balls in boxes X and Y, as given in the previous example. For instance, once a white ball is drawn, the probability it was drawn from box X is

$$P(X\,|\,W) = \frac{P(W\,|\,X)P(X)}{P(W\,|\,X)P(X) + P(W\,|\,Y)P(Y)} = \frac{P(XW)}{P(XW) + P(YW)}$$

$$= \frac{.6(.5)}{.6(.5) + .2(.5)} = \frac{.3}{.3 + .1} = .75$$

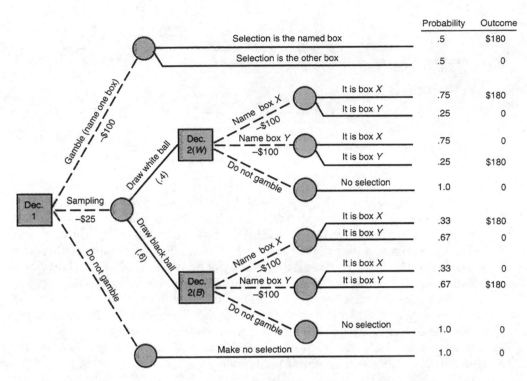

	Probability	Outcome
Selection is the named box	.5	$180
Selection is the other box	.5	0
It is box X	.75	$180
It is box Y	.25	0
It is box X	.75	0
It is box Y	.25	$180
No selection	1.0	0
It is box X	.33	$180
It is box Y	.67	0
It is box X	.33	0
It is box Y	.67	$180
No selection	1.0	0
Make no selection	1.0	0

FIGURE 14.8 Expanded decision trees for the pick-a-box gamble. Probabilities are based on boxes described in Fig. 14.7, but there is an added option of sampling one ball from a box before deciding to ante $100 for the chance to select a box. The fee for sampling is $25.

Similarly, the probability of drawing a white ball for the sample when the identity of the boxes is unknown is

$$P(W) = P(W \mid X)P(X) + P(W \mid Y)P(Y)$$
$$= .6(.5) + .2(.5) = .4$$

Or since there are 4 white balls among the 10 in the two boxes,

$$P(W) = \tfrac{4}{10} = .4$$

Given the probabilities and the payoffs for each outcome, we calculate the expected value of the sampling option by rolling back from decision point 2 to decision point 1. This means that the expected values from point 2 are calculated first and that the most profitable alternatives become the outcomes for point 1.

A payoff table in dollars for decision point 2(W) (a white ball drawn as the sample) is shown below:

	It is box X $P(X/W) = .75$	It is box Y $P(Y/W) = .25$	Expected value, $
Pick box X	$180 - 100 = 80$	-100	35
Pick box Y	-100	$180 - 100 = 80$	-55
Refuse gamble	0	0	0

The preferred alternative is clearly to pick box X when a white ball is drawn. By equivalent calculations, the box should be identified as Y at decision point 2(B) when a black ball is drawn, because the expected value EV of this choice is

$$\text{EV}(Y \text{ given } B) = (\$180 - \$100)(.67) + (-\$100)(.33) = \$20$$

as opposed to naming the box X for an expected value of $-\$40$ or quitting after the draw at no additional gain or loss.

A "pruned" decision tree is shown in Fig. 14.9. It displays the expected values for the original gamble and the outcomes for the sampling alternative. These outcomes are based on selecting the most advantageous alternatives from decision points 2(W) and 2(B). Given the likelihood of drawing a black ball or a white ball for the sample, we find that the expected value, given sampling information, is

$$\text{EV} | \text{SI} = \$35(.4) + \$20(.6) - \$25 - \$1$$

The option to buy a sample for $25 thus converts the long-term gain of the gamble from negative to positive, albeit barely profitable. The actual outcome of each round of gambling would be a loss of $25 + $100 = $125 or a gain of $180 - $125 = $55. Over a large number of rounds, the gambler averages a $1 gain per round.

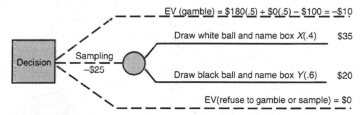

FIGURE 14.9 Pruned decision tree showing values for two alternatives and rolled-back outcomes from decision points 2(W) and 2(B) as determined from Fig. 14.8. Expected value of sampling alternative is $1, making it the preferred course of action for given data.

The value of information gained from sampling is the difference between the expected value of the sampling alternative and that of the *next-best alternative*. Without sampling, the best alternative is to refuse to gamble: EV(do not gamble) = $0.

$$\text{Expected value of sampling information (EVSI)} = \text{EV} \mid \text{SI} - \text{EV}$$
$$= \$1 - \$0 = \$1$$

Perfect information for the pick-a-box choice presumes prior knowledge of the identity of each box. Knowing which box is which eliminates the gamble and is consequently an unlikely proposition. But if it did exist, the gambler would pay $100 with complete assurance of winning $180 each time, a net gain of $80 per play. The value of perfect information is then $80 − $0 = $80.

14.4   **FORMULATION OF A DISCOUNTED DECISION TREE**

A warehousing problem of a small novelty manufacturing company will serve to illustrate a decision tree for successive decisions. The company is relatively new and has captured a limited segment of the novelty market. It must have additional storage space to meet customer demands and to allow more flexible production scheduling. A primary decision has been made to secure additional inventory storage.

An initial investigation has revealed the availability of only one suitable rental warehouse; it is available only if leased for 10 years. The warehouse has more space than is immediately required, but the company feels that some of the space could be subletted if desired. Estimates solicited from building contractors confirm that the construction of a new warehouse of equivalent size would amount to more than the $23,000 lease cost per year.

Another alternative is to build a small warehouse now and enlarge it if future business activity warrants expansion. The owners feel that in 3 years they will know whether the company's growth will support the addition. To evaluate the alternatives, estimates were made of possible business patterns and the likelihood of each. The optimistic forecasts are shown in Table 14.1.

The owners place the probability for increased growth during the next 3 years at .56 + .14 = .70. If the growth materializes, they can use more room than is available in the anticipated small warehouse. Therefore, if the owners initially decide to build, they must make a decision in 3 years about whether to add to the small warehouse or to find other means to obtain extra storage space. At that time the conditional probability that the company will continue to grow will be .56/.70 = .80. The spectrum of forecasts and alternatives can be summarized in a decision tree as shown in Fig. 14.10.

TABLE 14.1

Growth patterns for the novelty company

Growth pattern	Probability
No increase in activity for 10 years	.15
No increase for 3 years, but an expanded growth rate during the next 7 years	.15
Increasing growth for the next 3 years, but no increase during the following 7 years	.14
Increasing activity for full 10 years	.56

Outcomes. The outcomes for the warehouse proposals are rated according to expected costs. Initial building costs for a small warehouse should be accurate, but the estimated price for an addition is less firm because of possible changes in building conditions at the time of construction. Yearly rental fees for the leased warehouse are a fixed amount. Other annual costs are less certain. Savings, net positive cash flows, could result if the entire capacity is not required for the company's inventory and if the

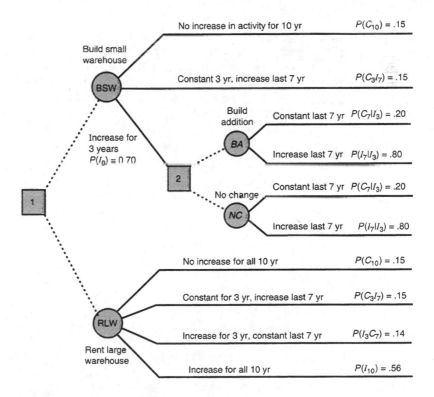

FIGURE 14.10
Decision tree with alternatives and forecasts.

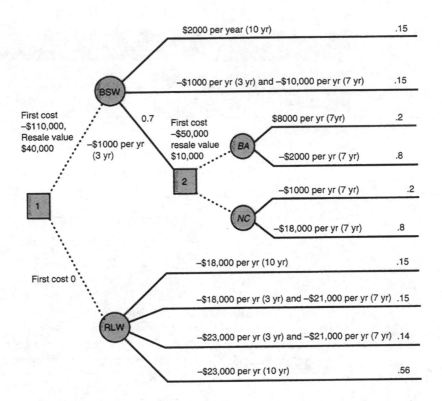

FIGURE 14.11
Costs associated with warehouse alternatives.

extra portion is rented. Conversely, additional costs are incurred when a lack of storage space forces production runs below the economical lot size or causes out-of-stock costs in supplying customers. Estimates of net annual costs for the outcomes of each alternative are tabulated in the decision tree of Fig. 14.11.

The cash flow estimates shown in the figure include the first costs associated with each alternative and the annual cost related to the outcomes. Building a small warehouse (BSW) has a first cost of $110,000 and a resale value of $40,000 after 10 years; renting a large warehouse (RLW) has no initial cost. The second decision point 3 years in the future is a choice between building an addition (BA) at a cost of $50,000 with a $10,000 resale value and making no change (NC). Net annual returns comprise repairs, taxes, insurance, leasing expense, and opportunity costs, as well as the savings from subletting when possible. The lease for the rental warehouse states an annual charge of $23,000, which includes taxes, insurance, and repairs. If there is no increase in the company's activities, this annual charge can be defrayed by $5000 from subletting extra space. Less rental income is anticipated when the company needs part of or all the space to handle its own increasing activity. The two periods of returns, 3 and 7 years, correspond to the original growth patterns indicated in Fig. 14.10.

Evaluation. Two types of calculations are involved in evaluating alternatives. The present values of receipts and expenditures are determined for each outcome and are then weighted according to their probability of occurrence. This procedure amounts to finding the expected value of the present worth of the outcomes. These expected values are compared at a decision point to select the most advantageous alternative.

Comparisons are made in a reverse chronological order. That is, the most distant decision point from time 0 is evaluated first. The selected alternative from the first decision then becomes an input to the next decision. The backward pass through successive points is continued until the primary decision is resolved.

For the warehouse example, the discounting procedure begins at decision point 2. At this time, 3 years away from the primary decision, the company must decide whether to build an addition to the plant or to make no change. The outcomes of each of these two alternatives depend on the level of business activity during the last 7 years of the study period. We will assume that the company uses an interest rate of 12 percent. The present worths of the four outcomes at decision point 2 are calculated as shown:

$$\text{PW(BA} \mid C_7) = -\$50,000 + \$10,000(P/F, 12, 7) + \$8000(P/A, 12, 7)$$
$$= -\$50,000 + \$10,000(0.45235) + \$8000(4.56376)$$
$$= -\$8966$$

$$\text{PW(BA} \mid I_7) = -\$50,000 + \$10,000(P/F, 12, 7) + (-\$2000)(P/A, 12, 7)$$
$$= -\$54,604$$

$$\text{PW(NC} \mid C_7) = -\$1000(P/A, 12, 7) = -\$1000(4.56376) = -\$4564$$

$$\text{PW(NC} \mid I_7) = -\$18,000(P/A, 12, 7) = -\$82,148$$

These present worths at decision point 2 are entered in a payoff table (Table 14.2), where the calculated expected values indicate a preference for the alternative to build an addition (BA).

TABLE 14.2

Payoff table for decision point 2

| | Company growth patterns, $ | | Expected costs |
Alternative	Constant (0.2)	Increase (0.8)	$(0.2C + 0.8I)$, $
BA	−8966	−54,604	−45,476
NC	−4564	−82,148	−66,631

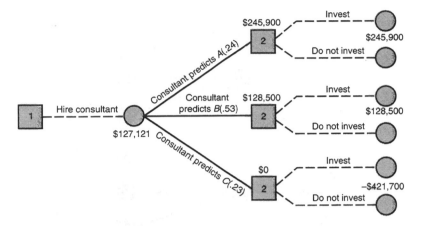

FIGURE 14.14
Decision tree for the hire-consultant alternative for Review Exercise 2.

The expected value from using the consultant's prediction is $127,121, which leads to

Value of additional information = EV(with added information)
$$- \text{EV(with original data)}$$
$$= \$127{,}121 - \$30{,}000 = \$97{,}121$$

The break-even point for purchasing additional information is therefore $97,121, which is the maximum amount the consultant should be paid.

EXERCISE 3
In converting job shop production to cellular manufacturing, management often face the decision of one-time conversion versus gradual conversion spread over time. The changeover costs are smaller if the entire production system is changed at the same time, compared with stepwise conversion. However, stepwise conversion is less risky, because we can dictate the level of automation as we see fit. Moreover, gradual conversion can serve as an investment sampling process. Complete conversion, although initially desirable, may appear unacceptable after additional information over time is garnered.

Consider a discrete parts manufacturing facility organized as a job shop. Management wishes to evaluate cellular manufacturing as a production alternative. Production can be organized into two identical cells. Management can change production to two cells simultaneously or can convert part of the system to one cell and observe its operation and production economics before making a decision on the second cell.

The operational performance of a cell is described by one of three outcomes: excellent, good, and poor. Based on studies of similar production organizations, management estimates the following probability distribution for the performance of a cell:

Performance	Probability
Excellent (E)	.5
Good (G)	.3
Poor (P)	.2

The conversion costs are $1,000,000 per cell. The expected annual returns associated with each cell operation are estimated to be $250,000 if the performance is excellent, $170,000 if good, and $50,000 if poor.

Management would consider converting the second cell after 3 years only if conversion of the first cell results in excellent or good performance. The conditional probabilities associated with the second phase of conversion are as follows:

If first-cell performance is	Then second-cell performance will be		
	Excellent	Good	Poor
Excellent	.90	.09	.01
Good	.25	.70	.05
Poor	.10	.20	.70

If the job shop arrangement is used exclusively, returns are expected to average $45,000 per year; partial conversion will result in annual returns of $100,000 of which $25,000 will be from the section of the facility using the job shop. Assume an interest rate of 10 percent over the 10-year study period.

Using a discounted decision tree, determine the best conversion strategy.

SOLUTION 3

The decision tree for the system described above is shown in Fig. 14.15. The discounting procedure begins at decision point 2, which is 3 years from the primary decision. The decision at this point is whether to establish the second manufacturing cell. The present worths for the alternatives at decision point $2E$ are calculated as shown. All outcomes are expressed in thousands of dollars.

$$PW(2E: \text{convert to cell 2}) = [.9(\$250 + \$250) + .09(\$170 + \$170) + .01$$
$$\times (\$50 + \$50)](P/A, 10, 7) - \$1000$$
$$= [.9(\$500) + .09(\$340) + .05(\$100)](4.86342) - \$1000$$
$$= \$1364$$

$$PW(2E: \text{do not convert}) = \$100(P/A, 10, 7) = \$487$$

At the decision point $2E$, the preferred choice is to establish the second production cell.

The present worth for converting to the second cell at decision point $2G$ is computed similarly.

$$PW(2G: \text{convert to cell 2}) = [.25(\$250 + \$250) + .7(\$170 + \$170) + .05$$
$$\times (\$50 + \$50)](P/A, 10, 7) - \$1000$$
$$= \$792$$

$$PW(2G: \text{do not convert}) = PW(2E: \text{do not convert}) = \$487$$

Thus, the preferred choice at decision point $2G$ is also to proceed with the second cell.

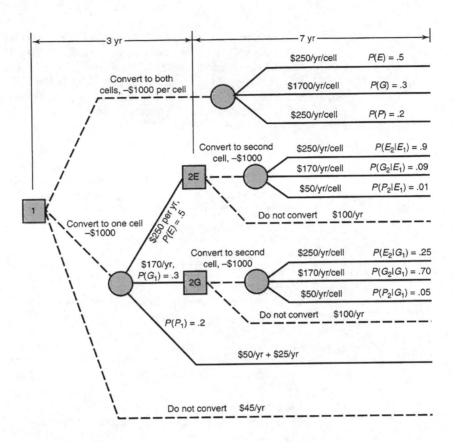

FIGURE 14.15
Decision tree for
Review Exercise 3.

Continuing along the same branch, we compute the present-worth value of stepwise conversion at decision point 1 as

$$
\begin{aligned}
\text{PW(stepwise conversion)} &= [\$1364(P/F,\ 10,\ 3) + \$250(P/A,\ 10,\ 3) - \$1000](.5) \\
&\quad + [\$792(P/F,\ 10,\ 3) + \$170(P/A,\ 10,\ 3) - \$1000](.3) \\
&\quad + [(\$50 + \$25)(P/A,\ 10,\ 10) - \$1000](.2) \\
&= [\$1364(.75132) + \$250(2.48685) - \$1000](.5) \\
&\quad + [\$792(.75132) + \$170(2.48685) - \$1000](.3) \\
&\quad + [\$75(6.14457) - \$1000](.2) \\
&= \$221
\end{aligned}
$$

The top branch is for establishing both manufacturing cells simultaneously. The present worth of outcomes for each cell is computed as

$$
\begin{aligned}
\text{PW(convert to 2 cells)} &= 2\{[\$250(.5) + \$170(.3) + \$50(.2)](P/A,\ 10,\ 10) - \$1000\} \\
&= \$286
\end{aligned}
$$

Finally, the option not to convert results in a net present value of

PW(do not convert) = $45(P/A, 10, 10) = \$277$

From this analysis the most economical alternative is to proceed with one-time conversion to two production cells.

14.7   PROBLEMS

14.1 When a machine is properly adjusted, it will produce an acceptable product 9 times in 10. When it is out of adjustment, the probability of an acceptable product is .4. The probability of the machine's being adjusted properly is .95.
  (a) If the first part tested after an adjustment is not acceptable, what is the probability that the machine was correctly adjusted?
  (b) If the first two parts were acceptable, what is the probability of a correctly adjusted machine?

14.2 New types of concrete mixes are tested in a laboratory by batching four test cylinders. The probability that a trial batch will yield the specified strength is .90 if the mix is properly prepared and tested. Occasionally, about 1 time in every 20, the trial batch will be improperly handled or the ingredients inaccurately measured. The probability that a poorly prepared mix will yield the specified strength is .20. If only one cylinder in a trial batch of four meets the specified strength, what is the probability that the mix was correctly prepared?

14.3 Ninety percent of the fruit received at a cannery comes from local growers. The fruit from local sources averages 80 percent grade 1 and 20 percent grade 2. The fruit obtained from other sources averages 40 percent grade 1 and 60 percent grade 2. The markings on a shipment of bins full of fruit were lost. One bin was sampled, and from five pieces of fruit inspected, four were of grade 1. What is the probability that the bin came from a local grower?

14.4 An Alberta oil operator owns a $5 million oil rig. It costs $75,000 to pull the drills to safety and batten down the rig in anticipation of a bad storm. An uninsured average loss of $400,000 results from a bad storm when no precautionary measures are taken. A weather forecasting service provides an assessment of the probability of a severe storm. Four out of five times that a severe storm is predicted with a probability of 1.0, it does occur. Only 1 severe storm in 100 arrives unpredicted. Should the rig owner pull the drills when the forecasting service predicts a storm at a probability of 1.0?

14.5 How much could be paid for perfect information for the investment decision described in Prob. 13.4?

14.6 A manufacturing company has been approached to produce a new product. If the product is a success, the company will make $100,000 (net present value) over the life of the product. However, if the product does not sell well in the market, the company expects to lose $40,000. A market survey indicates that the likelihood of the product's being a success to be .6.
  (a) Should the company commit to manufacturing the new product?
  (b) What is the expected value of perfect information?

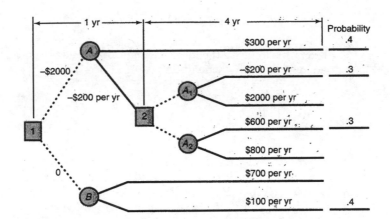

FIGURE 14.16
Figure for Prob. 14.7.

14.7 For the decision situation depicted in Fig. 14.16, capital is valued at 8 percent.

    (a) What is the expected profit at decision point 2?

    (b) Which alternative should be selected at decision point 1, and what is its expected value?

    (c) How much could be paid for perfect information?

14.8 A southwestern town is building an industrial park to encourage economic activity in the area. Three alternative-sized systems (in terms of pipe size plus appropriate pumps) are being considered to supply water to the site from the city reservoir. The small system will have a first cost of $300,000, the medium system will cost $450,000, and the cost of the large system will be $600,000. Water requirements at the still incomplete site depend on the companies that locate there. However, the construction of the water system must start now.

If the system is undersized, annual operating expenses will be quite high due to inefficient operation and accelerated pump wear. The following cost estimates have been developed:

Water system	Annual operating expenses for demand level, $		
	Low	**Medium**	**High**
Small	50,000	90,000	250,000
Medium	70,000	60,000	150,000
Large	100,000	110,000	120,000

The city predicts a 40 percent chance of low demand, a 30 percent chance of medium demand, and a 30 percent chance of high demand.

    (a) Assuming that the water system will be in use for 20 years, develop a decision tree for the situation and determine which system should be installed. Use an interest rate of 15 percent.

    (b) Determine the value of perfect information.

14.9 Plans are being developed for the construction of a new school. The city engineer now feels that the probability of *growth* G in the school area is .6 as opposed to a *stable* S census probability of .4. Two alternative designs are being considered. One is to build a medium-size school *(M)* with provisions for adding *(A)* onto it if needed, and the other is to construct a large *(L)* facility with the possibility of leasing part of the space to the city and county departments if the classroom space is not required.

The study period for the school in question is 15 years. It is believed that after 5 years the growth pattern will be evident. If the population is stable for 5 years, there is still a 50 percent chance it will remain stable for the rest of the 15-year period; there is no chance that the population will decrease. Given growth during the first 5 years, the probability of continued growth is .8, with a corresponding probability of .2 for a stable census during the next 10 years.

Additional data are as follows:

Estimated construction costs, $

Medium-size school to accommodate stable census	5,000,000
Addition to medium-size school to accommodate growth	4,000,000
Large-size school to accommodate a growing census	7,500,000
Remodeling *(R)* of large school to provide rental space if not all the classrooms are needed	500,000

Annual costs and income, $

Maintenance	
Medium-size school	200,000
Large or enlarged school	350,000
Revenue expected from rental space in a large school if all the capacity is not needed for classrooms	100,000
Busing and overcrowding costs if the school is not large enough to accommodate the population after first 5 years	500,000

The outcomes for the various options are labeled on the partially completed discounted decision tree in Fig. 14.17. Nodes are identified by the symbols above, and N means no change. The interest rate for the study is 7 percent.

   (a) Construct payoff tables for each decision point 2, and determine the preferred alternatives.

   (b) Develop a payoff table for decision point 1, and determine the preferred course of action for school construction.

14.10 The editor of a publishing house is deciding whether to accept a manuscript. She has already spent $1000 on the development of the manuscript and must now decide whether to

A_1 Reject the manuscript and forfeit the $1000

A_2 Accept the manuscript without obtaining an expert review

A_3 Obtain an expert review at a cost of $800

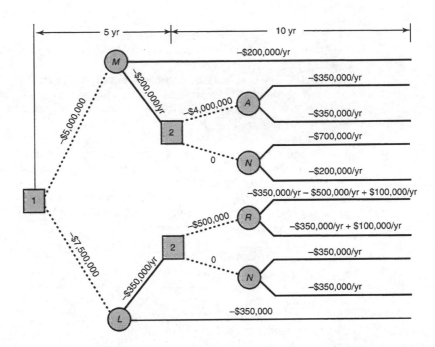

FIGURE 14.17
Partly completed decision tree for Prob. 14.9.

Data affecting the decision are given in the table below:

Decision and outcome if published	Editor-only evaluation (10 cases)	Evaluation by an expert (20 cases)			PW(net returns) manuscript if published, $
		Bad	**Fair**	**Good**	
M_0 Do not publish	4	9	0	0	0
M_1 Low demand	3	3	2	0	–10,000
M_2 Good sales	2	1	1	1	50,000
M_3 Bestseller	1	0	2	1	200,000

There are three possible market outcomes if the book is published: M_1, M_2, and M_3. Estimates for the present worth of revenues minus publishing costs are given for each market condition. Previous publishing decisions, made after reviewing, are indicated. The editor has accepted 6 out of the last 10 manuscripts of a similar nature and has obtained one bestseller. The expert has rated 20 books as bad, fair, or good for a fee of $800 per book and has had the success indicated in the table above.

(a) Construct a decision tree that represents the editor's alternatives. Indicate outcomes and associated probabilities.

(b) Calculate the expected value of sample information.

14.11 A small foundry has had trouble with its old arc furnace. This furnace has been completely depreciated for accounting purposes, but it could be sold currently for $60,000. The immediate alternatives are to overhaul and modify the old machine or to buy a current model that has many desirable features that could not be incorporated in the modification of the old machine. The plans are complicated by the general opinion in the industry that a breakthrough could be made in furnace technology in the near future.

The best estimate the foundry owners can make is that there is a 40 percent chance that a radically improved furnace will be available in about 3 years. If it is developed, the probability that it will make present models noncompetitive is .90 and that it will be only a minor improvement is .10.

The cost of modifying the old machine is $80,000, and the cost of a new, current-model machine is $250,000. Expected savings and resale values are given in the accompanying table, based on the following three possible future states:

S_1 = no technological breakthrough

S_2 = furnace developed that provides significant savings

S_3 = furnace developed that provides minor savings

Possible outcomes	Buy new		Modify	
	Savings per year, $	Resale at 8 years, $	Savings per year, $	Resale at 8 years, $
S_1	60,000	80,000	20,000	40,000
S_2	20,000	20,000	10,000	20,000
S_3	30,000	40,000	10,000	30,000

The table is based on a study period and life of 8 years for both furnaces. The sharp decreases in savings and salvage values in states 2 and 3 occur because the development of a radically different or even improved furnace would probably cut into the foundry's demand and its general competitive position.

Another alternative exists for the foundry. If the new type of furnace is developed in 3 years, the modified furnace could be sold at that time for $90,000 and the new one purchased for an estimated $450,000. This new furnace would provide a saving of $130,000 per year with a probability of .90 and $80,000 per year with a probability of .10. It will be worth $200,000, or $150,000 after 5 years, with respective probabilities of .90 and .10.

If a new machine is purchased now, it will be used for 8 years regardless of new developments.

Using a discounted decision tree, determine whether the old furnace should be modified or a new current model should be purchased. Interest is 10 percent.

14.12 A firm has produced a new product that was unusually successful; to meet the unexpectedly high demand, it will be necessary to add more production facilities. The troubling question is whether the high demand will continue, increase, or decrease. Plan A provides a permanent capacity increase and will be more profitable if the demand continues to increase. Plan B is a stopgap measure that can be converted to permanent capacity by a supplementary investment B' after 3 years, when the demand pattern is better known. For a steady or lower demand, plan B

is more profitable than plan A. The estimated future outcomes for an 8-year study period are shown in the table below:

First 3 years	Last 5 years	Probability
High	High	.40
High	Low	.20
Low	High	.30
Low	Low	.10

Initial cost estimates in dollars are as follows:

Plan A	1,000,000
Plan B	700,000
Plan B'	450,000

The supplementary investment B' in plan B will take place after the demand is known for the first 3 years.

Annual income estimates are as follows:

- Plan A with a high demand will yield a cash flow of $400,000 per year.
- Plan A with a low demand will yield $50,000 per year.
- Plan B with a high demand will yield $300,000 per year in the first 3 years and $200,000 annually in the last 5 years.
- Plan B combined with B' will yield $400,000 per year with high demand.
- Plan B combined with B' will yield $100,000 per year with low demand.
- Plan B with a low demand will yield $300,000 per year.

With interest at an annual rate of 8 percent, determine which plan or combination of plans appears most attractive.

14.13 The owners of the novelty company described in the chapter disagree about the solution of their storage problem. There is a minority feeling that more research should be done on the question. One member of the minority group is anxious to do such a study and estimates that it would cost about $5000 and would take approximately 6 months to complete. The company could limp through this period with existing inventory facilities. Although the other owners have faith in the person who would make the study, they feel that he is overconservative. Because of this attitude they estimate that (1) if company activity in the next 6 months is very strong, the probability that the study will indicate a continuation of increasing growth will be .60, and (2) if the next 6 months' activity is relatively constant, the chance of a forecast for increasing growth will be .10. On the basis of these estimates, an engineer in the company is asked to calculate the following:
  (a) The probability that the study will indicate increasing growth
  (b) If the study indicates increasing growth, the probability of continued increase and the chance of leveling off
  (c) If the study indicates no increase, the probability of increase and the chance of level activity

Carry out the engineer's assignment, and show the results in a decision-tree format without costs. (*Hint:* You must use the original estimates disclosed in the chapter example in conjunction with those in the problem. The decision tree has three primary alternatives.)

14.14 Engineering Service, a large consulting firm, is considering the acquisition of a computer to lower its project accounting and control costs. It can rent a large computer for $540,000 per year on a noncancelable but renewable 3-year lease. The other alternative is to buy a smaller computer at a cost of $600,000.

There is a probability of .70 for a high service demand in the next 3 years. If the demand is large in the first 3 years, the probability that it will continue to be large is .60. Expected annual net savings during a period of high demand are $900,000 from a large computer and $510,000 from a small model. If demand is low, the large computer will permit a saving of $420,000 per year, and the small computer's net annual saving will be $330,000. The probability of a continually low demand for the 6-year study period is .27.

After 3 years, the lease on the large computer could be terminated, and a smaller, used computer could be purchased for $360,000. Either purchased computer would have a negligible salvage value at the end of the 6-year period. Also, after 3 years the small computer could be sold for $360,000, and a large one could be leased for the remaining 3 years for $600,000 per year.

Assume that all receipts and disbursements are end-of-year payments and that the acceptable interest rate is 8 percent before taxes. Using a decision tree, determine the most attractive alternative for Engineering Services.

MULTIATTRIBUTE DECISION MAKING

Insight, understanding, ranking of priorities, and a "feel" for the complexity of an area are as important as precise, beautifully elegant mathematical models . . .

Peter F. Drucker, *Management, Tasks, Responsibilities, Practices,*
Harper and Row, Publishers, Inc., New York, 1974

Now that we are approaching the end of this book on engineering economy, it might be well to discuss the somewhat abstract topic of *decision making*. We have assumed that the engineering economist will develop data to assist the decision maker arrive at a logical and informed decision. Chapter 8 discussed benefit/cost approaches to economic problems where the methodologies did not necessarily rank alternatives in some feasible order. It would still be up to the decision maker to arrive at a decision. The purpose of this chapter is to discuss the decision-making process and to show some simple methods that will assist the decision maker.

A decision is a situation in which two or more alternatives or courses of action offer solutions to some issue. The purpose of decision analysis is to assist decision makers in selecting the "best" alternative for the issue under consideration. This chapter is concerned with selecting the preferred choice from a set of feasible alternatives.

A decision concerns what happens in the real world. A decision model provides a conceptualization of the real-world situation within a formal mathematical structure. Decision makers attempt to focus on the key aspects of the situation and to simplify the situation to a level that makes it easier to understand. Thus, decision models are approximations of reality that systematically structure the most important aspects of the situation.

Characteristics of the decision-making environment vary substantially. For example,

- It may involve well-defined quantitative attributes (or criteria), such as money, or attributes that are difficult to define and quantify, such as morale and welfare.
- It may range from being certain in terms of outcomes of any course of action to uncertain with regard to future events or actions.
- It may require a solution at one time versus requiring a set of interrelated sequential decisions over time.
- It may involve a single decision maker, such as purchasing an automobile or a computer for personal use, or a group of individuals with conflicting views with regard to the problem.

Many of the simpler decision problems involve quantitative attributes that are relatively easy to define, measure, and understand. The most familiar of these is money, measured in dollars or some other monetary unit. A number of other attributes involved in a decision problem might be easy to measure and convert to monetary units. Examples are workforce, machine utilization, reliability, and quality. So far in this text, our concern has been almost entirely with monetary attributes or attributes that can be easily converted to monetary units.

More complex decision problems involve attributes that are difficult to define and measure. Examples include employee morale, customer satisfaction, community reputation, appearance, and aesthetics. These attributes are referred to as *intangibles* or *qualitative attributes*. Intangibles are of particular interest in the public sector since many social services are either free or subsidized and since no market mechanism exists to establish economic equivalence. The implications associated with these factors must be presented in a comprehensive and consistent manner in the decision model. Multiattribute decision models integrate quantitative and qualitative attributes to produce an aggregate performance measure.

The overall strategy in quantitative decision models is *decomposition*. The decomposition process divides the problem into smaller problems; the results of the smaller problems are then aggregated to provide a solution to the original problem. Decomposing a complex problem into its components makes it easier for the decision maker to analyze the problem and explain and justify the results. The level of decomposition depends on the problem's complexity, time and resource availability, and the decision maker's expertise. The use of quantitative decision models does not eliminate human judgment. Rather their role is to provide decision makers with insights regarding the solution process and to facilitate the application of human judgment in a more systematic manner.

The multiattribute decision process uses a structured approach that consists of eight steps:

- Identify the decision makers.
- Identify the alternatives.
- Define the attributes.

- Determine the relative importance of attributes.
- Assess attribute values.
- Aggregate attribute values.
- Perform sensitivity analysis.
- Select the preferred alternative.

It should be emphasized that decision making is *not* a sequential process. Several activities, such as identifying alternatives and defining attributes, proceed in parallel. Each activity requires a number of iterations. For example, identifying alternatives involves selecting an initial list of potential alternatives. Some of these alternatives may be eliminated, others refined, and still new ones identified as the decision-making activity proceeds and more information becomes available.

15.1   DECISION MAKERS

The most obvious component of a decision-making environment is the decision makers. A decision refers to the process that begins with recognizing a need and that terminates with the selection and implementation of a particular course of action. The decision maker chooses from the selection of a course of action. A decision maker may consist of a single individual or a group of individuals, such as industrial or government organizations. An important task of the decision maker is to structure the problem, to identify the essential features of the problem to be modeled, and to define the criteria by which to measure the success of a decision.

Decision makers have their own styles of decision making. Individual decision making is affected by perceptual processes and personal habits and traits. Group decision making is influenced by the behavior of individuals in groups, individual perceptions concerning the distribution of power and authority in groups, and social and cultural norms within organizations. Both individual and group decision making is affected by the amount of information available to the decision maker, the amount of time in which the decision must be made, and the complexity of the choice itself.

Decisions are rarely free of bias. Bias is introduced in the decision process in several ways: in the choice of alternatives and attributes, in the weighting of attributes, and in the prediction and quantification of data. The effect of bias can be explored through sensitivity analysis. However, this is no slight accomplishment.

Including intangibles in the decision process further increases subjectivity. The dilemma includes choosing between using subjective assessments for certain contributing factors, while realizing that subjectivity detracts from dependability, and using only purely objective measurements that largely eliminate intangibles from being considered. Being aware of this dilemma is a prerequisite to deciding how to decide.

15.2   IDENTIFYING ALTERNATIVES

An *alternative* simply refers to a course of action that exists to meet some objective. We looked at identifying and defining alternatives in Chap. 6. The objective in any decision situation is to identify *feasible* alternatives. Feasible alternatives refer to alternatives that, upon preliminary evaluation, offer a viable course of action and that can be implemented within the time, information, and resource constraints of the decision maker.

Finding good feasible alternatives is an important component of the decision process, for the final outcome cannot be better than that allowed by the best alternative. There are many sources to draw upon in identifying and defining alternatives. These include the personal experience of the decision maker, comparisons between the current problem and previous problems successfully solved, examination of relevant literature, and experience of qualified experts.

EXAMPLE 15.1   **Use of T Chart for Screening Alternatives**

Generating alternatives requires the use of techniques such as brainstorming to enhance creativity. A brainstorming session could very well generate a hundred different ways to perform a certain function. Some of the ideas are probably so wild and impractical that they can be easily discarded. Other ideas are filtered through a screening process to test their feasibility. One method of screening is to compare each new alternative with the existing or conventional method by means of a *T chart*. The T chart consists of a list of criteria that an acceptable solution should satisfy and a place to mark whether the new design is better or worse than another design in reference to each criterion. A sample T chart is shown below:

Design *X*: present design	Better	Worse
Initial cost	✔	
Operating cost		✔
Reliability		✔
Appearance	✔	
Comfort		✔

Checkmarks, as used in the sample T chart, are usually adequate to eliminate less desirable ideas in a preliminary screening. Design *X* in the T chart above would probably be rejected because its lower first cost and more attractive appearance are outweighed by its lower reliability, decrease in comfort, and higher operating costs in comparison to the existing design. In a finer T chart screen, percentages replace checkmarks in the comparison.

15.3   IDENTIFYING ATTRIBUTES

The decision-making literature uses the terms *attribute* and *objective* interchangeably. We use *attribute,* on one hand, to represent characteristics associated with essential features of a system. For example, if the feature under consideration is forest habitat preservation, then attributes associated with this concept might be the populations of different animal and bird species, the quality of water in streams, and the acreage and distribution of different tree species in the forest. An *objective,* on the other hand, represents direction of improvement, e.g., improving the water quality in streams or increasing the population of certain animal species.

For an attribute to be useful, we need to define a scale to describe its relative levels. For example, a measure for water quality might be percentage of sedimentation per cubic meter of water, and a measure for species population might be the number per hectare of forest. As mentioned previously, attributes are quantitative when they can be expressed as numbers on a measurement scale, and they are qualitative when they have no natural measurement scale. Defining measurement scales for attributes introduces a new bias, for measurement scales associated with human systems are rarely neutral.

In many situations, it is difficult to define attributes that measure the direct effects of actions. However, it may be possible to develop *proxy attributes* that indirectly measure objectives. These are measures not necessarily of the direct effects but of effects that are directly related to actions that need to be measured. The employee turnover rate is frequently used as a proxy attribute for employee morale; market share, for a company's position and prestige.

Since system evaluation depends on attributes, these must be clearly selected and defined for measurement. Attributes may be developed through examination of relevant literature, observation of similar decision situations, and opinions. The danger in using opinions is that individuals may let their personal feelings take command over what they know are facts. Personal opinions are not necessarily bad sources of advice. In many instances they are the only source of advice. Even when more objective sources can be called upon, opinions may offer valuable insights about the decision problem. Several formal methods of obtaining subjective information are described below.

Consumer survey

A person who has actually bought a product or used services is the most logical source of information about that product's or service's sales appeal. Questions to the buyers are often part of the product's guarantee. Follow-up questionnaires are frequently mailed to purchasers of a large item, such as an automobile. Sometimes surveys are made of potential rather than actual consumers. Replies from this audience must be interpreted carefully, because consumers' tastes change very rapidly and their intentions or desires may be far removed from what they actually do.

Opinions of experts

An experienced sales force is in a position to observe both the actions of suppliers and the behavior of consumers. They can give warnings about changes in trends and the activities of competitors. Sales engineers are particularly well qualified to suggest design changes to improve a product's acceptance. The optimism or pessimism of individuals in the sales force can be balanced by averaging the predictions made by several sales representatives and sales managers.

Many *forecasts* used by executives are made by executives. The effect of individual biases is reduced by generating forecasts as a group effort. The mixture of interests and experience that ensures a good cross section of input makes consensus difficult to obtain.

Delphi method

The Delphi method is a systematic process for combining opinions into a reasoned consensus. The technique was developed at Rand Corporation, and it has gained fame in technical forecasting of future scientific developments. The procedure is to solicit and collate opinions about a certain subject from experts and to feed back digested appraisals to narrow the differences among opinions until near agreement is obtained.

A carefully prepared questionnaire is delivered to a panel of experts from professional specialties that pertain to the decision problem. The survey can be conducted in a group meeting or by mail. Each questionnaire solicits written opinions about specific topics and requests supporting reasons for the opinions. These reasons are summarized by the Delphi moderator to ensure the anonymity of responses and then are returned for consideration by the whole panel. The process is continued until the exchanged arguments and transfer of knowledge forge a consensus prediction. Advocates of the Delphi method claim that the anonymity of written responses preserves the desirable features of a committee of specialists while reducing the "bandwagon" and dominant-personality effects that unduly sway group opinions.

The procedure for identifying attributes is usually a multistep iteration. The iterative procedure may result in elimination of redundant attributes, combination of two or more attributes, or decomposition of an attribute into a number of attributes to facilitate the measurement process. The selected attributes should be[†]

- Complete, covering all aspects of the problem
- Operational, to be meaningfully used in the analysis
- Decomposable, to be broken down into parts for simplification and measurement
- Nonredundant, to avoid double counting of impacts
- Minimal, to minimize the problem dimension

[†]R. L. Keeney and H. Raiffa, *Decisions with Multiple Objectives: Preferences and Value Trade-offs,* John Wiley & Sons, Inc., New York, 1976.

The number of attributes is dependent on the characteristics of the system evaluated. As far as the number of attributes is concerned, minimal, concise, and manageable are the basic qualities sought.

EXAMPLE 15.2   **Nominal Group Process**

The *nominal group process (NGP)*, developed by André Delbecq and Andrew Van de Ven in 1968, is a powerful group technique used effectively in problem definition as well as alternative and attribute identification. It is designed to avoid the unproductive aspects of face-to-face meetings and to stimulate creative thinking. The NGP consists of six steps:

Step 1: Silent idea generation. The participants are given a formal problem statement. They are asked to generate ideas in response to the problem statement. Participants work silently and individually for about 15 minutes.

Step 2: Group round-robin listing of factors. Each individual reads one idea out loud to the group. Ideas are recorded. The process continues until all ideas are recorded. This phase is accomplished without any explanation or questions and comments from the group.

Step 3: Discussion and clarification of factors. Each factor listed in step 2 is discussed by the group. The primary objective is clarification. During the discussion, factors may be combined or new factors may be added to the list.

Step 4: Individual voting. To focus on the most important issues, each participant is asked to select the most important ideas from the list. The selections are collected and displayed.

Step 5: Discussion of voting results. The group discuss the ideas generated in step 4. New ideas may be introduced, but the general focus is on approaching consensus and clarifying misinformation.

Step 6: Final individual voting. Each participant ranks the most important ideas. Often a rating scale such as a 0-to-10 scale (0 = no importance, 10 = absolutely necessary) may be used. The number of factors that participants are directed to select is flexible, and it depends on the problem domain. Individual ratings are collected and tabulated.

EXAMPLE 15.3   **Attribute Selection in Automated Manufacturing**

Today's manufacturing environment is an integrated system of physical, information, and human components. Automated technologies such as flexible manufacturing systems, flexible machining systems, automated material handling, and robotics and vision systems are perceived by many manufacturers as the key to improving manufacturing productivity.

To compare integrated manufacturing systems is a complex and challenging task. Certain characteristics of manufacturing technologies make the comparison process more complex than that required for production technologies in the past. Purely economics-based comparisons are inadequate for these systems. Many of the advantages of newer technologies are not in cost reduction but relate to improved quality, increased manufacturing flexibility, faster delivery, improved information flow, and a more flexible and adaptable work environment. Whereas some of these attributes can be easily measured, others such as flexibility and integration are more difficult to quantify.

The attributes for comparing automated manufacturing technologies can be grouped into three broad categories, as follows:

1. Manufacturing costs
   1.1 Initial cost
       1.1.1 Plant and equipment
       1.1.2 Tooling
       1.1.3 Insurance and property taxes
       1.1.4 Space requirements
       1.1.5 Installation
   1.2 Operating and maintenance
       1.2.1 Operating and maintenance labor
       1.2.2 Hiring and training
       1.2.3 Materials and supplies
       1.2.4 Utilities
   1.3 Other costs
       1.3.1 Supervision
       1.3.2 Shipping, receiving, and distribution
       1.3.3 Scrap and rework
       1.3.4 Inventory holding and shortage
       1.3.5 Production control
       1.3.6 Information requirements
2. Technical attributes
   2.1 Flexibility to changes in market demand
   2.2 Flexibility to incorporate technological enhancements
   2.3 Flexibility to production disruptions
   2.4 Delivery performance
   2.5 Compatibility with existing system
   2.6 Quality
3. Social attributes
   3.1 Group morale
   3.2 Opportunities for individual growth
   3.3 Work environment including safety
   3.4 Management involvement and supervision

Manufacturing costs can be directly measured in dollars or some other monetary unit. Some of the technical attributes can be measured by using a quantifiable scale. For example, delivery performance can be measured by the percentage of orders that are delivered late, quality in terms of percentage of defective units, and flexibility to disruptions in production in terms of lost production time. However, flexibility to adapt to future technologies and changing markets is difficult to quantify and may require the use of a *subjective* scale. Clearly, the social attributes are intangibles. A real need exists to include such attributes in the evaluation and selection of manufacturing technologies.

EXAMPLE 15.4

Attribute Selection in Forest Resource Management

An area of current concern in Canada as well as other countries is the management of both public and private forests. The forest ecosystem represents a value-oriented decision-making environment. The demand for forest resources is affected more by economic and social factors than by any physical characteristics of the resources themselves. The problem involves multiple decision makers and interest groups. Different groups have different interests and different perceptions of the problem. Additional complexity is introduced by the changing values of interest groups over time. Examples include an increase in the demand for recreation and the preservation of old-growth forests for wildlife and other values.

Identifying objectives in forest resource management is a complex task. Here is an example set of objectives:

1. Ecological integrity
   1.1 Maintain habitat variety
   1.2 Maintain healthy forest (free of disease and fire potential)
   1.3 Protect special features, such as old-growth forests
2. Forest resource sustainability
   2.1 Protect fish and wildlife habitat
   2.2 Maintain attractive landscape
   2.3 Protect cultural resources
3. Timber harvesting
   3.1 Practice appropriate temporal harvesting policies
   3.2 Select appropriate silvicultural systems (care and cultivation of forest trees)

Compared to manufacturing technology implementation discussed in Example 15.3, the forest ecosystem is more complex. Reasons for this complexity include multiple interest groups, spatial and temporal dimensions of forest management, social needs and priorities that change over time, difficulty in developing acceptable attributes for the objectives defined above, and amount of data (physical, biological, economic, and social) required to estimate attribute values. Traditionally, the forest resource allocation decision has been treated primarily as an economic decision with the focus on timber-harvesting policies. Today's plans must recognize other objectives in selecting and implementing feasible implementation alternatives.

15.4   ATTRIBUTE WEIGHTING

In any decision environment, not all attributes are likely to be considered equally important. The purpose of attribute weights is to express the importance of each attribute relative to other attributes. A number of attribute-weighting procedures are based on the judgments of the decision makers. Some of these procedures are discussed below.

15.4.1   Equal Weighting

If estimates for attribute weights are not readily available due to resource and time constraints, the equal-weighting scheme can be used to assign initial attribute weights. In the equal-weighting scheme, all attributes are equally important and have equal weights. This is usually followed by sensitivity analysis to determine sensitivity of alternatives to variations in attribute weights.

15.4.2   Ranking Methods

The ranking methods require the decision maker to rank-order the attributes. Each attribute is then assigned a numerical rank. In case of ties, two or more equal ranks may be assigned an averaged value. Rank-sum weighting and rank-reciprocal weighting are two methods used to calculate importance weights by using assigned ranks.

In the rank-sum weighting method, the most important attribute is assigned the highest rank n (where n is the number of attributes). The least important attribute is assigned a rank of 1. If r_i is the rank of attribute i, the importance weight w_i for attribute i is given by

$$w_i = \frac{n - r_i + 1}{\sum\limits_{i=1}^{n} (n - r_i + 1)}$$

In the rank-reciprocal method, the rank of 1 is assigned to the most important attribute and the rank of n to the least important attribute. With the same notation,

$$w_i = \frac{1}{r_i \sum\limits_{i=1}^{n} \dfrac{1}{r_i}}$$

15.4.3 Ratio Method

Similar to the ranking methods, the ratio method starts off by arranging the attributes in a simple rank order. The least important attribute is assigned a weight of 10. The decision maker then assigns weights to other attributes, starting with the next-to-least-important attributes and working up the rank list to the most important attribute, such that the weights assigned reflect the importance of an attribute relative to the least important attribute. For example, if an attribute is considered three times as important as the least important attribute, it is assigned a weight of 30. Attributes considered to be equally important compared with the least important attribute are assigned the same weights. The weights are normalized after all numerical assignments have been made. Thus, if x_i is the numerical weight assigned to attribute i relative to the least important attribute, then the normalized weight w_i for attribute i is given by

$$w_i = \frac{x_i}{\sum\limits_{i=1}^{n} x_i}$$

The ratio method can be used to perform consistency checks on attribute weights. To perform consistency analysis, the least important attribute is dropped from the list of attributes, and the next-lowest attribute in the original rank list is now considered the least important attribute and is assigned a weight of 10. The decision maker is asked to assign weights to other attributes relative to this attribute. To be consistent, the ratios of weights obtained from these iterations should be comparable. The decision maker is asked to revise relative-importance judgments to ensure consistency.

As an example, consider a set of four attributes A, B, C, and D ranked in that sequence in order of decreasing rank order. In the first iteration, D is assigned a weight of 10, and the decision maker is asked to assign weights to C, B, and A that reflect their importance relative to D. Let the weights assigned to C, B, and A be 15, 30, and 40, respectively. Based on this assignment, the ratio of weights B:C is 2:1, A:C is 2.7:1, and A:B is 1.3:1. For a consistency check, D is dropped from the list, and C is assigned a weight of 10. The decision maker assigns weights to B and A relative to C. Let the weight of B relative to C be 30. Then the ratio of weights of B:C is 3:1. A 2:1 ratio was obtained for B:C in the previous iteration when D was the least important attribute. Clearly, in one case B is judged to be twice as important as C and in the other three times more important. Either one or both estimates need to be revised. Similarly, the other ratios can be compared for consistency.

15.4.4 Pairwise Comparison

In the pairwise comparison method, each attribute is paired with every other attribute for the purposes of comparison. A discrete scale is used to represent the degrees of importance. In a three-level scale, the digit 0 indicates *less important,* 1 indicates *equally important,* and 2 indicates *more important.* To illustrate the procedure, assume that the attributes of manufacturing costs, flexibility to change, and compatibility with the existing physical and information system are used to compare alternative production systems. The table below shows the results of pairwise comparison. Each column attribute is compared to each row attribute. The value below the principal diagonal is the complement of the value above the diagonal. Thus 0 is the complement of 2, and 1 is the complement of itself. In the table below, flexibility and cost, and flexibility and compatibility, are considered equally important, while cost is considered to be more important than compatibility. The importance weights are obtained by normalizing the sum of the scores corresponding to each column attribute: sum of scores $= 3 + 2 + 1 = 6$; weight for cost $= \text{cost}_{\text{sum}}/6 = 3/6 = .5$.

	Cost	Flexibility	Compatibility
Cost	—	1	0
Flexibility	1	—	1
Compatibility	2	1	
Sum	3	2	1
Weight	.500	.333	.167

15.4.5 Dunn-Rankin Procedure

The Dunn-Rankin procedure[†] can be used to develop attribute weights based on group input. Consider four attributes to be weighted by 10 decision makers or judges. A pairwise comparison is made of the attributes by each judge independently. A set of values resulting from such a comparison is shown below.

	A	B	C	D
A	—	9	8	6
B	1	—	4	3
C	2	6	—	4
D	4	7	6	—
Rank r_i	7	22	18	13

[†]P. Dunn-Rankin and F. J. King, "Multiple Comparisons in a Simplified Rank Method of Scaling," *Educational and Psychological Measurement,* vol. 29, no. 2, pp. 315–329, 1969.

An entry x_{ij} (i = row attribute, j = column attribute) in the table gives the number of judges who preferred attribute j to i. For example, 9 out of 10 judges preferred B to A. Also note that $x_{ij} + x_{ji}$ equals the number of judges. The rank r_i is the sum of each column.

Let n be the number of attributes and m be the number of judges. Then $m = 10$, $nm = 40$, and range $nm - m = 30$. The computations for attribute weights are shown in the table below:

Attribute i	r_i	(r_i/range)•100	Weight w_i
A	7	23	.116
D	13	43	.216
C	18	60	.302
B	22	73	.367

15.5   ATTRIBUTE VALUE ASSESSMENT

The measurement and assessment of attributes depend largely on the type of attributes. Measurement of quantitative attributes is based on direct measurement and data collection, or numerical value estimation using economic analysis, optimization techniques, and simulation. The assessment of qualitative attributes is generally based on an interval scale.

The techniques for economic analysis discussed in this text can be used to estimate economic attributes. Net present value, internal rate of return, benefit/cost ratio, and payback are some measures that can be used as measurement criteria.

A discussion of the use of optimization techniques in estimating quantitative attributes is beyond the scope of this text. Optimization techniques, such as linear programming, integer programming, and nonlinear programming, can be used to estimate certain types of attributes; examples in manufacturing applications include resource levels, production quantities, and product throughput times.

Because of attribute interaction and the stochastic nature of some attributes, analytical models including economic analysis and optimization techniques may not be adequate to estimate some system attributes. As discussed in Chap. 13, simulation is a powerful technique for analyzing complex systems, for it requires fewer assumptions than do analytical models. For many systems that are too complex to be modeled analytically, simulation becomes the only tool for obtaining relevant answers.

No ideal method has yet been devised to quantify intangibles. Quality point scales with several levels of qualitative terms are commonly used to assign different degrees of impact, agreement, or goodness. A five-level scale consists of *very low, low, average, high,* and *very high.* A standardized rating form that has written descriptions of each level of desirability is the most commonly used method for rating intangibles. The scales typically run from 0 to 10 with explanations of the attributes expected at each interval. Well-composed rating forms define, in easily understood language, the outcome that qualifies an alternative for each numbered rating. For example, government agencies engaged in research solicit bids from internal and outside investigators for conducting studies. A *request for proposals (RFP)* contains a statement of the technical requirements of the work and requests bidders to provide cost estimates, time schedules, and proof of competence. The replies are then evaluated by a board according to how well they meet the criteria of acceptance. A typical guideline for assigning numerical ratings to each criterion is given below:

Score		Description
10 9	Very good	Has a high probability of exceeding all requirements expressed in RFP
8 7 6	Normal	Will most likely meet minimum requirements and scope of work established in RFP
5 4 3	Below normal	May fail to meet stated minimum requirements but is of such a nature that it has correction potential
2 1	Unacceptable	Cannot be expected to meet stated minimum requirements and is of such a nature that drastic revision is necessary for correction

While you are using a rating scale, remember that it is important to keep referring to a mental standard that conforms to each level. In the RFP evaluation, the standards are defined in writing. Each rater likely has a different interpretation of what constitutes perfection, based on personal views and past exposures. It is not vital that all raters have the same absolute limits for their interval scale; it is vital that they be consistent in applying their own scales among alternatives.

A review of past ratings can improve future ratings. A numerical rating system is only as good as the rationale exercised in its use. A rater should be prepared to convince a questioner that the judgment was correct. Since intangible judgments are necessarily fragile, they deserve to be handled with care.

15.6 AGGREGATING ATTRIBUTE VALUES

Several models based on weighted attribute values are available. Multiplicative and exponential models have been proposed, but additive models are widely recommended and used.

The additive weighting method converts the multiattribute problem to a single-dimension problem. The aggregate score associated with each alternative is derived from the relationship

$$U_j = \sum_{i=1}^{n} w_i v_{ij}$$

where U_j = aggregate value for alternative j
   w_i = importance weight for attribute i
   v_{ij} = score of alternative j on attribute i
   n = number of attributes

In the above expression, v_{ij} represents single attribute values that are measured according to the procedures discussed in the previous section. Quantitative attribute values are expressed in different units of measure, such as dollars, days, or percentage of defects. These nonhomogeneous units must be converted to a common scale before the additive weighting model can be used. Also, the qualitative attributes must be converted to this common scale.

A common procedure is to convert all attributes to a 10-point dimensionless scale. Using the same scale to rate qualitative attributes eliminates the step of converting qualitative attributes to the common scale. The zero on this scale represents the least (minimum) attractive value for the attribute that is physically or practically attainable, while 10 represents the most (maximum) attractive attribute value that is practically attainable. The difference between the maximum and minimum values can be used as the basis of linear scale transformation.

Most decisions, personal or organizational, have economic overtones. The additive weighting model treats costs (or revenues) as any other attribute in the attribute set. This amounts to assigning a feasible range of possible values to costs, assigning a weight to cost that reflects its importance compared to other attributes, and then including it in the analysis while using the additive weighting relationship.

The single summary score for each alternative allows competing courses of action to be compared on an equivalent basis. A higher aggregate score signifies a more desirable alternative.

Consider the comparison of three prototypes of a new product design. Five independent attributes have been selected for evaluation: safety, cost, appearance, weight, and reliability. The importance weights of attributes, determined by using one of the weighting methods discussed in Sec. 15.4, are shown in Table 15.1. A cutoff score may be recognized that makes an alternative unacceptable. For example, $20 is considered the top limit for the product cost, and any alternative that exceeds this cutoff level is eliminated regardless of how well it scores on the other attributes.

Cost, weight, and reliability are ratio-scale measurements. Lower cost and lower weight are preferred, although a higher reliability is desired. All attribute measurements are converted to dimensionless numbers by taking a ratio of each attribute value to the best value available among the alternatives for that attribute. The best value is assumed to have a 10 rating. These ratios are used to convert the reliability figures to a 10-point scale:

| **TABLE 15.1** |

Attribute and comparison values for evaluating three product designs

	Safety	**Appearance**	**Cost, $**	**Weight, kg**	**Reliability**
Design 1	8	4	17.56	9.7	.96
Design 2	7	9	9.95	6.2	.81
Design 3	7	7	14.47	6.0	.90
Importance weight	.3	.13	.27	.1	.2
Cutoff value			20		

Design 1 $\qquad$ Design 2 $\qquad$ Design 3

$$\frac{0.96}{0.96} \times 10 = 10 \qquad \frac{0.81}{0.96} \times 10 = 8.4 \qquad \frac{0.90}{0.96} \times 10 = 9.4$$

since .96 is the highest reliability rating among the alternatives. In general, the lower and upper limits on attribute values do not have to be associated with any of the alternatives under consideration; they may represent realistic aspiration levels.

These are the converted cost scores:

Design 1 $\qquad$ Design 2 $\qquad$ Design 3

$$\frac{\$9.95}{\$17.56} \times 10 = 5.7 \qquad \frac{\$9.95}{\$9.95} \times 10 = 10 \qquad \frac{\$9.95}{\$14.47} \times 10 = 6.9$$

since $9.95 is the lowest cost for any alternative. None of the costs exceeded the $20 cutoff level, which would have eliminated an alternative from further consideration. Safety and appearance need no conversion because they are already rated on an interval scale with a top score of 10.

The final step is to multiply the attribute values by their respective importance weights and to add the resulting products for each alternative. The product design with the highest total score is the best alternative. As shown in Table 15.2 (next page), design 2 with a score of 8.62 is preferred to the other two prototypes.

.5.7   SENSITIVITY ANALYSIS

When queried, most decision makers express confidence in their ability but realistically admit that they are not exactly sure how competent they are. No one knows. The reason is that there is seldom a way to determine what the outcome would have been if a different course of action had been taken. Sensitivity analysis attempts to anticipate the consequences of selecting

15.9   PROBABILISTIC ADDITIVE WEIGHTING

The variability in decision outcomes is usually a result of variability associated with estimates of individual parameters. An alternative to sensitivity analysis is to directly incorporate discrete probability estimates into the additive weighting process. The range-of-estimates approach, described in Chap. 11, can be used to assess values of attributes that are reasonably likely to occur and the probability of occurrence associated with these values.

An electronics assembly operation considering three alternative material handling systems will illustrate the procedure. The material handling alternatives A, B, and C are to be evaluated on three attributes: cost, flexibility to change, and compatibility with the current system. The assessment of attribute weights for the three attributes using pairwise comparison was described in Sec. 15.4; the resulting weights were, respectively, .50, .333, and .167.

The attribute values and the results from the application of the additive weighting model, ignoring uncertainty, are shown in the following table. A 0-to-10 scale is used to express values of all three attributes; 10 is the highest attainable value, and 0 is the least attainable value.

Attribute	Weight	Alternative A	B	C
Cost	.500	6	5	9
Flexibility	.333	9	6	7
Compatibility	.167	9	7	3
Aggregate score		7.50	5.67	7.33

Now assume that cost and flexibility are uncertain attributes, whereas estimates for compatibility are fairly accurate. The worst, most likely, and best estimates, along with their associated probabilities for alternative A for cost and flexibility, are summarized as shown below:

	Cost Value	Probability	Flexibility Value	Probability
Worst	3	.3	7	.2
Most likely	6	.5	9	.7
Best	7	.2	9.5	.1

The expected value of cost is

$$\text{EV(cost)} = 3(.3) + 6(.5) + 7(.2)$$
$$= 5.3$$

and the variance of cost is

$$\text{Var(cost)} = (3^2)(.3) + (6^2)(.5) + (7^2)(.2) - (5.3)^2$$
$$= 2.41$$

In the notation used in Sec. 15.6, the expected value of attribute i for alternative j is computed as

$$\text{EV}(v_{ij}) = \sum_{i=1}^{m} p_{ij} x_{ij}$$

where m is the number of possible outcomes and p_{ij} and x_{ij} are the probabilities and outcome values, respectively, of attribute i for alternative j. The variance is computed as

$$\text{Var}(v_{ij}) = \sum_{i=1}^{m} p_{ij} x_{ij}^2 - [\text{EV}(v_{ij})]^2$$

The expected value and variance for flexibility, using the above expressions, are EV(flexibility) = 8.65 and Var(flexibility) = 0.7025.

Once the expected value and variance estimates for attributes are determined, the expected value and variance of the aggregate score for an alternative are calculated from the following expressions, where U_j represents the aggregate score for alternative j and n is the number of attributes:

$$\text{EV}(U_j) = \sum_{i=1}^{n} w_i \text{EV}(v_{ij})$$

$$\text{Var}(U_j) = \sum_{i=1}^{n} w_i^2 \text{Var}(v_{ij})$$

The data for alternative A are summarized below:

Attribute	Weight	Expected value	Variance
Cost	.500	5.3	2.41
Flexibility	.333	8.65	0.7025
Compatibility	.167	8.0	0

The expected value for the aggregate score for alternative A is

$$\begin{aligned} \text{EV}(U_A) &= (.5)(5.3) + (.333)(8.65) + (.167)(8) \\ &= 6.867 \end{aligned}$$

and the variance is

$$\begin{aligned} \text{Var}(U_A) &= (.5)^2(2.41) + (.333)^2(0.7025) + (.167)^2(0) \\ &= 0.68 \end{aligned}$$

The expected values and variances for the other alternatives can be computed similarly.

The shortage of pertinent information is a common handicap in incorporating uncertainty in the additive weighting model. Lack of information may be a result of a scarcity of historical data or the inability to extrapolate past trends to future conditions. In the absence of appropriate data, simple sensitivity analysis discussed in Sec. 15.7 can be used to evaluate the sensitivity of decisions to variations in attribute values.

15.10 JUSTIFICATION OF HIGH-TECHNOLOGY INVESTMENTS

The economics of *computer-integrated manufacturing (CIM)* is becoming more complex as technology advances. A growing set of initials is entering the vocabulary of analysts who evaluate high-technology investments. Among the better-known technologies are *computer-aided process planning (CAPP), computer-assisted design (CAD), computer-aided manufacturing (CAM), group technology (GT), automatic storage/retrieval system (AS/RS), manufacturing resource planning* (MRP II), *computer-aided engineering (CAE), flexible manufacturing system (FMS), computer-aided testing (CAT),* and robotics.

Some of these computer-driven systems are extremely expensive, whereas others are less costly than traditional methods for certain applications. All have the potential to yield very large jumps in productivity. They are usually more productive in terms of labor than manual or conventional automatic machines, offer more consistent and higher levels of quality, reduce scrap, shorten product lead times and manufacturing cycle times, lower inventory levels at both raw-material and in-process stages, allow more flexibility in reacting to demand fluctuations, and provide safer, more comfortable working conditions. Most of the benefits are quantifiable, but data may be difficult to obtain.

When conventional investment-justifying thinking is applied to automated systems, full credit may not be awarded to them. The major omission is the *synergy* that results when several subsystems, such as those listed above, are tied together into one overall system. When components of a system are evaluated individually, only those savings can be counted that were achieved by fitting the new component into the existing layout, which may not have the capacity to fully utilize the automated features of the addition. This process fails to recognize that the cost of a fully integrated system of automated components is greater than the sum of the benefits of its individual parts.

Other benefits of automated equipment may also be neglected because they are difficult to measure. The need for less management attention, more accurate controls, greater reliability, and the vastly increased flexibility of CIM components are difficult to determine, especially before the system is installed.

Considerations involved in justifying the acquisition of high-technology equipment can be illustrated by an evaluation of an automatic material handling system. Traditionally, automatic storage and retrieval systems have been justified by using savings in labor, inventory, and building costs to offset the project purchase price and operating cost of the equipment. Savings generally are grouped into two categories: hard and soft savings. Hard savings are those that are readily provable and measurable, leaning heavily on material-handling labor and building-occupancy cost. Other savings areas, principally indirect labor and inventory savings, are usually considered to be soft savings and are sometimes excluded from formal justification calculations.

The key obstacle to including indirect labor, inventory savings, damage control, response time, flexibility, and other soft benefits can be summarized in one word—*credibility*. First, confusion exists about the relation of system functions to the overall benefits that can be achieved by integrating AS/RS with automated production. Then, since benefits tend to be concentrated in areas that historically have not been well measured, people charged with preparing justifications do not know how or where to gather information. Finally, even if the savings are quantified, top management often does not believe that the savings will materialize, because of past failures to realize promised benefits from computerized equipment.

Because they are attuned to technological considerations and systems thinking, engineering economists tend to realize the significance of soft benefits and are prepared to search for them. The challenge is to be able to substantiate the soft savings to the satisfaction of the proposal reviewers. A set of attributes for justifying high-technology investments was discussed in Example 15.3.

15.11   REVIEW EXERCISES AND DISCUSSIONS

EXERCISE 1

PC/LAN (personal computer/local-area network) systems are changing the nature of information system design in production and office environments. These systems are no longer required to survive; they are needed to successfully compete.

A PC/LAN system consists of a core of one or two PCs that act as memory banks or *file servers* for any number of other PCs and workstations cabled to one another through a LAN. A PC/LAN system enables multiple-user operation, offers a much lower cost alternative, and is easier to use and implement than a mini or mainframe computer system.

A wide range of *packaged* PC/LAN systems are now commercially available that are developed, continuously enhanced, and maintained by companies distributing these systems. An important question for PC/LAN users is the selection of an appropriate system that meets their current and future needs.

A first step in this evaluation process is to identify attributes for comparing alternative PC/LAN systems. Attributes that can be used for this comparison process include the following:

1. *Installation and operating costs.* A number of different cost elements are included in this attribute: hardware, software, hardware and software maintenance, installation, user training, operating personnel, and other support costs.
2. *Functionality.* Refers to the technical features (hardware and software) and the functions and job applications performed by the system.
3. *Performance.* Capability of a system to perform the intended function in an accurate and timely manner.
4. *Ease of use.* Ability to effectively use the system easily (with minimal training).
5. *Connectivity.* Ability of the system to interface with other applications and systems.
6. *Flexibility.* Ability of the system to accommodate new applications and user needs over time.
7. *Reliability.* Ability of the system to perform its intended function for a specified period and to return to operational status after a failure within a specified time.
8. *Security.* Ability to provide access control against unauthorized use.

The choice among different PC/LAN systems is a complex one. The decision must rest on business needs and the ability of the system to help achieve organizational objectives. For most organizations this includes cost performance, quality performance, and on-time delivery.

EXERCISE 2

An independent data processing company is planning an image improvement and business expansion campaign. Three courses of action have been proposed:

A_1 Develop a staff to increase personal contacts with current and proposed clients; offer short courses and educational programs on the benefits of modern data processing methods.

A_2 Hire a staff to put out a professional newsletter about data processing activities; volunteer data processing services for community and charity projects.

A_3 Hire personnel to develop new service areas and offer customized service to potential customers; donate consulting time to charitable organizations.

Only one alternative can be implemented, owing to budgetary limitations.

The outcomes for each alternative are rated according to desired characteristics, and the importance of each criterion is ranked as shown below, where effectiveness and importance are rated on a 0-to-10 scale; 10 is the top rating:

	Annual cost, $	Immediate effectiveness	Long-range effectiveness
A_1	250,000	9	7
A_2	150,000	8	6
A_3	180,000	6	9
Importance	3	10	6

Using the additive model, determine the overall rankings for the three alternatives.

SOLUTION 2

The first step is to convert the annual cost to a dimensionless number; the least expensive alternative is, in effect, given the top rating of 10 by using it as the numerator in each of the cost/criterion ratios. The converted cost values are calculated as follows:

$$A_1 \qquad\qquad\qquad A_2 \qquad\qquad\qquad A_3$$

$$\frac{\$150,000}{\$250,000} \times 10 = 6 \qquad \frac{\$150,000}{\$150,000} \times 10 = 10 \qquad \frac{\$150,000}{\$180,000} \times 10 = 8.3$$

The other criteria already have interval-scale ratings and are consequently multiplied directly by their importance ratings. These are the aggregate values for the three alternatives:

$$A_1: \quad 6(3) + 9(10) + 7(6) \ = 150$$
$$A_2: \quad 10(3) + 8(10) + 6(6) = 146$$
$$A_3: \quad 8.3(3) + 6(10) + 9(6) = 139$$

The narrow edge given to A_1 over A_2 suggests that the subjective values used in the comparison model must be appraised carefully. For instance, increasing the importance rating for cost from 3 to 4, with all other figures unchanged, creates the same overall rating for the top two alternatives—156. Such tests of sensitivity reveal how large a shift in a factor is required to alter the preference from one option to another.

EXERCISE 3

The toughest part of a decision analysis is often the act of getting started. Inertia is a physical law that seems to have a counterpart in mental motion. Once mental activity gets underway and directed, things happen. It is comparatively easy to keep them happening after that first movement, even when there is an uncomfortable suspicion that not enough is known about the situation. As the solving process progresses, the uneasiness may be accompanied by frustrations in correlating facts and drawing meaningful interpretations from data. Better organization of data alleviates some of the difficulties by highlighting pertinent information. *Cause-and-effect (C&E)* diagrams assist in defining a problem by categorizing related factors to make their influence more observable.

In most situations the basic problem is known. The question concerns not how a mechanism works to convert inputs to outputs but which inputs (causes) are needed to solve the problem or to accomplish the mission to produce the wanted outputs (effects). Specific alternatives are not identified in the initial investigation. The characteristics (attributes) associated with the problem are identified and noted on the diagram. The C&E diagram generally leads to identification of potential solutions.

The visual impact tends to strengthen an investigation by suggesting additional considerations associated with the factors already recorded. Familiarity gained by the diagramming exercise reveals what data are needed to compare alternative courses of action.

The mechanics of constructing a C&E diagram are elementary, but the mental effort preceding the drawing is demanding. The first step is to develop a statement of the problem, situation, or objective. This is entered in a six-sided box shown in Fig. 15.1. Labeled ribs are then drawn to or from the cause-and-effect spine (bold arrows in Fig. 15.1) to specify the main causes and effects. Short definitions in ovals at the end of the rib arrows identify these main factors. Finally, smaller arrows identifying subfactors run to or from the main ribs, and, in turn, subfactor arrows can lead to or from these to provide greater detail. The construction procedure is illustrated in the following example.

The provincial Department of Vocational Training sent an industrial engineer to a local sheltered workshop to help overcome a production problem. The shop serves as a rehabilitation center for disabled workers. It provides training and work for the disabled in assembly operations and in the production of wood products such as pallets, packing cases, wishing wells, and picnic tables. The work is purposely designed to emphasize hand labor, and the processes consequently employ minimal mechanization.

A quality control problem occurred when the center began work on a contract to produce berry boxes. The customer threatened to cancel the contract if sturdier boxes were not produced within 1 month. The first analysis of the problem identified the causes and effects shown in Fig. 15.2. An obvious solution appeared to be to add an inspection station for outgoing boxes to ensure the use of good wood and adequate fastening. Then it was noticed that attention was being focused strictly on effects, not causes. Maybe it would be better to have the workers inspect as they produced (note 1 at the top of the diagram).

As a result of this internal inspection idea, attention was paid to the need for better physical facilities, brighter lights, lower work tables for wheelchair workers, jigs for more accurate stapling, etc. These and other considerations led to the addi-

FIGURE 15.1
Structure and purpose of a C&E diagram.

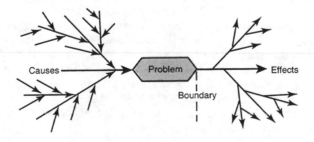

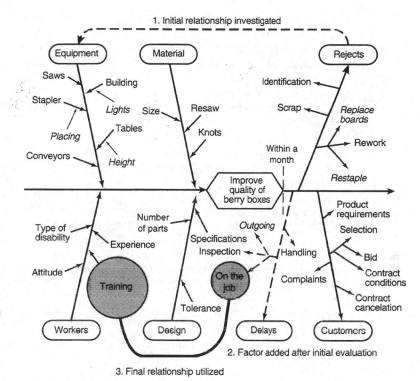

FIGURE 15.2
Initial and revised C&E diagram representing the production of berry boxes in a rehabilitation center. The steps in the solution are numbered in the order of their development.

tion of a new effect—delays (shown in Fig. 15.2 by note 2 and dashed arrows). To minimize delays, a suggestion was made to improve the motion patterns of workers. Finally, the subject of training was considered, and it was then recognized that training was currently directed to general skills, but little effort was made to tell individual workers what was expected of them and what particularly should be watched in satisfying each production contract.

Thus, the berry box problem was solved simply by informing the workers what was needed and how to do it with existing facilities. The answer is indicated by the connected and circled factors in the lower portion of the diagram. No investment funds were needed. Perhaps the answer may appear patently obvious, but how many times have sophisticated solutions been installed where a simple change could have produced the same results at lower cost and with less loss of dignity?

EXERCISE 4
Manufacturing costs are generally an important attribute in a production environment. As discussed earlier, the additive weighting model treats cost made like other attributes by assigning a range of possible values to it, assessing its importance weight with respect to other attributes, and then including it in the analysis with the additive model. An alternative approach for handling cost is to treat cost separately from other attributes until the end of the analysis and then to explore the sensitivity of the evaluation process to cost. A similar procedure for cost/utility analysis was examined in Chap. 8 (Review Exercise 4).

The procedure[†] consists in evaluating the aggregate score (or utility) for each alternative based on all attributes except cost. The resulting aggregate values are then mapped against cost, yielding a feasible cost/utility criteria space. As a first step, the procedure uses the concept of *dominance*. The aggregate values represent measures of desirability; obviously, one would not like to pay more for an alternative unless there were an increase in desirability. Consequently, alternatives that are inferior to others in cost and desirability can be eliminated from further consideration.

The set of noninferior alternatives is then evaluated by incremental cost/utility analysis. The objective is to select an alternative from the nondominated set that balances the increase in aggregate (utility) value against the incremental cost of a utility increase.

To illustrate the cost/utility tradeoff procedure, consider the following example. A manufacturing organization is considering the transition from functional layout to cellular manufacturing. Preliminary studies based on component classification schemes have indicated six potential cell configurations (alternatives). The objective is to evaluate the six alternatives on five attributes: changeover costs (A_1), space adequacy (A_2), flexibility in handling potential changes in workload (A_3), flexibility of the space layout to future expansion (A_4), and work flow pattern (A_5).

SOLUTION 4

The values of attributes A_2, A_3, A_4, and A_5, transformed to a dimensionless scale of range 0 to 100, and the changeover costs A_1 are shown in the following table. Also shown are the normalized importance weights for attributes A_2, A_3, A_4, and A_5.

| Attribute | Importance weight | Alternative | | | | | |
		C_1	C_2	C_3	C_4	C_5	C_6
A_1		$50,000	$53,500	$54,800	$61,000	$70,000	$53,400
A_2	.42	64	48	44	70	36	43
A_3	.25	60	50	48	50	48	50
A_4	.18	32	64	14	31	91	47
A_5	.15	6	59	76	66	36	53

The aggregate utility scores, based on attributes A_2 through A_5, for each of the six alternative cell configurations are computed by the additive weighting model. The aggregate scores and the changeover costs are summarized below, in ascending order of costs, and are shown graphically in Fig. 15.3:

[†]W. Edwards and J. R. Newman, *Multiattribute Evaluation,* pp. 81–89, copyright © 1982 by Sage Publications, Inc. Reprinted by permission of Sage Publications, Inc.

Alternative	Aggregate utility scores	Changeover costs, $
C_1	48.54	50,000
C_6	46.97	53,400
C_2	53.03	53,500
C_3	44.40	54,800
C_4	57.38	61,000
C_5	48.90	70,000

The approach uses a continuous piecewise-linear function for the surface representing the noninferior solutions. Any alternatives that fall below the concave line segment in Fig. 15.3 are eliminated from further analysis. The converse is also true. Any new alternative plotted on or above the curve would become a contender. Depending on its location, it could cause previous contenders to be dominated. Figure 15.3 shows that cell configurations C_3, C_5, and C_6 can be eliminated from consideration.

The table below lists the three contending alternatives, in order of increasing utilities and costs. Also shown are the successive differences in utilities and costs for the three contenders. The rightmost column shows the ratio of cost increment to utility increment and is, therefore, the dollar value of one utility point. Specifically, it is the dollar value for one utility point that would cause the decision maker to prefer the higher-cost alternative to the lowest-cost alternative. With respect to Fig. 15.3, the ratios represent the reciprocals of the slopes of the linear segments of the curve. If the dollar value of 1 utility point is less than $780, alternative C_1 is the preferred choice; if it is between $780 and $1724, alternative C_2 is the preferred choice; and if it is greater than $1724, alternative C_4 is the preferred choice.

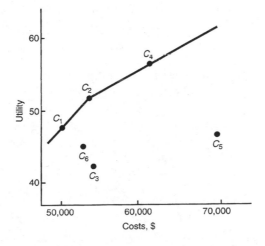

FIGURE 15.3
Graphical representation of aggregate utility values versus costs.

Alternative	Aggregate utility	Costs, $	Utility increment	Cost increment, $	Cost increment/ utility increment, $
C_1	48.54	50,000			
C_2	53.03	53,500	4.49	3500	779.51
C_4	57.38	61,000	4.35	7500	1724.14

Estimating the dollar value of 1 utility point is a difficult task. However, this judgment need not be made with much precision. The decision maker is asked to select an attribute about which he or she has firm and definite opinions. The decision maker is then asked to indicate the money that it would be worth to improve that attribute from its worst to its best acceptable value. Suppose that the attribute selected in this example is space adequacy (A_2) and that the decision maker would be willing to pay $60,000 to improve this value from 0 to 100 (worst value to best value on the transformed scale). Thus, a 100-point change in A_2 will change the aggregate utility score by $(0.42)(100) = 42$ points. The increase in aggregate utility of 42 points is worth $60,000; hence a 1-point change in utility is worth $60,000/42 = 1429. Based on this value, alternative C_2 is the preferred alternative.

15.12   PROBLEMS

15.1 Identify an attribute set for some of the problem situations listed below. Define an appropriate measure for each attribute.
  (a) Selecting a personal computer for your home and personal use
  (b) Selecting a job following graduation from college
  (c) Purchasing your first home
  (d) Selecting a transportation system for a project engineering manager of a construction company

15.2 For each of the situations selected in Prob. 15.1, identify a set of feasible alternatives, develop attribute weights for the attributes identified in Prob. 15.1, and then use the additive weighting model to compare the alternatives.

15.3 Review Exercise 1 presented attributes for comparing PC/LAN systems. Identify a number of LAN alternatives for your work environment. Define appropriate measures for each attribute, and estimate attribute values for each of the alternatives. Compare the alternatives, using the additive weighted model.

15.4 The provincial Transportation Department is planning to construct several highway rest stops. The purpose of such stops is to improve highway safety by encouraging motorists to get out of their cars and relax for a few minutes during long trips. The locations and appearance of the rest stops largely determine how much they are used. Identify attributes required to compare alternative sites and designs for rest stops. To get you started, some of the attributes are location, construction, design, upkeep, and safety.

15.5 Many innovative ideas have been proposed to solve the problems of intracity transportation. A poll to determine what consumers believe are the most important characteristics of a carrier-based city transportation service revealed the following attributes:

- Arrive and leave on schedule
- Have a seat for the whole trip
- No transfers during trip
- Low fares, comparable with the cost of using a car
- Shelters at pickup points
- Available at all hours
- Use of direct routes to shorten travel time
- Easy way to pay fares
- Space for packages
- Adjustable seats
- Clean vehicle interiors
- Adjustable air, light, and sound
- Coffee, refreshments, and reading material on board
- Stylish vehicle exterior

Develop attribute weights for the attributes, using one of the attribute weighting methods described in this chapter. Identify alternatives for intracity transportation and compare these, using the additive weighting model.

15.6 Five attributes have been identified to compare alternative bar-coding systems in an electronics operation:

A Cost
B Label size capabilities
C Vendor service capabilities
D Bar-code language capabilities
E Print quality

The following list of preferences was developed with the help of the manufacturing manager ($\succ$ means *preferred to*).

$$A \succ B \quad B = C \quad C \prec D \quad D = E$$
$$A \succ C \quad B = D \quad C \prec E$$
$$A \succ D \quad B \prec E$$
$$A \succ E$$

Use these rankings to determine the relative importance of the attributes.

15.7 Given the following matrix of outcomes for alternatives and attributes (higher values preferred for all attributes except A_1), which alternative will be selected if (a) all attributes are equally weighted and (b) A_2, A_3, and A_4 are equally weighted but A_1 is twice as important as A_2 (or A_3 or A_4)?

Alternative	Attribute			
	A_1	A_2	A_3	A_4
X_1	$10,000	7	8	Good
X_2	12,000	7	7	Very good
X_3	8,000	6	5	Fair
X_4	15,000	9	8	Excellent
Minimum acceptable value			5	Good

15.8 Three designs have been proposed for a new type of can opener. Careful studies have been conducted to evaluate the degree to which each design meets the desired attribute. The characteristics with familiar measurements were determined by design engineers. Opinions of many people were collected to obtain interval-scale ratings for intangible characteristics. The results are shown below:

Attribute	Design A	Design B	Design C
Cost (minimize)	$3.42	$5.84	$9.88
Cleanability (minimize time)	3.3 minutes	1.8 minutes	3.0 minutes
Reliability (maximize)	0.78	0.91	0.99
Size (minimize)	102 cubic inches	102 cubic inches	320 cubic inches
Appearance (maximize)	6	7	9
Safety (maximize)	7	9	9

(a) Assuming that all attributes are rated equally important, use the additive weighting model to determine the preferred design.

(b) Select importance weights for the attributes, using the ranking or the rating procedures, and apply the additive weighting model to determine the preferred design. Compare the results from part *a* with calculations based on your importance weights.

15.9 Prospective sites for a new chemical plant have been narrowed to three locations. The attribute criteria for each alternative and the importance of the attributes are shown in the following table. Higher interval-scale ratings show a preference. Which site is apparently more attractive? Comment on the sensitivity of the choice.

Attribute	Alternative			Importance weight
	Site 1	Site 2	Site 3	
Labor supply	2	8	9	9
Raw materials	3	10	5	8
Transportation	8	7	9	7
Cost of land	$200,000	$700,000	$400,000	5
Building costs	$2,000,000	$3,800,000	$1,800,000	6
Annual taxes and utility costs	$60,000	$120,000	$80,000	7
Climate	7	6	4	5

15.10 After a recent visit by occupational health and safety inspectors, a company must install better ventilation and filtering equipment or replace existing machines with newer versions having built-in controls. The costs of two alternatives that will satisfy safety codes are listed below:

	Add ventilation equipment to existing plant	Install new, improved machines
First cost	$80,000	$420,000
Present value of old machines	$150,000	$0
Economic life remaining	4 years	9 years
Salvage value at end of life	$0	$70,000
Added annual maintenance cost	$7,000	$0
Total annual operating costs	$36,000	$25,000

The company desires a rate of return of 9 percent on investments to improve operations and owing to current cash-availability problems seeks to minimize major capital allocations. Therefore, a priority system has been established to rate the desirability of alternative investments based on need, immediate cash outlays (net first cost), and total present worth, with relative-importance ratings of 10, 10, and 5, respectively. Both alternatives have the same score for need—10.

Assuming a before-tax economic evaluation for a 9-year study period, which alternative is preferred?

15.11 Sites for a new research laboratory have been narrowed to three locales. The construction cost of the plant will be approximately the same regardless of the location. However, the costs of land and intangible factors largely applicable to personnel recruitment vary considerably from one location to another. Based on the following figures, indicate which site should be selected.

Attribute	Site 1	Site 2	Site 3	Importance
Availability of technicians	7	10	2	10
Adequacy of contractors	5	9	5	8
Proximity to a university	10 km	40 km	30 km	8
Cost of land	$300,000	$400,000	$50,000	6
Recreational potential	7	2	10	4
Climate	6	1	9	2
Transportation	9	10	5	2

15.12 An electronics company would like to use a storage system for storing order archival data. The archival system stores information on a product's specifications, production sequence, and operators used in its production. This information is used in processing customer-returned defective items and assessing product quality and operator efficiency.

A manufacturing engineer has identified the following alternative systems:

S_1 Paper-based system (which is the current system).
S_2 Paper to microfiche system using in-house resources. Use of this system will require the purchase of a microfiche printer and reader system.
S_3 Paper to microfiche system using a service bureau, which may be able to provide faster service than in-house processing.
S_4 Magnetic tape to microfiche using a service bureau, where the company provides the magnetic tapes.
S_5 Computer to optical disk using in-house resources; this alternative will be able to store as much as 640 megabytes on a single disk but will require initial investment in computer and optical disk hardware and training and support.
S_6 Magnetic tape to optical disk using a service bureau, where the company provides the magnetic disks.

Five attributes have been identified for comparing the alternative systems:

A_1 Implementation cost: purchase and setup costs
A_2 Operating cost: maintenance, supplies, and service bureau fees
A_3 Staffing cost: cost of company staff to operate and maintain the system
A_4 Data accessibility: ease and timeliness of accessing information
A_5 Space: physical space required to store the system and records

The engineer has collected the following information on the six alternatives. All costs are on an annual basis. Also shown are the normalized attribute weights that the engineer has been able to assess through a survey of the system users.

	A_1	A_2	A_3	A_4	A_5
S_1	0	$1,213	$6,250	Poor	Poor
S_2	$2,000	12,000	36,000	Good	Good
S_3	2,000	5,460	2,500	Good	Good
S_4	2,000	3,000	2,500	Good	Good
S_5	17,923	0	1,923	Excellent	Very good
S_6	600	10,920	0	Very good	Excellent
Attribute weights	.30	.27	.24	.12	.07

(a) Use the additive weighting model to determine the preferred alternative.
(b) Explore the sensitivity of results to ±30 percent variations in weights for implementation costs, operating costs, and staffing costs.

15.13 An industrial engineer for a paper manufacturing company has developed three alternative layout designs for the packaging section of the plant. The three layouts are to be compared according to three attributes: configuration cost, work area flexibility, and product flow. The layouts were scored on each attribute with the help of manufacturing personnel. The results, converted to a 0-to-10 desirability scale with 10 being most desirable, are summarized below:

Layout	Attribute		
	Cost	**Flexibility**	**Product flow**
L_1	10	1	6
L_2	2	8	8
L_3	5	8	7

Cost was considered to be three times more important than flexibility and as important as product flow. Product flow was indicated to be twice as important as flexibility. Which layout alternative is selected by using the additive weighting model?

GLOSSARIES

1. Terms Commonly Used in Engineering Economics
2. Glossaire
3. Equation Symbols
4. Equations
5. Probability Concepts

GLOSSARY 1   **TERMS COMMONLY USED IN ENGINEERING ECONOMICS**

Accounting life   The period of time over which the asset cost will be allocated by the accountant.

Amortization   1. (*a*) As applied to a capitalized asset, the distribution of the initial cost by periodic charges to operations, as in depreciation; (*b*) the reduction of a debt by either periodic or irregular payments. 2. A plan to pay off a financial obligation according to some prearranged program.

Annual equivalent   In the time value of money, one of a sequence of equal end-of-year payments that would have the same financial effect when interest is considered as another payment or sequence of payments.

Annuity   1. An amount of money payable to a beneficiary at regular intervals for a prescribed time out of a fund reserved for that purpose. 2. A series of equal payments occurring at equal periods of time.

Assets   Resources of any kind owned by a company that are of value to the company.

Balance sheet   A display of the monetary values of a firm at a given time that equates assets to liabilities plus net worth.

Benefit/cost analysis An analysis in which all consequences of the investment are measured in or converted to economic terms.

Benefits Consequences of an investment either measured in or converted to economic terms.

Bond A means for an organization to raise money; most bonds bear interest semi-annually and are redeemable for a specified maturity value at a given date.

Bond valuation The present worth of the cash flow streams of dividends (interest) plus the discounted value of the bond redemption payment.

Book value Original cost of an asset less the accumulated depreciation.

Break-even chart A graphic representation of the relation between total income and total costs for various levels of production and sales, indicating areas of profit and loss.

Break-even point The rate of operations, output, or sales at which income will barely cover expenses.

Capital 1. The financial resources involved in establishing and sustaining an enterprise or a project. 2. Wealth that may be utilized to economic advantage.

Capital budgeting The allocation of funds to projects.

Capital cost allowance (CCA) Amount allowed by the Income Tax Act of Canada for depreciation expense.

Capital cost tax factor (CCTF) Coefficient used to calculate the present worth of tax savings (shields) due to the capital cost allowance.

Capital gains (losses) Profits (losses) on the sale of capital assets.

Capital gain or capital loss The gain or loss resulting from the sale of an asset. These are short-term if the asset is held for less than 1 year and long-term if held longer than 1 year.

Capitalized cost The present worth of a uniform series of periodic costs that continue for an indefinitely long time (hypothetically infinite).

Capital recovery 1. The act of charging periodically to operations amounts that will ultimately equal the amount of capital expenditure. 2. Replacement of the original cost of an asset plus interest. 3. The process of regaining the new investment in a project by means of revenue in excess of the costs from the project.

Capital recovery factor A factor used to calculate the sum of money required at the end of each of a series of periods to regain the net investment plus the compounded interest on the unrecovered balance.

Cash flow 1. The real dollars passing into and out of the treasury of a financial venture. 2. The flowback of profit plus depreciation from a given project.

Cash flow diagram A graphic representation of engineering economic decision data to facilitate problem understanding.

Cause-and-effect (C&E) diagram A diagram that displays the causes of a situation and the resulting effects.

Challenger The proposed property or equipment that is being considered as a replacement for the presently owned property or equipment (defender).

Common stocks Part of the capital of a business, which furnishes variable dividends and partial control through voting rights.

Compound-amount factor   1. The function of interest rate and time that determines the compound amount from a stated initial sum. 2. A factor that when multiplied by the single sum or uniform series of payments will give the future worth at compound interest of that single sum or series.

Compounding, continuous   1. A compound-interest situation in which the compounding period is zero and the number of periods is infinitely great. 2. A mathematical procedure for evaluating compound-amount factors based on a continuous interest function rather than discrete interest periods.

Compound interest   1. The type of interest that is periodically added to the amount of investment (or loan) so that subsequent interest is based on the cumulative amount. 2. The interest charges under the condition that interest is charged on any previous interest earned in any time period as well as on the principal.

Constant (or real) dollars   Cash flows from which the effect of inflation has been eliminated.

Consumers' surplus   The difference between what consumers actually pay for a public good or service and the maximum they would be willing to pay.

Contingency-dependent alternative   An alternative for which acceptance is dependent on the simultaneous acceptance of one or more related alternatives.

Correlation analysis   A study of the degree of relationship existing between variables.

Cost-effectiveness analysis   A diagnosis that includes all prospective consequences of a proposed investment, economic as well as noneconomic.

Cost index   A dimensionless number that indicates how cost for a class of items changes over time.

Cost of capital   The expense involved in borrowing capital, usually expressed as a percentage.

Costs   Consequences of an investment either measured in or converted to economic terms.

Cutoff rate of return   The after-tax rate of return determined by management that is based on the supply and demand for funds and will be used as a criterion for approving projects or investments; may or may not equal the minimum attractive rate of return.

Cyclic replacement   The replacement of an asset on a cyclic time basis based on a prior analysis to find the optimum cyclic time length, usually based on operational-cost minimization.

Debt   Portion of the capital that is borrowed including bonds and long-term notes.

Decisions under certainty   Decisions that assume complete information and no uncertainty connected with the analysis of the decisions.

Decisions under risk   Decisions for which the analyst elects to consider several possible futures whose probabilities can be estimated.

Decisions under uncertainty   Decisions for which the analyst elects to consider several possible futures, the probabilities of which cannot be estimated.

Decision tree   A graphical representation of the anatomy of a decision showing the interplay among a present decision, chance events, possible future decisions, and their results or payoffs.

Declining-balance depreciation A method of computing depreciation in which the annual charge is a fixed percentage of the depreciated book value at the beginning of the year to which the depreciation applies.

Defender Presently owned property or equipment that is being considered for replacement.

Deferred annuity A series of payments in which the first payment does not occur until later than the end of the first period.

Delphi procedure A systematic process for combining opinions into a reasoned consensus.

Dependent Events or alternatives that are related to each other in any way that influences the selection process.

Depletion 1. A form of capital recovery applicable to extractive property (e.g., mines). Can be on a unit-of-output basis just as straight-line depreciation relates to original or current appraisal of extent and value of deposit. 2. A lessening of the value of an asset because of a decrease in the quantity available. Similar to depreciation except that it refers to such natural resources as coal, oil, and timber in forests.

Depreciable property Property that is allowed a depreciation deduction or that can be amortized.

Depreciation 1. (*a*) Decline in value of a capitalized asset; (*b*) a form of capital recovery applicable to a property with 2 or more years' life span, in which an appropriate portion of the asset's value is periodically charged to current operations. 2. The loss of value because of obsolescence or attrition. In accounting, the allocation of this loss of value according to some plan.

Deterioration Condition of an asset that forces asset replacement; condition is manifested through excessive operating costs, increased maintenance costs, or higher rejection rates.

Direct cost The traceable cost that can be segregated and allocated against specific products, operations, or services.

Discounted cash flow 1. The present worth of a sequence in time of sums of money when the sequence is considered as a flow of cash into and/or out of an economic unit. 2. An investment analysis that compares the present worth of projected receipts and disbursements occurring at designated future times in order to estimate the rate of return from the investment or project.

Dumping A condition where a manufacturer sells a portion of the output at one sales price and the remaining output at a lower sales price.

Economic life The time, extending from the date of installation to the date of retirement from the intended service, over which a prudent owner expects to retain the property, in order to obtain a minimum cost.

Effective income tax rate Combined tax rate that includes federal, state, and possibly city taxes (also referred to as the **effective composite tax rate** or **combined marginal income tax rate).**

Effectiveness 1. The degree to which a strategic. or tactical plan achieves economic targets. 2. Consequences of an investment not measured in economic terms, e.g., reliability, safety, customer satisfaction.

Equity Portion of capital that belongs to the owners including retained earnings and common and preferred stocks.

Excise taxes Charges imposed on the *production* of certain products such as tobacco and alcohol.

Expected value A weighted mean of the possible outcomes of a random variable, with the probability outcomes used as weights.

External rate of return A rate of return that is feasible from the current economic conditions that is then assumed to be the rate of return for project fund reinvestments.

Face value A stated amount for which a bond may be redeemed at maturity.

First cost The initial cost of a capitalized property, including transporta- tion, installation, preparation for service, and other related initial expenditures.

Fixed cost A cost that tends to be unaffected by changes in the number of units produced.

Future (or actual) dollars Cash flows in the amount of money units actually exchanged at the time of transaction. Compare with **constant dollars** that have the effect of inflation removed from them.

Future worth 1. The equivalent value at a designated future date based on the time value of money. 2. The monetary sum at a given future time that is equivalent to one or more sums at given earlier times when interest is compounded at a given rate.

Goodwill Value inherent in the fixed and favorable consideration of customers arising from an established, well-known, and well-conducted business.

Gradient series A pattern of receipts or disbursements for a series that has a uniform linear (arithmetic or constant) or geometric increase in each time period.

Half-year rule For designated asset classes, Revenue Canada regulations reduce first year's depreciation to one-half the capital cost allowance (CCA).

Holding cost Total annual cost of holding an item in storage and interest foregone on money invested in the item.

Income taxes Taxes on personal and corporate income, usually in increasingly higher rates for higher incomes.

Incremental return The return expected for *additional* investment in an alternative over the amount invested in a smaller-investment alternative that is mutually exclusive from the larger-investment alternative.

Independence A condition where acceptance or rejection of an alternative has no effect on the acceptability of any other alternative.

Indirect cost The traceable or common cost that is not allocated against specific products, operations, or services but is allocated against all products, operations, or services by a predetermined formula.

Inflation A persistent rise in the general price level, usually resulting in the decline of purchasing power.

Intangibles Things that are difficult to define and measure quantitatively, such as employee morale and customer satisfaction.

Interest 1. (*a*) Financial share in a project or enterprise; (*b*) periodic compensation for the lending of money; (*c*) in engineering economic study, synonymous with required return, expected profit, or charge for the use of capital. 2. The cost for the use of capital. Sometimes referred to as the **time value of money**.

Interest rate, effective The true value of interest rate computed by equations for compound interest for a 1-year period.

Interest rate, continuous Effective interest rate when the number of compounding periods per year approaches infinity.

Interest rate, nominal Annual interest rate computed as the product of interest rate per period and the number of periods per year.

Internal rate of return 1. The rate of return on the unrecovered balance of the investment in a situation where the terminal balance is zero. 2. The interest rate at which the present worth of the cash flows of a project are zero.

Investment cost or first cost Capital required for the activities in the acquisition phase.

Investment risk profile A graphical representation that reveals the likelihood for an investment to realize various net present-worth returns.

Investment tax credit A reduction in income tax liability allowed for specific types of interest.

Isoquant An indifference line or curve which shows the combination of two or more variables that make the present worth of a proposal neither positive nor negative (indifference condition). It is used in studying two-parameter variations in sensitivity analysis.

Lease A contract between the owner of an asset, called a *lessor*, and a *lessee*, who makes periodic payments for the right to use the asset.

Life-cycle costing Study that gives attention to both direct and indirect cash flows over the complete life of a project.

Macroeconomics The study of entire economic systems in terms of income, flow of money, consumption, and general prices.

Marginal cost 1. The cost of one additional unit of production, activity, or service. 2. The rate of change of cost with production or output.

Marginal revenue 1. Money received from selling an additional unit of production, activity, or service. 2. The rate of change of revenue with production or output.

Microeconomics The study of activity in very small segments of the economy, such as a particular firm or household.

Midyear accounting convention Convention, often required for depreciation calculations, where cash flow in the first year is assumed to begin at the midpoint of that year and cash flow is assumed to end at the midpoint of the year following the actual cash flow's termination (at year $N + 1$).

Minimum attractive (acceptable) rate of return (MARR) The effective annual rate of return on investment which must meet the investor's threshold of acceptability.

Mixed investment An investment that has both positive and negative project balances when those balances are calculated by using a potential IRR value (root of the present-worth equation $= i^*$).

Modified accelerated cost recovery system (MACRS) Method prescribed by the Tax Reform Act of 1986 for the depreciation of property placed in service after 1986. It provides specific schedules for the depreciated recovery of investments in various property classes.

Multiattribute decision analysis Decision situation involving two or more choice alternatives requiring evaluation on multiple attributes or performance criteria.

Mutually exclusive alternative A choice such that the selection of it rules out the selection of all other alternatives in the set.

Net worth Current worth of investments in an organization.

Nominal group process Group technique used to stimulate creative thinking, such as in problem definition or alternative identification.

Nonsimple investment A situation that occurs when the cash flow at any time period for a project switches from positive to negative or negative to positive more than once.

Obsolescence Condition of an asset that forces replacement due to new developments or asset refinements.

Opportunity cost The cost of not being able to invest in an alternative because limited resources are being applied to another approved alternative and thus are not available for investment in other income-producing alternatives.

Overhead The portion of operating cost that cannot be clearly associated with particular operations or products. See **indirect costs.**

Ownership life The time that an asset is kept in service by an owner or owners.

Payback period 1. With respect to an investment, the number of years (or months) required for the related profit or savings in operating cost to equal the amount of said investment. 2. The time over which a machine, facility, or other investment has produced sufficient net revenue to recover its investment costs.

Payoff table Two-dimensional tabular format for organizing and displaying outcomes of alternative courses of action. Each row in the table represents an alternative with its outcomes arranged in columns according to respective future states.

Perpetual life Assumption made when, in an economic evaluation, an asset is treated as though it will last for ever.

Preferred stocks Part of the capital of a business, usually having fixed dividends and no voting rights.

Present worth 1. The equivalent value at present, based on the time value of money. 2. The monetary sum equivalent to a future sum or sums when interest is compounded at a given rate. 3. The discounted value of future sums.

Property taxes Local government charges on such items as land, buildings, machinery and equipment, and inventory.

Pure investment A situation where an investment's cash flow balances at any time are equal to or less than zero when calculated by using a potential IRR value (root of the present-worth equation = i^*).

Rate of return 1. The interest rate at which the present worth of cash flows of a project is zero. 2. The interest rate earned by an investment.

Recovery period The increment of years, as used in depreciation accounting, over which an asset's basis (original value) is recovered.

Repeated life An analysis based on the assumptions that an existing asset will be replaced with an asset having identical cash flows and that there is a continuing requirement for the asset's services.

Replacement 1. A broad concept embracing the selection of similar but new assets to replace existing assets. 2. The evaluation of entirely different ways of performing an asset's function.

Retained earnings Profits reinvested in an organization.

Risk Lack of predictability about the economic environment and about the outcomes and choices available in a decision situation.

Salvage value 1. The cost recovered or that could be recovered from a used property when it is removed, sold, or scrapped. A factor in the appraisal of property value and in computing depreciation. 2. The market value of a machine.

Sensitivity The relative magnitude of the change in one or more elements of an engineering economics problem that will reverse a decision among alternatives.

Simple interest 1. Interest that is not compounded; it is not added to the income-producing investment or loan. 2. The interest charges under the condition that interest in any period is charged only on the principal.

Simple investment A situation where the cash flows switch signs from positive to negative or negative to positive only once and the initial flow(s) are negative.

Simulation An analytical tool that derives sample data and statistical estimates of the system through repeated experimentation.

Sinking fund 1. A fund accumulated by periodic deposits and reserved exclusively for a specific purpose, such as retirement of a debt or replacement of a property. 2. A fund created by making periodic deposits (usually equal) at compound interest in order to accumulate a given sum at a given future time for some specific purpose.

Social discount rate The composite rate of interest used in evaluating public projects.

Spillover benefit or cost The financial effect of an activity on third parties not directly involved in a project or program.

Stock Representation of a share of ownership in a company (as opposed to a bond, which is basically a promissory note).

Straight-line depreciation Method of depreciation in which the annual depreciation charge is the same each year. According to Revenue Canada regulations, application of the half-year rule reduces first year's depreciation to one-half the capital cost allowance for an asset.

Strategy The setting of ultimate objectives.

Study period In engineering economic study, the time that is presumed to be spent in the schedule of events and appraisal of results. Often the anticipated life of the project under consideration, but a shorter time may be more appropriate for decision making.

Suboptimization Condition that occurs when (1) a subset of a larger problem is analyzed that optimizes the smaller problem but not necessarily the larger problem or (2) not all variables are included in an analysis because of the problem's complexity.

Sunk cost A cost, already paid, that is not relevant to the decision being made concerning the future. Capital already invested that for some reason cannot be retrieved.

Tactical suboptimization   A solution that optimizes tactical efficiency with little or no regard for strategic effectiveness.

Tangibles   Things that can be quantitatively measured or valued, such as items of cost and physical assets.

Taxable income   The portion of total revenue that remains after all deductions, including expenses incurred, permitted by tax laws and regulations have been taken.

Tax rate   Rate applied to taxable income that determines the amount of taxes owed.

Time value of money   1. The cumulative effect of elapsed time on the money value of an event, based on the earning power of equivalent invested funds. See **future worth** and **present worth**. 2. The expected interest rate that capital should or will earn.

Undepreciated capital cost (UCC)   The book value of an asset, used as the basis for determining the annual depreciation deduction for tax purposes.

Unit cost   Cost divided by number of units of output.

Variable cost   A cost that tends to fluctuate according to changes in the number of units produced. See **direct costs**.

Variance   Measure of the extent to which the outcomes of a random variable depart from their expected values.

Weighted cost of capital   A composite interest rate that represents the average cost of all acquired funding used by an organization.

Working capital   1. The portion of investment represented by current assets (assets that are not capitalized) less the current liabilities. The capital necessary to sustain operations. 2. Funds that are required to make the enterprise or project a going concern.

Yield   The ratio of return or profit to the associated investment, expressed as a percentage or decimal, usually on an annual basis.

GLOSSAIRE 2

actif: assets
actif à court terme: current assets
amortissement: depreciation, depletion, or amortization
amortissement dégressif: declining balance depreciation
amortissement du coût en capital (ACC): capital cost allowance (CCA)
amortissement linéaire: straight line depreciation
analyse coûts-avantages: benefit-cost analysis
analyse de sensibilité: sensitivity analysis
analyse du seuil de rentabilité: breakeven analysis
analyse financière: financial analysis
annuité: annuity
arbre de décision: decision tree
arbre de défaut: fault tree
bail d'exploitation: operating lease

bail financier: financial lease
bailleur: lessor
bénéfices réinvestis: retained earnings
biens publics: public goods
bilan: balance sheet (statement of financial position)
budgétisation des investissements: capital budgeting
capitalisation / actualisation continue: continuous compounding/discounting
capitaux propres (équité): net worth (equity)
comptabilité des coûts: cost accounting
contribution: contribution
courbe d'apprentissage: learning curve
courbe d'indifférence: indifference curve (isoquant)
coût d'opportunité: opportunity cost
coût du capital: cost of capital
coût du revient de cycle de vie: life cycle costing (LCC)
coût en capital non amorti: undepreciated capital cost (UCC)
coût fixe: fixed cost
coût initial: first cost (initial outlay)
coût variable: variable cost
coûts affectés: imputed costs
débenture: debenture
décisions dans un contexte aléatoire: decisions under risk
décisions dans un contexte certain: decisions under certainty
décisions dans un contexte incertain: decisions under uncertainty
défenseur: defender
délai de récupération: payback
demande de dépense: request for expenditure (RFE)
diagramme d'investissement acceptable (DIA): acceptable investment diagram (AID)
différentiel: incremental
effet de levier: leverage
efficacité: effectiveness
efficience: efficiency
équivalent annuel: annual equivalent
états des résultats: income (profit and loss) statement
externalités: spillovers (externalities)
facteur d'annuité: annuity factor
facteur d'intérêt: interest factor
facteur de coût en capital: capital cost tax factor (CCTF)
facteur de recouvrement du capital: capital recovery factor
flux de caisse actualisé (FCA): net cash flow (DCF)
flux de caisse net (FCN): net cash flow (NCF)
fonds d'amortissement: sinking fund
fonds de roulement: working capital
futur le plus probable: most probable future
gains (pertes) en capital: capital gains (losses)
gradient: gradient
immobilisations: capital assets
incitations fiscales: tax incentives

indice de rentabilité: profitability index
indice des prix: price index
inflation: inflation
intérêt composé: compound interest
intérêt simple: simple interest
irréductibles: irreducibles
locataire: lessee
manque à gagner minimax: minimax-regret
marginal: marginal
matrice des règlements: payoff matrix
maximax: maximax
maximin: maximin
méthode de multiple commun: common-multiple method
méthode de la période étudiée: study-period method
niveau d'aspiration: aspiration level
normes d'exploitation: standard operating procedures (SOP)
obligation: bond
opposant: challenger
passif: liabilities
passif à court terme: current liabilities
politique fiscale: fiscal policy
politique monétaire: monetary policy
profil de risque d'un investissement: investment risk profile
ratio d'équité: equity ratio
ratio d'exploitation: operating ratio
ratio de liquidité générale: current ratio
ratio de liquidité immédiate: acid test (quick) ratio
rationnement du capital: capital rationing
rendement: yield
remplacement: replacement
reports rétrospectifs (prospectifs): carrybacks (forwards)
risque: risk
risque financier: financial risk
rotation des stocks: inventory turnover
structure du capital: capital structure
structure financière: financial structure
taux de rendement externe: external rate of return
taux de rendement interne (TRI): internal rate of return (IRR)
taux de rendement multiple: multiple rates of return
taux de rendement requis (TRR): minimum acceptable rate of return (MARR)
taux d'excompte social: social discount rate
taux d'intérêt effectif: effective interest rate
taux d'intérêt nominal: nominal interest rate
valeur actualisée: present worth
valeur capitalisée: future worth
valeur comptable: book value
valeur de l'argent dans le temps: time value of money
valeur de récupération: salvage value
valeur d'usage: going concern value

valeur espérée: expected value
vie économique: economic life
vie de service: service life
VisiCalc: VisiCalc

GLOSSARY 3   EQUATION SYMBOLS

A	Annual rate
A'	Value added to gradient value to give actual cash flow
A/F	Annual rate given future value
A/G	Annual rate given gradient
A/P	Annual rate given present value
B/C	Benefit/cost ratio
$BV(n)$	Book value at period n
$CB(t)$	Current cash balance at time t
CCA	Capital cost allowance
CPW	Capitalized present worth when N is infinity
$DC(n)$	Depreciation charge at period n
e	Natural-logarithm base
e'	Computed interest rate in historical external rate-of-return method
EAC	Equivalent annual cost
EAW	Equivalent annual worth
ERR	External rate of return
f	Inflation rate
F	Future value
F/A	Future value given annual rate
F/P	Future value given present value
FW	Future worth
g	Geometric gradient value
G	Arithmetic gradient value
i	Specified interest rate
$i\%$	Implicit interest rate
i_∞	Continuous interest rate
i'	Pseudo-interest rate used in calculating the geometric gradient factor, method 2
i^*	Potential rate of return when present-worth equation has multiple roots when it is set to zero
i_{eff}	Effective interest rate
i_f	Combined interest-inflation rate
I	Simple interest accumulation
IRR	Internal rate of return
m	Number of compounding periods in 1 year
MARR	Minimum acceptable (attractive) rate of return
N	Number of time periods
NPW	Net present worth
P	Present value
P/A	Present value given annual rate
P/F	Present value given future value

PP	Payback period
PW	Present worth
R	Depreciation rate
r	Nominal interest rate
S	Salvage value
t	Effective tax rate
TTR	Total tax rate
UCC	Undepreciated capital cost
∞	Symbol for infinity

LOSSARY 4   BASIC EQUATIONS

For spreadsheet functions see App. C. The chapter where the equation was first presented or developed is given following equation caption. Occasionally, equation symbols are defined when their definitions are not the same as given in Glossary 3 (Equation Symbols) and the new definitions are accepted by convention. Basic probability concepts are covered in Glossary 5.

1. Arithmetic gradient conversion factor (to uniform series); Chap. 2:

$$A = G\left[\frac{1}{i} - \frac{N}{(1+i)^N - 1}\right] = G(A/G, i, N)$$

2. Benefit/cost comparison B/C; Chap. 8:

$$B/C = \frac{\text{present worth of benefits}}{\text{present worth of costs}}$$
$$= \frac{\text{equivalent annual benefits}}{\text{equivalent annual costs}}$$

3. Benefit/cost net present value; Chap. 8:

$$PW(B - C) = PW(\text{benefits}) - PW(\text{costs})$$

4. Book value in period n; Chap. 9: See *depreciation* (Equations 15, 16, and 17).
5. Break-even analysis—linear; Chap. 12:

Revenue/period $R = nP$

Total cost/period $C = nV + F$

Gross profit/period $Z = R - C$

Net profit/period $Z' = Z(1 - t)$

Break-even point $B = \dfrac{F}{P-V}$

where P = sales price per unit,
$\quad\ V$ = variable cost per unit
$\quad\ F$ = fixed cost

6. Capital cost allowance (CCA) tax shield; Chap. 9:

CCA tax shield in PW (full year) = $[(td)/(i+d)]$

CCA tax shield in PW (half-year rule) = $[(td)/(i+d)][(1+0.5i)/(1+i)]$

Capital cost tax factor = $1 - $ CCA tax shield

where t = tax rate
$\quad\ d$ = CCA (depreciation) rate
$\quad\ i$ = interest rate

7. Capital recovery factor (continuous compounding, discrete cash flow); Chap. 2:

$$A = P\left[\frac{e^{rN}(e^r-1)}{e^{rN}-1}\right]$$

8. Capital recovery factor (uniform series); Chap. 2:

$$A = P\left[\frac{i(1+i)^N}{(1+i)^N-1}\right] = P(A/P,\, i,\, N)$$

9. Capital recovery factor with infinite life; Chap. 4:

$$A = P\left[\frac{i(1+i)^N}{(1+i)^N-1}\right]$$
$$= Pi \qquad \text{as } N \to \infty$$

10. Capitalized present worth (CPW); Chap. 3:

$$\text{CPW} = P + A(P/A,\, i,\, \infty)$$
$$= P + \frac{A}{i}$$

11. Combined interest-inflation rate i_f; Chap. 10:

$$i_f = (1+i)(1+f) - 1$$

12. Compound-amount factor (single-payment, continuous compounding); Chap. 2:

$$F = P(e^{rN})$$

13. Compound-amount factor (single-payment); Chap. 2:

$$F = P(1 + i)^N = P(F/P, i, N)$$

14. Current and constant dollars; Chap. 10:
In period n:

Current dollars $= $ (constant dollars)$(F/P, f, n)$

Constant dollars $=$ (current dollars)$(P/F, f, n)$

15. Declining-balance method of calculating depreciation and book value; Chap. 9:

$$BV(n) = P(1\text{-depreciation rate})^n$$

$$DC(n) = BV(n - 1)(\text{depreciation rate})$$

where $BV(n)$ = book value at the end of year n
$BV(n - 1)$ = book value at the end of year $n - 1$
P = capital cost (depreciation cost)

16. Depletion rate of resource; Chap. 9:

$$\text{Depletion rate (\$/unit)} = \frac{\text{adjusted basis of resource}}{\text{remaining units of resource}}$$

17. Depreciation charge DC—declining-balance method; Chap. 9:

$$DC(n) = \frac{R}{N}\,[BV(n - 1)]$$

where $R = 1 - \left(\dfrac{S}{P}\right)^{1/N}$ $\quad S > 0$

$BV(n)$ = book value in period $n = P\left(\dfrac{S}{P}\right)^{n/N}$
$P = $ purchase price
N = useful life of asset

18. Depreciation—double-declining-balance method; Chap. 9:

$$R = \frac{200\%}{N}$$

$$BV(0) = P$$

$$DC(n) = BV(n - 1)R$$

$$BV(n) = BV(n - 1) - DC(n)$$

where $BV(n) \geq S$
P = purchase price
N = useful life of asset

19. Depreciation—straight-line per period; Chap. 9:

$$DC(n) = \frac{P - S}{N}$$

$$BV(n) = P - \frac{n}{N}(P - S)$$

where P = purchase price
N = useful life of asset
$BV(n)$ = book value in period n

20. Effective interest rate i_∞ (continuous) from nominal rate r; Chap. 2:

$$i_\infty = e^r - 1$$

21. Effective interest rate i_{eff} (discrete) from nominal rate r when compounded over m periods per year; Chap. 2:

$$i_{\text{eff}} = \left(1 + \frac{r}{m}\right)^m - 1$$

22. Effective tax rate t when state tax is deductible from federal taxes; Chap. 9:

t = state marginal tax rate + (1 − state marginal tax rate) (marginal federal rate)

23. Equivalent annual cost (EAC) for asset with P and S; Chap. 4:

$$\begin{aligned} EAC &= P(A/P, i, N) - S(A/F, i, N) \\ &= (P - S)(A/P, i, N) + Si \end{aligned}$$

24. Geometric gradient method 1 (g is percent gradient); Chap. 2:

$$P = \begin{cases} A'\left[\dfrac{1 - (1 + g)^N(1 + i)^{-N}}{i - g}\right] & \text{for } i \neq g \\[2ex] \dfrac{NA'}{1 + g} = \dfrac{NA'}{1 + i} & \text{for } i = g \end{cases}$$

25. Geometric gradient method 2 (g is percent gradient); Chap. 2:

$$P = \begin{cases} \dfrac{A}{1 + g}\left(P/A, \dfrac{1 + i}{1 + g} - 1, N\right) & \text{for } g < i \\[2ex] \dfrac{A'}{1 + i}\left(F/A, \dfrac{1 + g}{1 + i} - 1, N\right) & \text{for } g > i \\[2ex] \dfrac{NA'}{1 + g} = \dfrac{NA'}{1 + i} & \text{for } i = g \end{cases}$$

26. Historical external rate of return (HERR); Chap. 5: Solve for rate of return e' that allows

FW(receipts compounded at explicit interest rate $i\%$) = FW(disbursements compounded at e')

27. Internal rate of return (IRR)—simple investment; Chap. 5: Solve for i percent that allows

PW(incomes) = PW(disbursements)   then IRR = $i\%$

28. Internal rate of return (IRR)—project balance method; Chap. 5: Given MARR, solve for IRR so that

$$\sum_{t=1}^{N} [CB_{t-1}k(1 + MARR)^1 + CB_{t-1}(1 - k)(1 + IRR)^1 + CB_t] = 0$$

where $k = 1$ if $CB_{t-1} \geq 0$ and $k = 0$ otherwise; and CB_t = current cumulative cash balance at time t.

29. Internal rate of return (IRR), after-tax; Chap. 9:

$$IRR_{after\text{-}tax} \cong IRR_{before\text{-}tax}(1 - \text{effective income tax rate})$$

30. Multiattribute analysis; Chap. 15:
    a. Linear additive model—deterministic:

$$U_j = \sum_{i=1}^{n} w_i v_{ij}$$

where U_j = aggregate value for alternative j
        w_i = importance weight for attribute i
        v_{ij} = score of alternative j on attribute i
        n = number of attributes

b. Linear additive model—probabilistic:

$$EV(v_{ij}) = \sum_{i=1}^{m} p_{ij} x_{ij}$$

$$Var(v_{ij}) = \sum_{i=1}^{m} p_{ij} x_{ij}^2 - [EV(v_{ij})]^2$$

$$EV(U_j) = \sum_{i=1}^{n} w_i \, EV(v_{ij})$$

$$Var(U_j) = \sum_{i=1}^{n} w_i^2 \, Var(v_{ij})$$

where EV = expected value
      Var = variance
       m = number of possible outcome values
   p_{ij}, x_{ij} = probability and outcome values of attribute i on alternative j

31. Net present worth (NPW); Chap. 3:

NPW = PW(benefits) − PW(costs)

32. Payback period (PP); Chap. 3:

$$PP \cong \frac{\text{required investment}}{\text{annual receipts} - \text{annual disbursements}}$$
$$\cong \frac{\text{first cost}}{\text{net annual savings}}$$

33. Preferred-stock present worth; Chap. 3:

$$PW = \frac{\text{annual dividend of preferred stock}}{\text{annual rate of return expected by investor}}$$

34. Present-worth factor (single-payment); Chap. 2:

$$P = F \frac{1}{(1 + i)^N} = F(P/F, i, N)$$

35. Series compound-amount factor (continuous compounding, discrete cash flow); Chap. 2:

$$F = A \frac{e^{rN} - 1}{e^r - 1}$$

36. Series compound-amount factor (uniform series); Chap. 2:

$$F = A \frac{(1 + i)^N - 1}{i} = A(F/A, i, N)$$

37. Series present-worth factor (continuous compounding, discrete cash flow); Chap. 2:

$$P = A \frac{e^{rN} - 1}{e^{rN} (e^r - 1)}$$

38. Series present-worth factor (uniform series); Chap. 2:

$$P = A \frac{(1 + i)^N - 1}{i(1 + i)^N} = A(P/A, i, N)$$

39. Simple interest accumulation from P to F over N periods; Chap. 2:

$$F = P(1 + iN)$$

40. Simple interest earned by P over N periods; Chap. 2:

$$I = PiN$$

41. Sinking fund factor (continuous compounding, discrete cash flow); Chap. 2:

$$A = F \, \frac{e^r - 1}{e^{rN} - 1}$$

42. Sinking fund factor (uniform series); Chap. 2:

$$A = F \, \frac{i}{(1 + i)^N - 1} = F(A/F, i, N)$$

43. Taxable income; Chap. 9:

Taxable income = gross income − expenses − interest on debt − depreciation − other allowable deductions

44. Total tax rate (TTR); Chap. 5:

$$\text{TTR} = \frac{\Sigma \text{all taxes}}{\Sigma \text{taxable income}}$$

GLOSSARY 5   PROBABILITY CONCEPTS

1. For a random variable X,

$$\text{Expected value of } X = \text{EV}(X) = \sum_{i=1}^{n} P(X = x)x_i$$

$$\text{Variance of } X = \text{Var}(X) = \sum_{i=1}^{n} [x_i - \text{EV}(X)]^2 P(X = x_i)$$

$$= \sum_{i=1}^{n} P(X = x_i)x_i^2 - [\text{EV}(X)]^2$$

$$= \text{EV}(X^2) - [\text{EV}(X)]^2$$

$$\text{Standard deviation of } X = \sigma_x = \sqrt{\text{Var}(X)}$$

$$\text{Coefficient of variation} = \frac{\sigma_x}{\text{EV}(X)}$$

where n = number of possible outcomes for variable X

$$P(X = x_i) = \text{probability that } X = x_i$$

2. For a random variable X, defined as the sum or difference of other random variables ($X = A \pm B$),

$$EV(X) = EV(A) \pm EV(B)$$

$$Var(X) = Var(A) + Var(B) \pm Cov(AB)$$

where $Cov(AB)$ = covariance of variables A and B = 0 if A and B are independent

3. For a random variable X, defined as a product of other random variables [$X = (A)(B)$],

$$EV(X) = EV(A)EV(B)$$

$$Var(X) = [EV(A)]^2\sigma_B^2 + [EV(B)]^2\sigma_A^2 + \sigma_A^2\sigma_B^2$$

4. For two random variables X and Y,

Conditional probability of X given $Y = P(X \mid Y) = \dfrac{P(XY)}{P(Y)}$

where $P(XY)$ = joint probability of X and Y
$P(Y)$ = marginal probability of Y

$$= \sum_{i=1}^{n} P(Y \mid X = x_i)P(X = x_i)$$

CHEER 2.0 USER'S GUIDE†

CHEER (*computerized help for engineering economy results*) is a problem-solving aid for engineering economists. The program provides the following functions:

- Before-tax cash flow (BTCF) analysis
- After-tax cash flow (ATCF) analysis
- Sensitivity analysis
- Risk analysis
- Stand-alone functions:
  Interest table lookup
  Payback period
  Loan analysis

Written in Visual BASIC, CHEER provides a Windows environment. User interface with the program is through structured screens and menus. Graphical capabilities are provided for sensitivity analysis and risk analysis. The program provides complete file manipulation and editing features. Help is provided for each interface window; users may access the Help option at any time to obtain information on how to perform relevant operations.

---

†The authors thank Mr. Zhongkai Xu, Mr. Matthew Joab, and Ms. Deborah Cress for developing the CHEER program.

B.1   SYSTEM REQUIREMENTS

CHEER 2.0 requires an IBM or IBM compatible computer with 80486 or higher processor, Windows 3.1 or Windows 95, and a minimum of 2 megabytes of memory running on DOS 4.0 or a later version. The program comes in two diskettes. These contain a self-extracting file called ENGECON.EXE (in addition to CHEER 2.0, this file includes the SHEER files), which should be installed and run from the hard drive (C). The use of SHEER requires the installation of Quattro Pro for Windows (the spreadsheet program) on the hard drive.

The steps to be followed for installing CHEER 2.0 are as follows.

1. In the Windows program, choose Program Manager.
2. Click on File and select Run.
3. Insert Disk 1 in Drive A.
4. Type A:SETUP (It is assumed that the disk is in drive A.)
5. Install to C:ENGECON
6. Follow the remaining steps as directed by the program.
7. Once the program setup is complete, a CHEER icon will appear. Double click on the CHEER icon. This will lead to CHEER 2.0 directory, which includes icons for CHEER and SHEER.

B.2   DISCOUNTED CASH FLOW ANALYSIS

Discounted cash flow analysis includes BTCF, ATCF, and sensitivity analysis.

B.2.1   Features

1. The program requires the use of the mouse. The Tab key can be used for moving between items on a screen, and the Return key can control functions.
2. If certain parameters are not to be included in the analysis (e.g., inflation or loan), skip the fields corresponding to these parameters.
3. Limits on parameter values are as follows:
   a. Project life (as advised by the Help message).
   b. Initial investment is at time 0. Number of investments at times other than zero can be up to 20. Additional investments can be specified by using the noncontiguous cost option specified below.
   c. Cash flow streams, specified as a constant amount per period, an arithmetic gradient, or a geometric gradient:
      Positive cash flow streams: up to 5.
      Negative cash flow streams: up to 5.
   d. Noncontiguous cash flows:
      Positive cash flows: up to 20 (including salvage value).
      Negative cash flows: up to 20.

B.2.2   BTCF Analysis

To run CHEER 2.0, double click on CHEER icon. Printing graphics requires the use of Shift + Print Screen key combination on the keyboard.

After the introductory screen, the BTCF input is displayed. The input screen consists of three segments: a menu bar at the top, the input section, and a results section. The menu bar has three initial choices: File, Project, and Help. Clicking (mouse) on File displays the following pulldown menu (a brief explanation for each option is also provided):

New Project   Input data for a new project.
Open   Open (retrieve) an existing file.
Save Data   Save data to a file.
Save Results   Save results to a file.
Summary of Results   Show results on the screen.
Print   Send numerical results to the printer.
Exit   Exit to Windows.

Clicking on Project displays the functions available in CHEER 2.0. These correspond to the functions specified in the introductory comments of this User's Guide.

Some parameters (project life, initial investment, inflation rate, and interest rate) are specified on the initial BTCF screen. Selecting other parameters (clicking the mouse on appropriate fields) produces secondary screens. For continuous cash flow streams (revenues and operating/maintenance costs), users may specify cash flows as C (constant amount per period), A (constant amount change per period), or G (constant percentage change per period). If A or G is selected, a field requiring users to specify the change per period (amount for A, percentage for G) is activated. When the user is satisfied with data input, clicking on OK accepts the data; clicking on Clear clears data for the specific screen only. To clear all data and start with a new data set, select New Project from File.

Once data entry for BTCF is complete, click on Calculate to compute and display the results. If the interest rate is specified, then the following performance measures will be reported: PW, AW, FW, IRR. If no interest rate is specified, then only the IRR is computed. The program checks for multiple IRRs. Click on Summary of Results in File to display the BTCF table and results on the screen; selecting Print sends results to the printer.

B.2.3 Sensitivity Analysis

Sensitivity analysis can be performed on either before-tax or after-tax data. Select Sensitivity Analysis from Project in the main menu bar. Note that the sensitivity analysis option is activated only after BTCF or ATCF analyses have been completed. The system computes the effect of varying revenues, costs, salvage value, and interest rate by 50 percent in either direction of the expected value (specified in BTCF or ATCF sections) on the PW. The results are displayed in a tabular format and can be printed by clicking on Print. The graphical representation is displayed by selecting View and is printed by using the Shift + PrintScreen key combination on the keyboard. Users may return to the parent screen at any time by clicking on File, Exit.

B.2.4 ATCF Analysis

ATCF analysis requires the input data specified in the BTCF section plus additional information on depreciation, taxes, and loan (if involved). Click on After-Tax

Cash Flow in Project to display the main screen for ATCF analysis. The ATCF option is activated only after the BTCF analysis has been completed.

The major input for ATCF analysis is depreciation. Clicking on Depreciation Input produces a new screen that requires the following data to be input:

- Canadian tax depreciation regulations or other methods
- Number of assets to be depreciated (maximum = 5)
- For each depreciable asset:
    First year in which depreciation starts
    Depreciable amount
    Depreciation class

The depreciation class represents the depreciation procedure to be used. The following depreciation classes are provided: CCA declining-balance and straight-line classes, 6 MACRS property classes (3-, 5-, 7-, 10-, 15-, and 20-year), 2 MACRS classes for residential rental property and nonresidential real property (27.5- and 31.5-year), straight-line depreciation (based on MACRS midyear convention), constant rate depreciation (conventional straight-line depreciation), and year-by-year depreciation (for conventional depreciation procedures such as declining-balance and sum-of-years-digits).

Loan information is required if a loan is involved in the project. Loan input consists of the loan principal, loan interest rate, number of years before loan is repaid, and number of loan payments per year. The other input for ATCF analysis is the tax rate. Performance measures reported on completing ATCF analysis include PW, AW, FW, IRR if an after-tax interest rate is specified, and IRR if interest rate is not specified.

B.3 RISK ANALYSIS

Risk analysis is a separate program for analyzing the effect of uncertainty in parameter estimation on the PW of a project. Selecting Risk Analysis from Project displays a screen that requires the following input:

Stochastic parameters
1. Production rate (units/period)
2. Initial cost ($)
3. Revenues ($/unit or $)
4. Expenses ($/unit or $)
5. Salvage value ($)

Deterministic parameters
6. Interest rate
7. Study period
8. Number of simulation trials

Revenues (item 3) and expenses (item 4) each have two options: $/unit and $. The $ option is used for investigating variations in annual cash flows; if the $ option is selected, then the production rate (item 1) is deactivated. Selection of the $/unit option requires specification of a production rate. The $/unit option provides an opportunity to investigate changes at a microlevel, i.e., in the production rate, unit production costs, and unit sales price.

The values for each of the stochastic parameters may be specified as one of four choices (variables in parentheses represent the number of parameters required for the distribution):

- Constant or deterministic value
- Normal distribution (mean and variance)
- Triangular distribution (lower bound, mode, and upper bound)
- Uniform distribution (lower bound and upper bound)

Clicking on Start simulation in Simulation on the main screen for risk analysis initiates the simulation process. The user is prompted when simulation is complete. The numerical results can be observed by using File, View results; the graphical results by using Graph, Chart, View. Numerical results can be printed by using File, Print; graphical results by using the Shift + PrintScreen key combination on the keyboard.

B.4   STAND-ALONE FUNCTIONS

1. Table lookup computes discrete compound-interest factors. User input is project life and interest rate; computed values for eight interest factors are displayed on the screen.
2. Loan analysis computes loan (capital recovered, balance remaining, and interest) amounts per period. User input consists of four parameters: loan principal, loan interest rate, number of payment periods, and number of payments per period (a multiplier that allows the effect to be seen when increasing the amount of payment per period; e.g., 2 will double the payment per period.)
3. Payback period computes payback period, on either a nondiscounted or a discounted basis. For a nondiscounted payback period, the user specifies an initial investment, annual receipts, and annual costs. For a discounted payback period, in addition to the three parameters required for the nondiscounted payback computations, the user specifies an interest rate.

The results for the three stand-alone functions are obtained by clicking on Calculate. The results can be printed by clicking on File, Print.

SPREADSHEET USAGE AND SHEER USER'S GUIDE

C.1   SPREADSHEET USAGE[†]

As reported in App. B, this text has a computer program, called CHEER, that aids the analyst in arriving at solutions to complex engineering economic problems. CHEER is a user-friendly program that requires no programming by the user. Many engineering economists like to use spreadsheets (such as Lotus, Microsoft's Excel, Quattro Pro for Windows, and SuperCalc) since they can handle iterative calculations easily. Also, engineering students will be introduced to spreadsheet use in their introductory courses so it makes sense that many will want to use spreadsheets in their economic evaluations. The engineering economist should use all the tools available in solving problems, so commentary on the applicability of spreadsheets to engineering economic analysis is in order. CHEER and spreadsheets can be complementary, as we will see. Many times the analyst will find that CHEER provides faster table lookup, simple-to-use comprehensive risk and sensitivity analysis, fast IRR computations, and so on. Spreadsheets allow many of the CHEER operations to be performed, but the analyst will have to do considerable spreadsheet programming to try to match CHEER's capabilities. An advantage of spreadsheets, though, can be the ability of the user to output results in a report format that can be easily tailored to the analyst's needs. For example, many of the complex tables found in Chap. 9, for depreciation and tax analysis, were developed with a spreadsheet. Alloway[‡] suggests that the "correct" software

---

[†]Figures for this section appear on pages A-35 to A-44.
[‡]J. A. Alloway, "Technical Note—Spreadsheets: Enhancing Learning and Application of Engineering Economy Techniques," *The Engineering Economist,* vol. 39, no. 3, pp. 263–274, 1994. Published by the Institute of Industrial Engineers, Norcross, GA.

approach will depend on the amount of data, the degree of similarity between problems, and the user's familiarity with the software. The final results will be the same despite the approach chosen; only the level of effort required to reach them will differ.

The analyst will usually find three spreadsheets referenced for economic functions: Excel, Lotus, and Quattro Pro. We will add SuperCalc since some students will be familiar with it. In fact, the small examples using spreadsheets that will be presented shortly are done with Quattro Pro for Windows (which is closely akin to Lotus).

To facilitate the use of spreadsheet functions in solving some engineering economy problems, an integrated set of spreadsheet applications developed with Quattro Pro for Windows version 5.0 is provided with this text. We have chosen to call this software *SHEER* (*spreadsheet help for engineering economy results*) as a complement to the more comprehensive software package CHEER. The second part of this appendix will provide a brief user's guide for SHEER. This part of this appendix will introduce spreadsheets and their application to engineering economic analyses. It will also give small spreadsheet examples that will allow both numerical results *and* the associated formulas to be presented. Although these were developed by using Quattro Pro for Windows, readers who want to use a different spreadsheet software should find it a small task to translate the Quattro Pro examples for their desired systems. Tables C.1 and C.2 will greatly aid this process.

Alloway has shown the equivalence between the three prime spreadsheets with their annuity functions. Table C.1 adds some economic functions to Alloway's list and adds SuperCalc to make the group of spreadsheets number four. It follows from Table C.1 that we should be able to exactly define the engineering economy ANSI (American National Standards Institute) factors in terms of the economic functions. In fact, Eschenbach[†] shows the ANSI factors equivalence for functions of the three prime spreadsheets. Table C.2 modifies Eschenbach's development by adding SuperCalc to the spreadsheet list. Often there are multiple functions that find the same value in a spreadsheet; it should be apparent that a few additional functions could be alternates to some of the functions given in Table C.2.

This brief introduction to spreadsheet economic applications will not teach the reader how to develop complicated spreadsheets. It is a fairly simple matter to use a particular spreadsheet given the spreadsheet's User's Manual. Further, as mentioned earlier, most students will have been introduced to spreadsheet use early in their college courses.

We will now look at a few examples of the information given in Tables C.1 and C.2. Quattro Pro for Windows will be used in all these examples for simplicity. Also, as mentioned earlier, SHEER, using Quattro Pro will give the reader more flexibility to input his or her data and parameters for similar but larger-size problems.

[†]T. Eschenbach, "Technical Note—Using Spreadsheet Functions to Compute Arithmetic Gradients," *The Engineering Economist*, vol. 39, no. 3, pp. 275–280, 1994. Published by the Institute of Industrial Engineers, Norcross, GA.

TABLE C.1

Typical spreadsheet financial functions

Value to find	Quattro Pro	Lotus	Excel	SuperCalc
Present worth P	@NPV(i, cash flow, \<Type>)	@NPV(i, cash flow)	NPV(i, cash flow)	NPV(i, cash flow)
	@PVAL(i, N, A, \<F>, \<Type>) @PV(A, i, N)	@PV(A, i, N)	PV(i, N, A, \<F>, \<type>)	PV(A, i, N)
Future worth F	@FV(A, i, j N) @FVAL(i, N, A, \<P>, \<Type>)	@FV(A, i, N)	FV(i, N, A, \<P>, \<type>)	FV(A, i, N)
Annual worth A	@PMT(P, i, N) @PAYMT(i, N, P, \<F>, \<Type>)	@PMT(P, i, N)	PMT(i, N, P, \<F>, \<type>)	PMT(P, i, N)
Interest i	@RATE(F, P, N)	@RATE(F, P, N)	RATE(N, A, P, \<F>, \<type>, \<guess>)	RATE(F, P, N) ANRATE(A, P, N)
Number of periods N	@TERM(A, i, F) @CTERM(i, F, P) @NPER(i, A, P, \<F>, \<Type>)	@TERM(A, i, F) @CTERM(A, i, F)	NPER(i, A, P, \<F>, \<type>)	TERM(A, i, F) CTERM(i, F, P) ANTERM(A, i, P)
Internal interest rate of return (IRR)	@IRR(Guess, cash flow)	@IRR(guess, cash flow)	IRR(cash flow, guess)	IRR(guess,cash flow)
Portion of loan payment in period j (or start to end) that is principal	@PPAYMT(i, j, N, P, \<F>, \<Type>)	@PPAYMT(P, i, N, strt,\<end> \<type>,\<F>)	PPMT(i, j, N, P, \<F>, \<type>)	KPRIN(P, i, j, N)
Portion of loan payment in period j (or start to end) that is interest	@IPAYMT(i, j, N, P, \<F>, \<Type>)	@IPAYMT(P, i, N, strt, \<end>, \<type>, \<F>,)	IPMT(i, j, N, P, \<F>, \<type>)	KINT(P, i, N, j)
Double-declining-balance depreciation in period j	@DDB(P, S, N, j)	@DDB(P, S, N, j)	DDB(P, S,N, j, \<factor>)	DDB(P, S, N, j)
Straight-line depreciation in period j	@SLN(P, S, N)	@SLN(P, S, N)	SLN(P, S, N)	SLN(P, S, N)

TABLE C.1	CONTINUED

Notes: 1. "Cash flow" refers to a block of data, for example, A1..A20.
2. "Type" indicates if data are end-of-period or beginning-of-period. Default is end of period. Type = 0 is end of period, Type = 1 is beginning of period.
3. *<xyz>* indicates that item *xyz* is optional.
4. *<F>* or *<P>* refers to a nonzero value of *F* or *P*.
5. "Guess" is an estimate of the value to be input by the user.
6. "Factor" is the rate at which the declining balance declines. Default is 2 for double.
7. *P, S, N, A,* and *i* are the conventional engineering economy symbols.
8. *<Strt>* and *<end>* are starting and ending periods for cumulative principal. If *<end>* is omitted, then accumulation is just for start period.
9. Not all functions are applicable to all versions of the spreadsheets. The analyst should check the particular version's User's Guide. Not all the possible functions are included in this table.

EXAMPLE C.1 **ANSI Factors**

The six ANSI factors listed in Table C.2 will now be computed with spreadsheet functions and formulas. An interest rate *i* of 5 percent and a time length *N* of 5 will be used in each case. The output of Quattro Pro is given in Fig. C.1.

The six ANSI factor symbols are shown in cells A6 through A11 (A6..A11 is Quattro Pro's block-range nomenclature). The resulting factor values are shown in Fig. C.1*a*, column B, and the formulas actually typed to get the results are shown in the same column B cell locations in Fig. C.1*b*. The formulas shown in cells B6 through B11 in Fig. C.1*b* are the same as those given in Table C.2. The remaining examples will have results presented with the same two options just given: results and formulas.

The analyst who uses CHEER and spreadsheets will probably conclude that CHEER is a little more flexible and user-friendly with its ANSI factor lookup option, although SHEER will enhance the flexibility of the lookup process.

TABLE C.2				

Converting economic factors to spreadsheet functions

ANSI factor	Quattro Pro	Lotus	Excel	SuperCalc
$(P/F, i, N)$	@PVAL(i, N, 0, −1)	Find algebraically	PV(i, N, 0, −1)	Find algebraically
$(F/P, i, N)$	@FVAL(i, N, 0, −1)	Find algebraically	FV(i, N, 0, −1)	Find algebraically
$(P/A, i, N)$	@PV(1, i, N)	@PV(1, i, N)	PV(i, N, −1)	PV(1, i, N)
$(F/A, i, N)$	@FV(1, i, N)	@FV(1, i, N)	FV(i, N, −1)	FV(1, i, N)
$(A/P, i, N)$	@PAYMT(i, N, −1)	1/@PV(1, i, N)	PMT(i, N, −1)	PMT(1, i, N)
$(A/F, i, N)$	@PAYMT(i, N, 0 ,−1)	1/@FV(1, i, N)	PMT(i, N, 0, −1)	1/FV(1, i, N)

EXAMPLE C.2   **Cash Flow Equivalences**

In Example 3.2, we had an investment with the following cash flows:

End of period	Cash flow, $
1	−15,000
2	−15,000
3	−15,000
4	10,000
5	12,500
6	15,000
7	17,500
8	20,000

Given $i = 10$ percent, Example 3.2 asked for the present worth P of the investment. Also, we might want to calculate the future worth F and the equivalent annual worth EAW. Quattro Pro calculates these, as shown in Fig. C.2. We see that the cash flow data were inserted in column B (B8..B16). The results are given in columns C through F: P in C8, A in D8, and F in E8. Also, to exemplify spreadsheet functions, i is found in F8, given the F and P values just found in D8 and E8.

EXAMPLE C.3   **Capital and Interest Payments**

Table 4.1 gave interest paid and capital recovered, by time period, for an asset purchased with a loan of $40,000 at 10 percent interest over 4 years. The original table showed that in period 3, for example, the interest paid was $2190.05 and the capital recovered was $10,428.79. The annual payment is $12,618.83. Quattro Pro can be used to find the same interest and capital values as seen in Fig. C.3.

There is sometimes confusion about the sign (positive or negative) to insert for P, F, and A values in an economic analysis. We have chosen to use the convention that the loan of $40,000 is a positive income that forces the annual payments, capital recovered, and interest paid to be negative. The analyst should be careful to be consistent.

The financial functions in Fig. C.3b use a Quattro Pro convention that greatly simplifies increasing the number of time periods over the current four. The data given in cells C3 to C5 are used in *every* period by all three financial functions. If we wanted to copy the functions from period 4 to periods 5 through 10, we would want the "copy process" to recognize that the values given in cells C3 to C5 will not change cell location as the time period changes. If a formula at a particular time period used that time period in the formula, then we would want the formula in a new time period to use the new value. Fixing the data to a unique cell location is accomplished by using <$C$4> to represent cell <C4>. The dollar sign in front of <C> says that column C will not change as we increase the time period. Similarly, the dollar sign in front of the row value <4> indicates that the row value will not change as the period increases. In a hypothetical situation, we might have <C$4> or <$C4> to indicate partial fixing of the cell location. If the dollar sign is completely missing, the cell location's row and column values will both be adjusted as the time period increases. We will see later examples that have some cell locations fixed and others completely free to move.

Spreadsheet financial functions were originally designed to handle the loan payment type of problem. They do it very efficiently.

EXAMPLE C.4

Internal Rate of Return

Example 5.1 gave a cash flow stream from which an IRR was to be determined:

End of period	Cash flow, $
0	−80,000
1	650
2	650
3	650
4	650
5	150,650

An IRR value was computed manually in Chap. 5, by trial and error, and was found to be 14.04 percent. All the spreadsheets have the capability to determine an IRR. Quattro Pro gives the result shown in Fig. C.4.

The @IRR(guess,cash flow) function asks for an IRR guess to be input as an argument for the function. As seen in Fig. C.4b, we used a guess of 10 percent. Quattro Pro suggests that if you do not know a reasonable guess or if you suspect that multiple IRR values might exist, then you should insert @NA for the guess. Quattro Pro will return NA for the IRR value if it cannot converge on a single value in a reasonable number of iterations or if multiple IRR values are suspected. If the latter is expected, the user can insert multiple guesses in subsequent runs to try to find the various IRR values.

Now consider the cash flow stream given earlier in Example 5.4, which gave multiple-IRR results:

End of period	Cash flow, $
0	3,000
1	0
2	−10,000
3	2,000
4	2,000
5	2,000
6	2,000

Manually, in Chap. 5, we determined the IRR values to be 9.4 and 51 percent. CHEER gives approximate results for both values, probably close enough for an economic decision to be made directly. With CHEER, the income of $3000 at time 0 is input as an initial investment of –$3000 to allow an income to be received at the end of time 0. The CHEER approximate IRR values were 9.6 and 50.9 percent with a message indicating that the results should be within 0.1 percent of the actual results. The Quattro Pro results are given in Fig. C.5. Initially, @NA was used as the "IRR guess," and NA is returned as the value (cell C6 in Fig. C.5a). This tells us that something is wrong. We suspect multiple IRRs, so we try a guess of 0 percent. This gives the lower value of the IRR to be 9.58 percent in Fig. C.5a. Next, we try an IRR guess of 10 percent, which results in the second IRR value of 50.84 percent shown in cell E6.

As mentioned earlier, CHEER gave approximate multiple IRR values. These values could be inserted in the spreadsheet guesses to home in on closer values. This is an area where CHEER and spreadsheets can complement each other, helping the analyst to arrive at exact values for the multiple-IRR situation.

EXAMPLE C.5

Historical External Rate of Return

Following Example 5.4, it was suggested that the determination of an interest rate e' instead of an IRR would eliminate the possibility of multiple IRR values. This philosophy will be used with the same cash flow data just analyzed in Example C.4. The procedure compounds receipts at an explicit interest rate, probably the MARR value, while disbursements are compounded at the unknown e' value. The future worths F of the compounded disbursements are equated (or the sum is set equal to zero) so that the e' value can be found. In most situations, as with the spreadsheet approach, this will be a trial-and-error process.

Quattro Pro was used to solve this problem with the results shown in Fig. C.6. In Fig. C.6a, cells D10, E10, and F10 contain the e' guess, the MARR, and the value of N. As with Example 5.4, we used a MARR value of 15 percent. Varying the D10 value (e' guess) allows the analyst to see the effect on C17 (the total future shaded value), which we want to be almost zero in order to equate the compounded receipts with compounded disbursements. As can be seen, we ended up with a future sum equal to $0.75, which is almost zero. The value of e' turns out to be 14.06 percent, which is the same as the manual value found in Chap. 5 of 14.1 percent. How did Quattro Pro perform the calculations to determine if the e' or explicit interest rates should be used in each period?

The formula that calculated the future value (to the end of time period 6) for the cash flow value of $3000 at the end of period 0 is given in cell C10 of Fig. C.6b:

@IF(B10<0,B10*(1+$D$10)^($F$10–A10),B10*(1+$E$10)^($F$10–A10))

Using the referenced cell values, we can interpret this as follows:

If the cash flow at $t = 0$ is negative (disbursement), then the future value is (cash flow)$(1 + e')^{6-0}$; otherwise the cash flow is a receipt, and the future value is (cash flow)$(1 + MARR)^{6-0}$.

As seen in Fig. C.6b, the values in cells D10 to F10 are fixed and are used by the formulas in cells C10 to C16. Therefore, the $ convention is used in the formula address, that is, $D$10. Each of the cash flows in B10 to B16 and time periods A10 to A16 varies according to the time period. In this case, the $ convention is not used when those values are referenced, that is, A10 and B10. The formula in cell C10 was first developed and then copied to cells C11 to C16, with the result seen in Fig. C.6*b*. From time period 1, A10 increases to A11 while $D$10 stays the same in both time periods. It is a simple task to replicate (copy) the formula to subsequent cells by using a spreadsheet's replicate or the cut-and-paste editing capability, fixing certain cell values while indexing others in the manner just discussed.

Of course, the formulas given are only for Quattro Pro; the other spreadsheets would attack the problem in a similar manner.

EXAMPLE C.6

Project Balance Method Procedure

Section 5.5.4 applied the project balance method (PBM) procedure to the data we used in the previous two examples. To refresh the reader's memory, the PBM procedure, for any time period, applies an IRR guess to the previous period's accumulation of compounded cash flows. If this accumulation is negative, compounding is done with the IRR whereas the MARR (or other acceptable external interest rate) is applied if the accumulation is positive. As with the HERR procedure, the IRR is found when the compounded cash flow at the Nth time period approximately equals $0. To start the process, the compounded cash flow at the end of period 0 is set to the cash flow at the end of time 0. Using an IRR guess of 15 percent, the Quattro Pro solution is given in Fig. C.7*a*.

The current balance formula at $t = 1$ (cell C11, Fig. C.7c) is

@IF(C10<0,C10*(1+$D$10)+B11,C10*(1+$E$10)+B11)

This says that

> If the current balance at $t = 0$ is negative, then the new current balance (at $t = 1$) is the balance at [$t = 0$ times $(1 + \text{IRR})^1$ plus the cash flow at $t = 1$]; otherwise, the new current balance is the balance at $t = 0$ times $(1 + \text{MARR})^1$ plus the cash flow at $t = 1$.

The subsequent column C formulas are seen to be indexed in a manner similar to those in the previous example. The starting current cash flow balance at $t = 0$ is the cash flow value at $t = 0$, and so we see that the formula in cell C10 is simply B10, which brings in the cash value from cell B10.

The particular solution given in Fig. C.7*a* shows the accumulated balance at time period 6 to be −$564.13, which certainly is not $0. A guess of 12.34 percent gives an IRR of −$1.67 in Fig. C.7*a*, which is approximately $0. Not surprisingly, the same IRR value of 12.34 percent was found manually in Chap. 5.

EXAMPLE C.7

Depreciation and Book Value

Now, let's consider depreciation of an asset. Straight-line depreciation from Chap. 9 is trivial, but we can use spreadsheets to find the value. Example 9.2 considered an asset with $P = \$7000$, $S = \$0$, and $N = 5$. Example 9.2 originally showed this to be

$$DC(i) = \frac{P - S}{N} = \frac{\$7000 - \$0}{5} = \$1400$$

where $DC(i)$ is the depreciation cost in periods 1, 2, . . ., 5.

Example 9.3 applied the double-declining-balance depreciation to the same data. Chapter 9 found $DC(1) = \$2800$, $DC(2) = \$1680$, and $DC(3) = \$1008$. The spreadsheet results confirm these values, as seen in Fig. C.8a.

Now, suppose we want to find the book value BV as well as the depreciation cost. The book value for period j is computed by

$$BV(j) = BV(j - 1) - DC(j)$$

where $BV(0)$ = asset's price P. We insert columns D and E in Quattro Pro to allow us to compute both the depreciation and the book values, as shown in Fig. C.9.

With the double-declining-balance depreciation scheme for 5 time periods, the depreciation rate for each period is 200 percent/5, or 40 percent, of the previous period's book value. As an example, at time period 4 we would expect

$$DC(4) = 0.4\,BV(3) = 0.4(\$1512) = \$604.80$$

This will give a book value at time period 4 of

$$BV(4) = BV(3) - DC(4) = \$1512 - \$604.80 = \$907.20$$

This is exactly the value found in Fig. C.9a.

We also see, as expected, that the double-declining-balance method will not depreciate to $0 as does the straight-line depreciation method.

The reader should realize that the depreciation methods in spreadsheets often may not be used directly for tax purposes since half-year (or midyear) and other adjustments are usually required. Users can write their own procedures with spreadsheets to solve depreciation problems for tax purposes.

One final point regarding this example should be made relative to spreadsheet simplicity of use. Figure C.9 added two columns to the spreadsheet of Fig. C.8 while shifting the position of an existing column and its associated data (column C to column D). Shifting of data by rows and columns is a very simple process accomplished by marking the cells to be moved by using a mouse and then "dragging" the data to the locations desired. If the formulas had cell references that changed with the move, the editing cut-and-paste option would be used.

This completes the introduction to spreadsheets. CHEER handles most of the engineering economic computations without the user having to program. Spreadsheets allow the user to program unique situations and tailor company reports as needed. Both CHEER and spreadsheets should be in the analyst's "tool kit." We next give, starting on page A-45, a short introduction on how to use SHEER, the Quattro Pro spreadsheet program provided with this text.

FIG_1A	A	B
1	COMPUTATION OF ANSI ECONOMIC	
2	FACTORS WITH QUATTRO PRO	
3		
4	ANSI	FACTOR
5	FACTOR	VALUE
6	(P/F,10,5)	0.62092
7	(F/P,10,5)	1.61051
8	(P/A,10,5)	3.79079
9	(A/P,10,5)	0.26380
10	(F/A,10,5)	6.10510
11	(A/F,10,5)	0.16380

(a)

FIG_1B	A	B
1	COMPUTATION OF ANSI ECONOMIC	
2	FACTORS WITH QUATTRO PRO	
3		
4	ANSI	FACTOR
5	FACTOR	VALUE
6	(P/F,10,5)	@FVAL(0.1,5,0,-1)
7	(F/P,10,5)	@FVAL(0.1,5,0,-1)
8	(P/A,10,5)	@PV(1,0.1,5)
9	(A/P,10,5)	@PAYMT(0.1,5,-1)
10	(F/A,10,5)	@FV(1,0.1,5)
11	(A/F,10,5)	@PAYMT(0.1,5,0,-1)

(b)

FIGURE C.1

FIG_2A	A	B	C	D	E	F
1	COMPUTATION OF CASH FLOW EQUIVALENCES WITH QUATTRO PRO					
2						
3	NUMBER OF PERIODS:		8			
4	EXPLICIT INTEREST RATE:		10.00%			
5						COMPUTED
6	END OF	CASH	PRESENT	ANNUAL	FUTURE	RATE OF
7	PERIOD	FLOW	VALUE	VALUE	VALUE	RETURN
8	0	$0.00	$4,066.39	$762.22	$8,716.68	10.00%
9	1	-$15,000.00				
10	2	-$15,000.00				
11	3	-$15,000.00				
12	4	$10,000.00				
13	5	$12,500.00				
14	6	$15,000.00				
15	7	$17,500.00				
16	8	$20,000.00				

(a)

FIG_2B	A	B	C	D	E	F
1	COMPUTATION OF CASH FLOW EQUIVALENCES WITH QUATTRO PRO					
2						
3	NUMBER OF PERIODS:		8			
4	EXPLICIT INTEREST RATE:		10.00%			
5						COMPUTED
6	END OF	CASH	PRESENT	ANNUAL	FUTURE	RATE OF
7	PERIOD	FLOW	VALUE	VALUE	VALUE	RETURN
8	0	$0.00	@NPV(C4,B8..B16,1)	@PMT(C8,C4,C3)	@FV(D8,C4,C3)	@RATE(E8,C8,C3)
9	1	-$15,000.00				
10	2	-$15,000.00				
11	3	-$15,000.00				
12	4	$10,000.00				
13	5	$12,500.00				
14	6	$15,000.00				
15	7	$17,500.00				
16	8	$20,000.00				

(b)

FIGURE C.2

FIG_3A	A	B	C	D
1	CAPITAL AND INTEREST PAYMENTS USING QUATTRO PRO			
2				
3	NUMBER OF PERIODS:		4	
4	INTEREST RATE:		10.00%	
5	LOAN PRINCIPAL:		$40,000.00	
6				
7	END OF	ANNUAL	CAPITAL	INTEREST
8	PERIOD	PAYMENT	RECOVERED	PAID
9	1	-$12,618.83	-$8,618.83	-$4,000.00
10	2	-$12,618.83	-$9,480.72	-$3,138.12
11	3	-$12,618.83	-$10,428.79	-$2,190.05
12	4	-$12,618.83	-$11,471.67	-$1,147.17

(a)

FIG_3B	A	B	C	D
1	CAPITAL AND INTEREST PAYMENTS USING QUATTRO PRO			
2				
3	NUMBER OF PERIODS:		4	
4	INTEREST RATE:		10.00%	
5	LOAN PRINCIPAL:		$40,000.00	
6				
7	END OF	ANNUAL	CAPITAL	INTEREST
8	PERIOD	PAYMENT	RECOVERED	PAID
9	1	@PAYMT($C$4,$C$3,$C$5)	@PPAYMT($C$4,A9,$C$3,$C$5)	@IPAYMT($C$4,A9,$C$3,$C$5)
10	2	@PAYMT($C$4,$C$3,$C$5)	@PPAYMT($C$4,A10,$C$3,$C$5)	@IPAYMT($C$4,A10,$C$3,$C$5)
11	3	@PAYMT($C$4,$C$3,$C$5)	@PPAYMT($C$4,A11,$C$3,$C$5)	@IPAYMT($C$4,A11,$C$3,$C$5)
12	4	@PAYMT($C$4,$C$3,$C$5)	@PPAYMT($C$4,A12,$C$3,$C$5)	@IPAYMT($C$4,A12,$C$3,$C$5)

(b)

FIGURE C.3

FIG_4A	A	B	C
1	INTERNAL RATE OF RETURN		
2	(IRR) - SINGLE VALUE		
3	USING QUATTRO PRO		
4			
5	END OF	CASH	
6	PERIOD	FLOW	IRR
7	0	-$80,000.00	14.039%
8	1	$650.00	
9	2	$650.00	
10	3	$650.00	
11	4	$650.00	
12	5	$150,650.00	

(a)

FIG_4B	A	B	C
1	INTERNAL RATE OF RETURN		
2	(IRR) - SINGLE VALUE		
3	USING QUATTRO PRO		
4			
5	END OF	CASH	
6	PERIOD	FLOW	IRR
7	0	-$80,000.00	@IRR(10,B7..B12)
8	1	$650.00	
9	2	$650.00	
10	3	$650.00	
11	4	$650.00	
12	5	$150,650.00	

(b)

FIGURE C.4

FIG_5A	A	B	C	D	E
1	INTERNAL RATE OF RETURN (IRR) MULTIPLE VALUES				
2		USING QUATTRO PRO			
3					
4	END OF	CASH	INITIAL	IRR RESULT	IRR RESULT
5	PERIOD	FLOW	IRR RESULT	NUMBER ONE(%)	NUMBER TWO(%)
6	0	$3,000.00	NA	9.5818	50.8438
7	1	$0.00			
8	2	-$10,000.00			
9	3	$2,000.00			
10	4	$2,000.00			
11	5	$2,000.00			
12	6	$2,000.00			

(*a*)

FIG_5B	A	B	C	D	E
1	INTERNAL RATE OF RETURN (IRR) MULTIPLE VALUES				
2		USING QUATTRO PRO			
3					
4	END OF	CASH	INITIAL	IRR RESULT	IRR RESULT
5	PERIOD	FLOW	IRR RESULT	NUMBER ONE	NUMBER TWO
6	0	$3,000.00	@IRR(@NA,B6..B12)	@IRR(0,B6..B12)	@IRR(10,B6..B12)
7	1	$0.00			
8	2	-$10,000.00			
9	3	$2,000.00			
10	4	$2,000.00			
11	5	$2,000.00			
12	6	$2,000.00			

(*b*)

FIGURE C.5

FIG_6A	A	B	C	D	E	F
1	HISTORICAL EXTERNAL RATE OF RETURN (HERR) COMPUTATION					
2			USING QUATTRO PRO			
3						
4			FUTURE			
5			VALUE (IN			
6			TIME PERIOD 6)			
7			OF THE		EXPLICIT	NUMBER
8	END OF	CASH	CURRENT CASH	(e')	INTEREST	OF
9	PERIOD	FLOW	FLOW VALUE	GUESS(%)	RATE (%)	PERIODS
10	0	$3,000.00	$6,939.18	14.06	15.00	6
11	1	$0.00	$0.00			
12	2	−$10,000.00	−$16,925.19			
13	3	$2,000.00	$3,041.75			
14	4	$2,000.00	$2,645.00			
15	5	$2,000.00	$2,300.00			
16	6	$2,000.00	$2,000.00			
17	SUM OF FUTURE VALUES:		$0.75			

(a)

FIGURE C.6

FIG_6B	A	B	C	D	E	F
1	HISTORICAL EXTERNAL RATE OF RETURN (HERR) COMPUTATION					
2			USING QUATTRO PRO			
3						
4			FUTURE			
5			VALUE (IN			
6			TIME PERIOD 6)			
7			OF THE	(e')	EXPLICIT	NUMBER
8	END OF		CURRENT CASH		INTEREST	OF
9	PERIOD	CASH FLOW	FLOW VALUE	GUESS(%)	RATE (%)	PERIODS
10	0	$3,000.00	@IF(B10<0,B10*(1+$D$10)^($F$10-A10),B10*(1+$E$10)^($F$10-A10))	14.06	15.00	6
11	1	$0.00	@IF(B11<0,B11*(1+$D$10)^($F$10-A11),B11*(1+$E$10)^($F$10-A11))			
12	2	-$10,000.00	@IF(B12<0,B12*(1+$D$10)^($F$10-A12),B12*(1+$E$10)^($F$10-A12))			
13	3	$2,000.00	@IF(B13<0,B13*(1+$D$10)^($F$10-A13),B13*(1+$E$10)^($F$10-A13))			
14	4	$2,000.00	@IF(B14<0,B14*(1+$D$10)^($F$10-A14),B14*(1+$E$10)^($F$10-A14))			
15	5	$2,000.00	@IF(B15<0,B15*(1+$D$10)^($F$10-A15),B15*(1+$E$10)^($F$10-A15))			
16	6	$2,000.00	@IF(B16<0,B16*(1+$D$10)^($F$10-A10),B16*(1+$E$10)^($F$10-A16))			
17	SUM OF FUTURE VALUES:		@SUM(C10..C16)			

(b)

FIGURE C.6 continued

FIG_7A	A	B	C	D	E
1	PROJECT BALANCE METHOD IRR COMPUTATION USING				
2	AN EXTERNAL RATE OF RETURN (MARR)				
3	WITH QUATTRO PRO				
4	(USING AN IRR GUESS OF 15.00%)				
5					
6			CURRENT CASH		
7			FLOW BALANCE		EXPLICIT
8	END OF	CASH	USING IRR	IRR	INTEREST
9	PERIOD	FLOW	OR MARR	GUESS	RATE (MARR)
10	0	$3,000.00	$3,000.00	15.00	15.00
11	1	$0.00	$3,450.00		
12	2	-$10,000.00	-$6,032.50		
13	3	$2,000.00	-$4,937.38		
14	4	$2,000.00	-$3,677.98		
15	5	$2,000.00	-$2,229.68		
16	6	$2,000.00	-$564.13		

FIG_7A	A	B	C	D	E
1	PROJECT BALANCE METHOD IRR COMPUTATION USING				
2	AN EXTERNAL RATE OF RETURN (MARR)				
3	WITH QUATTRO PRO				
4	(USING AN IRR GUESS OF 15.00%)				
5					
6			CURRENT CASH		
7			FLOW BALANCE		EXPLICIT
8	END OF	CASH	USING IRR	IRR	INTEREST
9	PERIOD	FLOW	OR MARR	GUESS	RATE (MARR)
10	0	$3,000.00	$3,000.00	12.34	15.00
11	1	$0.00	$3,450.00		
12	2	-$10,000.00	-$6,032.50		
13	3	$2,000.00	-$4,776.91		
14	4	$2,000.00	-$3,366.38		
15	5	$2,000.00	-$1,781.79		
16	6	$2,000.00	-$1.67		

(a)

FIGURE C.7

FIG_7B	A	B	C	D	E
1	PROJECT BALANCE METHOD IRR COMPUTATION USING				
2	AN EXTERNAL RATE OF RETURN (MARR)				
3	WITH QUATTRO PRO				
4	(USING AN IRR GUESS OF 12.34%)				
5					
6			CURRENT CASH		
7			FLOW BALANCE		EXPLICIT
8	END OF	CASH	USING IRR	IRR	INTEREST
9	PERIOD	FLOW	OR MARR	GUESS	RATE (MARR)
10	0	$3,000.00	+B10	12.34%	15.00%
11	1	$0.00	@IF(C10<0,C10*(1+$D$10)+B11,C10*(1+$E$10)+B11)		
12	2	-$10,000.00	@IF(C11<0,C11*(1+$D$10)+B12,C11*(1+$E$10)+B12)		
13	3	$2,000.00	@IF(C12<0,C12*(1+$D$10)+B13,C12*(1+$E$10)+B13)		
14	4	$2,000.00	@IF(C13<0,C13*(1+$D$10)+B14,C13*(1+$E$10)+B14)		
15	5	$2,000.00	@IF(C14<0,C14*(1+$D$10)+B15,C14*(1+$E$10)+B15)		
16	6	$2,000.00	@IF(C15<0,C15*(1+$D$10)+B16,C15*(1+$E$10)+B16)		

(b)

FIGURE C.7   continued

FIG_8A	A	B	C
1	STRAIGHT LINE AND DOUBLE DECLINING		
2	BALANCE DEPRECIATION WITH QUATTRO PRO		
3			
4	PURCHASE PRICE:		7000.00
5	SALVAGE VALUE:		0.00
6	ASSET LIFE:		5
7			
8			DOUBLE
9		STRAIGHT	DECLINING
10	TIME	LINE	BALANCE
11	PERIOD	DEPRECIATION	DEPRECIATION
12	1	$1,400.00	$2,800.00
13	2	$1,400.00	$1,680.00
14	3	$1,400.00	$1,008.00
15	4	$1,400.00	$604.80
16	5	$1,400.00	$362.88
17		$7,000.00	$6,455.68

(a)

FIGURE C.8

FIG_8B	A	B	C
1	STRAIGHT LINE AND DOUBLE DECLINING		
2	BALANCE DEPRECIATION WITH QUATTRO PRO		
3			
4	PURCHASE PRICE:		7000.00
5	SALVAGE VALUE:		0.00
6	ASSET LIFE:		5
7			
8			DOUBLE
9		STRAIGHT	DECLINING
10	TIME	LINE	BALANCE
11	PERIOD	DEPRECIATION	DEPRECIATION
12	1	@SLN($C$4,$C$5,$C$6)	@DDB($C$4,$C$5,$C$6,A12)
13	2	@SLN($C$4,$C$5,$C$6)	@DDB($C$4,$C$5,$C$6,A13)
14	3	@SLN($C$4,$C$5,$C$6)	@DDB($C$4,$C$5,$C$6,A14)
15	4	@SLN($C$4,$C$5,$C$6)	@DDB($C$4,$C$5,$C$6,A15)
16	5	@SLN($C$4,$C$5,$C$6)	@DDB($C$4,$C$5,$C$6,A16)
17		@SUM(B12..B16)	@SUM(C12..C16)

(b)

FIGURE C.8   continued

FIG_9A	A	B	C	D	E
1	STRAIGHT LINE AND DOUBLE DECLINING BALANCE				
2	DEPRECIATION AND BOOK VALUES WITH QUATTRO PRO				
3					
4	PURCHASE PRICE:		7000.00		
5	SALVAGE VALUE:		0.00		
6	ASSET LIFE:		5		
7					BOOK VALUE
8				DOUBLE	WITH DOUBLE
9		STRAIGHT	BOOK VALUE	DECLINING	DECLINING
10	TIME	LINE	WITH STRAIGHT	BALANCE	BALANCE
11	PERIOD	DEPRECIATION	LINE DEPRECIATION	DEPRECIATION	DEPRECIATION
12	1	$1,400.00	$5,600.00	$2,800.00	$4,200.00
13	2	$1,400.00	$4,200.00	$1,680.00	$2,520.00
14	3	$1,400.00	$2,800.00	$1,008.00	$1,512.00
15	4	$1,400.00	$1,400.00	$604.80	$907.20
16	5	$1,400.00	$0.00	$362.88	$544.32
17		$7,000.00		$6,455.68	

(a)

FIGURE C.9

FIG_9B	A	B	C	D	E
1	STRAIGHT LINE AND DOUBLE DECLINING BALANCE				
2	DEPRECIATION AND BOOK VALUES WITH QUATTRO PRO				
3					
4	PURCHASE PRICE:		7000		
5	SALVAGE VALUE:		0		
6	ASSET LIFE:		5		
7					BOOK VALUE
8				DOUBLE	WITH DOUBLE
9		STRAIGHT	BOOK VALUE	DECLINING	DECLINING
10	TIME	LINE	WITH STRAIGHT	BALANCE	BALANCE
11	PERIOD	DEPRECIATION	LINE DEPRECIATION	DEPRECIATION	DEPRECIATION
12	1	@SLN($C$4,$C$5,$C$6)	+$C$4-B12	@DDB($C$4,$C$5,$C$6,A12)	+$C$4-D12
13	2	@SLN($C$4,$C$5,$C$6)	+C12-B13	@DDB($C$4,$C$5,$C$6,A13)	+E12-D13
14	3	@SLN($C$4,$C$5,$C$6)	+C13-B14	@DDB($C$4,$C$5,$C$6,A14)	+E13-D14
15	4	@SLN($C$4,$C$5,$C$6)	+C14-B15	@DDB($C$4,$C$5,$C$6,A15)	+E14-D15
16	5	@SLN($C$4,$C$5,$C$6)	+C15-B16	@DDB($C$4,$C$5,$C$6,A16)	+E15-D16
17		@SUM(B12..B16)		@SUM(D12..D16)	

(b)

FIGURE C.9 continued

SHEER USER'S GUIDE[†]

To be able to use SHEER, you will need to have Quattro Pro for Windows version 5.0 or higher installed on Drive C (hard drive). If you do not have Quattro Pro, you can modify the examples given in the previous section to fit your available spreadsheet software in order to accomplish a large percentage of what SHEER will do for you.

Assuming that you have installed Quattro Pro for Windows on your computer, the next step is to install CHEER 2.0 as directed in Appendix B. The CHEER 2.0 will automatically load SHEER.WB2. You can also use Quattro Pro's install menu to extract SHEER.WB2 from the hard drive (C).

To run SHEER, first double click on the CHEER 2.0 icon in the Windows screen. This will result in the display of the CHEER 2.0 directory. On the directory screen, double click on the SHEER icon. You will end up with the main menu shown in Fig. C.10. As can be seen on this index screen, 12 options can be accessed:

1. *ANSI factors.* This allows table lookup for the six discrete compound-interest factors listed earlier in Figure C.1a. In addition, the six continuous interest factors that are analogous to the discrete factors can be looked up, as can the present-worth and annual-worth linear gradient series factors.
2. *Loan payments.* This option determines a loan payment schedule, given the principal, interest rate, number of payment periods, and payments per period.
3. *CF equivalences.* Given a cash flow (CF) stream and interest rate, cash flow equivalencies for that stream are determined: present value, annual value, and future value.
4. *IRR.* An internal rate of return is computed, given a cash flow stream and an estimate of the IRR value. The user is allowed to input an IRR guess if desired.
5. *HERR.* The historical external rate of return (HERR) method is applied to a cash flow stream to determine the interest rate e' that, in conjunction with the MARR, will eliminate multiple possibilities for the IRR.
6. *PBM method.* The project balance method is applied to a stream of data to determine a unique value of the IRR, given that the MARR is applied to positive cash flow balances and the IRR is applied to negative cash flow balances.
7. *SL and DDB.* Given a principal, salvage value, interest rate, and number of periods, this option computes the straight-line (SL) and double-declining-balance (DDB) depreciation as well as the associated book values.
8. *CCA DB.* This option enables the user to solve capital cost allowance and after-tax cash flow problems according to Revenue Canada regulations for declining-balance type of assets. This method requires as input: cash flow, the CCA (depreciation) rate, number of years, interest rate, salvage (resale) value, whether half-year rule is applicable, tax rate, and capital gains tax rate. This option determines income tax effects including disposal tax effects.
9. *CCA SL.* This option is basically the same as 8 except that it is applicable to straight-line type of assets as defined by Revenue Canada.
10. *MACRS SL.* Using the 1986 modified accelerated cost recovery system (MACRS), this option determines the effect on income taxes for a cash flow stream of incomes, assuming straight-line depreciation. The user has to input

---

[†]Figures for this section appear on pages A-48 to A-62.

the cash flow stream, number of years, interest rate, unadjusted basis of the asset, and tax rate.

11. *MACRS ADM.* This is the same as the previous option except that the accelerated depreciation method (ADM) is utilized. In addition to the information listed in the previous option, the user has to input the MACRS class.

12. *ATCF calculation.* This option determines the after-tax cash flow (ATCF) and the present worth of the ATCF.

The menu buttons labelled *info1* to *info12* will give a brief discussion of what the associated spreadsheet option will accomplish, in case the reader forgets. This same information can be obtained through the Help option in any of the applications.

Example screens will now be given for each of the 12 applications using Quattro Pro for Windows. Most of the applications were discussed in the previous section, and it is assumed that the reader is familiar with the economic fundamentals associated with each application. Therefore, only a brief amount of information will be given in addition to the screen displays.

1. Computation of ANSI economic factors. (Fig. C.11) The user inputs the desired interest rate in cell B5 and the number of periods in cell D5 to get the compounding factors.

To return to the main menu for one of the other 12 applications, just click on the Return to Main Menu button at the top left corner of the spreadsheet screen. This process is the same for all 12 functions.

2. Loan payment schedule. (Figure C.12) The user inputs the required data in cells D6 to D9: principal, interest rate, number of payment periods, and payments per period. The computations are set up to allow up to 1000 payments. After data input, click on the calculate button to do calculation and error checking. An error message is displayed if the total number of payments exceed the allowable limit. All other functions have similar error check features.

3. Cash flow equivalences. (Fig. C.13) The user has to input the number of periods and the interest rate in cells B8 and C8, respectively. When the value for the number of periods is input, the required cells for cash flow entry are highlighted in column C. The user then has to input the cash flows. The copy function is very helpful when many of these values are the same. A cash flow stream limitation, as advised by the program, applies here as well as in the remaining applications. Clicking on the Calculate button will perform the calculations, error checking, and clearing unnecessary values. For example, if a problem with 10 values is run and the next problem has a smaller number of values, say 5, the program will automatically "zero out" the last 5 values from the previous problem. This "clearing procedure" is also automatically executed for the remaining functions.

4. Internal rate-of-return computations. (Fig. C.14) This is quite self-explanatory since notes are given on the screen to explain the IRR guess requirements. The program will automatically compute two IRR values if multiple roots exist. The user can specify a guess for an IRR possibility if desired.

5. Historical external rate-of-return method. (Fig. C.15) This computation will require several iterations by the user to achieve a satisfactory result. The user inputs the number of periods in cell B9 and the cash flow in the required cells in Column C. The explicit interest rate (usually MARR) is input in cell D9. Now the iterative process starts when the first try for e' is input to cell D9. Cell E13 will give the future sum of the cash flow values. If this is not close to zero, then another value for e' is input. It is then a simple search process to find the desired e' value.

6. Project balance method computations. (Fig. C.16) The PBM process is handled in the same manner as the HERR method except for the fact that the trial values are now an IRR guess to be input to cell C10. The MARR (or other external interest rate) is input to cell D10. The iterative process continues until the last current balance in column D is close to zero (in the example, this final balance is in cell D20). Of course, the cell location will vary as the number of periods changes.

7. Straight-line and double-declining-balance depreciation. (Fig. C.17) The user inputs the number of periods for which depreciation is needed, the principal value, and the salvage value in cells C10 to E10, respectively. The depreciation values and the book values will be displayed as shown in Fig. C.17.

8. Capital cost allowance (CCA) declining-balance class after tax analysis. (Fig. C.18) The user inputs the required data in cells B10 to I10 and highlighted area in Column C. The inputs include number of years, depreciation cost of assets, CCA rate, whether half-year rule is applicable, tax rate, capital gains tax rate, rate of return, salvage (or resale) value, and before-tax cash flow. The results are displayed as shown in Fig. C.18.

9. Capital cost allowance (CCA) straight-line class after tax analysis. (Figure C.19) This is the same as the previous option, except that Revenue Canada's straight-line classes are analyzed. See Figure C.19 for inputs and outputs.

10. MACRS straight-line depreciation method. (Fig. C.20) The user inputs the required data in cells C10 to F10 and the highlighted area in column C: number of years, rate of return, unadjusted basis of asset, tax rate, and before-tax cash flow. The results of the computations are displayed automatically on the bottom half of the screen depending on the number of time periods.

11. MACRS accelerated depreciation method. (Fig. C.21) This is basically the same as application 10 except that data are needed for the accelerated depreciation calculations. The user has to input the unadjusted basis of the asset and the MACRS class, with the class restrictions being indicated in the screen display figure. The depreciation percentages are automatically copied from the rate schedules shown in cells N19 to S30 (part 2) to the appropriate cells in column D (part 1) when the user inputs the MACRS class in cell F10.

12. After-tax computations (Fig. C.22 and Fig.C.23) This application can be undertaken in conjunction with CCA DB (as 12A) or CCA SL (as 12B) options. Examples are shown for CCA DB and CCA SL types of analyses. Here, more complex analyses can be carried out, such as handling debt capital in addition to other computations described under options 8 and 9.

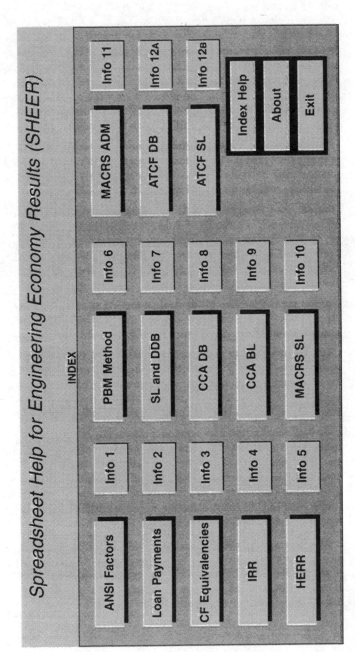

FIGURE C.10

ANSI_Factor	A	B	C	D
1	Rate i to Main Menu	Help		
2	COMPUTATION OF ANSI ECONOMIC FACTORS			
3			(Discrete Payment)	
4				
5	Interest Rate i :	10.0%	Period N:	5
6				
7				
8				
9		ANSI	Discrete	Continuous
10		FACTOR	Compounding	Compounding
11	Single	(F/P,i,N)	1.61051	1.64872
12	Payment	(P/F,i,N)	0.62092	0.60653
13		(A/F,i,N)	0.16380	0.16212
14	Uniform	(A/P,i,N)	0.26380	0.26729
15	Payment	(F/A,i,N)	6.10510	6.16826
16		(P/A,i,N)	3.79079	3.74124
17	Gradient	(A/G,i,N)	1.81013	1.80086
18	Series	(P/G,i,N)	6.86180	6.73745

FIGURE C.11

LOAN PAYMENT SCHEDULE

Return to Main Menu	Help	Calculate

Data Input

Principal	$40,000.00
Interest rate	10.00%
Number of payment periods	4
Payments per period	1

Data Output

Payment per period	$12,618.83
Effective interest rate per period	10.00%
Interest rate per period	10.00%
Total number of payments	4
Total Interest Paid	$10,475.33

Loan Payment Table

Payment	Interest Due	Payment Amount	Capital Recovered	Balance Remaining
0	$0.00	$0.00	$0.00	$40,000.00
1	4,000.00	12,618.83	8,618.83	31,381.17
2	3,138.12	12,618.83	9,480.71	21,900.46
3	2,190.05	12,618.83	10,428.78	11,471.67
4	1,147.17	12,618.84	11,471.67	0.00

FIGURE C.12

COMPUTATION OF CASH FLOW EQUIVALENCES

CF_Eq	B	C	D	E	F	G	H
1	Return to Main Menu		Help		Calculate		
2							
3							
4	**DATA INPUT**				**DATA OUTPUT**		
5							
6	Number of	Interest					Computed
7	Periods	Rate		Present	Annual	Future	Rate of
8	8	10.00%		Value	Value	Value	Return
9				$4,066.39	$762.22	$8,716.68	10.00%
10	End of	Cash					
11	Period	Flow					
12	0	$0.00					
13	1	-$15,000.00					
14	2	-$15,000.00					
15	3	-$15,000.00					
16	4	$10,000.00					
17	5	$12,500.00					
18	6	$15,000.00					
19	7	$17,500.00					
20	8	$20,000.00					

FIGURE C.13

IRR	B	C	D	E	F	G	H
1	Return to Main Menu		Help		Calculate		
2	COMPUTATION OF INTERNAL RATE OF RETURN(IRR)						
3							
4	DATA INPUT*			DATA OUTPUT**			
5							
6	Number of	User's Guess(%)		Single		Multiple IRR Values (%)	
7	Periods	(optional)		IRR	IRR Guess #1	IRR Guess #2	User's Guess
8	7	0.00		Value(%)	0	30	0
9				NA	9.581838	50.843761	9.581838
10	End of	Cash			There exist multiple IRR values!!!		
11	Period	Flow		NOTES:			
12	0	$0.00		* IRR guesses must be greater than -1.			
13	1	$3,000.00		** If multiple IRR values are suspected or no			
14	2	$0.00		convergence on a single value, the user			
15	3	-$10,000.00		needs to try multiple guesses in subsequent			
16	4	$2,000.00		runs to find the various IRR values.			
17	5	$2,000.00		The first two IRR results are based on IRR			
18	6	$2,000.00		(program) guesses # 1 and #2, respectively.			
19	7	$2,000.00		The last IRR result is based on the user's guess.			

FIGURE C.14

ERR	B	C	D	E
1	Return to Main Menu	Help	Calculate	
2	COMPUTATION OF HISTORICAL EXTERNAL RATE OF RETURN (HERR)			
3				
4		DATA INPUT		
5				
6	Number		Explicit	
7	Of	e'	Interest	
8	Periods	Guess	Rate	
9	6	14.06%	15.00%	
10				
11	End of	Cash	Future	SUM OF
12	Period	Flow	Value	FUTURE VALUES
13	0	$3,000.00	$6,939.18	$0.75
14	1	$0.00	$0.00	
15	2	-$10,000.00	-$16,925.19	
16	3	$2,000.00	$3,041.75	
17	4	$2,000.00	$2,645.00	
18	5	$2,000.00	$2,300.00	
19	6	$2,000.00	$2,000.00	

FIGURE C.15

PROJECT BALANCE METHOD COMPUTATION PROCESS
USING AN EXTERNAL RATE OF RETURN(MARR)

Return to Main Menu	Help	Calculate

DATA INPUT

Number		Explicit
Of	IRR	Interest
Periods	Guess	Rate(MARR)
6	12.34%	15.00%

End of Period	Cash Flow	Current Balance
0	$3,000.00	$3,000.00
1	$0.00	$3,450.00
2	-$10,000.00	-$6,032.50
3	$2,000.00	-$4,776.91
4	$2,000.00	-$3,366.38
5	$2,000.00	-$1,781.79
6	$2,000.00	-$1.67

FIGURE C.16

SL_DDB	B	C	D	E	F
1	Return to Main Menu		Help	Calculate	
2	COMPUTATION OF STRAIGHT LINE(SL) AND DOUBLE DECLINING				
3	BALANCE(DDB) DEPRECIATION AND BOOK VALUES				
4					
5			DATA INPUT		
6					
7					
8		Number	Principal	Salvage	
9		Of Periods	Value	Value	
10		5	$7,000.00	$0.00	
11					
12					
13					
14					
15					
16	Time	SL	Book Value	DDB	Book Value
17	Period	Depreciation	(SL)	Depreciation	(DDB)
18	1	$1,400.00	$5,600.00	$2,800.00	$4,200.00
19	2	$1,400.00	$4,200.00	$1,680.00	$2,520.00
20	3	$1,400.00	$2,800.00	$1,008.00	$1,512.00
21	4	$1,400.00	$1,400.00	$604.80	$907.20
22	5	$1,400.00	$0.00	$362.88	$544.32

FIGURE C.17

COMPUTATION OF CCA DECLINING BALANCE & AFTER TAX CASH FLOW

CCA_DB

Return to Main Menu | Help | Calculate

DATA INPUT

Number Of Years (N)	Deprec Cost of Asset (P)	CCA Rate (d)	Half Year Rule	Tax Rate (t)	Capital Gains Tax (gt)	Rate of Return (i)	Resale or Salvage Value
5	$45000	20%	yes	40%	20%	15%	$0

End Of Year (n) (1)	Before Tax Cash (2)	Dep. Rate (3)	Deprec Expense BVx(3) (4)	Taxable Income (2)-(4) (5)	Income Tax Rate (6)	Income Tax (5)x(6) (7)	After Tax Cash (2)-(7) (8)	Present-Worth Factor (P/F) (9)	PW of After Tax Cash Flow (8)x(9) (10)	TOTAL PRESENT WORTH Σ(10)
0	-45000						-45000.00	1.00000	-45000.00	-$3807.73
1	15700	0.10	4500.00	11200.00	0.40	4480.00	11220.00	0.86957	9756.58	
2	15700	0.20	8100.00	7600.00	0.40	3040.00	12660.00	0.75614	9572.73	
3	15700	0.20	6480.00	9220.00	0.40	3688.00	12012.00	0.65752	7898.13	
4	15700	0.20	5184.00	10516.00	0.40	4206.40	11493.60	0.57175	6571.47	
5	15700	0.20	4147.20	11552.80	0.40	4621.12	11078.88	0.49718	5508.20	
5	15700						0.00	0.49718	0.00	
5	15700						3791.73	0.49718	1885.17	

FIGURE C.18

Return to Main Menu	Help	Calculate

COMPUTATION OF CCA STRAIGHT LINE & AFTER TAX CASH FLOW

DATA INPUT

Number Of Years (N)	Deprec Cost of Asset (P)	CCA Rate (d)	Half Year Rule	Tax Rate (t)	Capital Gains Tax Rate (g)	Rate of Return (i)	Resale or Salvage Value
5	$45000	50%	yes	42%	21%	12%	$2000

End Of Year (t) (1)	Before Tax Cash (2)	Dep. Rate (3)	Deprec Expense (3)xP (4)	Taxable Income (2)-(4) (5)	Income Tax Rate (6)	Income Tax (5)x(8) (7)	After Tax Cash (2)-(7) (8)	Present-Worth Factor (P/F,I,N) (9)	PW of After Tax Cash Flow (8)x(9)	TOTAL PRESENT WORTH Σ(9)
0	-45000						-45000.00	1.00000	-45000.00	33596.71
1	15700	0.25	11250.00	4450.00	0.42	1869.00	13831.00	0.89286	12349.15	
2	15700	0.50	22500.00	-6800.00	0.42	-2856.00	18556.00	0.79719	14792.66	
3	15700	0.25	11250.00	4450.00	0.42	1869.00	13831.00	0.71178	9844.63	
4	15700			15700.00	0.42	6594.00	9106.00	0.63552	5787.05	
5	15700			15700.00	0.42	6594.00	9106.00	0.56743	5167.02	
5							2000.00	0.56743	1134.86	
5							-840.00	0.56743	-476.64	

FIGURE C.19

MACRS_SL	B	C	D	E	F	G	H	I	J	K
1	Return to Main Menu		Help		Calculate					
2	COMPUTATION OF MACRS STRAIGHT LINE DEPRECIATION METHOD									
3										
4										
5			DATA INPUT							
6										
7		Number	Rate of	Unadjusted	Tax					
8		Of Years	Return	Basis of Asset	Rate					
9		(N)	(i)	(P)	(t)					
10		5	10.00%	$1,500	35.00%					
11										
12										
13				Annual	Income			Present-	PW of	
14	End	Income		Depreciation	Less	Income	Income	Worth	Income	TOTAL
15	Of	Before	Depreciatio	Charge	Depreciation	Tax	Tax	Factor	Tax	OF
16	Year	Taxes and	Percentage	(3)xP	(2)-(4)	Rates	(5)x(6)	(P/F,i,n)	(7)x(8)	PRESENT
17	(n)	Depreciatio	(IRS)	(4)	(5)	(6)	(7)	(8)	(9)	WORTHS
18	(1)	(2)	(3)							
19	1	$500	10.00%	$150	$350	35%	$122	0.90909	$111	$382
20	2	$500	20.00%	$300	$200	35%	$70	0.82645	$58	
21	3	$500	20.00%	$300	$200	35%	$70	0.75131	$53	
22	4	$500	20.00%	$300	$200	35%	$70	0.68301	$48	
23	5	$500	20.00%	$300	$200	35%	$70	0.62092	$43	
	6	$500	10.00%	$150	$350	35%	$122	0.56447	$69	

FIGURE C.20

MACRS_ADM

| | Return to Main Menu | | Help | | Calculate | | | | |

COMPUTATION OF MACRS ACCELERATED DEPRECIATION METHOD

DATA INPUT

	Number Of Years (N)	Rate of Return (i)	Unadjusted Basis of Asset (P)	MACRS Class*	Tax Rate (t)
	5	10.00%	1500.00	5	35.00%

*Note: 3,5,7,10,15 or 20 only.

End Of Year (n) (1)	Income Before Taxes and Depreciation (2)	Depreciatio Percentage (IRS) (3)	Annual Depreciation Charge (3)xP (4)	Income Less Depreciation (2)-(4) (5)	Income Tax t x (5) (6)	Present-Worth Factor (P/F,i,n) (7)	PW of Income Tax (6)x(7) (8)	TOTAL OF PRESENT WORTHS
1	$500.00	20.00%	$300	$200	$70	0.90909	$64	$356
2	$500.00	32.00%	$480	$20	$7	0.82645	$6	
3	$500.00	19.20%	$288	$212	$74	0.75131	$56	
4	$500.00	11.52%	$173	$327	$115	0.68301	$78	
5	$500.00	11.52%	$173	$327	$115	0.62092	$71	
6	$500.00	5.76%	$86	$414	$145	0.56447	$82	

(a)

FIGURE C.21

MACRS_ADM	M	N 3-YEAR Property	O 5-YEAR Property	P 7-YEAR Property	Q 10-YEAR Property	R 15-YEAR Property	S 20-YEAR Property
16				MACRS Recovery Percentages			
19	1	0.3333	0.2	0.1429	0.1	0.05	0.0375
20	2	0.4445	0.32	0.245	0.18	0.095	0.0722
21	3	0.1481	0.192	0.1749	0.144	0.0855	0.0668
22	4	0.0741	0.1152	0.125	0.1152	0.077	0.0618
23	5		0.1152	0.0892	0.0922	0.0693	0.0517
24	6		0.0576	0.0892	0.0737	0.0623	0.0528
25	7			0.0892	0.0655	0.059	0.0489
26	8			0.0446	0.0655	0.059	0.0452
27	9				0.0655	0.059	0.0446
28	10				0.0655	0.059	0.0446
29	11				0.0328	0.059	0.0446
30	12					0.059	0.0446
31	13					0.059	0.0446
32	14					0.059	0.0446
33	15					0.059	0.0446
34	16					0.0295	0.0446
35	17						0.0446
36	18						0.0446
37	19						0.0446
38	20						0.0446
39	21						0.0223

(b)

FIGURE C.21 continued

ATCF_DB

COMPUTATION OF CCA DECLINING BALANCE & AFTER TAX CASH FLOW

DATA INPUT

							Resale or Salvage Value			
Number Of Years (N)	Deprec Cost of Asset (P)	CCA Rate (d)	Half Year Rule	Tax Rate (t)	Capital Gains Tax (ti)	Rate of Return (i)		Debt	Interest on Debt	
5	$45000	20%	yes	42%	21%	12%	$0	$20000	10%	

End Of Year (n) (1)	Before Tax Cash (2)	Dep. Rate (3)	Deprec Expense BVx(3) (4)	Interest Charges J10xK10 (5)	Taxable Income (2)-(4)-(5) (6)	Income Tax (6)x t (7)	After Tax Cash (2)-(5)-(7) (8)	Present-Worth Factor (P/F) (9)	PW of After Tax Cash Flow (8)x(9) (10)	TOTAL PRESENT WORTH Σ(10)
0	45000						-45000.00	1.0000	-45000.00	$3075.38
0	20000						20000.00	1.0000	20000.00	
1	15700	0.10	4500.00	2000.00	9200.00	3864.00	9836.00	0.8929	8782.56	
2	15700	0.20	8100.00	2000.00	5600.00	2352.00	11348.00	0.7972	9046.63	
3	15700	0.20	6480.00	2000.00	7220.00	3032.40	10687.60	0.7118	7593.20	
4	15700	0.20	5184.00	2000.00	8516.00	3576.72	10123.28	0.6355	6433.34	
5	15700	0.20	4147.20	2000.00	9552.80	4012.18	9887.82	0.5674	5496.87	
5							-20000.00	0.5674	-11348.00	
5							0.00	0.5674	0.00	
5							4354.56	0.5674	2470.78	

FIGURE C.22

COMPUTATION OF CCA STRAIGHT LINE & AFTER TAX CASH FLOW

ATCF_8L

DATA INPUT

	Number Of Years (N)	Deprec Cost of Asset (P)	CCA Rate (d)	Half Year Rule	Tax Rate (t)	Capital Gains Tax (gt)	Rate of Return	Resale or Salvage Value	Debt	Interest on Debt
	5	$45000	50%	yes	42%	21%	12%	$2000	$20000	10%

End Of Year (n) (1)	Before Tax Cash (2)	Dep. Rate (3)	Deprec Expense BVx(3) (4)	Interest Charges J10xK10 (5)	Taxable Income (2)-(4)-(5) (6)	Income Tax (6)x1 (7)	After Tax Cash (2)-(5)-(7) (8)	Present-Worth Factor (P/F) (9)	PW of After Tax Cash Flow (8)x(9) (10)	TOTAL PRESENT WORTH Σ(10)
0	-45000						-45000.00	1.00000	-45000.00	$6066.57
0	20000						20000.00	1.00000	20000.00	
1	15700	0.25	11250.00	2000.00	2450.00	1029.00	12671.00	0.89286	11313.43	
2	15700	0.50	22500.00	2000.00	-8800.00	-3696.00	17396.00	0.79719	13867.92	
3	15700	0.25	11250.00	2000.00	2450.00	1029.00	12671.00	0.71178	9018.96	
4	15700			2000.00	13700.00	5754.00	7946.00	0.63552	5049.84	
5	15700			2000.00	13700.00	5754.00	7946.00	0.56743	4508.80	
5							-20000.00	0.56743	-11348.60	
5							2000.00	0.56743	1134.86	
5							-840.00	0.56743	-476.64	

FIGURE C.23

C.3   REFERENCES

Novell Perfect Office, The Perfect Way to Make Your Numbers Count, User's Guide, Quattro Pro, Novell, Inc., Orem, UT, 1994.

Function Reference, Microsoft Excel, version 4.0, Microsoft Inc., Richmond, WA, 1992.

1-2-3 Release 5 for Windows Quick Reference, Que Corporation, Indianapolis, IN., 1994.

User's Guide for DOS, CA-SuperCalc version 5.0, Computer Associates, San Jose, CA, January 1992.

User's Guide Lotus 1-2-3 for Windows, release 4, Lotus Development Corp., Cambridge, MA, 1993.

User's Guide, Microsoft Excel, version 5.0, Microsoft Corp., Richmond, WA, 1993–1994.

DISCRETE COMPOUNDING INTEREST FACTORS

½% interest factors for discrete compounding periods

	SINGLE PAYMENT		UNIFORM SERIES					
	Compound Amount Factor	Present Worth Factor	Capital Recovery Factor	Present Worth Factor	Sinking Fund Factor	Compound Amount Factor	Gradient Factor	
N	(F/P,½,N)	(P/F,½,N)	(A/P,½,N)	(P/A,½,N)	(A/F,½,N)	(F/A,½,N)	(A/G,½,N)	N
1	1.00500	0.99502	1.00500	0.99502	1.00000	1.00000	0.00000	1
2	1.01003	0.99007	0.50375	1.98510	0.49875	2.00500	0.49875	2
3	1.01508	0.98515	0.33667	2.97025	0.33167	3.01503	0.99667	3
4	1.02015	0.98025	0.25313	3.95050	0.24813	4.03010	1.49377	4
5	1.02525	0.97537	0.20301	4.92587	0.19801	5.05025	1.99003	5
6	1.03038	0.97052	0.16960	5.89638	0.16460	6.07550	2.48545	6
7	1.03553	0.96569	0.14573	6.86207	0.14073	7.10588	2.98005	7
8	1.04071	0.96089	0.12783	7.82296	0.12283	8.14141	3.47382	8
9	1.04591	0.95610	0.11391	8.77906	0.10891	9.18212	3.96675	9
10	1.05114	0.95135	0.10277	9.73041	0.09777	10.22803	4.45885	10
11	1.05640	0.94661	0.09366	10.67703	0.08866	11.27917	4.95013	11
12	1.06168	0.94191	0.08607	11.61893	0.08107	12.33556	5.44057	12
13	1.06699	0.93722	0.07964	12.55615	0.07464	13.39724	5.93018	13
14	1.07232	0.93256	0.07414	13.48871	0.06914	14.46423	6.41896	14
15	1.07768	0.92792	0.06936	14.41662	0.06436	15.53655	6.90691	15
16	1.08307	0.92330	0.06519	15.00000	0.06019	16.61423	7.39403	16
17	1.08849	0.91871	0.06151	16.25863	0.05651	17.69730	7.88031	17
18	1.09393	0.91414	0.05823	17.17277	0.05323	18.78579	8.36577	18
19	1.09940	0.90959	0.05530	18.08236	0.05030	19.87972	8.85040	19
20	1.10490	0.90506	0.05267	18.98742	0.04767	20.97912	9.33419	20
21	1.11042	0.90056	0.05028	19.88798	0.04528	22.08401	9.81716	21
22	1.11597	0.89608	0.04811	20.78406	0.04311	23.19443	10.29929	22
23	1.12155	0.89162	0.04613	21.67568	0.04113	24.31040	10.78060	23
24	1.12716	0.88719	0.04432	22.56287	0.03932	25.43196	11.26107	24
25	1.13280	0.88277	0.04265	23.44564	0.03765	26.55912	11.74072	25
26	1.13846	0.87838	0.04111	24.32402	0.03611	27.69191	12.21953	26
27	1.14415	0.87401	0.03969	25.19803	0.03469	28.83037	12.69751	27
28	1.14987	0.86966	0.03836	26.06769	0.03336	29.97452	13.17467	28
29	1.15562	0.86533	0.03713	26.93302	0.03213	31.12439	13.65099	29
30	1.16140	0.86103	0.03598	27.79405	0.03098	32.28002	14.12649	30
31	1.16721	0.85675	0.03490	28.65080	0.02990	33.44142	14.60116	31
32	1.17304	0.85248	0.03389	29.50328	0.02889	34.60862	15.07499	32
33	1.17891	0.84824	0.03295	30.35153	0.02795	35.78167	15.54800	33
34	1.18480	0.84402	0.03206	31.19555	0.02706	36.96058	16.02018	34
35	1.19073	0.83982	0.03122	32.03537	0.02622	38.14538	16.49153	35
40	1.22079	0.81914	0.02765	36.17223	0.02265	44.15885	18.83585	40
45	1.25162	0.79896	0.02487	40.20720	0.01987	50.32416	21.15947	45
50	1.28323	0.77929	0.02265	44.14279	0.01765	56.64516	23.46242	50
55	1.31563	0.76009	0.02084	47.98145	0.01584	63.12577	25.74471	55
60	1.34885	0.74137	0.01933	51.72556	0.01433	69.77003	28.00638	60
65	1.38291	0.72311	0.01806	55.37746	0.01306	76.58206	30.24745	65
70	1.41783	0.70530	0.01697	58.93942	0.01197	83.56611	32.46796	70
75	1.45363	0.68793	0.01602	62.41365	0.01102	90.72650	34.66794	75
80	1.49034	0.67099	0.01520	65.80231	0.01020	98.06771	36.84742	80
85	1.52797	0.65446	0.01447	69.10750	0.00947	105.59430	39.00646	85
90	1.56655	0.63834	0.01383	72.33130	0.00883	113.31094	41.14508	90
95	1.60611	0.62262	0.01325	75.47569	0.00825	121.22243	43.26333	95
100	1.64667	0.60729	0.01273	78.54264	0.00773	129.33370	45.36126	100

1% interest factors for discrete compounding periods

	SINGLE PAYMENT		UNIFORM SERIES					
	Compound Amount Factor	Present Worth Factor	Capital Recovery Factor	Present Worth Factor	Sinking Fund Factor	Compound Amount Factor	Gradient Factor	
N	(F/P,1,N)	(P/F,1,N)	(A/P,1,N)	(P/A,1,N)	(A/F,1,N)	(F/A,1,N)	(A/G,1,N)	N
1	1.01000	0.99010	1.01000	0.99010	1.00000	1.00000	0.00000	1
2	1.02010	0.98030	0.50751	1.97040	0.49751	2.01000	0.49751	2
3	1.03030	0.97059	0.34002	2.94099	0.33002	3.03010	0.99337	3
4	1.04060	0.96098	0.25628	3.90197	0.24628	4.06040	1.48756	4
5	1.05101	0.95147	0.20604	4.85343	0.19604	5.10101	1.98010	5
6	1.06152	0.94205	0.17255	5.79548	0.16255	6.15202	2.47098	6
7	1.07214	0.93272	0.14863	6.72819	0.13863	7.21354	2.96020	7
8	1.08286	0.92348	0.13069	7.65168	0.12069	8.28567	3.44777	8
9	1.09369	0.91434	0.11674	8.56602	0.10674	9.36853	3.93367	9
10	1.10462	0.90529	0.10558	9.47130	0.09558	10.46221	4.41792	10
11	1.11567	0.89632	0.09645	10.36763	0.08645	11.56683	4.90052	11
12	1.12683	0.88745	0.08885	11.25508	0.07885	12.68250	5.38145	12
13	1.13809	0.87866	0.08241	12.13374	0.07241	13.80933	5.86073	13
14	1.14947	0.86996	0.07690	13.00370	0.06690	14.94742	6.33836	14
15	1.16097	0.86135	0.07212	13.86505	0.06212	16.09690	6.81433	15
16	1.17258	0.85282	0.06794	14.71787	0.05794	17.25786	7.28865	16
17	1.18430	0.84438	0.06426	15.56225	0.05426	18.43044	7.76131	17
18	1.19615	0.83602	0.06098	16.39827	0.05098	19.61475	8.23231	18
19	1.20811	0.82774	0.05805	17.22601	0.04805	20.81090	8.70167	19
20	1.22019	0.81954	0.05542	18.04555	0.04542	22.01900	9.16937	20
21	1.23239	0.81143	0.05303	18.85698	0.04303	23.23919	9.63542	21
22	1.24472	0.80340	0.05086	19.66038	0.04086	24.47159	10.09982	22
23	1.25716	0.79544	0.04889	20.45582	0.03889	25.71630	10.56257	23
24	1.26973	0.78757	0.04707	21.24339	0.03707	26.97346	11.02367	24
25	1.28243	0.77977	0.04541	22.02316	0.03541	28.24320	11.48312	25
26	1.29526	0.77205	0.04387	22.79520	0.03387	29.52563	11.94092	26
27	1.30821	0.76440	0.04245	23.55961	0.03245	30.82089	12.39707	27
28	1.32129	0.75684	0.04112	24.31644	0.03112	32.12910	12.85158	28
29	1.33450	0.74934	0.03990	25.06579	0.02990	33.45039	13.30444	29
30	1.34785	0.74192	0.03875	25.80771	0.02875	34.78489	13.75566	30
31	1.36133	0.73458	0.03768	26.54229	0.02768	36.13274	14.20523	31
32	1.37494	0.72730	0.03667	27.26959	0.02667	37.49407	14.65317	32
33	1.38869	0.72010	0.03573	27.98969	0.02573	38.86901	15.09946	33
34	1.40258	0.71297	0.03484	28.70267	0.02484	40.25770	15.54410	34
35	1.41660	0.70591	0.03400	29.40858	0.02400	41.66028	15.98711	35
40	1.48886	0.67165	0.03046	32.83469	0.02046	48.88637	18.17761	40
45	1.56481	0.63905	0.02771	36.09451	0.01771	56.48107	20.32730	45
50	1.64463	0.60804	0.02551	39.19612	0.01551	64.46318	22.43635	50
55	1.72852	0.57853	0.02373	42.14719	0.01373	72.85246	24.50495	55
60	1.81670	0.55045	0.02224	44.95504	0.01224	81.66967	26.53331	60
65	1.90937	0.52373	0.02100	47.62661	0.01100	90.93665	28.52167	65
70	2.00676	0.49831	0.01993	50.16851	0.00993	100.67634	30.47026	70
75	2.10913	0.47413	0.01902	52.58705	0.00902	110.91285	32.37934	75
80	2.21672	0.45112	0.01822	54.88821	0.00822	121.67152	34.24920	80
85	2.32979	0.42922	0.01752	57.07768	0.00752	132.97900	36.08013	85
90	2.44863	0.40839	0.01690	59.16088	0.00690	144.86327	37.87245	90
95	2.57354	0.38857	0.01636	61.14298	0.00636	157.35376	39.62648	95
100	2.70481	0.36971	0.01587	63.02888	0.00587	170.48138	41.34257	100

$1\frac{1}{2}$% interest factors for discrete compounding periods

| | SINGLE PAYMENT | | UNIFORM SERIES | | | | | |
| | Compound Amount Factor | Present Worth Factor | Capital Recovery Factor | Present Worth Factor | Sinking Fund Factor | Compound Amount Factor | Gradient Factor | |
N	(F/P,1½,N)	(P/F,1½,N)	(A/P,1½,N)	(P/A,1½,N)	(A/F,1½,N)	(F/A,1½,N)	(A/G,1½,N)	N
1	1.01500	0.98522	1.01500	0.98522	1.00000	1.00000	0.00000	1
2	1.03023	0.97066	0.51128	1.95588	0.49628	2.01500	0.49628	2
3	1.04568	0.95632	0.34338	2.91220	0.32838	3.04523	0.99007	3
4	1.06136	0.94218	0.25944	3.85438	0.24444	4.09090	1.48139	4
5	1.07728	0.92826	0.20909	4.78264	0.19409	5.15227	1.97023	5
6	1.09344	0.91454	0.17553	5.69719	0.16053	6.22955	2.45658	6
7	1.10984	0.90103	0.15156	6.59821	0.13656	7.32299	2.94046	7
8	1.12649	0.88771	0.13358	7.48593	0.11858	8.43284	3.42185	8
9	1.14339	0.87459	0.11961	8.36052	0.10461	9.55933	3.90077	9
10	1.16054	0.86167	0.10843	9.22218	0.09343	10.70272	4.37721	10
11	1.17795	0.84893	0.09929	10.07112	0.08429	11.86326	4.85118	11
12	1.19562	0.83639	0.09168	10.90751	0.07668	13.04121	5.32267	12
13	1.21355	0.82403	0.08524	11.73153	0.07024	14.23683	5.79169	13
14	1.23176	0.81185	0.07972	12.54338	0.06472	15.45038	6.25824	14
15	1.25023	0.79985	0.07494	13.34323	0.05994	16.68214	6.72231	15
16	1.26899	0.78803	0.07077	14.13126	0.05577	17.93237	7.18392	16
17	1.28802	0.77639	0.06708	14.90765	0.05208	19.20136	7.64306	17
18	1.30734	0.76491	0.06381	15.67256	0.04881	20.48938	8.09973	18
19	1.32695	0.75361	0.06088	16.42617	0.04588	21.79672	8.55394	19
20	1.34686	0.74247	0.05825	17.16864	0.04325	23.12367	9.00569	20
21	1.36706	0.73150	0.05587	17.90014	0.04087	24.47052	9.45497	21
22	1.38756	0.72069	0.05370	18.62082	0.03870	25.83758	9.90180	22
20	1.40838	0.71004	0.05173	19.33086	0.03673	27.22514	10.34618	23
24	1.42950	0.69954	0.04992	20.03041	0.03492	28.63352	10.78810	24
25	1.45095	0.68921	0.04826	20.71961	0.03326	30.06302	11.22758	25
26	1.47271	0.67902	0.04673	21.39863	0.03173	31.51397	11.66460	26
27	1.49480	0.66899	0.04532	22.06762	0.03032	32.98668	12.09918	27
28	1.51722	0.65910	0.04400	22.72672	0.02900	34.48148	12.53132	28
29	1.53998	0.64936	0.04278	23.37608	0.02778	35.99870	12.96102	29
30	1.56308	0.63976	0.04164	24.01584	0.02664	37.53868	13.38829	30
31	1.58653	0.63031	0.04057	24.64615	0.02557	39.10176	13.81312	31
32	1.61032	0.62099	0.03958	25.26714	0.02458	40.68829	14.23553	32
33	1.63448	0.61182	0.03864	25.87895	0.02364	42.29861	14.65550	33
34	1.65900	0.60277	0.03776	26.48173	0.02276	43.93309	15.07306	34
35	1.68388	0.59387	0.03693	27.07559	0.02193	45.59209	15.48820	35
40	1.81402	0.55126	0.03343	29.91585	0.01843	54.26789	17.52773	40
45	1.95421	0.51171	0.03072	32.55234	0.01572	63.61420	19.50739	45
50	2.10524	0.47500	0.02857	34.99969	0.01357	73.68283	21.42772	50
55	2.26794	0.44093	0.02683	37.27147	0.01183	84.52960	23.28936	55
60	2.44322	0.40930	0.02539	39.38027	0.01039	96.21465	25.09296	60
65	2.63204	0.37993	0.02419	41.33779	0.00919	108.80277	26.83925	65
70	2.83546	0.35268	0.02317	43.15487	0.00817	122.36375	28.52901	70
75	3.05459	0.32738	0.02230	44.84160	0.00730	136.97278	30.16306	75
80	3.29066	0.30389	0.02155	46.40732	0.00655	152.71085	31.74228	80
85	3.54498	0.28209	0.02089	47.86072	0.00589	169.66523	33.26756	85
90	3.81895	0.26185	0.02032	49.20985	0.00532	187.92990	34.73987	90
95	4.11409	0.24307	0.01982	50.46220	0.00482	207.60614	36.16018	95
100	4.43205	0.22563	0.01937	51.62470	0.00437	228.80304	37.52953	100

2% interest factors for discrete compounding periods

	SINGLE PAYMENT		UNIFORM SERIES					
	Compound Amount Factor	Present Worth Factor	Capital Recovery Factor	Present Worth Factor	Sinking Fund Factor	Compound Amount Factor	Gradient Factor	
N	(F/P,2,N)	(P/F,2,N)	(A/P,2,N)	(P/A,2,N)	(A/F,2,N)	(F/A,2,N)	(A/G,2,N)	N
1	1.02000	0.98039	1.02000	0.98039	1.00000	1.00000	0.00000	1
2	1.04040	0.96117	0.51505	1.94156	0.49505	2.02000	0.49505	2
3	1.06121	0.94232	0.34675	2.88388	0.32675	3.06040	0.98680	3
4	1.08243	0.92385	0.26262	3.80773	0.24262	4.12161	1.47625	4
5	1.10408	0.90573	0.21216	4.71346	0.19216	5.20404	1.96040	5
6	1.12616	0.88797	0.17853	5.60143	0.15853	6.30812	2.44226	6
7	1.14869	0.87056	0.15451	6.47199	0.13451	7.43428	2.92082	7
8	1.17166	0.85349	0.13651	7.32548	0.11651	8.58297	3.39608	8
9	1.19509	0.83676	0.12252	8.16224	0.10252	9.75463	3.86805	9
10	1.21899	0.82035	0.11133	8.98259	0.09133	10.94972	4.33674	10
11	1.24337	0.80426	0.10218	9.78685	0.08218	12.16872	4.80213	11
12	1.26824	0.78849	0.09456	10.57534	0.07456	13.41209	5.26424	12
13	1.29361	0.77303	0.08812	11.34837	0.06812	14.68033	5.72307	13
14	1.31948	0.75788	0.08260	12.10625	0.06260	15.97394	6.17862	14
15	1.34587	0.74301	0.07783	12.84926	0.05783	17.29342	6.63090	15
16	1.37279	0.72845	0.07365	13.57771	0.05365	18.63929	7.07990	16
17	1.40024	0.71416	0.06997	14.29187	0.04997	20.01207	7.52564	17
18	1.42825	0.70016	0.06670	14.99203	0.04670	21.41231	7.96811	18
19	1.45681	0.68643	0.06378	15.67846	0.04378	22.84056	8.40732	19
20	1.48595	0.67297	0.06116	16.35143	0.04116	24.29737	8.84328	20
21	1.51567	0.65978	0.05878	17.01121	0.03878	25.78332	9.27599	21
22	1.54598	0.64684	0.05663	17.65805	0.03663	27.29898	9.70546	22
23	1.57690	0.63416	0.05467	18.29220	0.03467	28.84496	10.13169	23
24	1.60844	0.62172	0.05287	18.91393	0.03287	30.42186	10.55468	24
25	1.64061	0.60953	0.05122	19.52346	0.03122	32.03030	10.97445	25
26	1.67342	0.59758	0.04970	20.12104	0.02970	33.67091	11.39100	26
27	1.70689	0.58586	0.04829	20.70690	0.02829	35.34432	11.80433	27
28	1.74102	0.57437	0.04699	21.28127	0.02699	37.05121	12.21446	28
29	1.77584	0.56311	0.04578	21.84438	0.02578	38.79223	12.62138	29
30	1.81136	0.55207	0.04465	22.39646	0.02465	40.56808	13.02512	30
31	1.84759	0.54125	0.04360	22.93770	0.02360	42.37944	13.42566	31
32	1.88454	0.53063	0.04261	23.46833	0.02261	44.22703	13.82303	32
33	1.92223	0.52023	0.04169	23.98856	0.02169	46.11157	14.21722	33
34	1.96068	0.51003	0.04082	24.49859	0.02082	48.03380	14.60826	34
35	1.99989	0.50003	0.04000	24.99862	0.02000	49.99448	14.99613	35
40	2.20804	0.45289	0.03656	27.35548	0.01656	60.40198	16.88850	40
45	2.43785	0.41020	0.03391	29.49016	0.01391	71.89271	18.70336	45
50	2.69159	0.37153	0.03182	31.42361	0.01182	84.57940	20.44198	50
55	2.97173	0.33650	0.03014	33.17479	0.01014	98.58653	22.10572	55
60	3.28103	0.30478	0.02877	34.76089	0.00877	114.05154	23.69610	60
65	3.62252	0.27605	0.02763	36.19747	0.00763	131.12616	25.21471	65
70	3.99956	0.25003	0.02667	37.49862	0.00667	149.97791	26.66323	70
75	4.41584	0.22648	0.02586	38.67711	0.00586	170.79177	28.04344	75
80	4.87544	0.20511	0.02516	39.74451	0.00516	193.77196	29.35718	80
85	5.38288	0.18577	0.02456	40.71129	0.00456	219.14394	30.60635	85
90	5.94313	0.16826	0.02405	41.58693	0.00405	247.15666	31.79292	90
95	6.56170	0.15240	0.02360	42.38002	0.00360	278.08496	32.91889	95
100	7.24465	0.13803	0.02320	43.09835	0.00320	312.23231	33.98628	100

$2\frac{1}{2}$% interest factors for discrete compounding periods

	SINGLE PAYMENT		UNIFORM SERIES					
	Compound Amount Factor	Present Worth Factor	Capital Recovery Factor	Present Worth Factor	Sinking Fund Factor	Compound Amount Factor	Gradient Factor	
N	$(F/P,2\frac{1}{2},N)$	$(P/F,2\frac{1}{2},N)$	$(A/P,2\frac{1}{2},N)$	$(P/A,2\frac{1}{2},N)$	$(A/F,2\frac{1}{2},N)$	$(F/A,2\frac{1}{2},N)$	$(A/G,2\frac{1}{2},N)$	N
1	1.02500	0.97561	1.02500	0.97561	1.00000	1.00000	0.00000	1
2	1.05063	0.95181	0.51883	1.92742	0.49383	2.02500	0.49383	2
3	1.07689	0.92860	0.35014	2.85602	0.32514	3.07563	0.98354	3
4	1.10381	0.90595	0.26582	3.76197	0.24082	4.15252	1.46914	4
5	1.13141	0.88385	0.21525	4.64583	0.19025	5.25633	1.95063	5
6	1.15969	0.86230	0.18155	5.50813	0.15655	6.38774	2.42801	6
7	1.18869	0.84127	0.15750	6.34939	0.13250	7.54743	2.90128	7
8	1.21840	0.82075	0.13947	7.17014	0.11447	8.73612	3.37045	8
9	1.24886	0.80073	0.12546	7.97087	0.10046	9.95452	3.83552	9
10	1.28008	0.78120	0.11426	8.75206	0.08926	11.20338	4.29649	10
11	1.31209	0.76214	0.10511	9.51421	0.08011	12.48347	4.75338	11
12	1.34489	0.74356	0.09749	10.25776	0.07249	13.79555	5.20618	12
13	1.37851	0.72542	0.09105	10.98318	0.06605	15.14044	5.65490	13
14	1.41297	0.70773	0.08554	11.69091	0.06054	16.51895	6.09955	14
15	1.44830	0.69047	0.08077	12.38138	0.05577	17.93193	6.54013	15
16	1.48451	0.67362	0.07660	13.05500	0.05160	19.38022	6.97665	16
17	1.52162	0.65720	0.07293	13.71220	0.04793	20.86473	7.40912	17
18	1.55966	0.64117	0.06967	14.35336	0.04467	22.38635	7.83754	18
19	1.59865	0.62553	0.06676	14.97889	0.04176	23.94601	8.26193	19
20	1.63862	0.61027	0.06415	15.58916	0.03915	25.54466	8.68230	20
21	1.67958	0.59539	0.06179	16.18455	0.03679	27.18327	9.09865	21
22	1.72157	0.58086	0.05965	16.76541	0.03465	28.86286	9.51099	22
23	1.76461	0.56670	0.05770	17.33211	0.03270	30.58443	9.91933	23
24	1.80873	0.55288	0.05591	17.88499	0.03091	32.34904	10.32369	24
25	1.85394	0.53939	0.05428	18.42438	0.02928	34.15776	10.72408	25
26	1.90029	0.52623	0.05277	18.95061	0.02777	36.01171	11.12050	26
27	1.94780	0.51340	0.05138	19.46401	0.02638	37.91200	11.51298	27
28	1.99650	0.50088	0.05009	19.96489	0.02509	39.85980	11.90152	28
29	2.04641	0.48866	0.04889	20.45355	0.02389	41.85630	12.28613	29
30	2.09757	0.47674	0.04778	20.93029	0.02278	43.90270	12.66683	30
31	2.15001	0.46511	0.04674	21.39541	0.02174	46.00027	13.04364	31
32	2.20376	0.45377	0.04577	21.84918	0.02077	48.15028	13.41656	32
33	2.25885	0.44270	0.04486	22.29188	0.01986	50.35403	13.78562	33
34	2.31532	0.43191	0.04401	22.72379	0.01901	52.61289	14.15082	34
35	2.37321	0.42137	0.04321	23.14516	0.01821	54.92821	14.51218	35
40	2.68506	0.37243	0.03984	25.10278	0.01484	67.40255	16.26203	40
45	3.03790	0.32917	0.03727	26.83302	0.01227	81.51613	17.91848	45
50	3.43711	0.29094	0.03526	28.36231	0.01026	97.48435	19.48389	50
55	3.88877	0.25715	0.03365	29.71398	0.00865	115.55092	20.96077	55
60	4.39979	0.22728	0.03235	30.90866	0.00735	135.99159	22.35185	60
65	4.97796	0.20089	0.03128	31.96458	0.00628	159.11833	23.65996	65
70	5.63210	0.17755	0.03040	32.89786	0.00540	185.28411	24.88807	70
75	6.37221	0.15693	0.02965	33.72274	0.00465	214.88830	26.03926	75
80	7.20957	0.13870	0.02903	34.45182	0.00403	248.38271	27.11666	80
85	8.15696	0.12259	0.02849	35.09621	0.00349	286.27857	28.12346	85
90	9.22886	0.10836	0.02804	35.66577	0.00304	329.15425	29.06288	90
95	10.44160	0.09577	0.02765	36.16917	0.00265	377.66415	29.93815	95
100	11.81372	0.08465	0.02731	36.61411	0.00231	432.54865	30.75249	100

3% interest factors for discrete compounding periods

	SINGLE PAYMENT		UNIFORM SERIES					
	Compound Amount Factor	Present Worth Factor	Capital Recovery Factor	Present Worth Factor	Sinking Fund Factor	Compound Amount Factor	Gradient Factor	
N	(F/P,3,N)	(P/F,3,N)	(A/P,3,N)	(P/A,3,N)	(A/F,3,N)	(F/A,3,N)	(A/G,3,N)	N
1	1.03000	0.97087	1.03000	0.97087	1.00000	1.00000	0.00000	1
2	1.06090	0.94260	0.52261	1.91347	0.49261	2.03000	0.49261	2
3	1.09273	0.91514	0.35353	2.82861	0.32353	3.09090	0.98030	3
4	1.12551	0.88849	0.26903	3.71710	0.23903	4.18363	1.46306	4
5	1.15927	0.86261	0.21835	4.57971	0.18835	5.30914	1.94090	5
6	1.19405	0.83748	0.18460	5.41719	0.15460	6.46841	2.41383	6
7	1.22987	0.81309	0.16051	6.23028	0.13051	7.66246	2.88185	7
8	1.26677	0.78941	0.14246	7.01969	0.11246	8.89234	3.34496	8
9	1.30477	0.76642	0.12843	7.78611	0.09843	10.15911	3.80318	9
10	1.34392	0.74409	0.11723	8.53020	0.08723	11.46388	4.25650	10
11	1.38423	0.72242	0.10808	9.25262	0.07808	12.80780	4.70494	11
12	1.42576	0.70138	0.10046	9.95400	0.07046	14.19203	5.14850	12
13	1.46853	0.68095	0.09403	10.63496	0.06403	15.61779	5.58720	13
14	1.51259	0.66112	0.08853	11.29607	0.05853	17.08632	6.02104	14
15	1.55797	0.64186	0.08377	11.93794	0.05377	18.59891	6.45004	15
16	1.60471	0.62317	0.07961	12.56110	0.04961	20.15688	6.87421	16
17	1.65285	0.60502	0.07595	13.16612	0.04595	21.76159	7.29357	17
18	1.70243	0.58739	0.07271	13.75351	0.04271	23.41444	7.70812	18
19	1.75351	0.57029	0.06981	14.32380	0.03981	25.11687	8.11788	19
20	1.80611	0.55368	0.06722	14.87747	0.03722	26.87037	8.52286	20
21	1.86029	0.53755	0.06487	15.41502	0.03487	28.67649	8.92309	21
22	1.91610	0.52189	0.06275	15.93692	0.03275	30.53678	9.31858	22
23	1.97359	0.50669	0.06081	16.44361	0.03081	32.45288	9.70934	23
24	2.03279	0.49193	0.05905	16.93554	0.02905	34.42647	10.09540	24
25	2.09378	0.47761	0.05743	17.41315	0.02743	36.45926	10.47677	25
26	2.15659	0.46369	0.05594	17.87684	0.02594	38.55304	10.85348	26
27	2.22129	0.45019	0.05456	18.32703	0.02456	40.70963	11.22554	27
28	2.28793	0.43708	0.05329	18.76411	0.02329	42.93092	11.59298	28
29	2.35657	0.42435	0.05211	19.18845	0.02211	45.21885	11.95582	29
30	2.42726	0.41199	0.05102	19.60044	0.02102	47.57542	12.31407	30
31	2.50008	0.39999	0.05000	20.00043	0.02000	50.00268	12.66777	31
32	2.57508	0.38834	0.04905	20.38877	0.01905	52.50276	13.01694	32
33	2.65234	0.37703	0.04816	20.76579	0.01816	55.07784	13.36160	33
34	2.73191	0.36604	0.04732	21.13184	0.01732	57.73018	13.70177	34
35	2.81386	0.35538	0.04654	21.48722	0.01654	60.46208	14.03749	35
40	3.26204	0.30656	0.04326	23.11477	0.01326	75.40126	15.65016	40
45	3.78160	0.26444	0.04079	24.51871	0.01079	92.71986	17.15557	45
50	4.38391	0.22811	0.03887	25.72976	0.00887	112.79687	18.55751	50
55	5.08215	0.19677	0.03735	26.77443	0.00735	136.07162	19.86004	55
60	5.89160	0.16973	0.03613	27.67556	0.00613	163.05344	21.06742	60
65	6.82998	0.14641	0.03515	28.45289	0.00515	194.33276	22.18407	65
70	7.91782	0.12630	0.03434	29.12342	0.00434	230.59406	23.21454	70
75	9.17893	0.10895	0.03367	29.70183	0.00367	272.63086	24.16342	75
80	10.64089	0.09398	0.03311	30.20076	0.00311	321.36302	25.03534	80
85	12.33571	0.08107	0.03265	30.63115	0.00265	377.85695	25.83490	85
90	14.30047	0.06993	0.03226	31.00241	0.00226	443.34890	26.56665	90
95	16.57816	0.06032	0.03193	31.32266	0.00193	519.27203	27.23505	95
100	19.21863	0.05203	0.03165	31.59891	0.00165	607.28773	27.84445	100

4% interest factors for discrete compounding periods

	SINGLE PAYMENT		UNIFORM SERIES					
	Compound Amount Factor	Present Worth Factor	Capital Recovery Factor	Present Worth Factor	Sinking Fund Factor	Compound Amount Factor	Gradient Factor	
N	(F/P,4,N)	(P/F,4,N)	(A/P,4,N)	(P/A,4,N)	(A/F,4,N)	(F/A,4,N)	(A/G,4,N)	N
1	1.04000	0.96154	1.04000	0.96154	1.00000	1.00000	0.00000	1
2	1.08160	0.92456	0.53020	1.88609	0.49020	2.04000	0.49020	2
3	1.12486	0.88900	0.36035	2.77509	0.32035	3.12160	0.97386	3
4	1.16986	0.85480	0.27549	3.62990	0.23549	4.24646	1.45100	4
5	1.21665	0.82193	0.22463	4.45182	0.18463	5.41632	1.92161	5
6	1.26532	0.79031	0.19076	5.24214	0.15076	6.63298	2.38571	6
7	1.31593	0.75992	0.16661	6.00205	0.12661	7.89829	2.84332	7
8	1.36857	0.73069	0.14853	6.73274	0.10853	9.21423	3.29443	8
9	1.42331	0.70259	0.13449	7.43533	0.09449	10.58280	3.73908	9
10	1.48024	0.67556	0.12329	8.11090	0.08329	12.00611	4.17726	10
11	1.53945	0.64958	0.11415	8.76048	0.07415	13.48635	4.60901	11
12	1.60103	0.62460	0.10655	9.38507	0.06655	15.02581	5.03435	12
13	1.66507	0.60057	0.10014	9.98565	0.06014	16.62684	5.45329	13
14	1.73168	0.57748	0.09467	10.56312	0.05467	18.29191	5.86586	14
15	1.80094	0.55526	0.08994	11.11839	0.04994	20.02359	6.27209	15
16	1.87298	0.53391	0.08582	11.65230	0.04582	21.82453	6.67200	16
17	1.94790	0.51337	0.08220	12.16567	0.04220	23.69751	7.06563	17
18	2.02582	0.49363	0.07899	12.65930	0.03899	25.64541	7.45300	18
19	2.10685	0.47464	0.07614	13.13394	0.03614	27.67123	7.83418	19
20	2.19112	0.45639	0.07358	13.59033	0.03358	29.77808	8.20912	20
21	2.27877	0.43883	0.07128	14.02916	0.03128	31.96920	8.57794	21
22	2.36992	0.42196	0.06920	14.45112	0.02920	34.24797	8.94065	22
23	2.46472	0.40573	0.06731	14.85684	0.02731	36.61789	9.29729	23
24	2.56330	0.39012	0.06559	15.24696	0.02559	39.08260	9.64790	24
25	2.66584	0.37512	0.06401	15.62208	0.02401	41.64591	9.99252	25
26	2.77247	0.36069	0.06257	15.98277	0.02257	44.31174	10.33120	26
27	2.88337	0.34682	0.06124	16.32959	0.02124	47.08421	10.66399	27
28	2.99870	0.33348	0.06001	16.66306	0.02001	49.96758	10.99092	28
29	3.11865	0.32065	0.05888	16.98371	0.01888	52.96629	11.31205	29
30	3.24340	0.30832	0.05783	17.29203	0.01783	56.08494	11.62743	30
31	3.37313	0.29646	0.05686	17.58849	0.01686	59.32834	11.93710	31
32	3.50806	0.28506	0.05595	17.87355	0.01595	62.70147	12.24113	32
33	3.64838	0.27409	0.05510	18.14765	0.01510	66.20953	12.53956	33
34	3.79432	0.26355	0.05431	18.41120	0.01431	69.85791	12.83244	34
35	3.94609	0.25342	0.05358	18.66461	0.01358	73.65222	13.11984	35
40	4.80102	0.20829	0.05052	19.79277	0.01052	95.02552	14.47651	40
45	5.84118	0.17120	0.04826	20.72004	0.00826	121.02939	15.70474	45
50	7.10668	0.14071	0.04655	21.48218	0.00655	152.66708	16.81225	50
55	8.64637	0.11566	0.04523	22.10861	0.00523	191.15917	17.80704	55
60	10.51963	0.09506	0.04420	22.62349	0.00420	237.99069	18.69723	60
65	12.79874	0.07813	0.04339	23.04668	0.00339	294.96838	19.49093	65
70	15.57162	0.06422	0.04275	23.39451	0.00275	364.29046	20.19614	70
75	18.94525	0.05278	0.04223	23.68041	0.00223	448.63137	20.82062	75
80	23.04980	0.04338	0.04181	23.91539	0.00181	551.24498	21.37185	80
85	28.04360	0.03566	0.04148	24.10853	0.00148	676.09012	21.85693	85
90	34.11933	0.02931	0.04121	24.26728	0.00121	827.98333	22.28255	90
95	41.51139	0.02409	0.04099	24.39776	0.00099	1012.78465	22.65498	95
100	50.50495	0.01980	0.04081	24.50500	0.00081	1237.62370	22.98000	100

5% interest factors for discrete compounding periods

	SINGLE PAYMENT		UNIFORM SERIES					
	Compound Amount Factor	Present Worth Factor	Capital Recovery Factor	Present Worth Factor	Sinking Fund Factor	Compound Amount Factor	Gradient Factor	
N	(F/P,5,N)	(P/F,5,N)	(A/P,5,N)	(P/A,5,N)	(A/F,5,N)	(F/A,5,N)	(A/G,5,N)	N
1	1.05000	0.95238	1.05000	0.95238	1.00000	1.00000	0.00000	1
2	1.10250	0.90703	0.53780	1.85941	0.48780	2.05000	0.48780	2
3	1.15763	0.86384	0.36721	2.72325	0.31721	3.15250	0.96749	3
4	1.21551	0.82270	0.28201	3.54595	0.23201	4.31013	1.43905	4
5	1.27628	0.78353	0.23097	4.32948	0.18097	5.52563	1.90252	5
6	1.34010	0.74622	0.19702	5.07569	0.14702	6.80191	2.35790	6
7	1.40710	0.71068	0.17282	5.78637	0.12282	8.14201	2.80523	7
8	1.47746	0.67684	0.15472	6.46321	0.10472	9.54911	3.24451	8
9	1.55133	0.64461	0.14069	7.10782	0.09069	11.02656	3.67579	9
10	1.62889	0.61391	0.12950	7.72173	0.07950	12.57789	4.09909	10
11	1.71034	0.58468	0.12039	8.30641	0.07039	14.20679	4.51444	11
12	1.79586	0.55684	0.11283	8.86325	0.06283	15.91713	4.92190	12
13	1.88565	0.53032	0.10646	9.39357	0.05646	17.71298	5.32150	13
14	1.97993	0.50507	0.10102	9.89864	0.05102	19.59863	5.71329	14
15	2.07893	0.48102	0.09634	10.37966	0.04634	21.57856	6.09731	15
16	2.18287	0.45811	0.09227	10.83777	0.04227	23.65749	6.47363	16
17	2.29202	0.43630	0.08870	11.27407	0.03870	25.84037	6.84229	17
18	2.40662	0.41552	0.08555	11.68959	0.03555	28.13238	7.20336	18
19	2.52695	0.39573	0.08275	12.08532	0.03275	30.53900	7.55690	19
20	2.65330	0.37689	0.08024	12.46221	0.03024	33.06595	7.90297	20
21	2.78596	0.35894	0.07800	12.82115	0.02800	35.71925	8.24164	21
22	2.92526	0.34185	0.07597	13.16300	0.02597	38.50521	8.57298	22
23	3.07152	0.32557	0.07414	13.48857	0.02414	41.43048	8.89706	23
24	3.22510	0.31007	0.07247	13.79864	0.02247	44.50200	9.21397	24
25	3.38635	0.29530	0.07095	14.09394	0.02095	47.72710	9.52377	25
26	3.55567	0.28124	0.06956	14.37519	0.01956	51.11345	9.82655	26
27	3.73346	0.26785	0.06829	14.64303	0.01829	54.66913	10.12240	27
28	3.92013	0.25509	0.06712	14.89813	0.01712	58.40258	10.41138	28
29	4.11614	0.24295	0.06605	15.14107	0.01605	62.32271	10.69360	29
30	4.32194	0.23138	0.06505	15.37245	0.01505	66.43885	10.96914	30
31	4.53804	0.22036	0.06413	15.59281	0.01413	70.76079	11.23809	31
32	4.76494	0.20987	0.06328	15.80268	0.01328	75.29883	11.50053	32
33	5.00319	0.19987	0.06249	16.00255	0.01249	80.06377	11.75657	33
34	5.25335	0.19035	0.06176	16.19290	0.01176	85.06696	12.00630	34
35	5.51602	0.18129	0.06107	16.37419	0.01107	90.32031	12.24980	35
40	7.03999	0.14205	0.05828	17.15909	0.00828	120.79977	13.37747	40
45	8.98501	0.11130	0.05626	17.77407	0.00626	159.70016	14.36444	45
50	11.46740	0.08720	0.05478	18.25593	0.00478	209.34800	15.22326	50
55	14.63563	0.06833	0.05367	18.63347	0.00367	272.71262	15.96645	55
60	18.67919	0.05354	0.05283	18.92929	0.00283	353.58372	16.60618	60
65	23.83990	0.04195	0.05219	19.16107	0.00219	456.79801	17.15410	65
70	30.42643	0.03287	0.05170	19.34268	0.00170	588.52851	17.62119	70
75	38.83269	0.02575	0.05132	19.48497	0.00132	756.65372	18.01759	75
80	49.56144	0.02018	0.05103	19.59646	0.00103	971.22882	18.35260	80
85	63.25435	0.01581	0.05080	19.68382	0.00080	1245.08707	18.63463	85
90	80.73037	0.01239	0.05063	19.75226	0.00063	1594.60730	18.87120	90
95	103.03468	0.00971	0.05049	19.80589	0.00049	2040.69353	19.06894	95
100	131.50126	0.00760	0.05038	19.84791	0.00038	2610.02516	19.23372	100

6% interest factors for discrete compounding periods

	SINGLE PAYMENT		UNIFORM SERIES					
	Compound Amount Factor	Present Worth Factor	Capital Recovery Factor	Present Worth Factor	Sinking Fund Factor	Compound Amount Factor	Gradient Factor	
N	(F/P,6,N)	(P/F,6,N)	(A/P,6,N)	(P/A,6,N)	(A/F,6,N)	(F/A,6,N)	(A/G,6,N)	N
1	1.06000	0.94340	1.06000	0.94340	1.00000	1.00000	0.00000	1
2	1.12360	0.89000	0.54544	1.83339	0.48544	2.06000	0.48544	2
3	1.19102	0.83962	0.37411	2.67301	0.31411	3.18360	0.96118	3
4	1.26248	0.79209	0.28859	3.46511	0.22859	4.37462	1.42723	4
5	1.33823	0.74726	0.23740	4.21236	0.17740	5.63709	1.88363	5
6	1.41852	0.70496	0.20336	4.91732	0.14336	6.97532	2.33040	6
7	1.50363	0.66506	0.17914	5.58238	0.11914	8.39384	2.76758	7
8	1.59385	0.62741	0.16104	6.20979	0.10104	9.89747	3.19521	8
9	1.68948	0.59190	0.14702	6.80169	0.08702	11.49132	3.61333	9
10	1.79085	0.55839	0.13587	7.36009	0.07587	13.18079	4.02201	10
11	1.89830	0.52679	0.12679	7.88687	0.06679	14.97164	4.42129	11
12	2.01220	0.49697	0.11928	8.38384	0.05928	16.86994	4.81126	12
13	2.13293	0.46884	0.11296	8.85268	0.05296	18.88214	5.19198	13
14	2.26090	0.44230	0.10758	9.29498	0.04758	21.01507	5.56352	14
15	2.39656	0.41727	0.10296	9.71225	0.04296	23.27597	5.92598	15
16	2.54035	0.39365	0.09895	10.10590	0.03895	25.67253	6.27943	16
17	2.69277	0.37136	0.09544	10.47726	0.03544	28.21288	6.62397	17
18	2.85434	0.35034	0.09236	10.82760	0.03236	30.90565	6.95970	18
19	3.02560	0.33051	0.08962	11.15812	0.02962	33.75999	7.28673	19
20	3.20714	0.31180	0.08718	11.46992	0.02718	36.78559	7.60515	20
21	3.39956	0.29416	0.08500	11.76408	0.02500	39.99273	7.91508	21
22	3.60354	0.27751	0.08305	12.04158	0.02305	43.39229	8.21662	22
23	3.81975	0.26180	0.08128	12.30338	0.02128	46.99583	8.50991	23
24	4.04893	0.24698	0.07968	12.55036	0.01968	50.81558	8.79506	24
25	4.29187	0.23300	0.07823	12.78336	0.01823	54.86451	9.07220	25
26	4.54938	0.21981	0.07690	13.00317	0.01690	59.15638	9.34145	26
27	4.82235	0.20737	0.07570	13.21053	0.01570	63.70577	9.60294	27
28	5.11169	0.19563	0.07459	13.40616	0.01459	68.52811	9.85681	28
29	5.41839	0.18456	0.07358	13.59072	0.01358	73.63980	10.10319	29
30	5.74349	0.17411	0.07265	13.76483	0.01265	79.05819	10.34221	30
31	6.08810	0.16425	0.07179	13.92909	0.01179	84.80168	10.57402	31
32	6.45339	0.15496	0.07100	14.08404	0.01100	90.88978	10.79875	32
33	6.84059	0.14619	0.07027	14.23023	0.01027	97.34316	11.01655	33
34	7.25103	0.13791	0.06960	14.36814	0.00960	104.18375	11.22756	34
35	7.68609	0.13011	0.06897	14.49825	0.00897	111.43478	11.43192	35
40	10.28572	0.09722	0.06646	15.04630	0.00646	154.76197	12.35898	40
45	13.76461	0.07265	0.06470	15.45583	0.00470	212.74351	13.14129	45
50	18.42015	0.05429	0.06344	15.76186	0.00344	290.33590	13.79643	50
55	24.65032	0.04057	0.06254	15.99054	0.00254	394.17203	14.34112	55
60	32.98769	0.03031	0.06188	16.16143	0.00188	533.12818	14.79095	60
65	44.14497	0.02265	0.06139	16.28912	0.00139	719.08286	15.16012	65
70	59.07593	0.01693	0.06103	16.38454	0.00103	967.93217	15.46135	70
75	79.05692	0.01265	0.06077	16.45585	0.00077	1300.94868	15.70583	75
80	105.79599	0.00945	0.06057	16.50913	0.00057	1746.59989	15.90328	80
85	141.57890	0.00706	0.06043	16.54895	0.00043	2342.98174	16.06202	85
90	189.46451	0.00528	0.06032	16.57870	0.00032	3141.07519	16.18912	90
95	253.54625	0.00394	0.06024	16.60093	0.00024	4209.10425	16.29050	95
100	339.30208	0.00295	0.06018	16.61755	0.00018	5638.36806	16.37107	100

7% interest factors for discrete compounding periods

	SINGLE PAYMENT		UNIFORM SERIES					
	Compound Amount Factor	Present Worth Factor	Capital Recovery Factor	Present Worth Factor	Sinking Fund Factor	Compound Amount Factor	Gradient Factor	
N	(F/P,7,N)	(P/F,7,N)	(A/P,7,N)	(P/A,7,N)	(A/F,7,N)	(F/A,7,N)	(A/G,7,N)	N
1	1.07000	0.93458	1.07000	0.93458	1.00000	1.00000	0.00000	1
2	1.14490	0.87344	0.55309	1.80802	0.48309	2.07000	0.48309	2
3	1.22504	0.81630	0.38105	2.62432	0.31105	3.21490	0.95493	3
4	1.31080	0.76290	0.29523	3.38721	0.22523	4.43994	1.41554	4
5	1.40255	0.71299	0.24389	4.10020	0.17389	5.75074	1.86495	5
6	1.50073	0.66634	0.20980	4.76654	0.13980	7.15329	2.30322	6
7	1.60578	0.62275	0.18555	5.38929	0.11555	8.65402	2.73039	7
8	1.71819	0.58201	0.16747	5.97130	0.09747	10.25980	3.14654	8
9	1.83846	0.54393	0.15349	6.51523	0.08349	11.97799	3.55174	9
10	1.96715	0.50835	0.14238	7.02358	0.07238	13.81645	3.94607	10
11	2.10485	0.47509	0.13336	7.49867	0.06336	15.78360	4.32963	11
12	2.25219	0.44401	0.12590	7.94269	0.05590	17.88845	4.70252	12
13	2.40985	0.41496	0.11965	8.35765	0.04965	20.14064	5.06484	13
14	2.57853	0.38782	0.11434	8.74547	0.04434	22.55049	5.41673	14
15	2.75903	0.36245	0.10979	9.10791	0.03979	25.12902	5.75829	15
16	2.95216	0.33873	0.10586	9.44665	0.03586	27.88805	6.08968	16
17	3.15882	0.31657	0.10243	9.76322	0.03243	30.84022	6.41102	17
18	3.37993	0.29586	0.09941	10.05909	0.02941	33.99903	6.72247	18
19	3.61653	0.27651	0.09675	10.33560	0.02675	37.37896	7.02418	19
20	3.86968	0.25842	0.09439	10.59401	0.02439	40.99549	7.31631	20
21	4.14056	0.24151	0.09229	10.83553	0.02229	44.86518	7.59901	21
22	4.43040	0.22571	0.09041	11.06124	0.02041	49.00574	7.87247	22
23	4.74053	0.21095	0.08871	11.27219	0.01871	53.43614	8.13685	23
24	5.07237	0.19715	0.08719	11.46933	0.01719	58.17667	8.39234	24
25	5.42743	0.18425	0.08581	11.65358	0.01581	63.24904	8.63910	25
26	5.80735	0.17220	0.08456	11.82578	0.01456	68.67647	8.87733	26
27	6.21387	0.16093	0.08343	11.98671	0.01343	74.48382	9.10722	27
28	6.64884	0.15040	0.08239	12.13711	0.01239	80.69769	9.32894	28
29	7.11426	0.14056	0.08145	12.27767	0.01145	87.34653	9.54270	29
30	7.61226	0.13137	0.08059	12.40904	0.01059	94.46079	9.74868	30
31	8.14511	0.12277	0.07980	12.53181	0.00980	102.07304	9.94708	31
32	8.71527	0.11474	0.07907	12.64656	0.00907	110.21815	10.13810	32
33	9.32534	0.10723	0.07841	12.75379	0.00841	118.93343	10.32191	33
34	9.97811	0.10022	0.07780	12.85401	0.00780	128.25876	10.49873	34
35	10.67658	0.09366	0.07723	12.94767	0.00723	138.23688	10.66873	35
40	14.97446	0.06678	0.07501	13.33171	0.00501	199.63511	11.42335	40
45	21.00245	0.04761	0.07350	13.60552	0.00350	285.74931	12.03599	45
50	29.45703	0.03395	0.07246	13.80075	0.00246	406.52893	12.52868	50
55	41.31500	0.02420	0.07174	13.93994	0.00174	575.92859	12.92146	55
60	57.94643	0.01726	0.07123	14.03918	0.00123	813.52038	13.23209	60
65	81.27286	0.01230	0.07087	14.10994	0.00087	1146.75516	13.47598	65
70	113.98939	0.00877	0.07062	14.16039	0.00062	1614.13417	13.66619	70
75	159.87602	0.00625	0.07044	14.19636	0.00044	2269.65742	13.81365	75
80	224.23439	0.00446	0.07031	14.22201	0.00031	3189.06268	13.92735	80
85	314.50033	0.00318	0.07022	14.24029	0.00022	4478.57612	14.01458	85
90	441.10298	0.00227	0.07016	14.25333	0.00016	6287.18543	14.08122	90
95	618.66975	0.00162	0.07011	14.26262	0.00011	8823.85354	14.13191	95
100	867.71633	0.00115	0.07008	14.26925	0.00008	12381.66179	14.17034	100

8% interest factors for discrete compounding periods

	SINGLE PAYMENT		UNIFORM SERIES					
	Compound Amount Factor	Present Worth Factor	Capital Recovery Factor	Present Worth Factor	Sinking Fund Factor	Compound Amount Factor	Gradient Factor	
N	(F/P,8,N)	(P/F,8,N)	(A/P,8,N)	(P/A,8,N)	(A/F,8,N)	(F/A,8,N)	(A/G,8,N)	N
1	1.08000	0.92593	1.08000	0.92593	1.00000	1.00000	0.00000	1
2	1.16640	0.85734	0.56077	1.78326	0.48077	2.08000	0.48077	2
3	1.25971	0.79383	0.38803	2.57710	0.30803	3.24640	0.94874	3
4	1.36049	0.73503	0.30192	3.31213	0.22192	4.50611	1.40396	4
5	1.46933	0.68058	0.25046	3.99271	0.17046	5.86660	1.84647	5
6	1.58687	0.63017	0.21632	4.62288	0.13632	7.33593	2.27635	6
7	1.71382	0.58349	0.19207	5.20637	0.11207	8.92280	2.69366	7
8	1.85093	0.54027	0.17401	5.74664	0.09401	10.63663	3.09852	8
9	1.99900	0.50025	0.16008	6.24689	0.08008	12.48756	3.49103	9
10	2.15892	0.46319	0.14903	6.71008	0.06903	14.48656	3.87131	10
11	2.33164	0.42888	0.14008	7.13896	0.06008	16.64549	4.23950	11
12	2.51817	0.39711	0.13270	7.53608	0.05270	18.97713	4.59575	12
13	2.71962	0.36770	0.12652	7.90378	0.04652	21.49530	4.94021	13
14	2.93719	0.34046	0.12130	8.24424	0.04130	24.21492	5.27305	14
15	0.17217	0.31524	0.11683	8.55948	0.03683	27.15211	5.59446	15
16	3.42594	0.29189	0.11298	8.85137	0.03298	30.32428	5.90463	16
17	3.70002	0.27027	0.10963	9.12164	0.02963	33.75023	6.20375	17
18	3.99602	0.25025	0.10670	9.37189	0.02670	37.45024	6.49203	18
19	4.31570	0.23171	0.10413	9.60360	0.02413	41.44626	6.76969	19
20	4.66096	0.21455	0.10185	9.81815	0.02185	45.76196	7.03695	20
21	5.03383	0.19866	0.09983	10.01680	0.01983	50.42292	7.29403	21
22	5.43654	0.18394	0.09803	10.20074	0.01803	55.45676	7.54118	22
23	5.87146	0.17032	0.09642	10.37106	0.01642	60.89330	7.77863	23
24	6.34118	0.15770	0.09498	10.52876	0.01498	66.76476	8.00661	24
25	6.84848	0.14602	0.09368	10.67478	0.01368	73.10594	8.22538	25
26	7.39635	0.13520	0.09251	10.80998	0.01251	79.95442	8.43518	26
27	7.98806	0.12519	0.09145	10.93516	0.01145	87.35077	8.63627	27
28	8.62711	0.11591	0.09049	11.05108	0.01049	95.33883	8.82888	28
29	9.31727	0.10733	0.08962	11.15841	0.00962	103.96594	9.01328	29
30	10.06266	0.09938	0.08883	11.25778	0.00883	113.28321	9.18971	30
31	10.86767	0.09202	0.08811	11.34980	0.00811	123.34587	9.35843	31
32	11.73708	0.08520	0.08745	11.43500	0.00745	134.21354	9.51967	32
33	12.67605	0.07889	0.08685	11.51389	0.00685	145.95062	9.67370	33
34	13.69013	0.07305	0.08630	11.58693	0.00630	158.62667	9.82075	34
35	14.78534	0.06763	0.08580	11.65457	0.00580	172.31680	9.96107	35
40	21.72452	0.04603	0.08386	11.92461	0.00386	259.05652	10.56992	40
45	31.92045	0.03133	0.08259	12.10840	0.00259	386.50562	11.04465	45
50	46.90161	0.02132	0.08174	12.23348	0.00174	573.77016	11.41071	50
55	68.91386	0.01451	0.08118	12.31861	0.00118	848.92320	11.69015	55
60	101.25706	0.00988	0.08080	12.37655	0.00080	1253.21330	11.90154	60
65	148.77985	0.00672	0.08054	12.41598	0.00054	1847.24808	12.06016	65
70	218.60641	0.00457	0.08037	12.44282	0.00037	2720.08007	12.17832	70
75	321.20453	0.00311	0.08025	12.46108	0.00025	4002.55662	12.26577	75
80	471.95483	0.00212	0.08017	12.47351	0.00017	5886.93543	12.33013	80
85	693.45649	0.00144	0.08012	12.48197	0.00012	8655.70611	12.37725	85
90	1018.91509	0.00098	0.08008	12.48773	0.00008	12723.93862	12.41158	90
95	1497.12055	0.00067	0.08005	12.49165	0.00005	18701.50686	12.43650	95
100	2199.76126	0.00045	0.08004	12.49432	0.00004	27484.51570	12.45452	100

9% interest factors for discrete compounding periods

N	SINGLE PAYMENT		UNIFORM SERIES					N
	Compound Amount Factor	Present Worth Factor	Capital Recovery Factor	Present Worth Factor	Sinking Fund Factor	Compound Amount Factor	Gradient Factor	
	(F/P,9,N)	(P/F,9,N)	(A/P,9,N)	(P/A,9,N)	(A/F,9,N)	(F/A,9,N)	(A/G,9,N)	
1	1.09000	0.91743	1.09000	0.91743	1.00000	1.00000	0.00000	1
2	1.18810	0.84168	0.56847	1.75911	0.47847	2.09000	0.47847	2
3	1.29503	0.77218	0.39505	2.53129	0.30505	3.27810	0.94262	3
4	1.41158	0.70843	0.30867	3.23972	0.21867	4.57313	1.39250	4
5	1.53862	0.64993	0.25709	3.88965	0.16709	5.98471	1.82820	5
6	1.67710	0.59627	0.22292	4.48592	0.13292	7.52333	2.24979	6
7	1.82804	0.54703	0.19869	5.03295	0.10869	9.20043	2.65740	7
8	1.99256	0.50187	0.18067	5.53482	0.09067	11.02847	3.05117	8
9	2.17189	0.46043	0.16680	5.99525	0.07680	13.02104	3.43123	9
10	2.36736	0.42241	0.15582	6.41766	0.06582	15.19293	3.79777	10
11	2.58043	0.38753	0.14695	6.80519	0.05695	17.56029	4.15096	11
12	2.81266	0.35553	0.13965	7.16073	0.04965	20.14072	4.49102	12
13	3.06580	0.32618	0.13357	7.48690	0.04357	22.95338	4.81816	13
14	3.34173	0.29925	0.12843	7.78615	0.03843	26.01919	5.13262	14
15	3.64248	0.27454	0.12406	8.06069	0.03406	29.36092	5.43463	15
16	3.97031	0.25187	0.12030	8.31256	0.03030	33.00340	5.72446	16
17	4.32763	0.23107	0.11705	8.54363	0.02705	36.97370	6.00238	17
18	4.71712	0.21199	0.11421	8.75563	0.02421	41.30134	6.26865	18
19	5.14166	0.19449	0.11173	8.95011	0.02173	46.01846	6.52358	19
20	5.60441	0.17843	0.10955	9.12855	0.01955	51.16012	6.76745	20
21	6.10881	0.16370	0.10762	9.29224	0.01762	56.76453	7.00056	21
22	6.65860	0.15018	0.10590	9.44243	0.01590	62.87334	7.22322	22
23	7.25787	0.13778	0.10438	9.58021	0.01438	69.53194	7.43574	23
24	7.91108	0.12640	0.10302	9.70661	0.01302	76.78981	7.63843	24
25	8.62308	0.11597	0.10181	9.82258	0.01181	84.70090	7.83160	25
26	9.39916	0.10639	0.10072	9.92897	0.01072	93.32398	8.01556	26
27	10.24508	0.09761	0.09973	10.02658	0.00973	102.72313	8.19064	27
28	11.16714	0.08955	0.09885	10.11613	0.00885	112.96822	8.35714	28
29	12.17218	0.08215	0.09806	10.19828	0.00806	124.13536	8.51538	29
30	13.26768	0.07537	0.09734	10.27365	0.00734	136.30754	8.66566	30
31	14.46177	0.06915	0.09669	10.34280	0.00669	149.57522	8.80829	31
32	15.76333	0.06344	0.09610	10.40624	0.00610	164.03699	8.94358	32
33	17.18203	0.05820	0.09556	10.46444	0.00556	179.80032	9.07181	33
34	18.72841	0.05339	0.09508	10.51784	0.00508	196.98234	9.19329	34
35	20.41397	0.04899	0.09464	10.56682	0.00464	215.71075	9.30829	35
40	31.40942	0.03184	0.09296	10.75736	0.00296	337.88245	9.79573	40
45	48.32729	0.02069	0.09190	10.88120	0.00190	525.85873	10.16029	45
50	74.35752	0.01345	0.09123	10.96168	0.00123	815.08356	10.42952	50
55	114.40826	0.00874	0.09079	11.01399	0.00079	1260.09180	10.62614	55
60	176.03129	0.00568	0.09051	11.04799	0.00051	1944.79213	10.76832	60
65	270.84596	0.00369	0.09033	11.07009	0.00033	2998.28847	10.87023	65
70	416.73009	0.00240	0.09022	11.08445	0.00022	4619.22318	10.94273	70
75	641.19089	0.00156	0.09014	11.09378	0.00014	7113.23215	10.99396	75
80	986.55167	0.00101	0.09009	11.09985	0.00009	10950.57409	11.02994	80
85	1517.93203	0.00066	0.09006	11.10379	0.00006	16854.80033	11.05508	85
90	2335.52658	0.00043	0.09004	11.10635	0.00004	25939.18425	11.07256	90
95	3593.49715	0.00028	0.09003	11.10802	0.00003	39916.63496	11.08467	95
100	5529.04079	0.00018	0.09002	11.10910	0.00002	61422.67546	11.09302	100

10% interest factors for discrete compounding periods

	SINGLE PAYMENT		UNIFORM SERIES					
	Compound Amount Factor	Present Worth Factor	Capital Recovery Factor	Present Worth Factor	Sinking Fund Factor	Compound Amount Factor	Gradient Factor	
N	(F/P,10,N)	(P/F,10,N)	(A/P,10,N)	(P/A,10,N)	(A/F,10,N)	(F/A,10,N)	(A/G,10,N)	N
1	1.10000	0.90909	1.10000	0.90909	1.00000	1.00000	0.00000	1
2	1.21000	0.82645	0.57619	1.73554	0.47619	2.10000	0.47619	2
3	1.33100	0.75131	0.40211	2.48685	0.30211	3.31000	0.93656	3
4	1.46410	0.68301	0.31547	3.16987	0.21547	4.64100	1.38117	4
5	1.61051	0.62092	0.26380	3.79079	0.16380	6.10510	1.81013	5
6	1.77156	0.56447	0.22961	4.35526	0.12961	7.71561	2.22356	6
7	1.94872	0.51316	0.20541	4.86842	0.10541	9.48717	2.62162	7
8	2.14359	0.46651	0.18744	5.33493	0.08744	11.43589	3.00448	8
9	2.35795	0.42410	0.17364	5.75902	0.07364	13.57948	3.37235	9
10	2.59374	0.38554	0.16275	6.14457	0.06275	15.93742	3.72546	10
11	2.85312	0.35049	0.15396	6.49506	0.05396	18.53117	4.06405	11
12	3.13843	0.31863	0.14676	6.81369	0.04676	21.38428	4.38840	12
13	3.45227	0.28966	0.14078	7.10336	0.04078	24.52271	4.69879	13
14	3.79750	0.26333	0.13575	7.36669	0.03575	27.97498	4.99553	14
15	4.17725	0.23939	0.13147	7.60608	0.03147	31.77248	5.27893	15
16	4.59497	0.21763	0.12782	7.82371	0.02782	35.94973	5.54934	16
17	5.05447	0.19784	0.12466	8.02155	0.02466	40.54470	5.80710	17
18	5.55992	0.17986	0.12193	8.20141	0.02193	45.59917	6.05256	18
19	6.11591	0.16351	0.11955	8.36492	0.01955	51.15909	6.28610	19
20	6.72750	0.14864	0.11746	8.51356	0.01746	57.27500	6.50808	20
21	7.40025	0.13513	0.11562	8.64869	0.01562	64.00250	6.71888	21
22	8.14027	0.12285	0.11401	8.77154	0.01401	71.40275	6.91889	22
23	8.95430	0.11168	0.11257	8.88322	0.01257	79.54302	7.10848	23
24	9.84973	0.10153	0.11130	8.98474	0.01130	88.49733	7.28805	24
25	10.83471	0.09230	0.11017	9.07704	0.01017	98.34706	7.45798	25
26	11.91818	0.08391	0.10916	9.16095	0.00916	109.18177	7.61865	26
27	13.10999	0.07628	0.10826	9.23722	0.00826	121.09994	7.77044	27
28	14.42099	0.06934	0.10745	9.30657	0.00745	134.20994	7.91372	28
29	15.86309	0.06304	0.10673	9.36961	0.00673	148.63093	8.04886	29
30	17.44940	0.05731	0.10608	9.42691	0.00608	164.49402	8.17623	30
31	19.19434	0.05210	0.10550	9.47901	0.00550	181.94342	8.29617	31
32	21.11378	0.04736	0.10497	9.52638	0.00497	201.13777	8.40905	32
33	23.22515	0.04306	0.10450	9.56943	0.00450	222.25154	8.51520	33
34	25.54767	0.03914	0.10407	9.60857	0.00407	245.47670	8.61494	34
35	28.10244	0.03558	0.10369	9.64416	0.00369	271.02437	8.70860	35
40	45.25926	0.02209	0.10226	9.77905	0.00226	442.59256	9.09623	40
45	72.89048	0.01372	0.10139	9.86281	0.00139	718.90484	9.37405	45
50	117.39085	0.00852	0.10086	9.91481	0.00086	1163.90853	9.57041	50
55	189.05914	0.00529	0.10053	9.94711	0.00053	1880.59142	9.70754	55
60	304.48164	0.00328	0.10033	9.96716	0.00033	3034.81640	9.80229	60
65	490.37073	0.00204	0.10020	9.97961	0.00020	4893.70725	9.86718	65
70	789.74696	0.00127	0.10013	9.98734	0.00013	7887.46957	9.91125	70
75	1271.89537	0.00079	0.10008	9.99214	0.00008	12708.95371	9.94099	75
80	2048.40021	0.00049	0.10005	9.99512	0.00005	20474.00215	9.96093	80
85	3298.96903	0.00030	0.10003	9.99697	0.00003	32979.69030	9.97423	85
90	5313.02261	0.00019	0.10002	9.99812	0.00002	53120.22612	9.98306	90
95	8556.67605	0.00012	0.10001	9.99883	0.00001	85556.76047	9.98890	95
100	13780.61234	0.00007	0.10001	9.99927	0.00001	137796.12340	9.99274	100

11% interest factors for discrete compounding periods

N	SINGLE PAYMENT		UNIFORM SERIES					N
	Compound Amount Factor	Present Worth Factor	Capital Recovery Factor	Present Worth Factor	Sinking Fund Factor	Compound Amount Factor	Gradient Factor	
	(F/P,11,N)	(P/F,11,N)	(A/P,11,N)	(P/A,11,N)	(A/F,11,N)	(F/A,11,N)	(A/G,11,N)	
1	1.11000	0.90090	1.11000	0.90090	1.00000	1.00000	0.00000	1
2	1.23210	0.81162	0.58393	1.71252	0.47393	2.11000	0.47393	2
3	1.36763	0.73119	0.40921	2.44371	0.29921	3.34210	0.93055	3
4	1.51807	0.65873	0.32233	3.10245	0.21233	4.70973	1.36995	4
5	1.68506	0.59345	0.27057	3.69590	0.16057	6.22780	1.79226	5
6	1.87041	0.53464	0.23638	4.23054	0.12638	7.91286	2.19764	6
7	2.07616	0.48166	0.21222	4.71220	0.10222	9.78327	2.58630	7
8	2.30454	0.43393	0.19432	5.14612	0.08432	11.85943	2.95847	8
9	2.55804	0.39092	0.18060	5.53705	0.07060	14.16397	3.31441	9
10	2.83942	0.35218	0.16980	5.88923	0.05980	16.72201	3.65442	10
11	3.15176	0.31728	0.16112	6.20652	0.05112	19.56143	3.97881	11
12	3.49845	0.28584	0.15403	6.49236	0.04403	22.71319	4.28793	12
13	3.88328	0.25751	0.14815	6.74987	0.03815	26.21164	4.58216	13
14	4.31044	0.23199	0.14323	6.98187	0.03323	30.09492	4.86187	14
15	4.78459	0.20900	0.13907	7.19087	0.02907	34.40536	5.12747	15
16	5.31089	0.18829	0.13552	7.37916	0.02552	39.18995	5.37938	16
17	5.89509	0.16963	0.13247	7.54879	0.02247	44.50084	5.61804	17
18	6.54355	0.15282	0.12984	7.70162	0.01984	50.39594	5.84389	18
19	7.26334	0.13768	0.12756	7.83929	0.01756	56.93949	6.05739	19
20	8.06231	0.12403	0.12558	7.96333	0.01558	64.20283	6.25898	20
21	8.94917	0.11174	0.12384	8.07507	0.01384	72.26514	6.44912	21
22	9.93357	0.10067	0.12231	8.17574	0.01231	81.21431	6.62829	22
23	11.02627	0.09069	0.12097	8.26643	0.01097	91.14788	6.79693	23
24	12.23916	0.08170	0.11979	8.34814	0.00979	102.17415	6.95552	24
25	13.58546	0.07361	0.11874	8.42174	0.00874	114.41331	7.10449	25
26	15.07986	0.06631	0.11781	8.48806	0.00781	127.99877	7.24430	26
27	16.73865	0.05974	0.11699	8.54780	0.00699	143.07864	7.37539	27
28	18.57990	0.05382	0.11626	8.60162	0.00626	159.81729	7.49818	28
29	20.62369	0.04849	0.11561	8.65011	0.00561	178.39719	7.61310	29
30	22.89230	0.04368	0.11502	8.69379	0.00502	199.02088	7.72056	30
31	25.41045	0.03935	0.11451	8.73315	0.00451	221.91317	7.82096	31
32	28.20560	0.03545	0.11404	8.76860	0.00404	247.32362	7.91468	32
33	31.30821	0.03194	0.11363	8.80054	0.00363	275.52922	8.00210	33
34	34.75212	0.02878	0.11326	8.82932	0.00326	306.83744	8.08356	34
35	38.57485	0.02592	0.11293	8.85524	0.00293	341.58955	8.15944	35
40	65.00087	0.01538	0.11172	8.95105	0.00172	581.82607	8.46592	40
45	109.53024	0.00913	0.11101	9.00791	0.00101	986.63856	8.67628	45
50	184.56483	0.00542	0.11060	9.04165	0.00060	1668.77115	8.81853	50

12% interest factors for discrete compounding periods

	SINGLE PAYMENT		UNIFORM SERIES					
	Compound Amount Factor	Present Worth Factor	Capital Recovery Factor	Present Worth Factor	Sinking Fund Factor	Compound Amount Factor	Gradient Factor	
N	(F/P,12,N)	(P/F,12,N)	(A/P,12,N)	(P/A,12,N)	(A/F,12,N)	(F/A,12,N)	(A/G,12,N)	N
1	1.12000	0.89286	1.12000	0.89286	1.00000	1.00000	0.00000	1
2	1.25440	0.79719	0.59170	1.69005	0.47170	2.12000	0.47170	2
3	1.40493	0.71178	0.41635	2.40183	0.29635	3.37440	0.92461	3
4	1.57352	0.63552	0.32923	3.03735	0.20923	4.77933	1.35885	4
5	1.76234	0.56743	0.27741	3.60478	0.15741	6.35285	1.77459	5
6	1.97382	0.50663	0.24323	4.11141	0.12323	8.11519	2.17205	6
7	2.21068	0.45235	0.21912	4.56376	0.09912	10.08901	2.55147	7
8	2.47596	0.40388	0.20130	4.96764	0.08130	12.29969	2.91314	8
9	2.77308	0.36061	0.18768	5.32825	0.06768	14.77566	3.25742	9
10	3.10585	0.32197	0.17698	5.65022	0.05698	17.54874	3.58465	10
11	3.47855	0.28748	0.16842	5.93770	0.04842	20.65458	3.89525	11
12	3.89598	0.25668	0.16144	6.19437	0.04144	24.13313	4.18965	12
13	4.36349	0.22917	0.15568	6.42355	0.03568	28.02911	4.46830	13
14	4.88711	0.20462	0.15087	6.62817	0.03087	32.39260	4.73169	14
15	5.47357	0.18270	0.14682	6.81086	0.02682	37.27971	4.98030	15
16	6.13039	0.16312	0.14339	6.97399	0.02339	42.75328	5.21466	16
17	6.86604	0.14564	0.14046	7.11963	0.02046	48.88367	5.43530	17
18	7.68997	0.13004	0.13794	7.24967	0.01794	55.74971	5.64274	18
19	8.61276	0.11611	0.13576	7.36578	0.01576	63.43968	5.83752	19
20	9.64629	0.10367	0.13388	7.46944	0.01388	72.05244	6.02020	20
21	10.80385	0.09256	0.13224	7.56200	0.01224	81.69874	6.19132	21
22	12.10031	0.08264	0.13081	7.64465	0.01081	92.50258	6.35141	22
23	13.55235	0.07379	0.12956	7.71843	0.00956	104.60289	6.50101	23
24	15.17863	0.06588	0.12846	7.78432	0.00846	118.15524	6.64064	24
25	17.00006	0.05882	0.12750	7.84314	0.00750	133.33387	6.77084	25
26	19.04007	0.05252	0.12665	7.89566	0.00665	150.33393	6.89210	26
27	21.32488	0.04689	0.12590	7.94255	0.00590	169.37401	7.00491	27
28	23.88387	0.04187	0.12524	7.98442	0.00524	190.69889	7.10976	28
29	26.74993	0.03738	0.12466	8.02181	0.00466	214.58275	7.20712	29
30	29.95992	0.03338	0.12414	8.05518	0.00414	241.33268	7.29742	30
31	33.55511	0.02980	0.12369	8.08499	0.00369	271.29261	7.38110	31
32	37.58173	0.02661	0.12328	8.11159	0.00328	304.84772	7.45858	32
33	42.09153	0.02376	0.12292	8.13535	0.00292	342.42945	7.53025	33
34	47.14252	0.02121	0.12260	8.15656	0.00260	384.52098	7.59649	34
35	52.79962	0.01894	0.12232	8.17550	0.00232	431.66350	7.65765	35
40	93.05097	0.01075	0.12130	8.24378	0.00130	767.09142	7.89879	40
45	163.98760	0.00610	0.12074	8.28252	0.00074	1358.23003	8.05724	45
50	289.00219	0.00346	0.12042	8.30450	0.00042	2400.01825	8.15972	50

13% interest factors for discrete compounding periods

	SINGLE PAYMENT		UNIFORM SERIES					
	Compound Amount Factor	Present Worth Factor	Capital Recovery Factor	Present Worth Factor	Sinking Fund Factor	Compound Amount Factor	Gradient Factor	
N	(F/P,13,N)	(P/F,13,N)	(A/P,13,N)	(P/A,13,N)	(A/F,13,N)	(F/A,13,N)	(A/G,13,N)	N
1	1.13000	0.88496	1.13000	0.88496	1.00000	1.00000	0.00000	1
2	1.27690	0.78315	0.59948	1.66810	0.46948	2.13000	0.46948	2
3	1.44290	0.69305	0.42352	2.36115	0.29352	3.40690	0.91872	3
4	1.63047	0.61332	0.33619	2.97447	0.20619	4.84980	1.34787	4
5	1.84244	0.54276	0.28431	3.51723	0.15431	6.48027	1.75713	5
6	2.08195	0.48032	0.25015	3.99755	0.12015	8.32271	2.14677	6
7	2.35261	0.42506	0.22611	4.42261	0.09611	10.40466	2.51711	7
8	2.65844	0.37616	0.20839	4.79877	0.07839	12.75726	2.86851	8
9	3.00404	0.33288	0.19487	5.13166	0.06487	15.41571	3.20138	9
10	3.39457	0.29459	0.18429	5.42624	0.05429	18.41975	3.51619	10
11	3.83586	0.26070	0.17584	5.68694	0.04584	21.81432	3.81342	11
12	4.33452	0.23071	0.16899	5.91765	0.03899	25.65018	4.09359	12
13	4.89801	0.20416	0.16335	6.12181	0.03335	29.98470	4.35727	13
14	5.53475	0.18068	0.15867	6.30249	0.02867	34.88271	4.60504	14
15	6.25427	0.15989	0.15474	6.46238	0.02474	40.41746	4.83749	15
16	7.06733	0.14150	0.15143	6.60388	0.02143	46.67173	5.05523	16
17	7.98608	0.12522	0.14861	6.72909	0.01861	53.73906	5.25890	17
18	9.02427	0.11081	0.14620	6.83991	0.01620	61.72514	5.44911	18
19	10.19742	0.09806	0.14413	6.93797	0.01413	70.74941	5.62651	19
20	11.52309	0.08678	0.14235	7.02475	0.01235	80.94683	5.79172	20
21	13.02109	0.07680	0.14081	7.10155	0.01081	92.46992	5.94538	21
22	14.71383	0.06796	0.13948	7.16951	0.00948	105.49101	6.08809	22
23	16.62663	0.06014	0.13832	7.22966	0.00832	120.20484	6.22046	23
24	18.78809	0.05323	0.13731	7.28288	0.00731	136.83147	6.34309	24
25	21.23054	0.04710	0.13643	7.32998	0.00643	155.61956	6.45655	25
26	23.99051	0.04168	0.13565	7.37167	0.00565	176.85010	6.56141	26
27	27.10928	0.03689	0.13498	7.40856	0.00498	200.84061	6.65819	27
28	30.63349	0.03264	0.13439	7.44120	0.00439	227.94989	6.74743	28
29	34.61584	0.02889	0.13387	7.47009	0.00387	258.58338	6.82962	29
30	39.11590	0.02557	0.13341	7.49565	0.00341	293.19922	6.90523	30
31	44.20096	0.02262	0.13301	7.51828	0.00301	332.31511	6.97473	31
32	49.94709	0.02002	0.13266	7.53830	0.00266	376.51608	7.03854	32
33	56.44021	0.01772	0.13234	7.55602	0.00234	426.46317	7.09707	33
34	63.77744	0.01568	0.13207	7.57170	0.00207	482.90338	7.15071	34
35	72.06851	0.01388	0.13183	7.58557	0.00183	546.68082	7.19983	35
40	132.78155	0.00753	0.13099	7.63438	0.00099	1013.70424	7.38878	40
45	244.64140	0.00409	0.13053	7.66086	0.00053	1874.16463	7.50761	45
50	450.73593	0.00222	0.13029	7.67524	0.00029	3459.50712	7.58113	50

14% interest factors for discrete compounding periods

	SINGLE PAYMENT		UNIFORM SERIES					
	Compound Amount Factor	Present Worth Factor	Capital Recovery Factor	Present Worth Factor	Sinking Fund Factor	Compound Amount Factor	Gradient Factor	
N	(F/P,14,N)	(P/F,14,N)	(A/P,14,N)	(P/A,14,N)	(A/F,14,N)	(F/A,14,N)	(A/G,14,N)	N
1	1.14000	0.87719	1.14000	0.87719	1.00000	1.00000	0.00000	1
2	1.29960	0.76947	0.60729	1.64666	0.46729	2.14000	0.46729	2
3	1.48154	0.67497	0.43073	2.32163	0.29073	3.43960	0.91290	3
4	1.68896	0.59208	0.34320	2.91371	0.20320	4.92114	1.33701	4
5	1.92541	0.51937	0.29128	3.43308	0.15128	6.61010	1.73987	5
6	2.19497	0.45559	0.25716	3.88867	0.11716	8.53552	2.12182	6
7	2.50227	0.39964	0.23319	4.28830	0.09319	10.73049	2.48324	7
8	2.85259	0.35056	0.21557	4.63886	0.07557	13.23276	2.82457	8
9	3.25195	0.30751	0.20217	4.94637	0.06217	16.08535	3.14632	9
10	3.70722	0.26974	0.19171	5.21612	0.05171	19.33730	3.44903	10
11	4.22623	0.23662	0.18339	5.45273	0.04339	23.04452	3.73331	11
12	4.81790	0.20756	0.17667	5.66029	0.03667	27.27075	3.99977	12
13	5.49241	0.18207	0.17116	5.84236	0.03116	32.08865	4.24909	13
14	6.26135	0.15971	0.16661	6.00207	0.02661	37.58107	4.48194	14
15	7.13794	0.14010	0.16281	6.14217	0.02281	43.84241	4.69904	15
16	8.13725	0.12289	0.15962	6.20506	0.01962	50.98035	4.90110	16
17	9.27646	0.10780	0.15692	6.37286	0.01692	59.11760	5.08884	17
18	10.57517	0.09456	0.15462	6.46742	0.01462	68.39407	5.26299	18
19	12.05569	0.08295	0.15266	6.55037	0.01266	78.96923	5.42429	19
20	13.74349	0.07276	0.15099	6.62313	0.01099	91.02493	5.57343	20
21	15.66758	0.06383	0.14954	6.68696	0.00964	104.76842	5.71113	21
22	17.86104	0.05599	0.14830	6.74294	0.00830	120.43600	5.83807	22
23	20.36158	0.04911	0.14723	6.79206	0.00723	138.29704	5.95494	23
24	23.21221	0.04308	0.14630	6.83514	0.00630	158.65862	6.06237	24
25	26.46192	0.03779	0.14550	6.87293	0.00550	181.87083	6.16100	25
26	30.16658	0.03315	0.14480	6.90608	0.00480	208.33274	6.25143	26
27	34.38991	0.02908	0.14419	6.93515	0.00419	238.49933	6.33423	27
28	39.20449	0.02551	0.14366	6.96066	0.00366	272.88923	6.40996	28
29	44.69312	0.02237	0.14320	6.98304	0.00320	312.09373	6.47914	29
30	50.95016	0.01963	0.14280	7.00266	0.00280	356.78685	6.54226	30
31	58.08318	0.01722	0.14245	7.01988	0.00245	407.73701	6.59979	31
32	66.21483	0.01510	0.14215	7.03498	0.00215	465.82019	6.65217	32
33	75.48490	0.01325	0.14188	7.04823	0.00188	532.03501	6.69981	33
34	86.05279	0.01162	0.14165	7.05985	0.00165	607.51991	6.74311	34
35	98.10018	0.01019	0.14144	7.07005	0.00144	693.57270	6.78240	35
40	188.88351	0.00529	0.14075	7.10504	0.00075	1342.02510	6.92996	40
45	363.67907	0.00275	0.14039	7.12322	0.00039	2590.56480	7.01878	45
50	700.23299	0.00143	0.14020	7.13266	0.00020	4994.52135	7.07135	50

15% interest factors for discrete compounding periods

	SINGLE PAYMENT		UNIFORM SERIES					
N	Compound Amount Factor	Present Worth Factor	Capital Recovery Factor	Present Worth Factor	Sinking Fund Factor	Compound Amount Factor	Gradient Factor	N
	(F/P,15,N)	(P/F,15,N)	(A/P,15,N)	(P/A,15,N)	(A/F,15,N)	(F/A,15,N)	(A/G,15,N)	
1	1.15000	0.86957	1.15000	0.86957	1.00000	1.00000	0.00000	1
2	1.32250	0.75614	0.61512	1.62571	0.46512	2.15000	0.46512	2
3	1.52088	0.65752	0.43798	2.28323	0.28798	3.47250	0.90713	3
4	1.74901	0.57175	0.35027	2.85498	0.20027	4.99338	1.32626	4
5	2.01136	0.49718	0.29832	3.35216	0.14832	6.74238	1.72281	5
6	2.31306	0.43233	0.26424	3.78448	0.11424	8.75374	2.09719	6
7	2.66002	0.37594	0.24036	4.16042	0.09036	11.06680	2.44985	7
8	3.05902	0.32690	0.22285	4.48732	0.07285	13.72682	2.78133	8
9	3.51788	0.28426	0.20957	4.77158	0.05957	16.78584	3.09223	9
10	4.04556	0.24718	0.19925	5.01877	0.04925	20.30372	3.38320	10
11	4.65239	0.21494	0.19107	5.23371	0.04107	24.34928	3.65494	11
12	5.35025	0.18691	0.18448	5.42062	0.03448	29.00167	3.90820	12
13	6.15279	0.16253	0.17911	5.58315	0.02911	34.35192	4.14376	13
14	7.07571	0.14133	0.17469	5.72448	0.02469	40.50471	4.36241	14
15	8.13706	0.12289	0.17102	5.84737	0.02102	47.58041	4.56496	15
16	9.35762	0.10686	0.16795	5.95423	0.01795	55.71747	4.75225	16
17	10.76126	0.09293	0.16537	6.04716	0.01537	65.07509	4.92509	17
18	12.37545	0.08081	0.16319	6.12797	0.01319	75.83636	5.08431	18
19	14.23177	0.07027	0.16134	6.19823	0.01134	88.21181	5.23073	19
20	16.36654	0.06110	0.15976	6.25933	0.00976	102.44358	5.36514	20
21	18.82152	0.05313	0.15842	6.31246	0.00842	118.81012	5.48832	21
22	21.64475	0.04620	0.15727	6.35866	0.00727	137.63164	5.60102	22
23	24.89146	0.04017	0.15628	6.39884	0.00628	159.27638	5.70398	23
24	28.62518	0.03493	0.15543	6.43377	0.00543	184.16784	5.79789	24
25	32.91895	0.03038	0.15470	6.46415	0.00470	212.79302	5.88343	25
26	37.85680	0.02642	0.15407	6.49056	0.00407	245.71197	5.96123	26
27	43.53531	0.02297	0.15353	6.51353	0.00353	283.56877	6.03190	27
28	50.06561	0.01997	0.15306	6.53351	0.00306	327.10408	6.09600	28
29	57.57545	0.01737	0.15265	6.55088	0.00265	377.16969	6.15408	29
30	66.21177	0.01510	0.15230	6.56598	0.00230	434.74515	6.20663	30
31	76.14354	0.01313	0.15200	6.57911	0.00200	500.95692	6.25412	31
32	87.56507	0.01142	0.15173	6.59053	0.00173	577.10046	6.29700	32
33	100.69983	0.00993	0.15150	6.60046	0.00150	664.66552	6.33567	33
34	115.80480	0.00864	0.15131	6.60910	0.00131	765.36535	6.37051	34
35	133.17552	0.00751	0.15113	6.61661	0.00113	881.17016	6.40187	35
40	267.86355	0.00373	0.15056	6.64178	0.00056	1779.09031	6.51678	40
45	538.76927	0.00186	0.15028	6.65429	0.00028	3585.12846	6.58299	45
50	1083.65744	0.00092	0.15014	6.66051	0.00014	7217.71628	6.62048	50

20% interest factors for discrete compounding periods

| | SINGLE PAYMENT | | UNIFORM SERIES | | | | | |
| | Compound Amount Factor | Present Worth Factor | Capital Recovery Factor | Present Worth Factor | Sinking Fund Factor | Compound Amount Factor | Gradient Factor | |
N	(F/P,20,N)	(P/F,20,N)	(A/P,20,N)	(P/A,20,N)	(A/F,20,N)	(F/A,20,N)	(A/G,20,N)	N
1	1.20000	0.83333	1.20000	0.83333	1.00000	1.00000	0.00000	1
2	1.44000	0.69444	0.65455	1.52778	0.45455	2.20000	0.45455	2
3	1.72800	0.57870	0.47473	2.10648	0.27473	3.64000	0.87912	3
4	2.07360	0.48225	0.38629	2.58873	0.18629	5.36800	1.27422	4
5	2.48832	0.40188	0.33438	2.99061	0.13438	7.44160	1.64051	5
6	2.98598	0.33490	0.30071	3.32551	0.10071	9.92992	1.97883	6
7	3.58318	0.27908	0.27742	3.60459	0.07742	12.91590	2.29016	7
8	4.29982	0.23257	0.26061	3.83716	0.06061	16.49908	2.57562	8
9	5.15978	0.19381	0.24808	4.03097	0.04808	20.79890	2.83642	9
10	6.19174	0.16151	0.23852	4.19247	0.03852	25.95868	3.07386	10
11	7.43008	0.13459	0.23110	4.32706	0.03110	32.15042	3.28929	11
12	8.91610	0.11216	0.22526	4.43922	0.02526	39.58050	3.48410	12
13	10.69932	0.09346	0.22062	4.53268	0.02062	48.49660	3.65970	13
14	12.83918	0.07789	0.21689	4.61057	0.01689	59.19592	3.81749	14
15	15.40702	0.06491	0.21388	4.67547	0.01388	72.03511	3.95884	15
16	18.48843	0.05409	0.21144	4.72956	0.01144	87.44213	4.08511	16
17	22.18611	0.04507	0.20944	4.77463	0.00944	105.93056	4.19759	17
18	26.62333	0.03756	0.20781	4.81219	0.00781	128.11667	4.29752	18
19	31.94800	0.03130	0.20646	4.84350	0.00646	154.74000	4.38607	19
20	38.33760	0.02608	0.20536	4.86958	0.00536	186.68800	4.46435	20
21	46.00512	0.02174	0.20444	4.89132	0.00444	225.02560	4.53339	21
22	55.20614	0.01811	0.20369	4.90943	0.00369	271.03072	4.59414	22
23	66.24737	0.01509	0.20307	4.92453	0.00307	326.23686	4.64750	23
24	79.49685	0.01258	0.20255	4.93710	0.00255	392.48424	4.69426	24
25	95.39622	0.01048	0.20212	4.94759	0.00212	471.98108	4.73516	25
26	114.47546	0.00874	0.20176	4.95632	0.00176	567.37730	4.77088	26
27	137.37055	0.00728	0.20147	4.96360	0.00147	681.85276	4.80201	27
28	164.84466	0.00607	0.20122	4.96967	0.00122	819.22331	4.82911	28
29	197.81359	0.00506	0.20102	4.97472	0.00102	984.06797	4.85265	29
30	237.37631	0.00421	0.20085	4.97894	0.00085	1181.88157	4.87308	30
31	284.85158	0.00351	0.20070	4.98245	0.00070	1419.25788	4.89079	31
32	341.82190	0.00293	0.20059	4.98537	0.00059	1704.10946	4.90611	32
33	410.18627	0.00244	0.20049	4.98781	0.00049	2045.93135	4.91935	33
34	492.22352	0.00203	0.20041	4.98984	0.00041	2456.11762	4.93079	34
35	590.66823	0.00169	0.20034	4.99154	0.00034	2948.34115	4.94064	35
40	1469.77157	0.00068	0.20014	4.99660	0.00014	7343.85784	4.97277	40
45	3657.26199	0.00027	0.20005	4.99863	0.00005	18281.30994	4.98769	45
50	9100.43815	0.00011	0.20002	4.99945	0.00002	45497.19075	4.99451	50

25% interest factors for discrete compounding periods

	SINGLE PAYMENT		UNIFORM SERIES					
	Compound Amount Factor	Present Worth Factor	Capital Recovery Factor	Present Worth Factor	Sinking Fund Factor	Compound Amount Factor	Gradient Factor	
N	(F/P,25,N)	(P/F,25,N)	(A/P,25,N)	(P/A,25,N)	(A/F,25,N)	(F/A,25,N)	(A/G,25,N)	N
1	1.25000	0.80000	1.25000	0.80000	1.00000	1.00000	0.00000	1
2	1.56250	0.64000	0.69444	1.44000	0.44444	2.25000	0.44444	2
3	1.95313	0.51200	0.51230	1.95200	0.26230	3.81250	0.85246	3
4	2.44141	0.40960	0.42344	2.36160	0.17344	5.76563	1.22493	4
5	3.05176	0.32768	0.37185	2.68928	0.12185	8.20703	1.56307	5
6	3.81470	0.26214	0.33882	2.95142	0.08882	11.25879	1.86833	6
7	4.76837	0.20972	0.31634	3.16114	0.06634	15.07349	2.14243	7
8	5.96046	0.16777	0.30040	3.32891	0.05040	19.84186	2.38725	8
9	7.45058	0.13422	0.28876	3.46313	0.03876	25.80232	2.60478	9
10	9.31323	0.10737	0.28007	3.57050	0.03007	33.25290	2.79710	10
11	11.64153	0.08590	0.27349	3.65640	0.02349	42.56613	2.96631	11
12	14.55192	0.06872	0.26845	3.72512	0.01845	54.20766	3.11452	12
13	18.18989	0.05498	0.26454	3.78010	0.01454	68.75958	3.24374	13
14	22.73737	0.04398	0.26150	3.82408	0.01150	86.94947	3.35595	14
15	28.42171	0.03518	0.25912	3.85926	0.00912	109.68684	3.45299	15
16	35.52714	0.02815	0.25724	3.88741	0.00724	138.10855	3.53660	16
17	44.40892	0.02252	0.25576	3.90993	0.00576	173.63568	3.60838	17
18	55.51115	0.01801	0.25459	3.92794	0.00459	218.04460	3.66979	18
19	69.38894	0.01441	0.25366	3.94235	0.00366	273.55576	3.72218	19
20	86.73617	0.01153	0.25292	3.95388	0.00292	342.94470	3.76673	20
21	108.42022	0.00922	0.25233	3.96311	0.00233	429.68087	3.80451	21
22	135.52527	0.00738	0.25186	3.97049	0.00186	538.10109	3.83646	22
23	169.40659	0.00590	0.25148	3.97639	0.00148	673.62636	3.86343	23
24	211.75824	0.00472	0.25119	3.98111	0.00119	843.03295	3.88613	24
25	264.69780	0.00378	0.25095	3.98489	0.00095	1054.79118	3.90519	25
26	330.87225	0.00302	0.25076	3.98791	0.00076	1319.48898	3.92118	26
27	413.59031	0.00242	0.25061	3.99033	0.00061	1650.36123	3.93456	27
28	516.98788	0.00193	0.25048	3.99226	0.00048	2063.95153	3.94574	28
29	646.23485	0.00155	0.25039	3.99381	0.00039	2580.93941	3.95506	29
30	807.79357	0.00124	0.25031	3.99505	0.00031	3227.17427	3.96282	30
31	1009.74196	0.00099	0.25025	3.99604	0.00025	4034.96783	3.96927	31
32	1262.17745	0.00079	0.25020	3.99683	0.00020	5044.70979	3.97463	32
33	1577.72181	0.00063	0.25016	3.99746	0.00016	6306.88724	3.97907	33
34	1972.15226	0.00051	0.25013	3.99797	0.00013	7884.60905	3.98275	34
35	2465.19033	0.00041	0.25010	3.99838	0.00010	9856.76132	3.98580	35

30% interest factors for discrete compounding periods

	SINGLE PAYMENT		UNIFORM SERIES					
	Compound Amount Factor	Present Worth Factor	Capital Recovery Factor	Present Worth Factor	Sinking Fund Factor	Compound Amount Factor	Gradient Factor	
N	(F/P,30,N)	(P/F,30,N)	(A/P,30,N)	(P/A,30,N)	(A/F,30,N)	(F/A,30,N)	(A/G,30,N)	N
1	1.30000	0.76923	1.30000	0.76923	1.00000	1.00000	0.00000	1
2	1.69000	0.59172	0.73478	1.36095	0.43478	2.30000	0.43478	2
3	2.19700	0.45517	0.55063	1.81611	0.25063	3.99000	0.82707	3
4	2.85610	0.35013	0.46163	2.16624	0.16163	6.18700	1.17828	4
5	3.71293	0.26933	0.41058	2.43557	0.11058	9.04310	1.49031	5
6	4.82681	0.20718	0.37839	2.64275	0.07839	12.75603	1.76545	6
7	6.27485	0.15937	0.35687	2.80211	0.05687	17.58284	2.00628	7
8	8.15731	0.12259	0.34192	2.92470	0.04192	23.85769	2.21559	8
9	10.60450	0.09430	0.33124	3.01900	0.03124	32.01500	2.39627	9
10	13.78585	0.07254	0.32346	3.09154	0.02346	42.61950	2.55122	10
11	17.92160	0.05580	0.31773	3.14734	0.01773	56.40535	2.68328	11
12	23.29809	0.04292	0.31345	3.19026	0.01345	74.32695	2.79517	12
13	30.28751	0.03302	0.31024	3.22328	0.01024	97.62504	2.88946	13
14	39.37376	0.02540	0.30782	3.24867	0.00782	127.91255	2.96850	14
15	51.18589	0.01954	0.30598	3.26821	0.00598	167.00031	3.03444	15
16	66.54106	0.01503	0.30458	3.28324	0.00458	218.47220	3.08921	16
17	86.50416	0.01156	0.30351	3.29480	0.00351	285.01386	3.13451	17
18	112.45541	0.00889	0.30269	3.30369	0.00269	371.51802	3.17183	18
19	146.19203	0.00684	0.30207	3.31053	0.00207	483.97343	3.20247	19
20	190.04964	0.00526	0.30159	3.31579	0.00159	630.16546	3.22754	20
21	247.06453	0.00405	0.30122	3.31984	0.00122	820.21510	3.24799	21
22	321.18389	0.00311	0.30094	3.32296	0.00094	1067.27963	3.26462	22
23	417.53905	0.00239	0.30072	3.32535	0.00072	1388.46351	3.27812	23
24	542.80077	0.00184	0.30055	3.32719	0.00055	1806.00257	3.28904	24
25	705.64100	0.00142	0.30043	3.32861	0.00043	2348.80334	3.29786	25
26	917.33330	0.00109	0.30033	3.32970	0.00033	3054.44434	3.30496	26
27	1192.53329	0.00084	0.30025	3.33054	0.00025	3971.77764	3.31067	27
28	1550.29328	0.00065	0.30019	3.33118	0.00019	5164.31093	3.31526	28
29	2015.38126	0.00050	0.30015	3.33168	0.00015	6714.60421	3.31894	29
30	2619.99564	0.00038	0.30011	3.33206	0.00011	8729.98548	3.32188	30
31	3405.99434	0.00029	0.30009	3.33235	0.00009	11349.98112	3.32423	31
32	4427.79264	0.00023	0.30007	3.33258	0.00007	14755.97546	3.32610	32
33	5756.13043	0.00017	0.30005	3.33275	0.00005	19183.76810	3.32760	33
34	7482.96956	0.00013	0.30004	3.33289	0.00004	24939.89853	3.32879	34
35	9727.86043	0.00010	0.30003	3.33299	0.00003	32422.86808	3.32974	35

40% interest factors for discrete compounding periods

	SINGLE PAYMENT		UNIFORM SERIES					
	Compound Amount Factor	Present Worth Factor	Capital Recovery Factor	Present Worth Factor	Sinking Fund Factor	Compound Amount Factor	Gradient Factor	
N	(F/P,40,N)	(P/F,40,N)	(A/P,40,N)	(P/A,40,N)	(A/F,40,N)	(F/A,40,N)	(A/G,40,N)	N
1	1.40000	0.71429	1.40000	0.71429	1.00000	1.00000	0.00000	1
2	1.96000	0.51020	0.81667	1.22449	0.41667	2.40000	0.41667	2
3	2.74400	0.36443	0.62936	1.58892	0.22936	4.36000	0.77982	3
4	3.84160	0.26031	0.54077	1.84923	0.14077	7.10400	1.09234	4
5	5.37824	0.18593	0.49136	2.03516	0.09136	10.94560	1.35799	5
6	7.52954	0.13281	0.46126	2.16797	0.06126	16.32384	1.58110	6
7	10.54135	0.09486	0.44192	2.26284	0.04192	23.85338	1.76635	7
8	14.75789	0.06776	0.42907	2.33060	0.02907	34.39473	1.91852	8
9	20.66105	0.04840	0.42034	2.37900	0.02034	49.15262	2.04224	9
10	28.92547	0.03457	0.41432	2.41357	0.01432	69.81366	2.14190	10
11	40.49565	0.02469	0.41013	2.43826	0.01013	98.73913	2.22149	11
12	56.69391	0.01764	0.40718	2.45590	0.00718	139.23478	2.28454	12
13	79.37148	0.01260	0.40510	2.46850	0.00510	195.92869	2.33412	13
14	111.12007	0.00900	0.40363	2.47750	0.00363	275.30017	2.37287	14
15	155.56810	0.00643	0.40259	2.48393	0.00259	386.42024	2.40296	15
16	217.79533	0.00459	0.40185	2.48852	0.00185	541.98833	2.42620	16
17	304.91347	0.00328	0.40132	2.49180	0.00132	759.78367	2.44406	17
18	426.87885	0.00234	0.40094	2.49414	0.00094	1064.69714	2.45773	18
19	597.63040	0.00167	0.40067	2.49582	0.00067	1491.57599	2.46815	19
20	836.68255	0.00120	0.40048	2.49701	0.00048	2089.20639	2.47607	20
21	1171.35558	0.00085	0.40034	2.49787	0.00034	2925.88894	2.48206	21
22	1639.89781	0.00061	0.40024	2.49848	0.00024	4097.24452	2.48658	22
23	2295.85693	0.00044	0.40017	2.49891	0.00017	5737.14232	2.48998	23
24	3214.19970	0.00031	0.40012	2.49922	0.00012	8032.99925	2.49253	24
25	4499.87958	0.00022	0.40009	2.49944	0.00009	11247.19895	2.49444	25

50% interest factors for discrete compounding periods

	SINGLE PAYMENT		UNIFORM SERIES					
	Compound Amount Factor	Present Worth Factor	Capital Recovery Factor	Present Worth Factor	Sinking Fund Factor	Compound Amount Factor	Gradient Factor	
N	(F/P,50,N)	(P/F,50,N)	(A/P,50,N)	(P/A,50,N)	(A/F,50,N)	(F/A,50,N)	(A/G,50,N)	N
1	1.50000	0.66667	1.50000	0.66667	1.00000	1.00000	0.00000	1
2	2.25000	0.44444	0.90000	1.11111	0.40000	2.50000	0.40000	2
3	3.37500	0.29630	0.71053	1.40741	0.21053	4.75000	0.73684	3
4	5.06250	0.19753	0.62308	1.60494	0.12308	8.12500	1.01538	4
5	7.59375	0.13169	0.57583	1.73663	0.07583	13.18750	1.24171	5
6	11.39063	0.08779	0.54812	1.82442	0.04812	20.78125	1.42256	6
7	17.08594	0.05853	0.53108	1.88294	0.03108	32.17188	1.56484	7
8	25.62891	0.03902	0.52030	1.92196	0.02030	49.25781	1.67518	8
9	38.44336	0.02601	0.51335	1.94798	0.01335	74.88672	1.75964	9
10	57.66504	0.01734	0.50882	1.96532	0.00882	113.33008	1.82352	10
11	86.49756	0.01156	0.50585	1.97688	0.00585	170.99512	1.87134	11
12	129.74634	0.00771	0.50388	1.98459	0.00388	257.49268	1.90679	12
13	194.61951	0.00514	0.50258	1.98972	0.00258	387.23901	1.93286	13
14	291.92926	0.00343	0.50172	1.99315	0.00172	581.85852	1.95188	14
15	437.89389	0.00228	0.50114	1.99543	0.00114	873.78778	1.96567	15
16	656.84084	0.00152	0.50076	1.99696	0.00076	1311.68107	1.97560	16
17	985.26125	0.00101	0.50051	1.99797	0.00051	1968.52251	1.98273	17
18	1477.89188	0.00068	0.50034	1.99865	0.00034	2953.78376	1.98781	18
19	2216.83782	0.00045	0.50023	1.99910	0.00023	4431.67564	1.99143	19
20	3325.25673	0.00030	0.50015	1.99940	0.00015	6648.51346	1.99398	20
21	4987.88510	0.00020	0.50010	1.99960	0.00010	9973.77019	1.99579	21
22	7481.82764	0.00013	0.50007	1.99973	0.00007	14961.65520	1.99708	22
23	11222.74146	0.00009	0.50004	1.99982	0.00004	22443.48293	1.99795	23
24	16834.11220	0.00006	0.50003	1.99988	0.00003	33666.22439	1.99857	24
25	25251.16829	0.00004	0.50002	1.99992	0.00002	50500.33659	1.99901	25

60% interest factors for discrete compounding periods

| | SINGLE PAYMENT | | UNIFORM SERIES | | | | | |
| | Compound Amount Factor | Present Worth Factor | Capital Recovery Factor | Present Worth Factor | Sinking Fund Factor | Compound Amount Factor | Gradient Factor | |
N	(F/P,60,N)	(P/F,60,N)	(A/P,60,N)	(P/A,60,N)	(A/F,60,N)	(F/A,60,N)	(A/G,60,N)	N
1	1.60000	0.62500	1.60000	0.62500	1.00000	1.00000	0.00000	1
2	2.56000	0.39063	0.98462	1.01563	0.38462	2.60000	0.38462	2
3	4.09600	0.24414	0.79380	1.25977	0.19380	5.16000	0.69767	3
4	6.55360	0.15259	0.70804	1.41235	0.10804	9.25600	0.94641	4
5	10.48576	0.09537	0.66325	1.50772	0.06325	15.80960	1.13956	5
6	16.77722	0.05960	0.63803	1.56733	0.03803	26.29536	1.28637	6
7	26.84355	0.03725	0.62322	1.60458	0.02322	43.07258	1.39581	7
8	42.94967	0.02328	0.61430	1.62786	0.01430	69.91612	1.47596	8
9	68.71948	0.01455	0.60886	1.64241	0.00886	112.86579	1.53377	9
10	109.95116	0.00909	0.60551	1.65151	0.00551	181.58527	1.57488	10
11	175.92186	0.00568	0.60343	1.65719	0.00343	291.53643	1.60378	11
12	281.47498	0.00355	0.60214	1.66075	0.00214	467.45829	1.62388	12
13	450.35996	0.00222	0.60134	1.66297	0.00134	748.93327	1.63774	13
14	720.57594	0.00139	0.60083	1.66435	0.00083	1199.29323	1.64721	14
15	1152.92150	0.00087	0.60052	1.66522	0.00052	1919.86917	1.65364	15
16	1844.67441	0.00054	0.60033	1.66576	0.00033	3072.79068	1.65799	16
17	2951.47905	0.00034	0.60020	1.66610	0.00020	4917.46509	1.66090	17
18	4722.36648	0.00021	0.60013	1.66631	0.00013	7868.94414	1.66285	18
19	7555.78637	0.00013	0.60008	1.66645	0.00008	12591.31062	1.66415	19
20	12089.25820	0.00008	0.60005	1.66653	0.00005	20147.09699	1.66501	20

70% interest factors for discrete compounding periods

| | SINGLE PAYMENT | | UNIFORM SERIES | | | | | |
N	Compound Amount Factor (F/P,70,N)	Present Worth Factor (P/F,70,N)	Capital Recovery Factor (A/P,70,N)	Present Worth Factor (P/A,70,N)	Sinking Fund Factor (A/F,70,N)	Compound Amount Factor (F/A,70,N)	Gradient Factor (A/G,70,N)	N
1	1.70000	0.58824	1.70000	0.58824	1.00000	1.00000	0.00000	1
2	2.89000	0.34602	1.07037	0.93426	0.37037	2.70000	0.37037	2
3	4.91300	0.20354	0.87889	1.13780	0.17889	5.59000	0.66190	3
4	8.35210	0.11973	0.79521	1.25753	0.09521	10.50300	0.88451	4
5	14.19857	0.07043	0.75304	1.32796	0.05304	18.85510	1.04974	5
6	24.13757	0.04143	0.73025	1.36939	0.03025	33.05367	1.16925	6
7	41.03387	0.02437	0.71749	1.39376	0.01749	57.19124	1.25372	7
8	69.75757	0.01434	0.71018	1.40809	0.01018	98.22511	1.31222	8
9	118.58788	0.00843	0.70595	1.41652	0.00595	167.98268	1.35203	9
10	201.59639	0.00496	0.70349	1.42149	0.00349	286.57056	1.37872	10
11	342.71896	0.00292	0.70205	1.42440	0.00205	488.16995	1.39638	11
12	582.62224	0.00172	0.70120	1.42612	0.00120	830.88891	1.40794	12
13	990.45780	0.00101	0.70071	1.42713	0.00071	1413.51115	1.41540	13
14	1683.77827	0.00059	0.70042	1.42772	0.00042	2403.96895	1.42025	14
15	2862.42305	0.00005	0.70024	1.42807	0.00024	4087.74722	1.42333	15
16	4866.11919	0.00021	0.70014	1.42828	0.00014	6950.17027	1.42528	16
17	8272.40262	0.00012	0.70008	1.42840	0.00008	11816.28946	1.42652	17
18	14063.08445	0.00007	0.70005	1.42847	0.00005	20088.69207	1.42729	18
19	23907.24357	0.00004	0.70003	1.42851	0.00003	34151.77653	1.42778	19
20	40642.31407	0.00002	0.70002	1.42854	0.00002	68059.02009	1.42808	20

80% interest factors for discrete compounding periods

| | SINGLE PAYMENT | | UNIFORM SERIES | | | | | |
N	Compound Amount Factor (F/P,80,N)	Present Worth Factor (P/F,80,N)	Capital Recovery Factor (A/P,80,N)	Present Worth Factor (P/A,80,N)	Sinking Fund Factor (A/F,80,N)	Compound Amount Factor (F/A,80,N)	Gradient Factor (A/G,80,N)	N
1	1.80000	0.55556	1.80000	0.55556	1.00000	1.00000	0.00000	1
2	3.24000	0.30864	1.15714	0.86420	0.35714	2.80000	0.35714	2
3	5.83200	0.17147	0.96556	1.03567	0.16556	6.04000	0.62914	3
4	10.49760	0.09526	0.88423	1.13093	0.08423	11.87200	0.82884	4
5	18.89568	0.05292	0.84470	1.18385	0.04470	22.36960	0.97060	5
6	34.01222	0.02940	0.82423	1.21325	0.02423	41.26528	1.06825	6
7	61.22200	0.01633	0.81328	1.22958	0.01328	75.27750	1.13376	7
8	110.19961	0.00907	0.80733	1.23866	0.00733	136.49951	1.17674	8
9	198.35929	0.00504	0.80405	1.24370	0.00405	246.69911	1.20440	9
10	357.04672	0.00280	0.80225	1.24650	0.00225	445.05840	1.22191	10
11	642.68410	0.00156	0.80125	1.24806	0.00125	802.10513	1.23286	11
12	1156.83138	0.00086	0.80069	1.24892	0.00069	1444.78923	1.23962	12
13	2082.29649	0.00048	0.80038	1.24940	0.00038	2601.62061	1.24375	13
14	3748.13368	0.00027	0.80021	1.24967	0.00021	4683.91709	1.24626	14
15	6746.64062	0.00015	0.80012	1.24981	0.00012	8432.05077	1.24778	15

90% interest factors for discrete compounding periods

	SINGLE PAYMENT		UNIFORM SERIES					
	Compound Amount Factor	Present Worth Factor	Capital Recovery Factor	Present Worth Factor	Sinking Fund Factor	Compound Amount Factor	Gradient Factor	
N	(F/P,90,N)	(P/F,90,N)	(A/P,90,N)	(P/A,90,N)	(A/F,90,N)	(F/A,90,N)	(A/G,90,N)	N
1	1.90000	0.52632	1.90000	0.52632	1.00000	1.00000	0.00000	1
2	3.61000	0.27701	1.24483	0.80332	0.34483	2.90000	0.34483	2
3	6.85900	0.14579	1.05361	0.94912	0.15361	6.51000	0.59908	3
4	13.03210	0.07673	0.97480	1.02585	0.07480	13.36900	0.77867	4
5	24.76099	0.04039	0.93788	1.06624	0.03788	26.40110	0.90068	5
6	47.04588	0.02126	0.91955	1.08749	0.01955	51.16209	0.98081	6
7	89.38717	0.01119	0.91018	1.09868	0.01018	98.20797	1.03191	7
8	169.83563	0.00589	0.90533	1.10457	0.00533	187.59514	1.06373	8
9	322.68770	0.00310	0.90280	1.10767	0.00280	357.43078	1.08313	9
10	613.10663	0.00163	0.90147	1.10930	0.00147	680.11847	1.09477	10

100% interest factors for discrete compounding periods

	SINGLE PAYMENT		UNIFORM SERIES					
	Compound Amount Factor	Present Worth Factor	Capital Recovery Factor	Present Worth Factor	Sinking Fund Factor	Compound Amount Factor	Gradient Factor	
N	(F/P,100,N)	(P/F,100,N)	(A/P,100,N)	(P/A,100,N)	(A/F,100,N)	(F/A,100,N)	(A/G,100,N)	N
1	2.00000	0.50000	2.00000	0.50000	1.00000	1.00000	0.00000	1
2	4.00000	0.25000	1.33333	0.75000	0.33333	3.00000	0.33333	2
3	8.00000	0.12500	1.14286	0.87500	0.14286	7.00000	0.57143	3
4	16.00000	0.06250	1.06667	0.93750	0.06667	15.00000	0.73333	4
5	32.00000	0.03125	1.03226	0.96875	0.03226	31.00000	0.83871	5
6	64.00000	0.01563	1.01587	0.98438	0.01587	63.00000	0.90476	6
7	128.00000	0.00781	1.00787	0.99219	0.00787	127.00000	0.94488	7
8	256.00000	0.00391	1.00392	0.99609	0.00392	255.00000	0.96863	8
9	512.00000	0.00195	1.00196	0.99805	0.00196	511.00000	0.98239	9
10	1024.00000	0.00098	1.00098	0.99902	0.00098	1023.00000	0.99022	10

CONTINUOUS-FLOW, CONTINUOUS-COMPOUNDING INTEREST FACTORS

Effective interest rate of 5%; $r = 4.879\%$

N	$(\bar{A}/P,4.879,N)$	$(P/\bar{A},4.879,N)$	$(\bar{A}/F,4.879,N)$	$(F/\bar{A},4.879,N)$	N
1	1.02459	0.97600	0.97580	1.02480	1
2	0.52479	1.90552	0.47600	2.10083	2
3	0.35832	2.79078	0.30953	3.23067	3
4	0.27519	3.63388	0.22640	4.41700	4
5	0.22539	4.43684	0.17660	5.66265	5
6	0.19225	5.20155	0.14346	6.97057	6
7	0.16864	5.92986	0.11985	8.34390	7
8	0.15098	6.62348	0.10219	9.78589	8
9	0.13729	7.28408	0.08850	11.29998	9
10	0.12637	7.91321	0.07758	12.88977	10
11	0.11748	8.51239	0.06869	14.55905	11
12	0.11010	9.08304	0.06131	16.31180	12
13	0.10388	9.62651	0.05509	18.15219	13
14	0.09858	10.14411	0.04979	20.08459	14
15	0.09401	10.63705	0.04522	22.11361	15
16	0.09004	11.10652	0.04125	24.24408	16
17	0.08655	11.55364	0.03776	26.48108	17
18	0.08348	11.97947	0.03469	28.82993	18
19	0.08074	12.38501	0.03195	31.29621	19
20	0.07830	12.77125	0.02951	33.88582	20
21	0.07611	13.13909	0.02732	36.60490	21
22	0.07413	13.48942	0.02534	39.45993	22
23	0.07234	13.82307	0.02355	42.45772	23
24	0.07072	14.14083	0.02193	45.60540	24
25	0.06924	14.44345	0.02045	48.91045	25
26	0.06788	14.73167	0.01909	52.38076	26
27	0.06664	15.00616	0.01785	56.02459	27
28	0.06550	15.26758	0.01671	59.85061	28
29	0.06445	15.51655	0.01566	63.86792	29
30	0.06348	15.75367	0.01469	68.08611	30
31	0.06258	15.97949	0.01379	72.51520	31
32	0.06175	16.19456	0.01296	77.16574	32
33	0.06098	16.39939	0.01219	82.04881	33
34	0.06026	16.59447	0.01147	87.17603	34
35	0.05959	16.78026	0.01080	92.55962	35
40	0.05687	17.58462	0.00808	123.79468	40
45	0.05490	18.21485	0.00611	163.65939	45
50	0.05345	18.70866	0.00466	214.53793	50

Effective interest rate of 6%; $r = 5.827\%$

N	$(\bar{A}/P, 5.827, N)$	$(P/\bar{A}, 5.827, N)$	$(\bar{A}/F, 5.827, N)$	$(F/\bar{A}, 5.827, N)$	N
1	1.02942	0.97142	0.97115	1.02971	1
2	0.52970	1.88786	0.47143	2.12120	2
3	0.36332	2.75242	0.30505	3.27819	3
4	0.28027	3.56804	0.22200	4.50459	4
5	0.23055	4.33750	0.17228	5.80458	5
6	0.19750	5.06340	0.13923	7.18257	6
7	0.17397	5.74821	0.11570	8.64324	7
8	0.15639	6.39425	0.09812	10.19156	8
9	0.14278	7.00373	0.08451	11.83277	9
10	0.13195	7.57871	0.07368	13.57246	10
11	0.12314	8.12114	0.06487	15.41653	11
12	0.11584	8.63287	0.05757	17.37125	12
13	0.10970	9.11563	0.05143	19.44326	13
14	0.10448	9.57106	0.04621	21.63958	14
15	0.09999	10.00072	0.04172	23.96769	15
16	0.09810	10.40605	0.03783	26.43549	16
17	0.09269	10.78844	0.03442	29.05136	17
18	0.08969	11.14919	0.03142	31.82418	18
19	0.08704	11.48951	0.02877	34.76338	19
20	0.08467	11.81057	0.02640	37.87893	20
21	0.08255	12.11346	0.02428	41.18142	21
22	0.08065	12.39920	0.02238	44.68207	22
23	0.07893	12.66877	0.02066	48.39275	23
24	0.07738	12.92308	0.01911	52.32608	24
25	0.07597	13.16300	0.01770	56.49542	25
26	0.07469	13.38933	0.01642	60.91492	26
27	0.07351	13.60285	0.01524	65.59959	27
28	0.07244	13.80429	0.01417	70.56535	28
29	0.07146	13.99432	0.01319	75.82906	29
30	0.07055	14.17360	0.01228	81.40860	30
31	0.06972	14.34273	0.01145	87.32292	31
32	0.06895	14.50228	0.01068	93.59211	32
33	0.06825	14.65281	0.00998	100.23745	33
34	0.06759	14.79481	0.00932	107.28153	34
35	0.06698	14.92878	0.00871	114.74825	35
40	0.06454	15.49308	0.00627	159.36446	40
45	0.06283	15.91477	0.00456	219.07134	45
50	0.06161	16.22987	0.00334	298.97306	50

Effective interest rate of 7%; $r = 6.766\%$

N	$(\bar{A}/P,6.766,N)$	$(P/\bar{A},6.766,N)$	$(\bar{A}/F,6.766,N)$	$(F/\bar{A},6.766,N)$	N
1	1.03421	0.96692	0.96655	1.03461	1
2	0.53459	1.87058	0.46693	2.14164	2
3	0.36831	2.71513	0.30065	3.32616	3
4	0.28535	3.50442	0.21769	4.59360	4
5	0.23573	4.24207	0.16807	5.94977	5
6	0.20278	4.93147	0.13512	7.40086	6
7	0.17935	5.57576	0.11169	8.95354	7
8	0.16187	6.17791	0.09421	10.61491	8
9	0.14835	6.74066	0.08069	12.39257	9
10	0.13762	7.26659	0.06996	14.29468	10
11	0.12890	7.75812	0.06124	16.32993	11
12	0.12169	8.21749	0.05403	18.50766	12
13	0.11565	8.64681	0.04799	20.83783	13
14	0.11052	9.04804	0.04286	23.33111	14
15	0.10612	9.42302	0.03846	25.99893	15
16	0.10232	9.77347	0.03466	28.85350	16
17	0.09900	10.10099	0.03134	31.90789	17
18	0.09609	10.40708	0.02843	35.17609	18
19	0.09352	10.69315	0.02586	38.67308	19
20	0.09124	10.96051	0.02358	42.41485	20
21	0.08920	11.21037	0.02154	46.41856	21
22	0.08738	11.44389	0.01972	50.70253	22
23	0.08575	11.66213	0.01809	55.28639	23
24	0.08427	11.86609	0.01661	60.19112	24
25	0.08294	12.05671	0.01528	65.43920	25
26	0.08173	12.23486	0.01407	71.05464	26
27	0.08064	12.40135	0.01298	77.06317	27
28	0.07964	12.55695	0.01198	83.49231	28
29	0.07873	12.70238	0.01107	90.37150	29
30	0.07789	12.83828	0.01023	97.73224	30
31	0.07713	12.96530	0.00947	105.60825	31
32	0.07643	13.08401	0.00877	114.03559	32
33	0.07579	13.19495	0.00813	123.05285	33
34	0.07520	13.29863	0.00754	132.70133	34
35	0.07465	13.39553	0.00699	143.02522	35
40	0.07250	13.79284	0.00484	206.55140	40
45	0.07104	14.07611	0.00338	295.65074	45
50	0.07004	14.27807	0.00238	420.61803	50

Effective interest rate of 8%; $r = 7.696\%$

N	$(\bar{A}/P,7.696,N)$	$(P/\bar{A},7.696,N)$	$(\bar{A}/F,7.696,N)$	$(F/\bar{A},7.696,N)$	N
1	1.03897	0.96249	0.96201	1.03949	1
2	0.53947	1.85368	0.46251	2.16213	2
3	0.37329	2.67886	0.29633	3.37459	3
4	0.29045	3.44292	0.21349	4.68403	4
5	0.24094	4.15038	0.16398	6.09824	5
6	0.20810	4.80544	0.13114	7.62558	6
7	0.18478	5.41197	0.10782	9.27510	7
8	0.16740	5.97358	0.09044	11.05659	8
9	0.15400	6.49359	0.07704	12.98059	9
10	0.14337	6.97507	0.06641	15.05850	10
11	0.13475	7.42090	0.05779	17.30265	11
12	0.12765	7.83370	0.05069	19.72633	12
13	0.12171	8.21592	0.04475	22.34390	13
14	0.11669	8.56983	0.03973	25.17088	14
15	0.11239	8.89752	0.03543	28.22401	15
16	0.10868	9.20094	0.03172	31.52138	16
17	0.10546	9.48189	0.02850	35.08254	17
18	0.10265	9.74203	0.02569	38.92859	18
19	0.10017	9.98289	0.02321	43.08232	19
20	0.09798	10.20592	0.02102	47.56835	20
21	0.09604	10.41242	0.01908	52.41325	21
22	0.09431	10.60363	0.01735	57.64574	22
23	0.09276	10.78067	0.01580	63.29682	23
24	0.09137	10.94460	0.01441	69.39998	24
25	0.09012	11.09639	0.01316	75.99138	25
26	0.08899	11.23694	0.01203	83.11010	26
27	0.08797	11.36707	0.01101	90.79830	27
28	0.08705	11.48756	0.01009	99.10154	28
29	0.08621	11.59913	0.00925	108.06904	29
30	0.08545	11.70244	0.00849	117.75393	30
31	0.08476	11.79809	0.00780	128.21360	31
32	0.08413	11.88666	0.00717	139.51003	32
33	0.08355	11.96866	0.00659	151.71016	33
34	0.08302	12.04460	0.00606	164.88629	34
35	0.08254	12.11490	0.00558	179.11650	35
40	0.08067	12.39562	0.00371	269.27776	40
45	0.07945	12.58668	0.00249	401.75356	45
50	0.07864	12.71671	0.00168	596.40295	50

Effective interest rate of 9%; $r = 8.618\%$

N	$(\bar{A}/P,8.618,N)$	$(P/\bar{A},8.618,N)$	$(\bar{A}/F,8.618,N)$	$(F/\bar{A},8.618,N)$	N
1	1.04371	0.95812	0.95753	1.04435	1
2	0.54433	1.83713	0.45815	2.18270	2
3	0.37828	2.64356	0.29210	3.42351	3
4	0.29556	3.38340	0.20938	4.77599	4
5	0.24618	4.06215	0.16000	6.25019	5
6	0.21345	4.68486	0.12727	7.85708	6
7	0.19025	5.25615	0.10407	9.60859	7
8	0.17300	5.78026	0.08682	11.51775	8
9	0.15972	6.26110	0.07354	13.59873	9
10	0.14920	6.70224	0.06302	15.86700	10
11	0.14071	7.10695	0.05453	18.33943	11
12	0.13372	7.47824	0.04754	21.03438	12
13	0.12790	7.81888	0.04172	23.97188	13
14	0.12298	8.13139	0.03680	27.17376	14
15	0.11879	8.41810	0.03261	30.66382	15
16	0.11519	8.68113	0.02901	34.46800	16
17	0.11208	8.92244	0.02590	38.61456	17
18	0.10936	9.14383	0.02318	43.13432	18
19	0.10699	9.34693	0.02081	48.06088	19
20	0.10490	9.53327	0.01872	53.43083	20
21	0.10305	9.70422	0.01687	59.28409	21
22	0.10141	9.86106	0.01523	65.66417	22
23	0.09995	10.00494	0.01377	72.61846	23
24	0.09865	10.13695	0.01247	80.19866	24
25	0.09748	10.25805	0.01130	88.46110	25
26	0.09644	10.36916	0.01026	97.46717	26
27	0.09550	10.47109	0.00932	107.28382	27
28	0.09466	10.56460	0.00848	117.98399	28
29	0.09389	10.65039	0.00771	129.64720	29
30	0.09320	10.72910	0.00702	142.36012	30
31	0.09258	10.80131	0.00640	156.21725	31
32	0.09202	10.86756	0.00584	171.32155	32
33	0.09151	10.92834	0.00533	187.78527	33
34	0.09104	10.98410	0.00486	205.73077	34
35	0.09062	11.03525	0.00444	225.29141	35
40	0.08901	11.23422	0.00283	352.89295	40
45	0.08800	11.36354	0.00182	549.22600	45
50	0.08735	11.44759	0.00117	851.31220	50

Effective interest rate of 10%; $r = 9.531\%$

N	$(\bar{A}/P, 9.531, N)$	$(P/\bar{A}, 9.531, N)$	$(\bar{A}/F, 9.531, N)$	$(F/\bar{A}, 9.531, N)$	N
1	1.04841	0.95382	0.95310	1.04921	1
2	0.54917	1.82094	0.45386	2.20333	2
3	0.38326	2.60922	0.28795	3.47287	3
4	0.30068	3.32584	0.20537	4.86936	4
5	0.25143	3.97732	0.15612	6.40550	5
6	0.21884	4.56957	0.12353	8.09526	6
7	0.19577	5.10798	0.10046	9.95399	7
8	0.17865	5.59744	0.08334	11.99859	8
9	0.16550	6.04241	0.07019	14.24765	9
10	0.15511	6.44692	0.05980	16.72162	10
11	0.14674	6.81466	0.05143	19.44299	11
12	0.13988	7.14897	0.04457	22.43649	12
13	0.13418	7.45289	0.03887	25.72934	13
14	0.12938	7.72918	0.03407	29.35147	14
15	0.12531	7.98035	0.03000	33.33582	15
16	0.12182	8.20869	0.02651	37.71860	16
17	0.11882	8.41627	0.02351	42.53966	17
18	0.11621	8.60498	0.02090	47.84282	18
19	0.11394	8.77653	0.01863	53.67630	19
20	0.11195	8.93249	0.01664	60.09313	20
21	0.11020	9.07427	0.01489	67.15163	21
22	0.10866	9.20316	0.01335	74.91599	22
23	0.10729	9.32034	0.01198	83.45678	23
24	0.10608	9.42686	0.01077	92.85164	24
25	0.10500	9.52370	0.00969	103.18600	25
26	0.10404	9.61173	0.00873	114.55378	26
27	0.10318	9.69176	0.00787	127.05834	27
28	0.10241	9.76452	0.00710	140.81336	28
29	0.10172	9.83066	0.00641	155.94387	29
30	0.10110	9.89079	0.00579	172.58743	30
31	0.10055	9.94545	0.00524	190.89535	31
32	0.10005	9.99515	0.00474	211.03405	32
33	0.09960	10.04032	0.00429	233.18662	33
34	0.09919	10.08139	0.00388	257.55444	34
35	0.09883	10.11872	0.00352	284.35904	35
40	0.09746	10.26026	0.00215	464.36817	40
45	0.09664	10.34813	0.00133	754.27441	45
50	0.09613	10.40270	0.00082	1221.17089	50

Effective interest rate of 11%; $r = 10.436\%$

N	$(\bar{A}/P,10.436,N)$	$(P/\bar{A},10.436,N)$	$(\bar{A}/F,10.436,N)$	$(F/\bar{A},10.436,N)$	N
1	1.05309	0.94959	0.94873	1.05404	1
2	0.55399	1.80507	0.44963	2.22403	2
3	0.38823	2.57578	0.28387	3.52272	3
4	0.30580	3.27011	0.20144	4.96426	4
5	0.25670	3.89564	0.15234	6.56437	5
6	0.22426	4.45917	0.11990	8.34050	6
7	0.20133	4.96686	0.09697	10.31200	7
8	0.18436	5.42424	0.08000	12.50036	8
9	0.17134	5.83629	0.06698	14.92944	9
10	0.16110	6.20751	0.05674	17.62572	10
11	0.15286	6.54194	0.04850	20.61860	11
12	0.14613	6.84323	0.04177	23.94069	12
13	0.14055	7.11466	0.03619	27.62820	13
14	0.13588	7.35919	0.03152	31.72135	14
15	0.13193	7.57949	0.02757	36.26474	15
16	0.12857	7.77796	0.02421	41.30791	16
17	0.12568	7.95676	0.02132	46.90582	17
18	0.12319	8.11784	0.01883	53.11950	18
19	0.12102	8.26296	0.01666	60.01669	19
20	0.11914	8.39370	0.01478	67.67257	20
21	0.11749	8.51148	0.01313	76.17059	21
22	0.11604	8.61759	0.01168	85.60340	22
23	0.11477	8.71318	0.01041	96.07381	23
24	0.11365	8.79930	0.00929	107.69598	24
25	0.11265	8.87689	0.00829	120.59658	25
26	0.11177	8.94678	0.00741	134.91624	26
27	0.11099	9.00975	0.00663	150.81107	27
28	0.11030	9.06649	0.00594	168.45433	28
29	0.10968	9.11759	0.00532	188.03834	29
30	0.10913	9.16364	0.00477	209.77660	30
31	0.10864	9.20512	0.00428	233.90607	31
32	0.10820	9.24249	0.00384	260.68977	32
33	0.10780	9.27615	0.00344	290.41969	33
34	0.10745	9.30648	0.00309	323.41989	34
35	0.10714	9.33381	0.00278	360.05012	35
40	0.10599	9.43480	0.00163	613.26972	40
45	0.10532	9.49473	0.00096	1039.95943	45
50	0.10493	9.53030	0.00057	1758.95636	50

Effective interest rate of 12%; $r = 11.333\%$

N	$(\bar{A}/P,11.333,N)$	$(P/\bar{A},11.333,N)$	$(\bar{A}/F,11.333,N)$	$(F/\bar{A},11.333,N)$	N
1	1.05774	0.94542	0.94441	1.05887	1
2	0.55880	1.78954	0.44547	2.24480	2
3	0.39320	2.54322	0.27987	3.57305	3
4	0.31093	3.21614	0.19760	5.06069	4
5	0.26199	3.81697	0.14866	6.72684	5
6	0.22970	4.35342	0.11637	8.59294	6
7	0.20694	4.83239	0.09361	10.68298	7
8	0.19011	5.26005	0.07678	13.02382	8
9	0.17725	5.64188	0.06392	15.64556	9
10	0.16715	5.98280	0.05382	18.58192	10
11	0.15905	6.28720	0.04572	21.87065	11
12	0.15246	6.55898	0.03913	25.55402	12
13	0.14702	6.80164	0.03369	29.67941	13
14	0.14248	7.01830	0.02915	34.29985	14
15	0.13866	7.21175	0.02533	39.47475	15
16	0.13542	7.38447	0.02209	45.27065	16
17	0.13265	7.53868	0.01932	51.76206	17
18	0.13027	7.67637	0.01694	59.03245	18
19	0.12822	7.79931	0.01489	67.17530	19
20	0.12644	7.90908	0.01311	76.29530	20
21	0.12489	8.00709	0.01156	86.50972	21
22	0.12354	8.09459	0.01021	97.94988	22
23	0.12236	8.17272	0.00903	110.76288	23
24	0.12132	8.24248	0.00799	125.11346	24
25	0.12041	8.30476	0.00708	141.18612	25
26	0.11961	8.36037	0.00628	159.18753	26
27	0.11891	8.41002	0.00558	179.34914	27
28	0.11828	8.45436	0.00495	201.93017	28
29	0.11773	8.49394	0.00440	227.22095	29
30	0.11724	8.52928	0.00391	255.54667	30
31	0.11681	8.56084	0.00348	287.27151	31
32	0.11643	8.58901	0.00310	322.80338	32
33	0.11609	8.61416	0.00276	362.59913	33
34	0.11579	8.63662	0.00246	407.17043	34
35	0.11552	8.65668	0.00219	457.09035	35
40	0.11456	8.72897	0.00123	812.28151	40
45	0.11403	8.76998	0.00070	1438.25382	45
50	0.11372	8.79326	0.00039	2541.43817	50

Effective interest rate of 13%; $r = 12.222\%$

N	$(\bar{A}/P,12.222,N)$	$(P/\bar{A},12.222,N)$	$(\bar{A}/F,12.222,N)$	$(F/\bar{A},12.222,N)$	N
1	1.06235	0.94131	0.94013	1.06368	1
2	0.56360	1.77432	0.44138	2.26564	2
3	0.39817	2.51149	0.27595	3.62385	3
4	0.31607	3.16386	0.19385	5.15864	4
5	0.26730	3.74118	0.14508	6.89296	5
6	0.23518	4.25207	0.11296	8.85274	6
7	0.21258	4.70419	0.09036	11.06729	7
8	0.19591	5.10430	0.07369	13.56975	8
9	0.18320	5.45837	0.06098	16.39753	9
10	0.17326	5.77171	0.05104	19.59293	10
11	0.16532	6.04900	0.04310	23.20374	11
12	0.15887	6.29439	0.03665	27.28397	12
13	0.15357	6.51155	0.03135	31.89463	13
14	0.14917	6.70373	0.02695	37.10470	14
15	0.14548	6.87379	0.02326	42.99208	15
16	0.14236	7.02429	0.02014	49.64485	16
17	0.13971	7.15748	0.01749	57.16249	17
18	0.13745	7.27534	0.01523	65.65744	18
19	0.13551	7.37965	0.01329	75.25676	19
20	0.13383	7.47195	0.01161	86.10402	20
21	0.13239	7.55364	0.01017	98.36145	21
22	0.13113	7.62592	0.00891	112.21238	22
23	0.13004	7.68989	0.00782	127.86397	23
24	0.12909	7.74650	0.00687	145.55030	24
25	0.12826	7.79660	0.00604	165.53591	25
26	0.12754	7.84094	0.00532	188.11970	26
27	0.12690	7.88017	0.00468	213.63944	27
28	0.12634	7.91489	0.00412	242.47681	28
29	0.12586	7.94562	0.00364	275.06313	29
30	0.12543	7.97281	0.00321	311.88575	30
31	0.12505	7.99687	0.00283	353.49541	31
32	0.12472	8.01817	0.00250	400.51443	32
33	0.12442	8.03701	0.00220	453.64606	33
34	0.12417	8.05369	0.00195	513.68494	34
35	0.12394	8.06845	0.00172	581.52903	35
40	0.12315	8.12035	0.00093	1078.33518	40
45	0.12272	8.14853	0.00050	1993.67914	45
50	0.12249	8.16382	0.00027	3680.16101	50

:ffective interest rate of 14%; r = 13.103%

N	$(\bar{A}/P,13.103,N)$	$(P/\bar{A},13.103,N)$	$(\bar{A}/F,13.103,N)$	$(F/\bar{A},13.103,N)$	N
1	1.06695	0.93726	0.93592	1.06847	1
2	0.56837	1.75941	0.43734	2.28653	2
3	0.40313	2.48059	0.27210	3.67513	3
4	0.32121	3.11321	0.19018	5.25812	4
5	0.27262	3.66814	0.14159	7.06274	5
6	0.24068	4.15491	0.10965	9.12001	6
7	0.21825	4.58191	0.08722	11.46531	7
8	0.20176	4.95647	0.07073	14.13895	8
9	0.18921	5.28503	0.05818	17.18690	9
10	0.17943	5.57323	0.04840	20.66157	10
11	0.17164	5.82605	0.04061	24.62271	11
12	0.16535	6.04782	0.03432	29.13841	12
13	0.16020	6.24235	0.02917	34.28631	13
14	0.15593	6.41299	0.02490	40.15494	14
15	0.15238	6.56267	0.02135	46.84518	15
16	0.14939	6.69398	0.01836	54.47207	16
17	0.14686	6.80915	0.01583	63.16674	17
18	0.14471	6.91019	0.01368	73.07868	18
19	0.14288	6.99881	0.01185	84.37832	19
20	0.14131	7.07655	0.01028	97.25992	20
21	0.13996	7.14475	0.00893	111.94498	21
22	0.13880	7.20457	0.00777	128.68597	22
23	0.13780	7.25704	0.00677	147.77073	23
24	0.13693	7.30307	0.00590	169.52740	24
25	0.13618	7.34344	0.00515	194.33004	25
26	0.13552	7.37886	0.00449	222.60510	26
27	0.13495	7.40993	0.00392	254.83873	27
28	0.13446	7.43718	0.00343	291.58513	28
29	0.13403	7.46109	0.00300	333.47610	29
30	0.13365	7.48206	0.00262	381.23189	30
31	0.13333	7.50045	0.00230	435.67358	31
32	0.13304	7.51659	0.00201	497.73722	32
33	0.13279	7.53074	0.00176	568.48989	33
34	0.13257	7.54316	0.00154	649.14807	34
35	0.13238	7.55405	0.00135	741.09856	35
40	0.13173	7.59144	0.00070	1433.99712	40
45	0.13139	7.61086	0.00036	2768.12569	45
50	0.13122	7.62094	0.00019	5336.89863	50

Effective interest rate of 15%; $r = 13.976\%$

N	$(\bar{A}/P,13.976,N)$	$(P/\bar{A},13.976,N)$	$(\bar{A}/F,13.976,N)$	$(F/\bar{A},13.976,N)$	N
1	1.07151	0.93326	0.93175	1.07325	1
2	0.57313	1.74480	0.43337	2.30749	2
3	0.40808	2.45049	0.26832	3.72686	3
4	0.32636	3.06413	0.18660	5.35913	4
5	0.27795	3.59773	0.13819	7.23625	5
6	0.24620	4.06173	0.10644	9.39492	6
7	0.22395	4.46521	0.08419	11.87739	7
8	0.20764	4.81606	0.06788	14.73222	8
9	0.19527	5.12115	0.05551	18.01527	9
10	0.18565	5.38645	0.04589	21.79078	10
11	0.17803	5.61714	0.03827	26.13260	11
12	0.17189	5.81775	0.03213	31.12568	12
13	0.16688	5.99219	0.02712	36.86772	13
14	0.16276	6.14387	0.02300	43.47105	14
15	0.15934	6.27577	0.01958	51.06486	15
16	0.15648	6.39047	0.01672	59.79773	16
17	0.15408	6.49020	0.01432	69.84050	17
18	0.15205	6.57693	0.01229	81.38967	18
19	0.15032	6.65235	0.01056	94.67120	19
20	0.14886	6.71793	0.00910	109.94492	20
21	0.14760	6.77495	0.00784	127.50966	21
22	0.14653	6.82454	0.00677	147.70908	22
23	0.14561	6.86766	0.00585	170.93836	23
24	0.14482	6.90515	0.00506	197.65199	24
25	0.14414	6.93776	0.00438	228.37260	25
26	0.14355	6.96611	0.00379	263.70123	26
27	0.14305	6.99076	0.00329	304.32908	27
28	0.14261	7.01220	0.00285	351.05101	28
29	0.14223	7.03084	0.00247	404.78113	29
30	0.14190	7.04705	0.00214	466.57065	30
31	0.14162	7.06115	0.00186	537.62846	31
32	0.14137	7.07341	0.00161	619.34478	32
33	0.14116	7.08406	0.00140	713.31836	33
34	0.14098	7.09333	0.00122	821.38777	34
35	0.14082	7.10139	0.00106	945.66736	35
40	0.14028	7.12841	0.00052	1909.29261	40
45	0.14002	7.14184	0.00026	3847.46837	45
50	0.13989	7.14852	0.00013	7745.79424	50

Effective interest rate of 20%; $r = 18.232$

N	$(\bar{A}/P, 18.232, N)$	$(P/\bar{A}, 18.232, N)$	$(\bar{A}/F, 18.232, N)$	$(F/\bar{A}, 18.232, N)$	N
1	1.09393	0.91414	0.91161	1.09696	1
2	0.59669	1.67592	0.41437	2.41331	2
3	0.43276	2.31074	0.25044	3.99294	3
4	0.35214	2.83975	0.16982	5.88848	4
5	0.30482	3.28060	0.12250	8.16312	5
6	0.27412	3.64798	0.09180	10.89269	6
7	0.25290	3.95412	0.07058	14.16818	7
8	0.23757	4.20924	0.05525	18.09875	8
9	0.22615	4.42184	0.04383	22.81542	9
10	0.21744	4.59901	0.03512	28.47543	10
11	0.21067	4.74665	0.02835	35.26742	11
12	0.20535	4.86969	0.02303	43.41780	12
13	0.20112	4.97221	0.01880	53.19824	13
14	0.19772	5.05766	0.01540	64.93476	14
15	0.19498	5.12886	0.01266	79.01855	15
16	0.19275	5.18819	0.01043	95.91907	16
17	0.19093	5.23763	0.00861	116.19967	17
18	0.18944	5.27884	0.00712	140.53635	18
19	0.18821	5.31318	0.00589	169.74032	19
20	0.18720	5.34179	0.00488	204.78503	20
21	0.18637	5.36564	0.00405	246.83861	21
22	0.18568	5.38551	0.00336	297.30284	22
23	0.18511	5.40207	0.00279	357.85981	23
24	0.18464	5.41586	0.00232	430.52807	24
25	0.18425	5.42736	0.00193	517.72984	25
26	0.18393	5.43695	0.00161	622.37180	26
27	0.18366	5.44493	0.00134	747.94196	27
28	0.18343	5.45159	0.00111	898.62592	28
29	0.18325	5.45713	0.00093	1079.44638	29
30	0.18309	5.46175	0.00077	1296.43060	30
31	0.18296	5.46561	0.00064	1556.81126	31
32	0.18285	5.46882	0.00053	1869.26757	32
33	0.18277	5.47149	0.00045	2244.21456	33
34	0.18269	5.47372	0.00037	2694.15024	34
35	0.18263	5.47558	0.00031	3234.07221	35
40	0.18244	5.48113	0.00012	8055.50705	40
45	0.18237	5.48336	0.00005	20052.68640	45
50	0.18234	5.48426	0.00002	49905.27535	50

AREAS OF A STANDARD NORMAL DISTRIBUTION

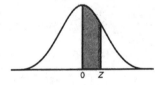

An entry in the table is the proportion under the entire curve that is between $Z = 0$ and a positive value of Z. Areas for negative values of Z are obtained by symmetry. The areas correspond to probabilities. Thus the area between $Z = 0$ and $Z = 2$ is .4772, which leads to a probability of .5000 − .4772 = .0228 that Z will be larger than 2 in a normally distributed population. By symmetry, the probability that Z is less than −2 is .5000 − .4772 = .0228.

Z	.00	.01	.02	.03	.04	.05	.06	.07	.08	.09
.0	.0000	.0040	.0080	.0120	.0160	.0199	.0239	.0279	.0319	.0359
.1	.0398	.0438	.0478	.0517	.0557	.0596	.0636	.0675	.0714	.0753
.2	.0793	.0832	.0871	.0910	.0948	.0987	.1026	.1064	.1103	.1141
.3	.1179	.1217	.1255	.1293	.1331	.1368	.1406	.1443	.1480	.1517
.4	.1554	.1591	.1628	.1664	.1700	.1736	.1772	.1808	.1844	.1879
.5	.1915	.1950	.1985	.2019	.2054	.2088	.2123	.2157	.2190	.2234
.6	.2257	.2291	.2324	.2357	.2389	.2422	.2454	.2486	.2517	.2549
.7	.2580	.2614	.2642	.2673	.2703	.2734	.2764	.2794	.2823	.2852
.8	.2881	.2910	.2939	.2967	.2995	.3023	.3051	.3078	.3106	.3133
.9	.3159	.3186	.3212	.3238	.3264	.3289	.3315	.3340	.3365	.3389
1.0	.3413	.3438	.3461	.3485	.3508	.3531	.3554	.3577	.3599	.3621
1.1	.3643	.3665	.3686	.3708	.3729	.3749	.3770	.3790	.3810	.3830
1.2	.3849	.3869	.3888	.3907	.3925	.3944	.3962	.3980	.3997	.4015
1.3	.4032	.4049	.4066	.4082	.4099	.4115	.4131	.4147	.4162	.4177
1.4	.4192	.4207	.4222	.4236	.4251	.4265	.4279	.4292	.4306	.4319

z	.00	.01	.02	.03	.04	.05	.06	.07	.08	.09
1.5	.4332	.4345	.4357	.4370	.4382	.4394	.4406	.4418	.4429	.4441
1.6	.4452	.4463	.4474	.4484	.4495	.4505	.4515	.4525	.4535	.4545
1.7	.4554	.4564	.4573	.4582	.4591	.4599	.4608	.4616	.4625	.4633
1.8	.4641	.4649	.4656	.4664	.4671	.4678	.4686	.4693	.4699	.4706
1.9	.4713	.4719	.4726	.4732	.4738	.4744	.4750	.4756	.4761	.4767
2.0	.4772	.4778	.4783	.4788	.4793	.4798	.4803	.4808	.4812	.4817
2.1	.4821	.4826	.4830	.4834	.4838	.4842	.4846	.4850	.4854	.4857
2.2	.4861	.4864	.4868	.4871	.4875	.4878	.4881	.4884	.4887	.4890
2.3	.4893	.4896	.4898	.4901	.4904	.4906	.4909	.4911	.4913	.4916
2.4	.4918	.4920	.4922	.4925	.4927	.4929	.4931	.4932	.4934	.4936
2.5	.4938	.4940	.4941	.4943	.4945	.4946	.4948	.4949	.4951	.4952
2.6	.4953	.4955	.4956	.4957	.4959	.4960	.4961	.4962	.4963	.4964
2.7	.4965	.4966	.4967	.4968	.4969	.4970	.4971	.4972	.4973	.4974
2.8	.4974	.4975	.4976	.4977	.4977	.4978	.4979	.4979	.4980	.4981
2.9	.4981	.4982	.4982	.4983	.4984	.4984	.4985	.4985	.4986	.4986
3.0	.4987	.4987	.4987	.4988	.4988	.4989	.4989	.4989	.4990	.4990

SOLUTIONS TO SELECTED PROBLEMS

To problem solvers: Engineering economic problems can often be solved in more than one way, and so intermediate answers can be misleading. Also, one method may give very minor numerical changes from another method. So do not spend an inordinate length of time trying to match a solution exactly. It is possible that errors have been made in the solutions, and the authors would be very grateful if these could be brought to their attention. Answers to most of the odd-numbered problems are given, but where the question asks for assumptions and estimated data, no solution is given. When a sequence of answers shows the solution methodology, we have given only partial solutions.

CHAPTER 1

1.7. 654 parts

1.9. We should not change the 18-month decision.

1A.1. (*a*) $Q = 4000 - 2000P$

    (*b*) (i) $Q = 2500$

        (ii) $Q = 1000$

    (*c*) Change in gross revenue = $500

    (*d*) Do not raise price.

1A.3. (*a*) $Q = 1000$

    (*b*) $Q = 2000$

    (*c*) $Q = \$0.2$ million

1A.5. The effect of an increase in price due to a shift in demand function is being compensated by the drop in price due to the supply curve shift.

CHAPTER 2

2.1. $P = \$1093.75$

2.3. $i = 3.8\%$

2.5. Ordinary simple interest: $38.89; exact simple interest: $38.36

2.7. $F = \$126.25$

2.9. Interest earned = $987.28

2.11.   4 years: $F = \$6312.40$
        8 years: $F = \$7969.25$
       12 years: $F = \$10,061.00$
       The interest earned will not be exactly double in twice the time.

2.13. (a) $i_{\text{eff}} = 19.56\%$
       (b) Interest paid = $307.34

2.15. $A = \$179.90$

2.17. The out-of-pocket difference is $161.40.

2.19. $P = \$8414.67$

2.23. (a) 2,526,950
       (b) 33,065,960

2.25. (a) $F = \$8160$
       (b) $F = \$7623.42$
       (d) $F = \$8166.97$
       (e) $F = \$7727.47$ CHEER was used to find values for (F/P, 1, 36) and
           (F/P, 1, 48).

2.27. $i = 9.144\%$

2.29. $P = \$1603.05$

2.31. $29,900.90   CHEER was used to find (P/A, 1, 64).

2.35. (a) $193.30
       (b) $1598.00

2.37. $A = \$13,448.08$

2.39. PW = $10,021.58

2.41. Nominal interest rate = 4.8%

CHAPTER 3

3.1. PW = $226,967

3.3. FW = $412,431.85

3.5. PW = $228,857

3.7. Sales price of land = $22,273

3.9. PW = $1390.91

3.11. $PW_{\text{elec car}} = -\$18,633.89$
       $PW_{\text{gas car}} = -\$19,618.83$

3.13. $PW_{\text{mach } A} = -\$57,955$
       $PW_{\text{mach } B} = -\$53,175$

3.15. Salvage value = $443,030

3.17. Capitalized cost of ditch and tunnel system = $533,333; capitalized cost of
       flume system = $526,450

3.19. PW = $280,999

3.21. $PW_3 = \$668,207$

3.23. $PW_A = \$28,749$; $PW_B = \$29,772$; $PW_C = \$27,420$

3.25. (a) PW cost of deferred investment = $2,146,628
       (b) PW cost of immediate investment = $2,353,519

3.27. $FW_{\text{robot } A} = \$51,582$; $FW_{\text{robot } B} = \$57,803$; $FW_{\text{robot } C} = \$44,271$

3.29. Building first costs available = $1,110,818

3.31. $P = \$4556.85$

3.33. PW = $4587

CHAPTER 4

4.1. $3784.50

4.3. 0.1 cent per liter

4.5. Equivalent monthly worth = $6,471

4.7. Difference between anticipated equivalent annual costs ($1351.34) and actual ($1828.32) is $476.98 more than expected.

4.9. Purchase EAC = $4827.84; lease EAC = $3450.04

4.11. EAC_{IC} = $2331; EAC_{UC} = $2071

4.13. $EAW_{robot\ A}$ = $15,286; $EAW_{robot\ B}$ = $17,130; $EAW_{robot\ C}$ = $13,119

4.15. $EAW_{method\ 1}$ = –$45,625; $EAW_{method\ 2}$ = –$67,002

4.17. Number of months is between 21 and 22, which really means 22 months.

4.19. PW = $41,051

4.21. A = $10,231

4.23. Subcontracting EAC = $115,376; leasing EAC = $112,913

4.25. Minimum annual revenue = $4,516,180

4.27. Beta salvage value = $5472

4.29. Alternative 1 monthly payment = $1047.51; alternative 2 monthly payment = $1017.00

4.31. Immediate replacement: EAC = $249,129

4.33. EAC_A = $267,425; EAC_B = $261,422; EAC_C = $275,226; EAC_D = $260,261

CHAPTER 5

5.1. i = 6.7%

5.3. i = 9.4%

5.5. (a) 21.97%

 (b) Receipt in period 1 = $1528.27

5.7. (a) 18.90%

 (b) 0%

 (c) 13.14%

5.9. i_{eff} = 30.91%

5.11. Nominal annual rate = 18.06%, effective annual rate = 19.63%

5.13. (a) Plan A: i = 18.28%, plan B: i = 13.66%

 (b) Rate of return$_{A \to B}$ = 6% (found with CHEER)

 (d) The project balance method is not justified. State a reason!

5.15. Rate of return$_X$ = 14.87%, rate of return$_Y$ = 20.76%

5.17. Rate of return (by CHEER) = 14.42%

5.19. IRR = 14.43%

5.21. IRR = 16.71%

5.23. IRR = 22.11% *Note:* The PW equation is quite complex, and so solving manually by trial and error will be difficult. CHEER was used to get this solution.

5.25. IRR = 31.14%

5.27. IRR = 5.795%

5.29. i = 7.08%

5.31. i^* = 17.8% (solved directly from equation)

5.33. IRR = 21.3%

CHAPTER 6

Only partial answers are given for Probs. 6.1, 6.3, 6.5, 6.7, 6.15, 6.17, 6.25, and 6.29.

6.1. IRR_1 = 16.66%

 $IRR_{1 \to 2}$ = 11.69%

6.3. $IRR_{14 \to 16} = 20.6\%$

6.5. (a) $IRR_X = 11.39\%$

6.7. $IRR_{robot\ C} = 9.73\%$, $IRR_{robot\ A \to robot\ B} = 77.72\%$

6.9. $EAW_A = \$5098$, $EAW_B = \$9355$, $EAW_C = -\$341.19$

6.11. $EAC_a = \$29,086$; $EAC_b = \$24,808$; $EAC_c = \$26,800$

6.13. $PW_1 = \$151,430$; $PW_2 = \$144,312$; $PW_3 = \$145,324$; $PW_4 = \$155,838$

6.15. $IRR_F = 6.40\%$, $IRR_C = 4.76\%$, $IRR_{B \to A} = 10.37\%$

6.17. $IRR_{park} = 12.05\%$, $IRR_{park \to park+swim} = 25.41\%$

6.19. (a) Proposal C

(b) All of them

6.21. (a) Proposal B; PW = \$3676

(b) Proposal B

6.23. (a) Recommend alternative 4

(b) Recommend alternative 3

6.25. (a) Recommend design D, using incremental IRR analysis; $IRR_{C \to D} = 21.11\%$

(b) Capitalized $cost_A = CC_A$. $CC_A = \$14,253,857$; $CC_B = \$13,500,143$; $CC_C = \$13,268,571$; $CC_D = \$11,532,857$

6.27. (a) $PW_J = \$33,434$; $PW_K = \$2968$

(b) $PW_J = \$51,350$; $PW_K = \$34,006$

6.29. $IRR_{1 \to 2} = 48.79\%$

$IRR_{2 \to 4} = 7.85\%$

6.31. IRR = 12.02%

CHAPTER 7

7.1. Annual cost of new machine = \$8803. Cost of holding old machine 1 more year = \$7340.

7.3. Salvage value = \$6452

7.5. (a) $EAC_{machine\ 1} = \$12,856$; $EAC_{presently\ avail\ mach} = \$12,330$

7.7. $EAC_{old\ car} = \$2301$, $EAC_{new\ car} = \$3851$

7.9. $EAC_{current\ system} = \$13,938$; $EAC_{modified\ system} = \$12,778$; $EAC_{pulse-jet\ system} = \$11,920$

7.11. $EAC_1 = \$3032$; $EAC_2 = \$2837$; $EAC_3 = \$2549$

7.13. This will be very difficult to accomplish without computer assistance. CHEER will not handle a problem over 30 periods, although interest factors can be computed that have time periods > 30. CHEER determined the interest factors, and a spreadsheet was used to determine PW values. By trial and error it was found that the lease monthly cost would be \$526.

7.15. Replace the pump at the end of 4 years of service.

7.17. Replace every 3 years.

7.19. Replace the old machines 1 year from now.

7.21. Keep the buses for their 6-year service life.

7.23. Purchase the challenger now.

7.25. (a) $EAC_{def} = \$44,777$

(b) $EAC_{chal} = \$42,242$; $EAC_{def\ 1st\ year} = \$34,048$

7.27. Economic life = 5 years

7.31. Economic life = 5 years

CHAPTER 8

8.1. Partial solutions are given:

(a) $B/C_F = 1.15$; $B/C_G = 1.76$

(b) $B/C_F = 1.22$; $B/C_G = 1.89$

  (c) Proposal F
  (d) Proposal C
  (e) Proposal G (based on $B - C$)
  (f) Select proposal G.
  (g) Select proposal G.
8.3. Partial solutions: $B/C_{\text{ferry}} = 1.2$; $B/C_{\text{low bridge}\to\text{2d design}} = 1.45$
8.5. Partial solutions: $B/C_{\text{ferry}} = 1.12$; $B/C_{\text{ferry}\to\text{low-level bridge}} = 9.19$
8.7. Solution depends on student's assumptions and data.
8.9. $B/C_A = 2.47$. Select alternative A.
8.11. At least 14 accidents
8.13. (a) Reject all alternatives.
  (b) Reject all alternatives.
  (c) Recommend alternative B.
8.15. Plan 2 is recommended.
8.17. Picnic: \$1.49 per visit; picnic + camping: \$1.66 per visit; picnic + camping + cabin: \$4.11 per visit
8.19. (a) Function of student data
  (b) This is a function of the weighting scheme in part a. One solution: \$407,736 per fatality or injury
8.21. (a) $B/C = 1.38$, but it depends on assumptions!
8.25. (a) \$210,000
  (b) 300,000 units (draw a diagram!)
  (c) Additional benefits = \$135,000
  (d) \$180,000
  (e) \$240,000
8.27. Solutions are based on assumptions for the most part. We will leave it up to the student to justify the results.

CHAPTER 9

9.1. NPW = \$8,896.61; a year-by-year analysis by CHEER gives \$8,884.12
9.3. (a) Depreciation charge = \$50.00
  Book value at the end of year 4 = \$200
  (b) Depreciation charge during year 5 = \$34.08
  Book value at the end of year 4 = \$227.23
9.5. (a) Maximum allowable rate = 0.1667
  (b) Accumulated depreciation = \$25,000
  (c) Book value = \$47,385
9.7. Macro Inc.: 44.84%; total income tax = \$2,017,800
  Maso Ltd.: 44.34%; total income tax = \$221,700
  Micro Co.: 17.84%; total income tax = \$8920
9.9. Before-tax IRR = 15.1%; After-tax IRR = 8.3%
9.11. After-tax IRR is slightly below 11%.
9.13. If the interest rate is 7.7 percent or less, the new lot should be purchased. Interest rates over 7.7 percent favor continuing payment on the older lot.
9.15. (a) Before-tax PW = \$9765.00
  (b) After-tax PW = \$556.20; CHEER results in \$555.47
9.17. Tax effect for years 1 to 8 (excluding investment):

Year	After-tax cash flow	Year	After-tax cash flow
1	$3600	5	$2099.16
2	6120	6	1469.41
3	4284	7	1028.59
4	2998.80	8	720.01
		8*	1260.02*

*Disposal tax effect

PW of tax effect (years 1 to 8) (excluding investment) = $17,181.82

9.19. (a) Rate of return before tax = 26.6%; use of CHEER gives 26.49%

(b) Approximate after-tax rate of return = 15.43%

(c) Actual after-tax rate of return = 13.20%; use of CHEER gives 13.149%

9.21. EAW (after-tax) = –$14,539.97; a year-by-year analysis by CHEER gives –$14,693.75

CHAPTER 10

10.1. (a) 4.5%

(b) 2.3%

10.3. $3.31 (for a per-unit cost of $1)

10.5. $2,433

10.7. (a) 15.5% (b) $121

10.9. $16,800

10.11. $3471 per year

10.13. PW = $137,762

10.15. PW = –$263.10

10.17. (a) IRR = 14.2%

(b) IRR = 12.9%

CHAPTER 11

11.3. $3056

11.7. $7706

11.9. Annual receipts

11.15. (a) PW(objective estimate) = $39,739

(b) PW(less favorable estimate) = –$254,347

(c) PW(more favorable estimate) = $242,522

CHAPTER 12

12.1. 226,364 barrels per year

12.3. (a) 100 campers per week; (b) $9600; (c) $3000

12.5. (a) 45% (b) 31 units

12.7. 35,159 kilometers

12.9. Minimum crew plus one finisher and one laborer; total cost = $184.80

12.11. (a) Original line: $CC_A = 0.06030$, $CC_B = 0.14070$, $CC_C = 0.20101$. New line: $CC_A = 0.05657$, $CC_B = 0.10649$, $CC_C = 0.11980$, $CC_D = 0.10649$

(b) Z(original line) = $100,000; Z(new line) = $92,499

12.13. $130,000

12.15. $1,274,372

12.17. (a) 3040 units

(b) Use machine A for the production of less than or equal to 406 units, and use machine B for the production of more than 406 units.

12.19. (b) $1,750,000; (c) $1,080,000

12.21. (a) Break-even points: $n_1 = 3.26$, $n_2 = 6.23$; (b) 4.91

CHAPTER 13
13.1. EV(add new facilities) = $345,000; EV(increase utilization) = $260,000
13.3. Method 1 at $0.80
13.7. (a) 20%
13.9. EV(PW) = $80,452; SD(PW) = $7485
13.11. (a) Rank: *B, D, E, C, F, A*
    (b) Rank: *D, F, B, E, A, C*
13.13. (a) EV(PW) = $9859; SD(PW) = $4262
    (b) P(loss) = 1%
13.15. (a) EV(PW) = $21,532; SD(PW) = $2125
    (b) EV(PW) = $21,532; SD(PW) = $2014
13.17. EV(AW) = $7404; Var(AW) = 46,493,183
13.19. P(loss) = .25
13.21. (a) EV(annual profit) = $49,500; Var(annual profit) = 2.364×10^8
    (b) EV(PW) = $40,561; SD(PW) = 1.7826×10^4
13.23. Cost of individual replacement = $323 per week; cost of preventive replacement = $321 per week
13.25. Four standby machines
13.27. (a) $15.19 per week
    (b) Use 4-week plan at $14.39 per unit per week.
    (c) $16.77 per unit per week
13.33. (a) Site *C* is dominated. (b) SW (c) NW (d) NE (e) NW (f) NE or SW
13.35. (a) A_1 or A_3
    (b) 12
    (c) A_1 from $\alpha = 0$ to $\alpha = 0.5$; A_2 from $\alpha = 0.5$ to $\alpha = 1.0$; indifferent at $\alpha = 0.5$
    (d) A_1

CHAPTER 14
14.1. (a) 0.76; (b) 0.99
14.3. 0.98
14.5. $240,000
14.7. (a) EV(A_1) = $4438
    (b) EV(B) = $1837
    (c) EV(PI) = $0
14.9. (a) Decision point 2 for medium (*M*) school: EV(A) = −$6,458,225; EV(*N*) = −$4,214,100
    Decision point 2 for large (*L*) school: EV(*R*) = −$4,011,749; EV(*N*) = −$2,458,224
    (b) EV(*M*) = −$8,023,403; EV(*L*) = −$10,687,728
14.11. EV(modify) = $85,708; EV(buy new) = $112,160
14.13. (a) 0.45
    (b) 0.933, 0.067
    (c) 0.509, 0.491

CHAPTER 15
15.7. (a) Alternative X_4; (b) alternative X_4
15.9. Site 3
15.11. Site 1
15.13. Alternative L_1

SELECTED
REFERENCES

BOOKS

Adler, Hans A., *Economic Appraisal of Transport Projects, A Manual with Case Studies, Revised and Expanded Edition*, published for the World Bank, The John Hopkins University Press, Baltimore, 1987.

American Telephone and Telegraph, *Engineering Economy*, McGraw-Hill Book Co., New York, 1977.

Au, T., and T. P. Au, *Engineering Economics for Capital Investment Analysis*, Allyn and Bacon, Inc., Boston, 1992.

Barish, N. N., and S. Kaplan, *Economic Analysis for Engineering and Managerial Decision Making*, McGraw-Hill Book Co., New York, 1978

Bierman, H., and S. Smidt, *The Capital Budgeting Decision: Economic Analysis of Investment Projects*, Macmillan Publ. Co., New York, 1984.

Blank, L. T., and A. J. Tarquin, *Engineering Economy*, McGraw-Hill Book Co., New York, 1989.

Bunn, D. W., *Applied Decision Analysis*, McGraw-Hill Book Co., New York, 1984.

Bussey, L. E., and T. G. Eschenbach, *The Economic Analysis of Industrial Projects*, Prentice-Hall, Inc., Englewood Cliffs, NJ, 1992.

Byrd, J., Jr., and L. T. Moore, *Decision Models for Management*, McGraw-Hill Book Co., New York, 1982.

Canada, J. R., and W. G. Sullivan, *Economic and Multiattribute Evaluation of Advanced Manufacturing Systems*, Prentice-Hall, Inc., Englewood Cliffs, NJ, 1989.

Canada, J. R., and J. A. White, Jr., *Capital Investment Decision Analysis for Management and Engineering*, Prentice-Hall, Inc., Englewood Cliffs, NJ, 1980.

Collier, C. A., *Engineering Cost Analysis*, Harper & Row, Publishers, New York, 1982.

Cooper, D. F., and C. B. Chapman, *Risk Analysis for Large Projects: Models, Methods and Cases,* John Wiley & Sons, Inc., New York, 1987.

Coopers & Lybrand, *International Tax Networks, 1995, International Tax Summaries, A Guide for Planning and Decisions,* J. Wiley, Toronto/New York, 1995.

Cornell, A. H., *The Decision-Maker's Handbook,* Prentice-Hall, Inc., Englewood Cliffs, NJ, 1980.

DeGarmo, E. P., W. G. Sullivan, and J. A. Bontadelli, *Engineering Economy,* Macmillan Publ. Co., New York, 1993.

Easton, A., *Complex Managerial Decisions Involving Multiple Objectives,* Robert E. Krieger Publ. Co., Huntington, NY, 1980.

Edwards, W., and J. R. Newman, *Multi-attribute Evaluation,* Sage Publ. Co., Beverly Hills, CA, 1983.

Eilon, S., B. Gold, and J. Soesan, *Applied Productivity Analysis for Industry,* Pergamon Press, Oxford, England, 1976.

English, J. M., *Cost Effectiveness: The Economic Evaluation of Engineered Systems,* John Wiley & Sons, Inc., New York, 1968.

Fabrycky, W. J., and B. S. Blanchard, *Life-Cycle Cost and Economic Analysis,* Prentice-Hall, Inc., Englewood Cliffs, NJ, 1991.

Fabrycky, W. J., and G. J. Thuesen, *Economic Decision Analysis,* Prentice-Hall, Inc., Englewood Cliffs, NJ, 1974.

Farrar, D. E., *The Investment Decision under Uncertainty,* Prentice-Hall, Inc., Englewood Cliffs, NJ, 1962.

Fleischer, G. A., *Risk and Uncertainty: Non-deterministic Decision Making in Engineering Economy,* American Institute of Industrial Engineers, Norcross, GA, 1975.

Fleischer, G. A., *Engineering Economy: Capital Allocation Theory,* Brooks/Cole Publishing Company, Monterey, CA, 1984.

Fleischer, G. A., *Introduction to Engineering Economy,* PWS Publishing Company, Boston, 1994.

Frost, M. J., *How to Use Cost Benefit Analysis in Project Appraisal,* John Wiley & Sons, Inc., New York, 1975.

Goicoecha, A., D. R. Hasen, and L. Duckstein, *Multiobjective Decision Analysis with Engineering and Business Applications,* John Wiley & Sons, Inc., New York, 1982.

Gonen, T., *Engineering Economy for Engineering Managers,* John Wiley & Sons, New York, 1993.

Grant, E. L., W. G. Ireson, and R. S. Leavenworth, *Principles of Engineering Economy,* John Wiley & Sons, Inc., New York, 1990.

Haley, C. W., and L. D. Schall, *The Theory of Financial Decisions,* McGraw-Hill Book Co., New York, 1979.

Hertz, D. B., and H. Thomas, *Risk Analysis and Its Applications,* John Wiley & Sons, Inc., New York, 1983.

Holloway, C. A., *Decision Making under Uncertainty,* Prentice-Hall, Inc., Englewood Cliffs, NJ, 1979.

Hull, J. C., *The Evaluation of Risk in Business Investment,* Pergamon Press, New York, 1980.

Jelen, F. C., and J. H. Black, *Cost and Optimization Engineering,* McGraw-Hill Book Co., New York, 1983.

Keeney, R. L., and H. Raiffa, *Decisions with Multiple Objectives: Preferences and Value Tradeoffs,* John Wiley & Sons, Inc., New York, 1976.

Kleinfeld, I. H., *Engineering and Managerial Economics,* CBS College Publ., New York, 1986.

Lang, H. J., *Cost Analysis for Capital Investment Decisions,* Marcel Dekker, Inc., New York, 1989.

Lang, H. J., and D. N. Merino, *The Selection Process for Capital Projects,* John Wiley & Sons, Inc., New York, 1993.

Lin, S. A. Y., *Theory and Measurement of Economic Externalities,* Academic Press, New York, 1976.

Mao, J. C. T., *Quantitative Analysis of Financial Decisions,* Macmillan Publ. Co., New York, 1969.

Mayer, R. R., *Capital Expenditure Analysis for Managers and Engineers,* Waveland Press, Prospect Heights, IL, 1978.

Morris, W. T., *Engineering Economic Analysis,* Reston Publ. Co., Reston, VA, 1976.

Newnan, D. G., *Engineering Economic Analysis,* 3d ed., Engineering Press, San Jose, CA, 1988.

Nolan, J.L., A. Woznick, W.T. LeGro, D.C. Alexander, K.C. Shippey, E.G. Hinkelman, H.I. Vera, M.F. Pasero, *Mexico Business, The Portable Encyclopedia for Doing Business With Mexico,* World Trade Press, San Rafael, CA, 1994.

Oakford, R. V., *Capital Budgeting: A Quantitative Evaluation of Investment Alternatives,* Ronald Press, New York, 1970.

Ostwald, P. F., *Cost Estimating for Engineering and Management,* Prentice-Hall, Inc., Englewood Cliffs, NJ, 1984.

Palm, T., and A. Qayum, *Private and Public Investment Analysis,* South-Western Publ. Co., Cincinnati, OH, 1985.

Park, C. S., *Contemporary Engineering Economics,* Addision-Wesley Publ. Co., Reading, MA, 1993.

Park, C. S., and G. P. Sharp-Bette, *Advanced Engineering Economics,* John Wiley & Sons, Inc., New York, 1990.

Radford, K. J., *Managerial Decision Making,* Reston Publ. Co., Reston, VA, 1975.

Schall, L. D., and C. W. Haley, *Financial Management,* McGraw-Hill Book Co., New York, 1977.

Steiner, H. M., *Engineering Economic Principles,* McGraw-Hill Book Co., New York, 1992.

Stevens, G. T., Jr., *Economics and Financial Analysis of Capital Investments,* John Wiley & Sons, Inc., New York, 1979.

Stuart, R. D., *Cost Estimating,* John Wiley & Sons, Inc., New York, 1982.

Taylor, G. A., *Managerial and Engineering Economy,* Van Nostrand Reinhold Co., New York, 1980.

Thuesen, G. J., and W. J. Fabrycky, *Engineering Economy,* Prentice-Hall, Inc., Englewood Cliffs, NJ, 1993.

Wellington, A. M., *The Economic Theory of Railway Location,* John Wiley & Sons, Inc., New York, 1887.

White, J. A., M. H. Agee, and K. E. Case, *Principles of Engineering Economic Analysis,* John Wiley & Sons, Inc., New York, 1989.

Wilkes, F. M., *Capital Budgeting Techniques,* John Wiley & Sons, Inc., New York, 1977.

Young, D., *Modern Engineering Economy,* John Wiley & Sons, Inc., New York, 1992.

Zeleny, M., *Multiple Criteria Decision Making,* McGraw-Hill Book Co., New York, 1982.

GOVERNMENT AND OTHER DOCUMENTS

Bank of Nova Scotia, *Scotiabank 1994 Annual Report,* Ottawa.

CCH Canada Limited, *Preparing Your Corporation Tax Returns,* Don Mills, Ontario, 1994.

Cordukes, P.A.(Editor), *Submission and Evaluation of Proposals for Private Power Generation Projects in Developing Countries,* World Bank Discussion Paper 250, 1994.

Corel Corporation, *1994 Annual Report,* Ottawa.

Ernst & Young, *Worldwide Corporate Tax Guide,* 1994 Edition.

Hanna N., K. Guy, and E. Arnold, *The Diffusion of Information Technology, Experience of Industrial Countries and Lessons for Developing Countries,* World Bank Discussion Paper 281, Washington, D.C., 1995.

Hoekman, B., and P. Sauve, *Liberalizing Trade in Services,* World Bank Discussion Paper 243, Washington D.C., 1994.

Mathieson, Donal J., and Liliane Rojas-Suarez, *Liberalization of the Capital Account, Experience and Issues,* International Monetary Fund, Washington, D.C., March 1993.

Pechman, Joseph A., *Comparative Tax Systems: Europe, Canada and Japan,* The Brookings Institution, 1987.

Public Works and Government Services Canada, *Northumberland Strait Crossing Project, A Link to the Future,* May 26, 1995 (Internet).

Revenue Canada, *Income Tax Act, Capital Cost Allowance — General Comments, Interpretation Bulletin, IT-285R2,* Ottawa, March 1994.

Revenue Canada, *T2 Corporation Income Tax Guide,* Ottawa, 1994.

Royal Commission on National Passenger Transportation, *Directions: The Final Report,* Government of Canada, Ottawa, 1992.

The World Bank, *The World Bank and the Environment,* Fiscal 1993, Washington D.C.

The World Bank, *Making Development Sustainable, The World Bank Group and the Environment,* Fiscal 1994, Washington, D.C.

ARTICLES

Pertinent articles are named throughout the text. The most frequently cited sources for subjects associated with engineering economics are listed below:

IIE Transactions
American Institute of Industrial Engineers: *Conference Proceedings*
Harvard Business Review
Industrial Engineering (called *The Journal of Industrial Engineering* prior to
    January 1969)
Journal of Business
Journal of Cost Analysis
Journal of Finance
Journal of Financial and Quantitative Analysis
Journal of Manufacturing Systems
Management Science
Sloan Management Review
The Economic Journal
The Engineering Economist

JOURNAL/CONFERENCE ARTICLES

American Society of Civil Engineers, "Engineers from Three Countries Reach Mutual
    Recognition Agreement," *ASCE News*, vol. 20, no.7, American Society of Civil Engineers, New York, p. 1, July, 1995.

Ashton, B. W., "The Design and Control of Long-Life Capital Projects," *Proceedings of 1986 Fall Industrial Engineering Conference,* Boston, December 7–10, 1986, pp. 95–98, Institute of Industrial Engineers, Norcross, GA.

Barr, W. R., "Risk Analysis Application and Capital Investment Evaluation," *Proceedings of Spring Annual Industrial Engineering and World Productivity Conference,* Detroit, MI, May 17–20, 1981, pp. 418–422, Institute of Industrial Engineers, Norcross, GA.

Beaves, R. G., "Net Present Values and Rates of Return; Implicit and Explicit Reinvestment Assumptions," *The Engineering Economist,* vol. 33, no. 4, pp. 275–302 summer 1988.

Bein, Peter, "Cost-Benefit Basis of Highway Investment Appraisal and Road Pricing," *Proceedings, Canadian Transportation Research Forum 29th Annual Meeting*, Victoria, B.C. May 15–18, 1994, pp. 743–757.

Buck, J. R., "Risk Analysis Method Can Help Make Firms' Investments Less of a Gamble," *Industrial Engineering,* vol. 14, no. 11, pp. 35–41, 1987.

Canada, J. R., "Annotated Bibliography on Justification of Computer Integrated Manufacturing Systems," *The Engineering Economist,* vol. 31, no. 2, pp. 137–163, 1986.

Canada, J. R., "Non-traditional Method for Evaluating CIM Opportunities Assigns Weights to Intangibles," *Industrial Engineering,* vol. 18, no. 3, pp. 66–71, 1986.

Canada, J. R., and H. M. Wadsworth, "Methods for Quantifying Risk in Economic Analyses of Capital Projects," *The Journal of Industrial Engineering,* vol. 19, no. 1, pp. 103–108, 1968.

Dunn-Rankin, P., "Multiple Comparisons in a Simplified Rank Method of Scaling," *Educational and Psychological Measurement,* vol. 29, no. 2, pp. 315–329, 1969.

Eckenrode, R. H., "Weighting Multiple Criteria," *Management Science,* vol. 12, no. 3, pp. 180–192, 1965.

Eschenbach, T. G., and R. J. Gimpel, "Stochastic Sensitivity Analysis," *The Engineering Economist,* vol. 35, no. 4, pp. 305–321, 1990.

Falkner, C. H., and S. Benhajla, "Multiattribute Decision Models in the Justification of CIM Systems," *The Engineering Economist,* vol. 35, no. 2, pp. 91–114, 1990.

Garner, David P., and Peep Korgemagi, "Ontario's Highway 407 Project," *Proceedings, 1995 Annual Conference of the Canadian Society for Civil Engineering,* Ottawa, V.III, pp. 97–106.

Greer, W. R., Jr., "Capital Budgeting Analysis with the Timing of Events Uncertain," *The Accounting Review,* vol. 45, no. 1, pp. 103–114, 1970.

Harder, S. W., and L. T. Blank, "The Role for Computer Simulation in the Economic Analysis of Manufacturing Systems," *Proceedings of Winter Simulation Conference,* Arlington, VA, December 12–14, 1983, pp. 199–206. Institute of Electrical and Electronic Engineers, New York, NY.

Hertz, D. B., "Risk Analysis in Capital Investment," *Harvard Business Review,* vol. 42, no. 1, pp. 141–152, 1964.

Hillier, F. S., "The Derivation of Probabilistic Information for the Evaluation of Risky Investments," *Management Science,* vol. 9, no. 4, pp. 443–457, 1963.

Hoff, George C., and Radoslar Elomor, "Concrete Production for the Hibernia Platform," *Proceedings, 1995 Annual Conference of the Canadian Society for Civil Engineering,* Ottawa, V.III, pp. 693–716.

Khan, A.M., "Maglev vs. High Speed Rail in the Quebec City–Windsor Corridor: A Comparison of Costs and Revenues," *Proceedings of the International Conference on High Speed Ground Transportation Systems,* edited by V.A. Bondada and Roger L. Wayson, American Society of Civil Engineers (ASCE), New York, 1992.

Kulkarni, J., and H. R. Parsaei, "Economic Justification of Flexible Manufacturing Systems: A Bibliographic Analysis of Literature," in H. R. Parsaei, T. L. Ward, and W. Karwowski, eds., *Justification Methods for Computer Integrated Manufacturing Systems,* Elsevier Science Publ., Amsterdam, The Netherlands, 1990, pp. 275–309.

Lee, T. S., "Economic Analysis in the Context of Incomplete Knowledge," *Proceedings of International Industrial Engineering Conference,* Orlando, FL, May 22–25, 1988, pp. 95–100. Institute of Electrical and Electronic Engineers, New York, NY.

Leung, Lawrence C., and Gerald A. Fleischer, "Depreciation and Tax Policies in Certain East Asian Countries," *Engineering Costs and Production Economics,* V.16, no. 2, p. 125, April, 1989.

Lohmann, J., "The IRR, NPV and the Fallacy of the Reinvestment Assumption," *The Engineering Economist,* vol. 38, no. 3, pp. 303–330, 1993.

Martin, Bernie, and Ata M. Khan, "Environmental Issues of the New Intermodal Tunnel, Canada/U.S.," *Proceedings, 1996 Annual Conference of the Canadian Society for Civil Engineering,* Edmonton, 1996.

Meredith, J. R., and M. M. Hill, "Justifying New Manufacturing Systems: A Managerial Approach," *Sloan Management Review,* vol. 28, no. 4, pp. 49–61, 1987.

Meredith, J. R., and N. C. Suresh, "Justification Techniques for Advanced Manufacturing Technologies," *International Journal of Production Research,* vol. 24, no. 5, pp. 1043–1057, 1986.

Michaels, L. T., W. T. Muir, and R. G. Eiler, "Improving Technology Cost-Benefit Analysis," *Material Handling Engineering,* vol. 39, no. 2, pp. 49–54, 1984.

Park, C. S., and Y. K. Son, "An Economic Evaluation Model for Advanced Manufacturing Systems," *The Engineering Economist,* vol. 34, no. 1, pp. 1–26, 1988.

Pike, R., "Do Sophisticated Capital Budgeting Approaches Improve Investment Decision-Making Effectiveness?" *The Engineering Economist,* vol. 34, no. 2, pp. 149–161, 1989.

Proctor, M. D., and J. R. Canada, "Past and Present Methods of Manufacturing Investment Evaluation: A Review of Empirical and Theoretical Literature," *The Engineering Economist,* vol. 38, no. 1, pp. 45–58, 1992.

Randhawa, S. U., and T. M. West, "Uncertainty Modeling in CIM Investment Analysis," *CIM Review,* vol. 6, no. 1, pp. 32–36, 1989.

Randhawa, S. U., and T. M. West, "Evaluating Automated Manufacturing Technologies: Part I—Concepts and Literature Review," *Computer-Integrated Manufacturing Systems,* vol. 15, no. 3, pp. 208–218, 1992.

Smith, L. L., "Using Isoquants for Economic Decision Making under Uncertainty," *International Journal of Industrial Engineering,* vol. 1, no. 2, pp. 109–118, 1994.

Son, Y. K., "A Comprehensive Bibliography on Justification of Advanced Manufacturing Technologies," *The Engineering Economist,* vol. 38, no. 1, pp. 59–71, 1992.

Sullivan, W. G., "Replacement Decisions in High Technology Industries—Where Are Those Models When You Need Them?" *Proceedings of 1984 Annual International Industrial Engineering Conference,* Chicago, May 6–10, 1984, pp. 119–128, Institute of Industrial Engineers, Norcross, GA.

Sullivan, W. G., "Models IEs Can Use to Include Strategic, Non-monetary Factors in Automation Decisions," *Industrial Engineering,* vol. 81, no. 3, pp. 42–50, 1986.

Van Horne, J. C., "The Analysis of Uncertainty Resolution in Capital Budgeting for New Products," *Management Science,* vol. 15, no. 8, pp. 376–386, 1969.

West, T. M., and S. U. Randhawa, "Multicriteria Evaluation of Manufacturing Systems," in B. Prasad, ed., *CAD/CAM, Robotics and Factories of the Future: Proceedings of Third International Conference,* Springer-Verlag, New York, 1989, pp. 271–275.

Wong, Brenda, and Dominique Lord, "Feasibility for a Reserves HOV Lane for the Approach of the Victoria Bridge During the Morning Peak Period," *1991 Annual Meeting of the Canadian Transportation Research Forum,* pp. 872–892.

INDEX